Scott Foresman - Addison Wesley
MIDDLE SCHOOL MATH
Course 1

Randall I. Charles   John A. Dossey   Steven J. Leinwand
Cathy L. Seeley   Charles B. Vonder Embse

L. Carey Bolster • Janet H. Caldwell • Dwight A. Cooley • Warren D. Crown
Linda Proudfit • Alma B. Ramírez • Jeanne F. Ramos • Freddie Lee Renfro
David Robitaille • Jane Swafford

Scott Foresman
Addison Wesley

Editorial Offices: Menlo Park, California • Glenview, Illinois
Sales Offices: Reading, Massachusetts • Atlanta, Georgia • Glenview, Illinois
Carrollton, Texas • Menlo Park, California

http://www.sf.aw.com

Cover artist: Robert Silvers, 28, started taking photographs and playing with computers at the same time, about 19 years ago. He always thought of computer programming as a way to express himself much as he does with photography. Silvers has melded his interests to produce the image on this cover.

Printed in the United States of America

ISBN 0-201-69016-0

8 9 10-VH-01 00 99

FROM THE AUTHORS

Dear Student,

     We have designed a unique mathematics program that answers the question students your age have been asking for years about their math lessons: "When am I ever going to use this?"

     In *Scott Foresman - Addison Wesley Middle School Math*, you'll learn about math in your own world and develop problem-solving techniques that will work for you in everyday life. The chapters have two or three sections, each with a useful math topic and an interesting theme. For example, you'll relate fractions to floods, algebra to the Oregon Trail, and geometry to origami.

     Each section begins with an opportunity to explore new topics and make your own conjectures. Lessons are presented clearly with examples and chances to try the math yourself. Then, real kids like you and your friends say what they think about each concept and show how they understand it. And every section contains links to the World Wide Web, making your math book a dynamic link to an ever-expanding universe of knowledge.

     You will soon realize how mathematics is not only useful, but also connected to you and your life as you continue to experience the real world. We trust that each of you will gain the knowledge necessary to be successful and to be everything you want to be.

Randall I. Charles   *John A. Dossey*   *Steven J. Leinwand*

       Cathy L. Seeley   *Charles B. Vonder Embse*

L. Carey Bolster   *Janet H. Caldwell*   *Dwight A. Cooley*   *Warren D. Crown*   *Linda Proudfit*

Alma B. Ramírez   *Jeanne F. Ramos*   *Freddie Lee Renfro*   *David Robitaille*   *Jane Swafford*

Authors

L. Carey Bolster
Public Broadcasting System
Alexandria, Virginia

Randall I. Charles
San Jose State University
San Jose, California

Warren D. Crown
Rutgers, the State University of New Jersey
New Brunswick, New Jersey

Steven J. Leinwand
Connecticut Department of Education
Hartford, Connecticut

Alma B. Ramírez
Oakland Charter Academy
Oakland, California

Freddie Lee Renfro
Fort Bend Independent School District
Sugarland, Texas

Cathy L. Seeley
Texas SSI in Math and Science
Austin, Texas

Charles B. Vonder Embse
Central Michigan University
Mount Pleasant, Michigan

Janet H. Caldwell
Rowan College of New Jersey
Glassboro, New Jersey

Dwight A. Cooley
M. L. Phillips Elementary School
Fort Worth, Texas

John A. Dossey
Illinois State University
Normal, Illinois

Linda Proudfit
Governors State University
University Park, Illinois

Jeanne F. Ramos
Nobel Middle School
Los Angeles, California

David Robitaille
University of British Columbia
Vancouver, British Columbia, Canada

Jane Swafford
Illinois State University
Normal, Illinois

Problem Solving in Chapter 1

Search for patterns in data concerning shark habits, Presidential candidates, and top-ranked athletes.

TECHNOLOGY

- Spreadsheet
- Calculator
- World Wide Web
- Interactive CD-ROM

X Algebra

See how to plot points and interpret algebraic information in different types of graphs.

CHAPTER

| 1 | 2 | 3 | 4 | 5 | 6 | 7 | 8 | 9 | 10 | 11 | 12 |

STATISTICS - REAL WORLD USE OF WHOLE NUMBERS...2

Problem Solving in Chapter 2

Present information concerning space probes, collections, and deep-sea diving to demonstrate your decision-making skills.

TECHNOLOGY

- Spreadsheet
- Calculator
- World Wide Web
- Interactive CD-ROM

𝑥 Algebra

See how to use one of the basic units of algebra — the variable.

CHAPTER

| 1 | **2** | 3 | 4 | 5 | 6 | 7 | 8 | 9 | 10 | 11 | 12 |

CONNECTING ARITHMETIC TO ALGEBRA...62

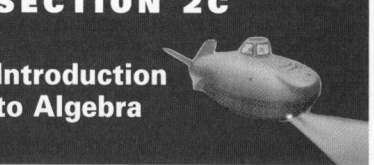

Problem Solving in Chapter 3

Use decimal information about either spiders, currencies of the world, or the Oregon Trail to design different plans of action.

TECHNOLOGY

- Spreadsheet
- Calculator
- World Wide Web
- Interactive CD-ROM

x Algebra

See how to use mental math to solve decimal equations.

CHAPTER

| 1 | 2 | **3** | 4 | 5 | 6 | 7 | 8 | 9 | 10 | 11 | 12 |

DECIMALS...134

Problem Solving
in Chapter 4

Practice drawing charts and dia-grams about garbage, shopping malls, and unusual inventions.

TECHNOLOGY

- Geometry Software
- Calculator
- World Wide Web
- Interactive CD-ROM

𝓍 Algebra

See how formulas can help you find the areas of polygons and circles.

CHAPTER

| 1 | 2 | 3 | **4** | 5 | 6 | 7 | 8 | 9 | 10 | 11 | 12 |

MEASUREMENT...206

Problem Solving in Chapter 5

Look for numerical patterns in clocks and calendars, and in tools of the trade, to make accurate and reliable predictions.

TECHNOLOGY

- Spreadsheet
- Calculator
- World Wide Web
- Interactive CD-ROM

Algebra

Learn more about basic number theory facts and fraction notation, two important building blocks of algebra.

CHAPTER

| 1 | 2 | 3 | 4 | **5** | 6 | 7 | 8 | 9 | 10 | 11 | 12 |

PATTERNS AND NUMBER THEORY...266

SECTION 5A
Number Theory

SECTION 5B
Connecting Fractions and Decimals

Problem Solving in Chapter 6

Use logical reasoning to discover new information about blood, and then use data tables and charts to predict flood patterns.

TECHNOLOGY

- Fraction Calculator
- World Wide Web
- Interactive CD-ROM

Algebra

See how to use like denominators to solve fraction equations.

CHAPTER

| 1 | 2 | 3 | 4 | 5 | **6** | 7 | 8 | 9 | 10 | 11 | 12 |

ADDING AND SUBTRACTING FRACTIONS...320

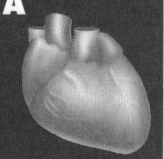

Problem Solving
in Chapter 7

TECHNOLOGY

(x) **Algebra**

Act out real-world situations involving recipes and unusual measurements to understand how fractions can be used in everyday life.

• Fraction Calculator
• World Wide Web
• Interactive CD-ROM

See how to use reciprocals to solve fraction equations.

CHAPTER

1	2	3	4	5	6	**7**	8	9	10	11	12

MULTIPLYING AND DIVIDING FRACTIONS...362

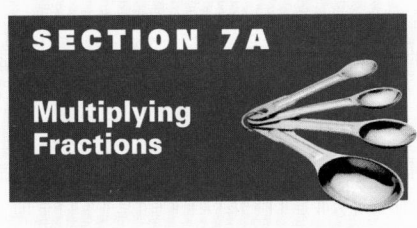

Problem Solving in Chapter 8

Draw diagrams and build models to communicate important geometry concepts in origami, crystals, and Islamic art.

TECHNOLOGY

- Geometry Software
- Calculator
- World Wide Web
- Interactive CD-ROM

X Algebra

Use algebraic thinking as you classify polygons and look for numerical relationships within polygons.

CHAPTER

| 1 | 2 | 3 | 4 | 5 | 6 | 7 | **8** | 9 | 10 | 11 | 12 |

THE GEOMETRY OF POLYGONS...404

Problem Solving in Chapter 9

Demonstrate how integers can be used to describe ideas in earth science and treasure maps.

TECHNOLOGY

• Spreadsheet
• Calculator
• World Wide Web
• Interactive CD-ROM

x Algebra

See how equations can be graphed on a coordinate plane.

CHAPTER

| 1 | 2 | 3 | 4 | 5 | 6 | 7 | 8 | **9** | 10 | 11 | 12 |

INTEGERS AND THE COORDINATE PLANE...464

Problem Solving in Chapter 10

Determine how information about fire prevention, statues, and rain forests can help you make predictions and identify patterns.

TECHNOLOGY

- Spreadsheet
- Calculator
- World Wide Web
- Interactive CD-ROM

Algebra

See how proportions can be solved using algebra.

CHAPTER

| 1 | 2 | 3 | 4 | 5 | 6 | 7 | 8 | 9 | **10** | 11 | 12 |

RATIO, PROPORTION, AND PERCENT...510

PROBLEM SOLVING FOCUS **Checking for a Reasonable Answer** **512**

Problem Solving in Chapter 11

Use data concerning packages and aquariums to explain the advantages and disadvantages of a particular solution.

TECHNOLOGY

- Spreadsheet
- Calculator
- World Wide Web
- Interactive CD-ROM

𝑥 Algebra

See how methods for finding surface area can be summarized using variables.

CHAPTER

| 1 | 2 | 3 | 4 | 5 | 6 | 7 | 8 | 9 | 10 | **11** | 12 |

SOLIDS AND MEASUREMENT...576

Problem Solving in Chapter 12

Investigate how solving simpler problems can help you find complex solutions concerning disasters and game design.

TECHNOLOGY

- Spreadsheet
- Calculator
- World Wide Web
- Interactive CD-ROM

Algebra

See the relationship between probability formulas and area formulas.

CHAPTER

| 1 | 2 | 3 | 4 | 5 | 6 | 7 | 8 | 9 | 10 | 11 | **12** |

PROBABILITY...622

PROBLEM SOLVING FOCUS **Checking for a Reasonable Answer** **624**

Internet Connections

The world of math is connected to the world around you in so many interesting ways. We'd like to invite you to explore these connections on the World Wide Web.

To begin your journey, you will need a web browser. Use your browser to visit the home page for *Mathsurf* by typing in *http://www.mathsurf.com.*

You'll find more web addresses at the top of each chapter opener and section opener that send you directly to pages that relate to your chapter or section.

SEARCH

ecimals

3

Entertainment Link
www.mathsurf.com/6/ch3/ent

...n/6/ch3/social

Science Link
www.mathsurf.com/6/ch3/science

Arts & Literature

In *The Gift of the Magi*, O. Henry stated "One dollar and eighty-...

KEY MATH IDEA...

Decimal numbers can be used... that are in between whole nu...

Decimal place values...

...dies

...edited as one
...of the first cultures
...to use the number 0.
...Without this digit,
...our current base 10
...system wouldn't
...be possible.

People of the World

In Europe, a comma is used in place of a decimal point. The number 42.37 in the United States would be 42,37 in Europe.

Entertainment

In 1988, Carl Lewis won the Olympic gold medal for the 100-meter dash by completing the race in 9.92 seconds.

134

SECTION
3A

Decimal Concepts

www.m...

Science Link   www...

www.mathsurf.com/6/ch3/spiders

It ...n Arm and a Leg ...
... and a Leg ...

...to get three Chi...
...der for a...
not, this wasn't an order for flowers.
It was an order for tarantulas!
   To some people, tarantulas and
other spiders are fearsome creatures
that should be avoided. To others,
spiders are fascinating creatures
that have hunting and mating habits
as varied as those of any animal.
People who study spiders are called
arachnologists (a-rak-NAH-luh-jists).
They spend thousands of dollars and
hours studying these eight-legged
wonders.
   Mathematics plays an important
role in the work of an arachnologist.
Spiders are small creatures. When you
study and describe spiders, you need
to use numbers that are small and precise.
Mathematics provides you with such numbers.

1 Why are some people afraid of spiders?

2 What sort of information do you think is important to arachnologists who are studying a particular species of spider?

3 Why do you need to use small numbers when studying spiders?

137

Problem Solving and Applications

Math is all around you. Having good math skills can help you solve problems every day. What kinds of problems can you solve using mathematics?

Problem Solving
Understand
Plan
Solve
Look Back

Problem Solving STRATEGIES

Problem Solving TIP

WHAT DO YOU THINK?

Sharks

Australian Shark Attacks

Number of attacks: 15, 13, 11, 9, 7, 5, 3, 1, 0
Distance from shore (meters): 0-10, 11-50, 51-100, 101-600

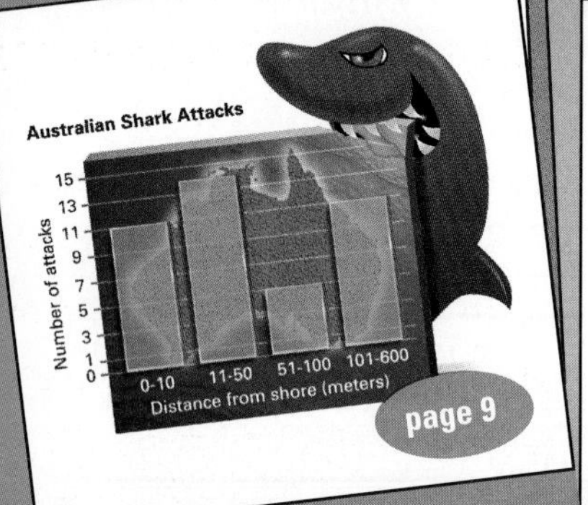

page 9

Where is the safest place to swim when you are in shark-infested waters?

Unusual Measurements

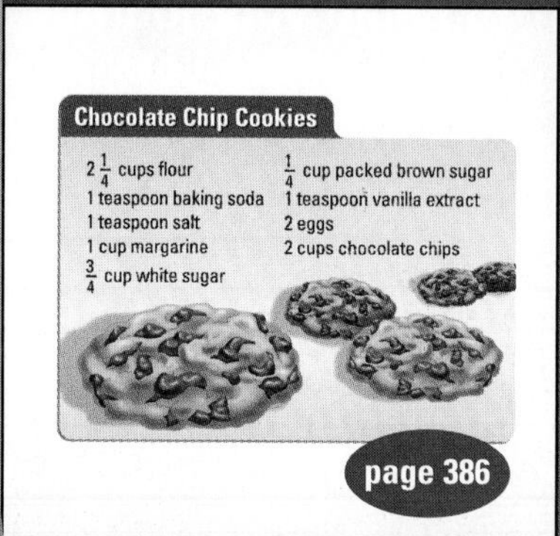

Chocolate Chip Cookies

2¼ cups flour
1 teaspoon baking soda
1 teaspoon salt
1 cup margarine
¾ cup white sugar
¼ cup packed brown sugar
1 teaspoon vanilla extract
2 eggs
2 cups chocolate chips

page 386

How can you adjust a recipe to serve a large number of people?

Treasure Maps

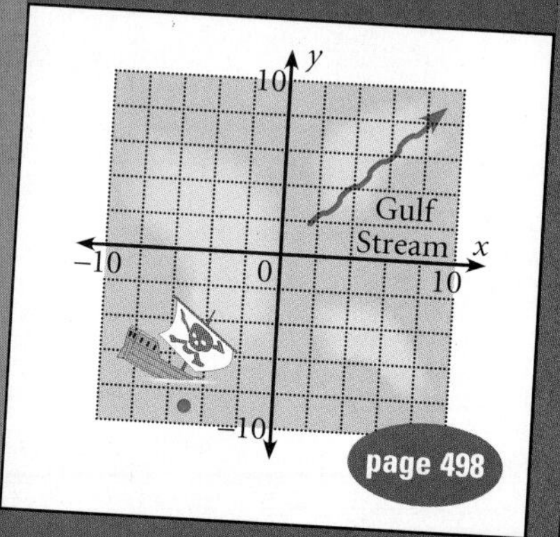

Gulf Stream

page 498

How can you locate a specific point on a map?

Origami

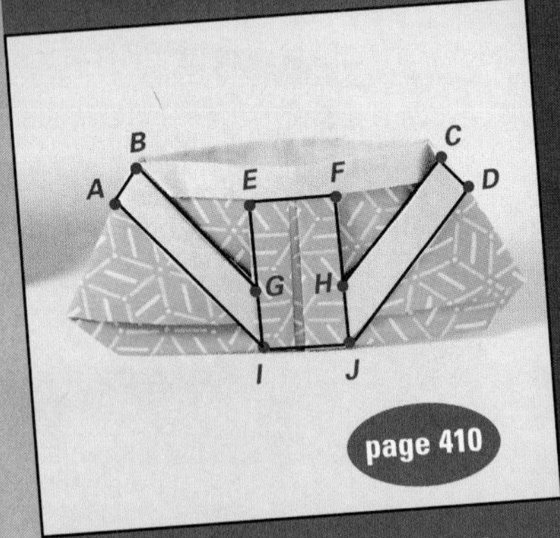

B, C, A, E, F, D, G, H, I, J

page 410

How can you describe the folding instructions for making origami figures?

Garbage

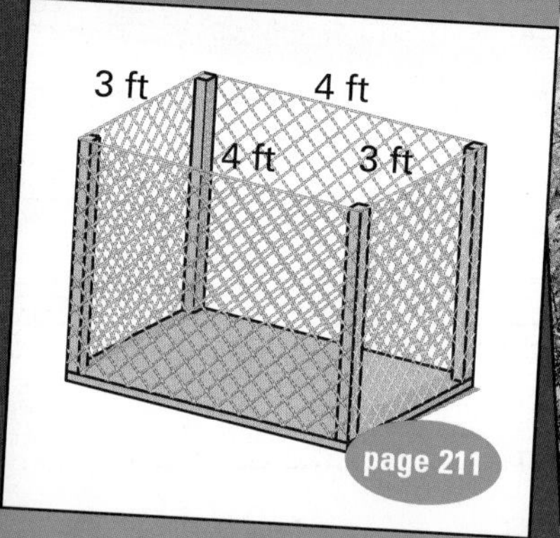

3 ft, 4 ft, 4 ft, 3 ft

page 211

How much material do you need to build a composter?

Clocks & Calendars

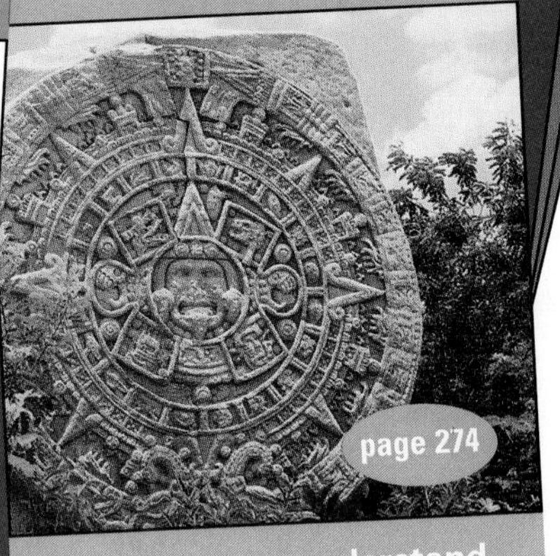

page 274

How can you understand the ancient Aztecs' methods for recording time?

Math is also connected to the other subjects you are studying. Look here to find some examples of how math is connected to:

PROBLEM SOLVING HAND BOOK

You solve some kinds of problems almost every day, such as what to wear for school or when to leave to get to school on time. You solve these problems so often that you don't even have to think to come up with an answer.

Other problems are more difficult to solve. How do you get home if you missed the bus? How can you earn enough money to buy a new bicycle? Finding solutions to these kinds of problems requires good problem-solving skills.

Learning mathematics is an excellent way to practice and improve your problem-solving skills. Mathematics gives you the chance to solve problems alone and with groups. It can help you learn more about how to use data and technology. It also helps you to think in a logical, step-by-step way.

Keep in mind that some problems in math have a "right" answer, but many have more than one answer. People may disagree about which answer is the best, and they may ask you, "What do YOU think?" Answering this question can help you develop a wide range of strategies to use when faced with challenging problems.

The students shown here will share their thinking with you throughout this book. But the key question will always be

"What do you think?"

1. What kinds of problems do you solve almost every day?

2. For what kinds of problems do you need to understand and use mathematics?

3. How can a problem have more than one answer?

Solving Problems

You've solved many problems in your previous math classes. Now you'll look more closely at some methods that can help you solve problems. ◄

Problem Solving

Problem solving can be complicated. Some problems include lots of information. Sometimes information is missing. There might be several ways to solve a problem. Your first answer might be unreasonable, or it might not even answer the question.

A good understanding of mathematics can help when solving problems. But you need to know more than just how to do math. You need to decide what math to do. Should you add the numbers or subtract them? Would the problem be easier to do with decimals or with fractions? Math is a tool for problem solving. As with any tool, you need to make good choices about how to use it.

You need a plan or a strategy to solve any problem. A plan or strategy will help you to understand the problem, to decide on a good approach, to work out a creative solution, and to see if your solution makes sense.

Problem Solving

Understand

Plan

Solve

Look Back

PROBLEM-SOLVING GUIDELINES

① UNDERSTAND the Problem

- What do you know?
- What do you need to find out?

② Develop a PLAN

- Have you ever solved a similar problem?
- What strategies can you use?
- Estimate an answer.

③ SOLVE the Problem

- Do you need to try another strategy?
- What is the solution?

④ LOOK BACK

- Did you answer the right question?
- Does your answer make sense?

Example

How many ways can you make 25¢ using only dimes, nickels, and pennies?

❶ UNDERSTAND the Problem

You *know* that the problem uses only dimes, nickels and pennies. You *need to find* the number of ways you can make 25¢ with these coins.

❷ Develop a PLAN

You've *solved similar problems* involving making a total amount of money. One *strategy* is to list possible combinations as they come to mind.

❸ SOLVE the Problem

#1: 2 dimes, 5 pennies   #2: 2 dimes, 1 nickel

#3: 5 pennies, 2 nickels, 1 dime   #4: 5 pennies, 2 dimes

Notice that the list is not very organized. Some possibilities, such as 25 pennies, are missing. Also, combination #1 and combination #4 are the same.

So *try another strategy*. The number of pennies will always have to be a multiple of 5. So list all of the possible combinations with 0, 5, 10, 15, 20, and 25 pennies.

(0 pennies)   #1: 2 dimes, 1 nickel   #2: 1 dime, 3 nickels   #3: 5 nickels

(5 pennies)   #4: 2 dimes, 5 pennies   #5: 1 dime, 2 nickels, 5 pennies
                      #6: 4 nickels, 5 pennies

(10 pennies) #7: 1 dime, 1 nickel, 10 pennies   #8: 3 nickels, 10 pennies

(15 pennies) #9: 1 dime, 15 pennies   #10: 2 nickels, 15 pennies

(20 pennies) #11: 1 nickel, 20 pennies (25 pennies) #12: 25 pennies

The solution is that there are 12 combinations.

❹ LOOK BACK

The *right question was answered*. The list is organized and does not have any repeated combinations, so *the answer makes sense*.

Check | Your Understanding

1. Would the problem be harder or easier if you were not allowed to use pennies? Explain.

2. Describe a problem that you could solve using a similar method.

3. Why is it important to have a plan before you begin a solution?

Problem Solving
STRATEGIES

• Look for a Pattern
• Make an Organized List
• Make a Table
• Guess and Check
• Work Backward
• Use Logical Reasoning
• Draw a Diagram
• Solve a Simpler Problem

Look for a Pattern

Sometimes the numbers in a problem form a pattern. To solve the problem, find the rule that creates the pattern. Then use the rule to find the answer. ◄

Example

Marsha's hourly wage as a dog groomer increases by a fixed amount each year. She earned $4.75 per hour her first year on the job and $5.60 per hour her second year. Find her hourly wage during her fifth year of work.

Second-year wage:	$5.60
First-year wage:	− 4.75
Wage increase:	$0.85

The rule is that Marsha's wages increase by $0.85 each year.

Use the rule to continue the pattern:

Third-year wage:	$5.60 + $0.85 = $6.45
Fourth-year wage:	$6.45 + $0.85 = $7.30
Fifth-year wage:	$7.30 + $0.85 = $8.15

During her fifth year, she earned $8.15 per hour.

Try It

a. During their first year of life, swordfish increase in weight at a regular rate. A swordfish weighed 14 pounds at age 1 month and 28 pounds at age 2 months. How much did it weigh at age 6 months?

b. This year, the average price of Concert File CDs went from $13.95 to $12.49. If the price continues to change at the same rate, how much will they cost next year?

Make an Organized List

Problem Solving
STRATEGIES

• Look for a Pattern
• Make an Organized List
• Make a Table
• Guess and Check
• Work Backward
• Use Logical Reasoning
• Draw a Diagram
• Solve a Simpler Problem

Sometimes you need to find the number of ways in which something can be done. To solve the problem, make a list of all the ways and count them. It is important to organize your list so that you don't miss any possibilities, or repeat any of them. ◄

Example

At the Healthy Bowl Restaurant, you can order a garden salad with or without dressing, with or without croutons, and with or without bacon bits. If the manager wants to list all the possible combinations in the menu, how many combinations must she list?

One way to organize a list is to pick one item and list all the combinations that include that one item. Then, pick a second item and list all the combinations that include the second item but not the first.

First list the dressing choices: D

DC   DB

DCB

Now, list the crouton choices without dressing:

C

CB

Now, list the bacon bit choices without dressing or croutons:

B

Finally, list any choices without dressing, croutons, or bacon bits:

no toppings

There are 8 combinations.

Try It

a. There are 5 pitchers and 3 catchers on the Middle School baseball team. How many pitcher-catcher pairs can the coach choose from?

b. Flavor-Filled Ice Cream has four flavors of soft-serve ice cream. How many ways could you choose two different flavors?

Problem Solving

STRATEGIES

• Look for a Pattern
• Make an Organized List
• Make a Table
• Guess and Check
• Work Backward
• Use Logical Reasoning
• Draw a Diagram
• Solve a Simpler Problem

Make a Table

A problem involving a relationship between two sets of numbers can often be solved by making a table. A table helps you organize data so that you can see the numerical relationship and find the answer. ◄

Example

Carl mailed ads for his new craft business to three friends. He asked each friend to mail three copies to friends. Each friend was then to mail ads to three of *their* friends, and so on. How many ads were sent in the sixth mailing?

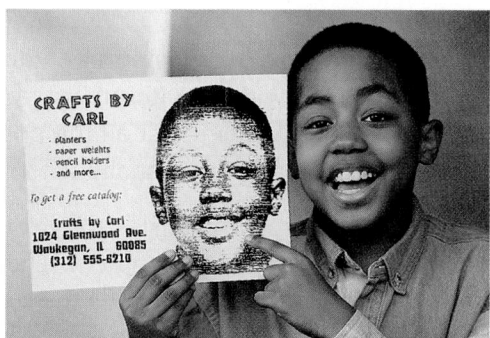

Make a table to organize data about the mailings.

Mailing	1	2	3
Number sent	3	$3 \times 3 = 9$	$3 \times 3 \times 3 = 27$

The table helps you see the relationship between the number of a mailing and the number of ads sent. In mailing **1,** 3 is multiplied by itself **one time.** In mailing **2,** 3 is multiplied by itself **two times.** In mailing **3,** 3 is multiplied by itself **three times.**

So, to find the number of ads in mailing **6** multiply 3 by itself **six times.**

$3 \times 3 \times 3 \times 3 \times 3 \times 3 = 729$

In the sixth mailing, 729 ads were sent.

Try It

a. Every person has 2 parents, 4 grandparents, 8 great-grandparents, and so on. Record this information in a table. Then find how many great-great-great-great-great-great grandparents everyone has.

b. For every 2 bald eagles seen by visitors to the Audubon Eagle Sanctuary, 7 golden eagles are seen. Make a table showing the number of golden eagles seen when 2, 4, and 6 bald eagles are seen. Then find the number of bald eagles seen for 56 golden eagles.

Guess and Check

Problem Solving
STRATEGIES

- Look for a Pattern
- Make an Organized List
- Make a Table
- Guess and Check
- Work Backward
- Use Logical Reasoning
- Draw a Diagram
- Solve a Simpler Problem

If you're not sure how to solve a problem, make an educated guess at the answer. Check your guess. If it's wrong, use what you've learned in checking your guess to make a better guess. Continue to guess, check, and revise until you find the answer. ◄

Example

Twenty-five dolphins and killer whales perform at Sea Circus. There are 13 more dolphins than killer whales. How many of each animal are there?

	Dolphins	Killer Whales
Guess: Make an educated guess: $15 + 10 = 25$	15	10
Check: There should be 13 more dolphins.	$15 - 10 = 5$	
Think: The difference isn't big enough. I need more dolphins.		
Revise: $20 + 5 = 25$	20	5
Check:	$20 - 5 = 15$	
Think: I'm closer, but now I have slightly too many dolphins.		
Revise: $19 + 6 = 25$	19	6
Check:	$19 - 6 = 13$ ✔	

There are 19 dolphins and 6 killer whales.

Try It

a. Before going on vacation, Vanessa bought 21 rolls of film. She bought twice as many rolls of print film as slide film. How many rolls of each type did she buy?

b. One weekend, Allan worked a total of 17 hours helping his uncle paint his cabin. They worked 3 hours more on Saturday than they worked on Sunday. How many hours did they work each day?

Problem Solving STRATEGIES

- Look for a Pattern
- Make an Organized List
- Make a Table
- Guess and Check
- **Work Backward**
- Use Logical Reasoning
- Draw a Diagram
- Solve a Simpler Problem

Work Backward

A problem may tell you what happened at the end of a series of steps and ask you to find what happened at the beginning. To solve the problem, work backward step-by-step to the beginning. ◄

Example

Ed was deciding when to get up in the morning. He needed 45 minutes to get ready for school. His bus ride took 25 minutes. He wanted to get to school 20 minutes early to do some library research. If school starts at 8:30, what time should he get up?

The problem describes three steps occurring in order (getting ready, riding the bus, doing research). It also tells you the end result (school starts at 8:30). To solve the problem, work backward to the beginning.

Step	What Happened	Conclusion
3	Ed did research for 20 minutes. Then it was 8:30.	Before this step, the time was 20 minutes before 8:30, or 8:10.
2	He rode the bus for 25 minutes. Then it was 8:10.	Before this step, the time was 25 minutes before 8:10, or 7:45.
1	He spent 45 minutes getting ready. Then it was 7:45.	Before this step, the time was 45 minutes before 7:45, or 7:00.

Ed should get up at 7:00.

Try It

a. One winter night, the temperature fell 14 degrees between midnight and 6 A.M. Between 6 A.M. and 10 A.M., the temperature doubled. By noon it had risen another 11 degrees, to 33°F. Find the midnight temperature.

b. Lake Erie is half as wide as Lake Michigan. Lake Erie is 5 miles wider than Lake Ontario. Lake Superior is 3 times as wide as Lake Ontario. Lake Superior is 159 miles wide. How wide is Lake Michigan?

Use Logical Reasoning

Problem Solving STRATEGIES

- Look for a Pattern
- Make an Organized List
- Make a Table
- Guess and Check
- Work Backward
- **Use Logical Reasoning**
- Draw a Diagram
- Solve a Simpler Problem

To solve a problem using logical reasoning, decide how the facts of the problem relate to each other. Then work your way step-by-step from the given facts to a sensible solution. Along the way, avoid making false assumptions or drawing unreasonable conclusions. ◄

Example

Arnie, Becca, and Chad collect stamps, coins, and rocks, though not necessarily in that order. Becca is the sister of the rock collector. Chad once had lunch with both the rock collector and the stamp collector. Match each person with his or her hobby.

Take clues one at a time. Use a grid to keep track of your conclusions.

1. Becca is the sister of the rock collector. So she is not the rock collector.

	Stamps	Coins	Rocks
Arnie			
Becca			no
Chad			

2. Chad once had lunch with the rock collector and the stamp collector.

	Stamps	Coins	Rocks
Arnie			
Becca			no
Chad	no		no

Chad must collect coins.

Becca must collect stamps.

That means Arnie collects rocks.

	Stamps	Coins	Rocks
Arnie	no	no	yes
Becca	yes	no	no
Chad	no	yes	no

Try It

a. Tim, Mei, and Jamal are in 6th, 7th, and 8th grades, though not necessarily in that order. Mei is not in 8th grade. The 6th grader is in chorus with Tim and band with Mei. Match the students with their grades.

b. Sid, Todd, and Maria play soccer, baseball, and tennis, though not necessarily in that order. Maria doesn't play tennis. Sid rides the bus with the baseball and tennis players. Match the students and their sports.

Draw a Diagram

Some problems are visual. They may involve objects, places, or physical situations. To solve such a problem, draw a diagram to help you see relationships among the given data. Then use the relationships to find the answer. ◄

Example

All the city blocks in Sunnyville are the same size. Geena starts her paper route at the corner of two streets. She goes 8 blocks south, 13 blocks west, 8 blocks north, and 6 blocks east. How far is she from her starting point when she is done?

To get a clearer picture of what is happening, draw a diagram of Geena's route.

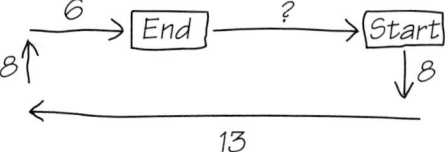

The diagram shows that at the end of her route, Geena is 13 – 6 blocks from her starting point.

13 – 6 = 7

When she finishes, Geena is 7 blocks from her starting point.

Try It

a. After leaving a warehouse, a trucker drove 28 miles south to make a delivery. The trucker then made three more deliveries, driving 13 miles west, 43 miles north, and 13 miles east. How far was the trucker from the warehouse?

b. The roots of an elm tree reach 17 feet into the ground. A robin's nest is 13 feet from the top of the tree. From treetop to root-bottom, the tree measures 52 feet. How far above the ground is the nest?

Solve a Simpler Problem

Problem Solving

STRATEGIES

- Look for a Pattern
- Make an Organized List
- Make a Table
- Guess and Check
- Work Backward
- Use Logical Reasoning
- Draw a Diagram
- Solve a Simpler Problem

A problem may seem very complex. It may contain large numbers or appear to require many steps to solve. Instead of solving the given problem, solve a similar but simpler problem. Look for shortcuts, patterns, and relationships. Then use what you've learned to solve the original problem. ◄

Example

A diagonal is a line that connects two points in a figure that are not already connected by a side. For example, you can draw nine diagonals inside a 6-sided figure. How many diagonals can you draw inside an 8-sided figure?

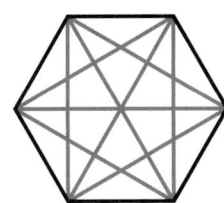

You could draw an 8-sided figure and draw and count the number of diagonals. But that could be very complicated.

Instead, look at some very simple figures.

3-sided figure:
0 diagonals

4-sided figure:
2 diagonals

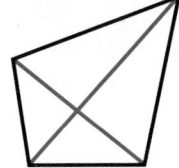

5-sided figure:
5 diagonals

Notice that from a 3-sided to a 4-sided figure, 2 diagonals are added. From a 4-sided to a 5-sided figure, 3 diagonals are added. From a 5-sided to a 6-sided figure, 4 diagonals are added.

A 7-sided figure would have 14 diagonals (9 + 5). An 8-sided figure would have 20 diagonals (14 + 6). A 9-sided figure would have 27 diagonals (20 + 7).

Try It

a. Each side of each triangle is 1 in. long. If there were 42 triangles in a row, what would the combined length of all of their sides be?

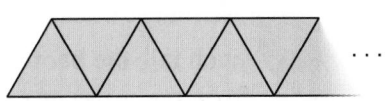

b. A bell rang 22 times. Each ring lasted 4 seconds. Two seconds elapsed between rings. How long did the ringing last?

Science Link
www.mathsurf.com/6/ch1/science

Entertainment

When it comes to houses with televisions, China is an outlier. 227,500,000 homes in China have televisions. The country with the next greatest number of televisions, the United States, has only 94,200,000.

People of the World

Charts and graphs in Japan's *Asahi Shimbun* newspaper are seen by over 12,500,000 people every day. That's about four times the population of the state of Oklahoma.

Science

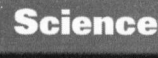

If a bar graph showed the planets' distances from the Sun, and the bar representing Mercury's distance was one inch tall, the bar for Pluto's distance would be 9 feet tall.

Numbers

Social Studies Link
www.mathsurf.com/6/ch1/social

Arts & Literature

The letter that appears most often in English writings is "e." It is followed by "t," "a," "i," and "n."

KEY MATH IDEAS

Graphs can be used to compare numbers to each other, to compare numbers over time, and to compare numbers as part of a whole.

A scatterplot is a graph that can help determine if there is a relationship between two sets of data.

You can use stem-and-leaf diagrams to display data in intervals.

A large set of data can be described by listing the value that falls in the exact middle of the data, as well as the value that appears most often.

The mean, or average, of a set of data can also describe the data.

Social Studies

The mean temperature in Norilsk, Russia, is 12.4 °F. Water freezes at temperatures below 32 °F.

CHAPTER PROJECT

Problem Solving
Understand
Plan
Solve
Look Back

In this project, you will collect data about an interesting location somewhere in the world. Other students will have to guess the location you chose based on your data. Begin by thinking of a place in the world that you find interesting and want to learn more about.

Problem Solving Focus

Read each problem, and answer the questions about the problem.

Reading the Problem

Before you can solve a problem, you must understand the information given in the problem. Answering questions about the problem can help you organize the information and develop a plan for finding a solution.

1 Krakatoa, a famous volcano in Indonesia, once erupted so loudly that people over 3000 miles away could hear it. One hundred and two years later, Nevado del Ruiz in Columbia erupted. This took place 316 years after the 1669 eruption of Mount Etna in Italy. In what year was Krakatoa's loud eruption?

a. What is the problem about?

b. What is the problem asking for?

c. When did Mount Etna erupt?

d. Which volcano erupted first, Nevado del Ruiz or Mount Etna?

e. Write and answer a question of your own.

2 Kilauea is a volcano in Hawaii. It is about half the height of Canlaon in the Philippines. On-Take in Japan is about 2000 feet taller than Canlaon. If the total height of the three volcanoes is about 22,000 feet, about how tall is each volcano?

a. What is the problem about?

b. What is the problem asking for?

c. How many times shorter than Canlaon is Kilauea?

d. Of the three volcanoes, which is the tallest?

e. Write and answer a question of your own.

4

DANGER! SHARK ATTACK!

You walk alone on the beach, the water splashing against your feet. Suddenly, you feel a presence. A single animal that threatens your very life. You turn around and scream in horror at the sight of … a dog!

Silly, maybe, but it's statistically sound. Each year, about 18 people in the United States are killed by dogs. In the past 100 years, only 59 people worldwide have been killed by sharks. There are more than 350 species of sharks, but only about 30 of them are known to have attacked humans.

Sharks are fascinating and often misunderstood. Suppose you were a marine biologist who wanted to study sharks to better understand them. How would you decide the best places to go and the best sharks to study? One way would be to refer to graphs that display data on shark attacks. Graphs allow you to compare numerical data, display it visually, and look for patterns and trends.

1 Why do you think more people are killed by dogs than by sharks?

2 Why might a graph of data be better than a list of data?

5

1-1 Reading Graphs

► **Lesson Link** In the past, you've learned the importance of using information to make decisions. Graphs are a useful way to organize information. ◄

You'll Learn ...

■ to read numbers from different types of graphs

■ to compare numbers within the same graph

... How It's Used

Marine biologists use graphs to find relationships between marine life and factors in their environment when developing research plans.

Vocabulary

bar graph

pictograph

line graph

circle graph

Explore   Graphs of Data

Attacking the Data

Use the graphs to answer the questions.

Australian Shark Attacks

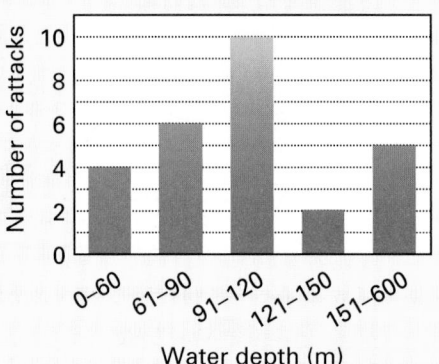

Australian Shark Attacks

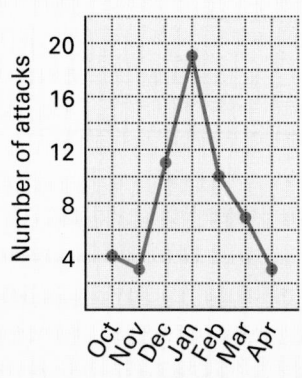

Australian Shark Attacks

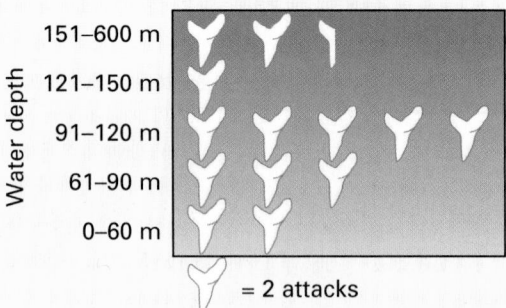

Times of Shark Attacks

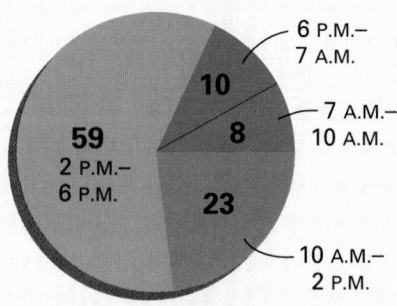

1. At what depth do most shark attacks occur? Name the graph(s) you can use to determine this.

2. In which month do the fewest attacks occur? The most attacks?

3. At what time of day do most shark attacks occur?

4. How many attacks were studied to produce each graph? Explain how you found your answers.

A **bar graph** uses vertical or horizontal bars to display numerical information. The length of the bar tells you the number it represents.

Example 1

How much deeper than a free diver can a scuba diver dive?

Look at the bar for the free diver. It represents a depth of about 15 meters. The scuba diver bar represents 50 meters. Since $50 - 15 = 35$, the scuba diver can dive about 35 meters deeper.

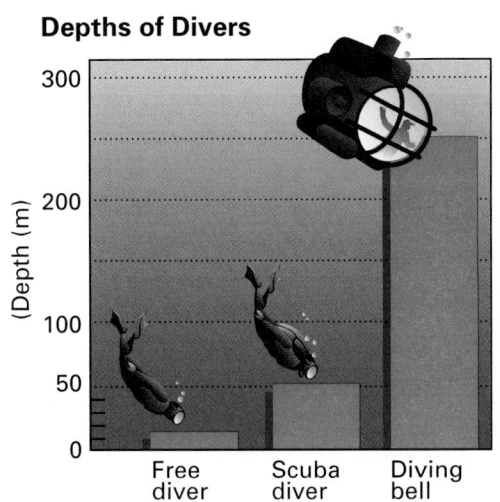

Depths of Divers

A **pictograph** uses symbols to represent data. All of the symbols have the same value. To determine the measure of an item in a pictograph, count the number of symbols and multiply by the value of the symbol.

Example 2

About how many species of animals are there in the San Antonio Zoo?

In the pictograph, the number of species of animals in the San Antonio Zoo is represented by 7 symbols. Each symbol equals 100 species.

$7 \times 100 = 700$

There are about 700 species.

Zoos with Most Species of Animals

San Diego

Cincinnati

San Antonio

Bronx

Key 🐘 = 100 species

MENTAL MATH

A simple way to compute 7×100 is to compute 7×1 and annex two zeros to the end of the answer.

Try It

Use the bar graph or the pictograph to answer each question.

a. How much deeper can a diver in a diving bell dive than a scuba diver?

b. About how many species of animals are in the San Diego Zoo?

A **line graph** often shows how data changes over time. Each dot represents an item of data. The height of the dot represents the value of the data. The time is shown by how far to the right the dot is.

Example 3

Find the value of a 1980 Rickey Henderson baseball card in 1992.

Find the dot above the 1992 on the year line. The dot is directly to the right of the value 150.

A card was worth $150 in 1992.

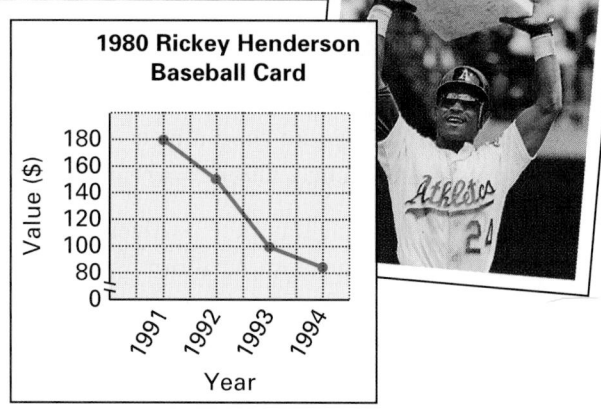

A **circle graph** shows how portions of a set of data compare with the whole set. The larger the value of the data, the wider the wedge that represents the value.

Example 4

Retailers were asked to name the technology they preferred for advertising. Which technology was most favored?

The largest wedge in the graph represents the Internet. It was the most favored technology.

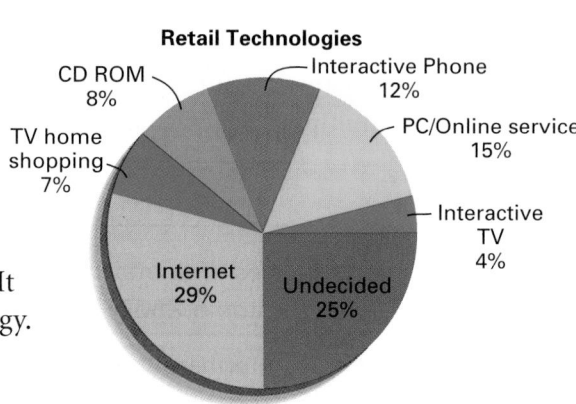

Try It

Use the line graph or the circle graph to answer each question.

a. In what year was a Rickey Henderson card worth about $100?

b. Which technology was the least preferred for advertising?

Check | Your Understanding

1. How does each type of graph show the value of a data item?

2. For each graph, how can you tell which value is the highest number? The lowest number?

Practice and Apply

Getting Started Fill in the blank with the name of the graph described.

1. A _____ uses symbols to represent data and a key to show the value of each symbol.

2. A _____ shows data as a set of connected points.

3. In a _____, the data is broken into parts of a whole.

Science Use the Shark Attack graph to answer each question.

4. What is the total number of shark attacks shown in the data?   41

5. Which bar represents the most shark attacks? The fewest shark attacks?

6. Do more shark attacks take place within 50 m from shore or 51–600 m from shore?

7. How many bars represent a number of attacks that is greater than 10?

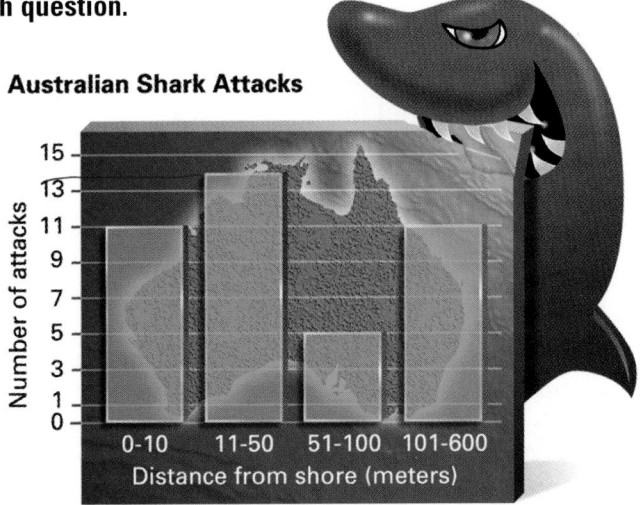

Australian Shark Attacks

Use the Cost of Raising a Child graph for Exercises 8–11.

8. What is the cost of transportation?

9. For each $100 a parent spends on raising a child to age 18, how much more is spent on housing and clothes than on education?

10. **Test Prep** For each $300 spent, estimate how much is spent for food and clothes.

   Ⓐ $329   Ⓑ $90

   Ⓒ $29   Ⓓ $130

11. Which costs are about twice as much as the cost of education? Five times as much? Eleven times as much?

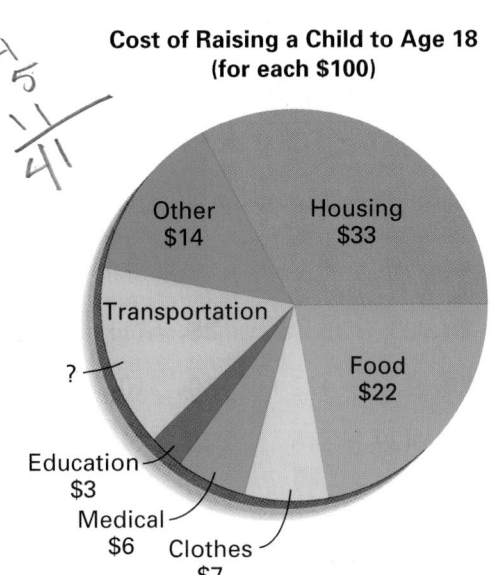

Cost of Raising a Child to Age 18
(for each $100)

Problem Solving and Reasoning

Ocean sizes are often measured in square miles. Use this measurement and the graph to answer each question.

12. Number Sense What is the size of the Arctic Ocean?

13. Operation Sense The total area of the Pacific, Atlantic, and Indian Oceans is 124,000,000 square miles. How many square miles is the Pacific Ocean?

14. Critical Thinking What's the difference in square miles between the sizes of the Indian Ocean and the Atlantic Ocean?

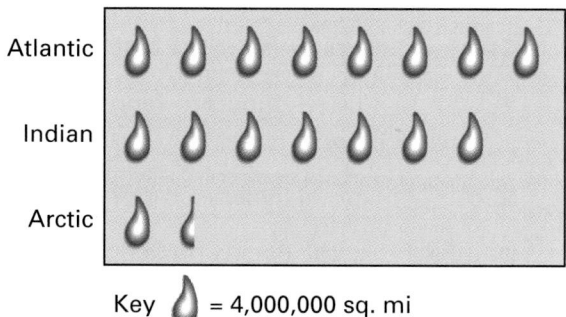

Ocean Sizes

Atlantic

Indian

Arctic

Key ⬭ = 4,000,000 sq. mi

Use the **CD-ROM Sales** graph to answer each question.

15. Communicate Describe the change(s) in the data overall and from year to year.

16. How many CD-ROMs were sold in 1992?

17. What's the difference between the number of CD-ROMs sold in 1993 and the number sold in 1994?

18. What year showed the biggest increase in CD-ROM sales?

19. Critical Thinking How many CD-ROM sales would you expect in the year 2000?

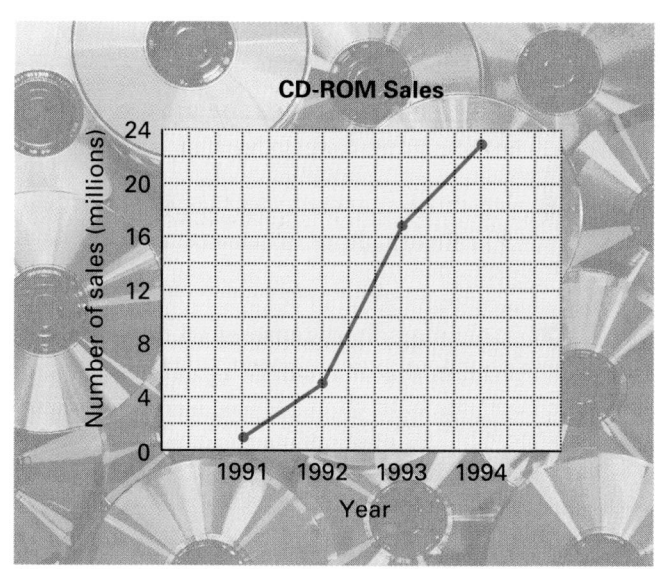

CD-ROM Sales

Mixed Review

Write each as a number. *[Previous course]*

20. four hundred thirty-seven

21. five thousand one hundred six

22. two thousand six hundred eleven

23. eight thousand twenty-two

Add. *[Previous course]*

24. 23 + 35	**25.** 61 + 29	**26.** 456 + 43	**27.** 712 + 94	**28.** 888 + 612
29. 272 + 422	**30.** 510 + 501	**31.** 348 + 282	**32.** 638 + 804	**33.** 135 + 298
34. 429 + 316	**35.** 612 + 178	**36.** 543 + 799	**37.** 702 + 298	**38.** 941 + 62
39. 667 + 919	**40.** 52 + 452	**41.** 300 + 300	**42.** 185 + 468	**43.** 472 + 584

Misleading Graphs

▶ **Lesson Link**   In the last lesson, you learned some of the ways that a graph can give you a better understanding of data. Now you will see how a graph can *mis*lead you. ◀

You'll Learn ...

■ to identify common ways that a graph can suggest misleading relationships

... How It's Used

Consumers have to check graphs to see if they could be misleading before deciding which product to buy or which service to use.

Explore   Misleading Graphs

Monstro and Mighty

Monstro is a blue shark who lives at the Oceanside Aquarium. Mighty is another blue shark who lives at the Deep Sea Aquarium. Each aquarium created a graph showing the weights of the two sharks. An independent marine biologist also drew a graph. The three graphs are shown below.

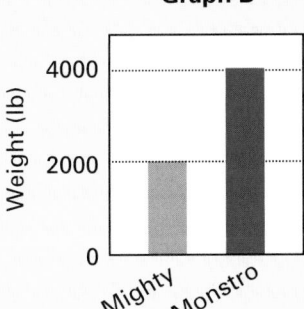

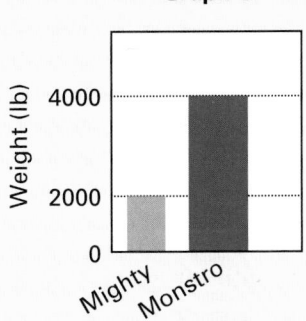

Graph A   **Graph B**   **Graph C**

1. Which graph do you think was made by the owners of Monstro at the Oceanside Aquarium? Why?

2. Which graph do you think was made by the owners of Mighty at the Deep Sea Aquarium? Why?

3. Which graph shows that Monstro weighs 4000 pounds and Mighty weighs 2000 pounds?

4. If you were writing a newspaper article about Monstro and Mighty, which graph do you think would be the best one to use? Why?

Learn   Misleading Graphs

There are many ways to make a graph that can mislead a careless reader. One way is to start labeling the graph at a number other than zero without indicating that some numbers have been skipped.

Example 1

Is the great white shark twice as long as the mako shark?

In graph Ⓐ, the top bar is twice as long as the bottom bar. But the value for the great white shark, 16, is not twice the value for the mako shark, 13.

In graph Ⓑ, the great white shark is clearly not twice as long. When the bar graph starts at 0, the graph is not misleading.

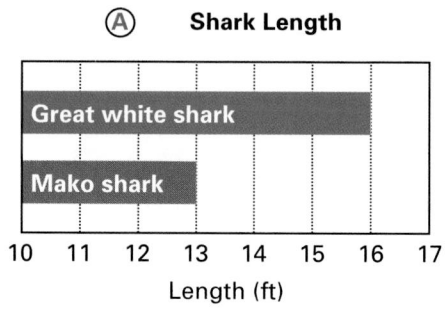

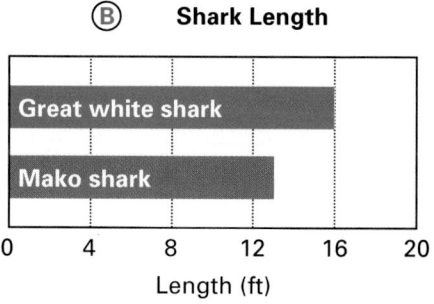

Example 2

Is the hippo able to hold its breath for twice as long as the sea otter?

Both bars start at zero, and the hippo bar is twice as tall as the sea otter bar. But the data values show that a sea otter can hold its breath for 5 minutes and the hippo for 15 minutes—three times as long as a sea otter.

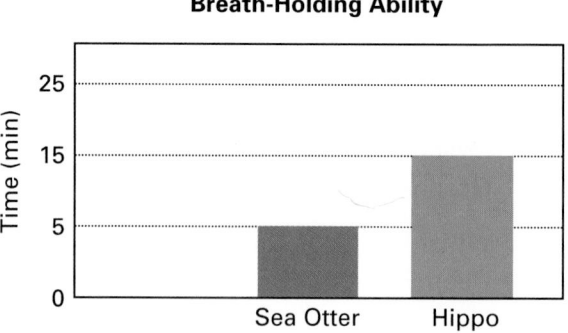

A misleading impression is created because the 5–15 space covers more values than the 0–5 space, but both spaces have equal heights.

A graph can mislead by lengthening or shortening the spaces between data values in order to give a certain impression.

Example 3

Which admission price went up more quickly?

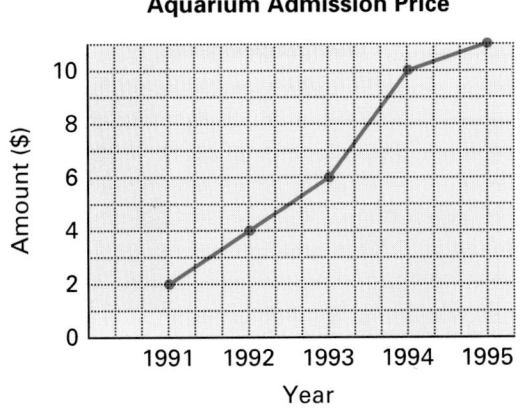

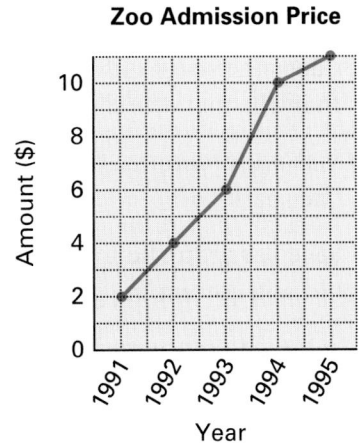

In the right graph, the years are much closer together, so the line appears to climb more rapidly. But both graphs show exactly the same data. Neither admission price went up more quickly.

Try It

Explain how each graph could create a misleading impression.

a.

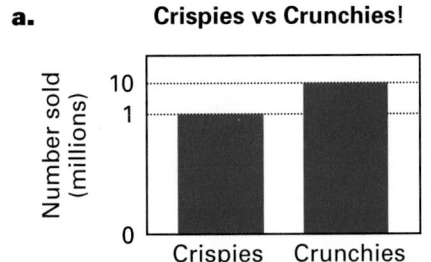

b.

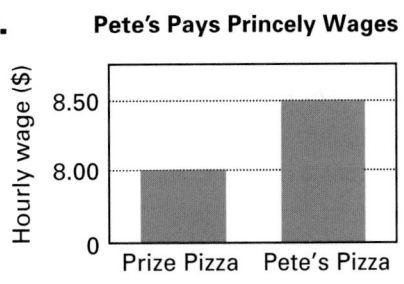

Test Prep

Many graphs can be misleading because the vertical scale has been drawn incorrectly. When evaluating a graph for misleading impressions, check the vertical scale first.

Check   Your Understanding

1. What should you look at to determine if a graph is misleading?

2. Why might someone want to create a misleading graph? Give examples from everyday life.

Practice and Apply

Getting Started Use the Life Span graph for Exercises 1–5.

1. What is the information in the graph about?

2. How many times taller does the shark's life span bar appear to be than the manatee's?

3. Read the graph. What is the approximate life span of the manatee? The shark?

4. **Communicate** Could the bar graph be misleading? If so, how would you correct the graph?

5. **Test Prep** What is the difference in the life spans of the shark and the manatee?

   Ⓐ about 4 yr   Ⓑ about 40 yr
   Ⓒ about 50 yr   Ⓓ about 100 yr

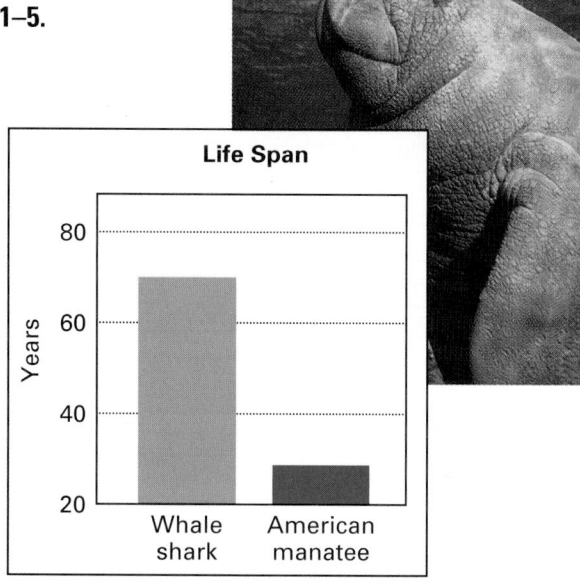

Use the Calories Needed graphs for Exercises 6–10.

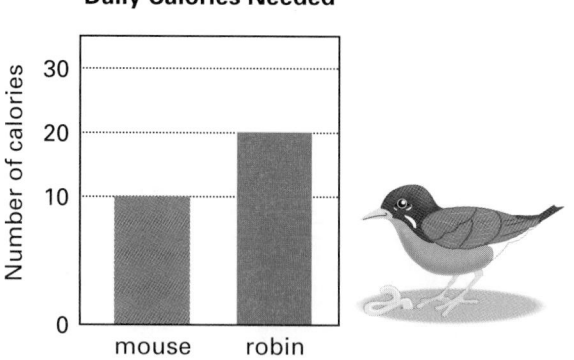

6. **Science** How many calories a day does a mouse need? A robin?

7. For each graph, the robin's calorie bar appears to be how many times greater than the mouse's calorie bar?

8. **Communicate** Do you think either graph is misleading? Explain.

9. How many calories does each animal need in a month that has 30 days?

10. **Science** If a cat needs 370 calories a day, how many days would it take for a mouse to eat the number of calories a cat needs each day?

Problem Solving and Reasoning

Use the Population graphs to answer Exercises 11–13.

U.S. Population of 5–13 Year-Olds

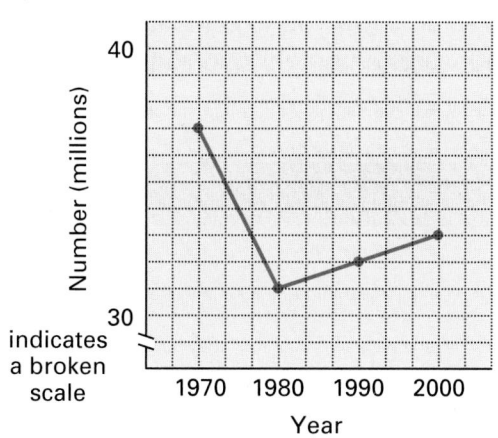

U.S. Population of 5–13 Year-Olds

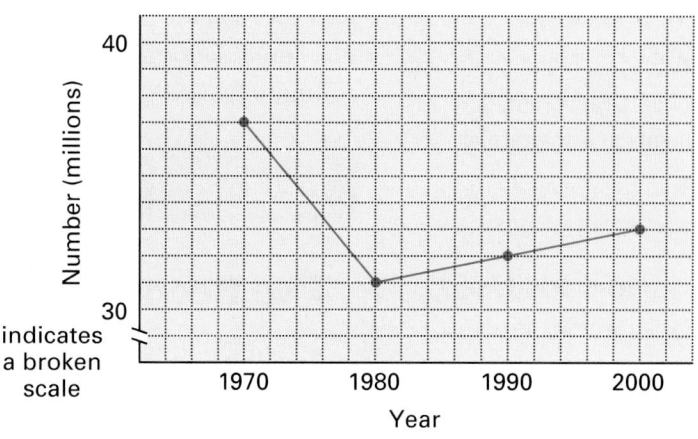

11. **Critical Thinking** How many more 5–13 year-olds will there be in the year 2000 than there were in the year when their population was the smallest?

12. **Critical Thinking** What do you think the population of 5–13 year-olds will be in the year 2010?

13. **Communicate** Why might someone want to represent the information with the second graph?

Mixed Review

Write each number in words. [*Previous course*]

14. 639   15. 204   16. 883   17. 913

18. 6728   19. 8912   20. 2856   21. 1045

Subtract. [*Previous course*]

22. 239 − 51   23. 681 − 67   24. 714 − 80   25. 809 − 37

26. 489 − 211   27. 503 − 432   28. 932 − 601   29. 883 − 577

Project Progress

Start to collect data about the location you have chosen. Try to find data that has lots of numbers in it. You may want to look for data in your school library, your local public library, a travel agency, and the newspaper.

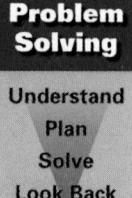

Problem Solving

Understand
Plan
Solve
Look Back

Scatterplots and Trends

You'll Learn ...

■ to identify the two pieces of data represented by points in a scatterplot

■ to determine if a scatterplot suggests a trend

... How It's Used

Medical researchers use scatterplots to find relationships between data from medical tests and the health of patients.

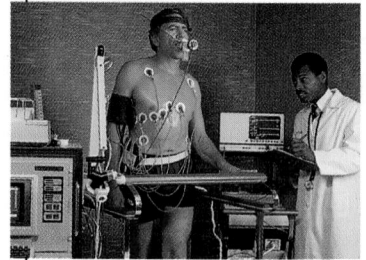

Vocabulary

scatterplot

trend

► Lesson Link The graphs you have seen so far allow you to compare values in a single set of numerical data. This lesson focuses on graphs that allow you to compare two sets of data. ◄

Explore | Graphing Points

I've Been Framed!

1. Nine points labeled *A* through *I* are plotted on the graph. Each of the frames shows one of the nine points plotted by itself. For each frame, determine which of the nine points is shown.

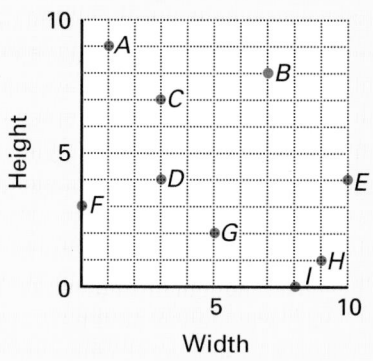

Frame 1

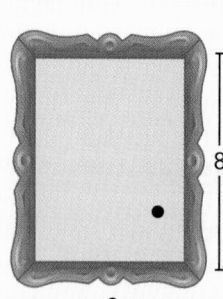

Frame 2

Frame 3

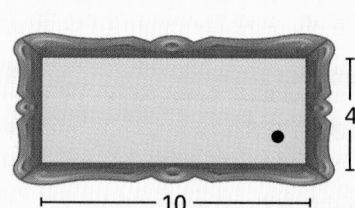

2. How did you decide which point appeared in each frame?

3. Choose a point that didn't appear in one of the three frames and draw a frame for it. Have another student decide which point you framed.

4. Give directions for how to get from the lower left corner of the graph to one of the points on the graph. Use words like "Go to the right so many squares" and "Go up so many squares."

The graphs you have studied so far display individual items of data. For example, each bar in a bar graph represents one number. Sometimes data occurs in pairs. A graph that shows paired data is called a **scatterplot**.

Each point on a scatterplot represents *two* data values. To find the two values, start in the lower left corner. Find one value by counting how far *right* you must go until you are under the point. Find the second value by counting how far *up* you must go to reach the point.

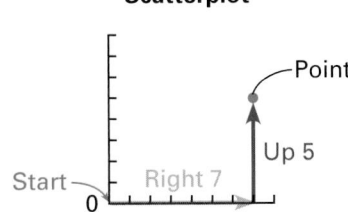

Scatterplot

Example 1

The scatterplot compares the speeds of a mako shark (M) and two great blue sharks (GBS 1 and GBS 2) to their lengths. Give the length and speed of each shark.

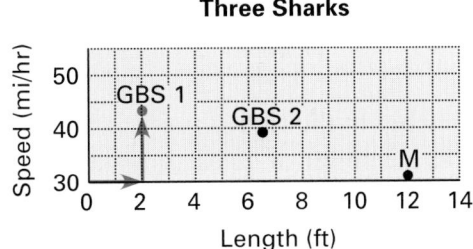

Three Sharks

To reach data point GBS 1, go right to 2 feet and up to about 43 mi/hr. This means that the first great blue shark was 2 feet long and traveled 43 mi/hr.

Second great blue shark:	Length: $6\frac{1}{2}$ feet	Speed: 39 mi/hr
Mako shark:	Length: 12 feet	Speed: 31 mi/hr

Try It

For each point in the graph, estimate the data represented by the point.

a. A

b. B

c. C

d. D

e. E

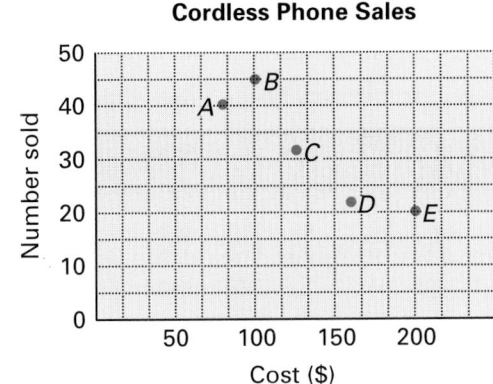

Cordless Phone Sales

▶ **Science Link**

The male mako shark usually grows to $6\frac{1}{2}$ feet long. The female shark grows to 9 feet long. Mako sharks have been known to grow up to 13 feet long.

Sometimes the points in a scatterplot suggest a relationship between the two measured quantities. Look again at the scatterplot in Example 1. Notice that the farther to the right a point is, the farther down it is. This suggests that for the sharks in the experiment, the longer a shark was, the slower it swam. A relationship between two sets of data that shows a pattern like this is called a **trend**.

Examples

For each graph, determine if there is a trend.

2 **Earthquakes and Damaged Houses**

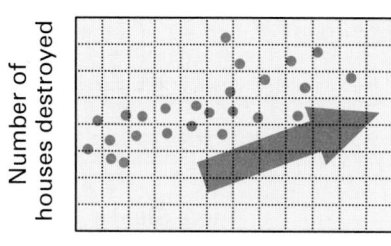

The farther to the right a point is, the farther up it is. This suggests that the greater the power of an earthquake, the greater the number of houses that are destroyed.

3 **Earthquakes and Red Houses**

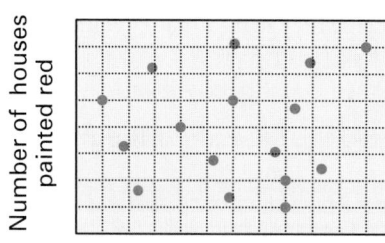

The points don't fall into any particular pattern. This suggests that there is no trend between the power of an earthquake and the number of red houses.

Study TIP

When you have a hard time with homework, check the Examples. They often show step-by-step how to do the homework problems.

| **Check** | **Your Understanding** |

1. In what ways are a line graph and a scatterplot similar? In what ways are they different?

2. Give an example of two sets of related data that might increase together. Give an example where one increases as the other decreases.

Practice and Apply

Getting Started For each point on the graph, describe:

a. How far to the right and how far up on the graph it is.

b. The weight and the length the point represents.

1. *A*   **2.** *B*   **3.** *C*

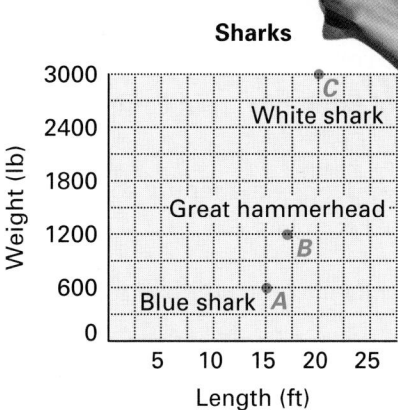

Sharks

For each scatterplot, determine if there is a trend. If there is, describe the pattern of the data.

4. Age and Height

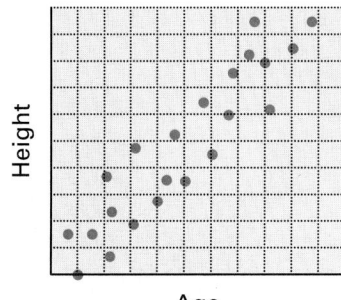

5. Exercise and Height

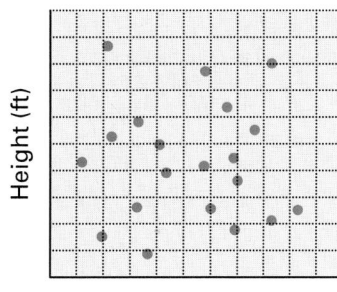

6. Sleep and Scores

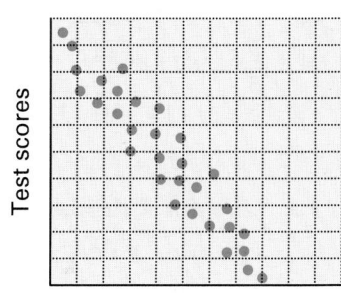

Use the Olympics graph to answer Exercises 7 and 8.

7. **Test Prep** Which two points represent the same values for number of postal stamps?

Ⓐ *A* and *C*   Ⓑ *C* and *E*

Ⓒ *B* and *D*   Ⓓ *A* and *D*

8. Estimation Which point represents a number of events that is about four times greater than the number of stamps? About how many events and how many stamps does this point represent?

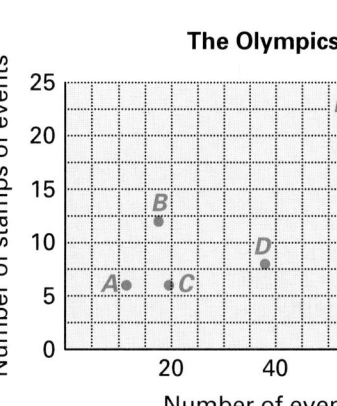

The Olympics

Problem Solving and Reasoning

9. Critical Thinking For each situation, describe what the pattern in a scatterplot would look like.

   a. The hours you work per week compared to your weekly salary

   b. A person's age compared to the amount of sleep needed

   c. The number of books you read compared to the scores on your math tests

   d. The number of people in a family compared to the amount they spend on groceries each week

Use the Calorie Requirements graph for Exercises 10–12.

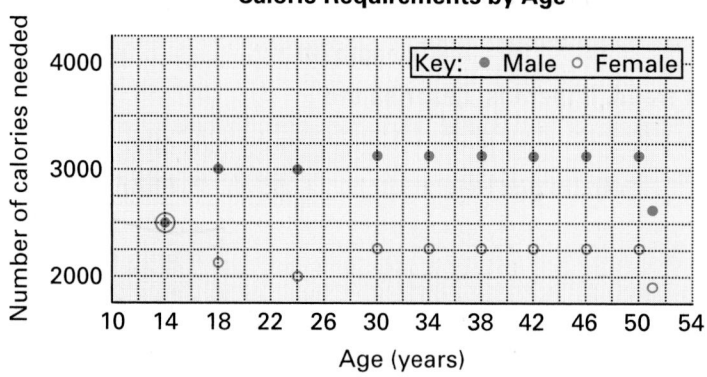

Calorie Requirements by Age

10. Critical Thinking At what age(s) do males need the most calories? Females?

11. Communicate At what age is the difference in calorie needs the greatest between males and females? The smallest? How can you tell?

12. Critical Thinking What pattern is shown in the data for males? For females? For males and females?

13.  In your own words, describe and sketch the kinds of patterns you have seen in scatterplots.

Mixed Review

Write each as a number. *[Previous course]*

14. nine hundred twenty-nine

15. six thousand six hundred six

16. four thousand ninety-eight

17. eight thousand nine hundred

Multiply. *[Previous course]*

18. 6 × 425   **19.** 9 × 481   **20.** 2 × 804   **21.** 8 × 236

At the beginning of this section, you saw how information from graphs can help you make sensible decisions. Now you will have an opportunity to use graphs to make some decisions of your own.

Danger! Shark Attack!

Shark attacks are extremely rare. Millions of people swim in the ocean each year without fear of sharks. The graphs give information on some of the very few attacks that have actually occurred.

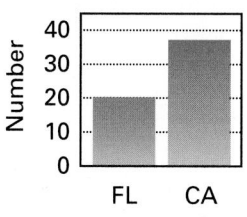

U.S. Shark Attacks

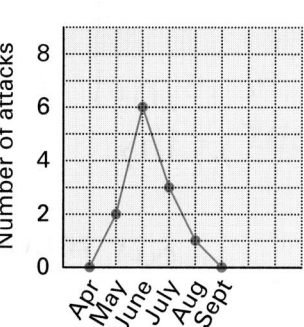

Twelve Florida Attacks

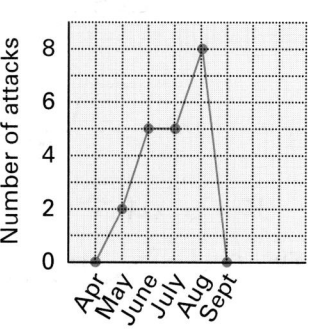

Twenty California Attacks

California Shark Attacks

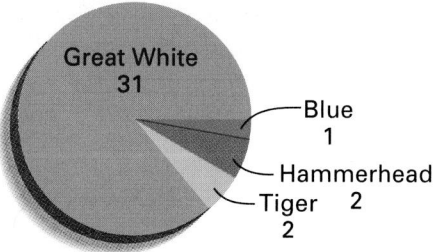

Florida Shark Attacks

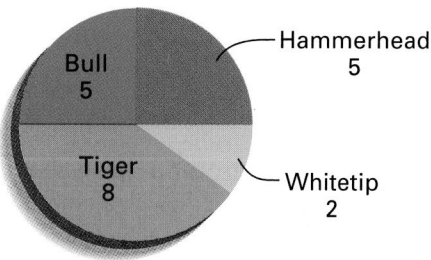

You are a scientist who wants to study shark attacks during June.

1. Which species appears to attack humans the most?

2. Which state has more attacks? How many more? How did you determine this?

3. During the month of May, which state has more shark attacks? How did you determine this?

4. If you can study only one species in the month of June, which state should you go to? Explain how you made your decision.

21

1. **Communicate** Explain how it is possible to read the symbols in a picto-graph and determine their number values. *i'll tell you verbally*

Use the bar graph for Exercises 2–5.

2. Which special had the most viewers? *The sharks*

3. How many more viewers watched *The Sharks* than watched *Great Moments*? *3 more*

4. What was the least watched show? *Great Moments*

5. Could the graph be misleading? Explain. *yes, starts w/ 15, not 0.*

Most-Watched Nature TV Specials

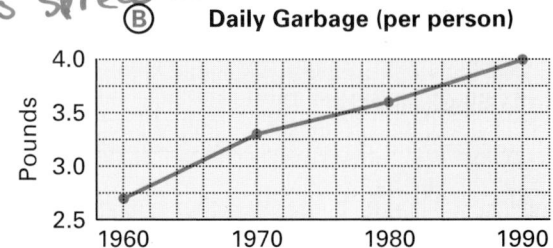

Industry Use the line graphs for Exercises 6–8.

6. In 1980, how much garbage did each person generate in a day? A family of four in a day? *→ about 3.5 lbs*

7. Describe the change in the data over time. *goes up ↑*

8. How are the two graphs alike? How are they different? *same data* *B. is spread out more ↔*

Ⓐ **Daily Garbage (per person)**

Ⓑ **Daily Garbage (per person)**

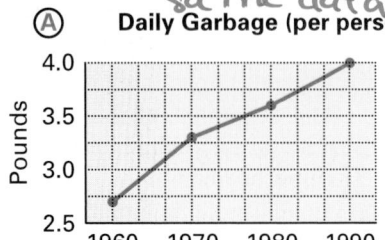

9. **Journal** Sketch an example of a scatterplot pattern that shows a trend and describe the trend.

amount of tobacco packs/day *11 12 13 14 → year*

Test Prep

You can compare two kinds of data on a circle graph by finding their differences or stating how many times larger one appears than another.

10. Which statement accurately compares the red apples to the yellow apples?

   Ⓐ There are four times more red apples than yellow apples.
   Ⓑ There are about half as many red apples as yellow apples.
   Ⓒ There are 38 more red apples than yellow apples.
   Ⓓ There are 48 fewer yellow apples than red apples.

Apples Delivered

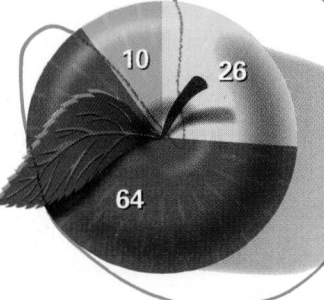

SECTION 1B

Displaying Data

▶ Civics Link ▶ History Link ▶ www.mathsurf.com/6/ch1/Presidents

Job Opportunity for Ambitious American

Does this sound like a good opportunity? The salary may seem high, but when you consider what a difficult job the President of the United States has, the salary may not be a surprise. Every day, the President has to organize and interpret vast amounts of information. This information is critical in making decisions that influence the lives of millions of people.

One way the President can better understand information is by using mathematics. Mathematical tools like frequency graphs, line plots, bar graphs, and stem-and-leaf diagrams help to sort and give shape to data.

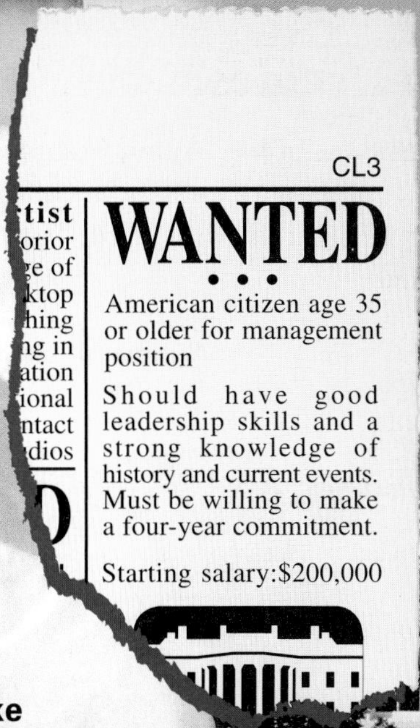

CL3
WANTED
American citizen age 35 or older for management position
Should have good leadership skills and a strong knowledge of history and current events. Must be willing to make a four-year commitment.
Starting salary:$200,000

1 What sort of information does the president need to sort and organize?

2 Why is it important for numerical information to be organized?

Tallies, Frequency Charts, and Line Plots

You'll Learn …

■ to organize data using tallies and frequency charts

■ to use a line plot to show the shape of a data set

… How It's Used

Advertising executives use frequency charts and line plots to organize and communicate about data on public opinion.

Vocabulary

tally marks

frequency chart

line plot

▶ **Lesson Link**   In the last section, you saw various ways to display data on graphs. Before data can be displayed, it must be carefully organized. ◀

Explore   Organizing Data

Who Decides?

The President of the United States is not chosen directly by the voters. Instead, voters choose people called *electors.* The electors meet after the election to elect the President. The map lists the number of electors for each state.

Number of Electors for Each State

1. Organize the data so that you can quickly tell how many states have 3 electoral vote, how many have 4, how many have 5, and so on.

2. What is the most common number of electors? Second most common?

3. Why do you think different states have different numbers of electors?

4. What patterns can you see in the organized data that you can't easily see from the map?

Tally marks are used to organize a large set of data. Each tally mark indicates one time that the value appeared in the data.

A **frequency chart** can help you list the data quickly. Each value that appeared in the data is followed by the number of times it appeared.

Example 1

Use the data to make a frequency chart. For each age, how many states specify that age in their law?

Ages at Which State Laws Require Children to Be in School									
State	Age	State	Age	State	Age	State	Age	State	Age
CA	6	KS	7	MO	7	NH	6	UT	6
DE	5	MA	6	MT	7	OH	5	VA	5
FL	6	MD	5	NC	7	PA	8	WA	8
ID	6	ME	7	ND	7	TN	7	WI	6
IN	7	MN	6	NE	7	TX	6	WY	7

List ages in order. → **Age**

Make a tally mark for each data item. → **Tally Marks**

Count tally marks to find the frequency. → **Frequency**

Age	Tally Marks	Frequency
5	‖‖	4
6	‖‖‖ ‖‖‖	9
7	‖‖‖ ‖‖‖	10
8	‖	2

Four states require children to be in school at age 5, nine states at age 6, ten states at age 7, and two at age 8.

Try It

a. Make a frequency chart of the test scores. Use these groups: under 60; 60–69; 70–79; 80–89; 90–100.

b. How many students scored 80–89? Less than 70?

History Test Scores				
81	95	77	64	85
62	79	92	100	61
83	55	84	83	91
75	83	72	84	95

Problem Solving TIP

Some data sets are more easily organized if you put the data into groups. This way, you have fewer categories, and more data per category.

A **line plot** shows the shape of a set of data. It is similar to a set of tally marks that has been turned onto its side. Instead of tally marks, a line plot uses ×'s.

Age	Tally
5	||||
6	╫╫ ||||
7	╫╫ ╫╫
8	||

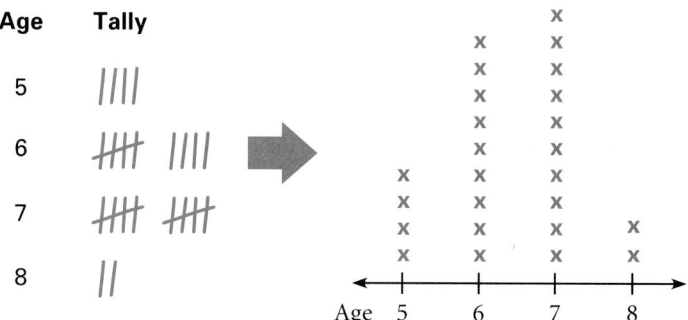

Example 2

Make a line plot of the data. What does the line plot show?

Number of Children of 20th-Century Presidents and First Ladies					
2	5	3	3	0	2
2	5	1	1	2	2
2	4	4	2	6	1

The line plot shows that 2 is the most common number of children, 0 and 6 are the least common, and 3, 4, and 5 all appear with the same frequency.

Problem Solving TIP

It may be useful to scan the data before you start to tally it. This gives you an idea of how high and how low the numbers will be.

Try It

The table gives the results of a survey of 20 middle school students. Make a line plot of the data. What picture of the data does the line plot show?

Average Phone Calls Made (daily)				
2	3	5	2	3
1	0	3	4	2
1	5	3	4	3
2	3	1	4	3

Check | **Your Understanding**

1. How are frequency charts and line plots similar? How are they different?

2. Can the same information be shown in a frequency chart and a line plot? Explain.

Practice and Apply

1. **Getting Started** Record each data set in a tally chart.

   a. 5, 4, 1, 3, 3, 6, 10, 4, 7, 3, 1, 1, 2, 1, 4

   b. 23, 21, 18, 20, 19, 22, 17, 22, 21, 20, 19, 20, 13, 20

   c. 2000, 4000, 5000, 2500, 2000, 1500, 6500, 6000, 4000, 3500

Make a frequency chart for each set of tally marks.

2. Hours spent doing home-work each week

Hours	Tally
4	||||
5	‖‖‖ ||
6	‖‖‖ ‖‖‖ |||
7	‖‖‖ ||||
8	‖‖‖ ‖‖‖ ‖‖‖ |
9	‖‖‖ ‖‖‖ |
10	‖‖‖ ||

3. Shoes in your closet

Shoes	Tally
2	‖‖‖
4	‖‖‖ |
6	‖‖‖ ||||
8	‖‖‖ ‖‖‖ |||
10	‖‖‖ ‖‖‖ ‖‖‖ |
12	‖‖‖ ‖‖‖ ‖‖‖ |||

4. Hair length

Length (in)	Tally
1	|
2	‖‖‖ |||
3	‖‖‖ ‖‖‖
4	‖‖‖
5	|||
6	||
7	|

5. **History** Draw a line plot of the ages of the first ten Presidents when they took office.

Age of First Ten Presidents

Age	Frequency
49	1
54	1
57	4
58	1
61	2
68	1

6. **Geography** Draw a line plot of the number of states bordering each state in the United States.

Borders	Frequency
0	2
1	2
2	4
3	8
4	12
5	11
6	8
7	1
8	2

7. **History** If the President signs a bill from the Congress, that bill becomes a law. If the President doesn't think it should become a law, he or she can veto the bill.

a. Make a frequency chart for the data in the table.

b. Make a line plot for the data in the table.

President	Number of Vetoes	President	Number of Vetoes
Washington	2	Jackson	12
J. Adams	0	Van Buren	0
Jefferson	0	W. Harrison	0
Madison	7	Tyler	10
Monroe	2	Polk	3
J. Q. Adams	0	Taylor	0

"They can't say I'm not doing anything"

from HERBLOCK: A CARTOONIST'S LIFE (Macmillan Publishing, 1993)

Problem Solving and Reasoning

8. **Critical Thinking** Does the frequency chart show a data set with mostly even numbers or mostly odd numbers? Explain.

Age	Frequency
5	2
6	5
7	6

9. **Communicate** How does a line plot show the shape of a data set?

10. **Journal** What is the purpose of a frequency chart? A line plot?

Mixed Review

Write each number in words. *[Previous course]*

11. 217   **12.** 356   **13.** 616   **14.** 491   **15.** 609   **16.** 773

17. 2143   **18.** 3781   **19.** 9611   **20.** 5505   **21.** 4302   **22.** 9933

Divide. *[Previous course]*

23. 50 ÷ 2   **24.** 66 ÷ 3   **25.** 84 ÷ 4   **26.** 96 ÷ 6   **27.** 88 ÷ 8

28. 98 ÷ 7   **29.** 95 ÷ 5   **30.** 87 ÷ 2   **31.** 74 ÷ 3   **32.** 57 ÷ 1

Project Progress

After you have collected numerical data about your location, think about the best way to display your data. You might want to consider using frequency charts, line plots, or bar graphs.

Problem Solving

Understand
Plan
Solve
Look Back

Scales and Bar Graphs

▶ **Lesson Link**   You know how to read and interpret a bar graph. Now you will construct a bar graph. ◀

A bar graph is a way to visually display and compare numerical data. The **scale** of a bar graph is the "ruler" that measures the heights of the bars. The **intervals** are the equal divisions marked on the scale to make it easier to read. The lines on which a bar graph is built are the **horizontal axis** and the **vertical axis**.

Vertical axis

Scale

← Intervals

Horizontal axis

You'll Learn ...

■ to make a bar graph

... How It's Used

Political analysts use bar graphs to communicate the popularity of presidential candidates.

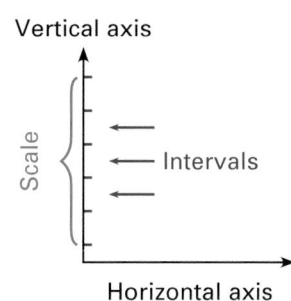

Vocabulary

scale

interval

horizontal axis

vertical axis

range

Explore   Scales on Bar Graphs

Tipping the Scales for Victory!

Materials: Spreadsheet software

The map shows five regions of the country and the number of electoral votes each region casts for President. Presidential candidates often try to attract voters regionally rather than nationwide. A candidate who can win great popularity in three regions is likely to win the election.

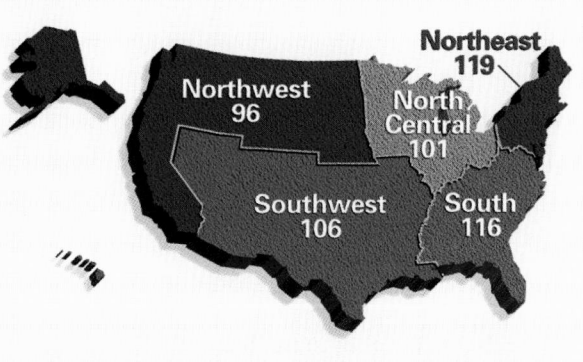

Northeast 119

Northwest 96

North Central 101

Southwest 106

South 116

1. On a blank spreadsheet, enter the names of each region in column A. Enter the electoral vote totals in column B.

2. Using the data in the spreadsheet, draw a bar graph.

3. Using the data in the spreadsheet, draw a second bar graph. This time, use a small number for the scale.

4. Using the data in the spreadsheet, draw a third bar graph. This time, use a !arge number for the scale.

5. Explain how the choice of scale affects the look of a bar graph.

Learn | Scales and Bar Graphs

The **range** of a data set refers to the difference between the highest value and the lowest value. For this data set, the highest value is 31, and the lowest is 28. The difference, $31 - 28$, is 3. The range is 3.

When data in a set are spread fairly evenly from low values to high values, it is often best to start the scale on a bar graph at 0.

Number of Days in Month			
31	28	31	30
31	30	31	31
30	31	30	31

Example 1

A political party is a group of citizens who want to influence the government by having their members elected to government offices. The first 42 U.S. Presidents came from five political parties. Use the data to make a bar graph.

Party	Number of Presidents
Democratic	15
Democratic-Republican	4
Federalist	2
Republican	17
Whig	4

Top value of scale must be greater than 17. Numbers ending in zero are easy to understand and to divide into intervals. Therefore 20 is a good choice for the top of the scale.

The lowest number in the data is 2. Data are spread fairly evenly across the range from 2 to 17, so zero is a convenient choice for the bottom of the scale.

20
15
10 ← It is easy to divide 20 into intervals of 5, but you could also use intervals of 2, 4, or 10.
5
0

Represent each party with vertical bars of the same width. Label the bars and give the graph a title.

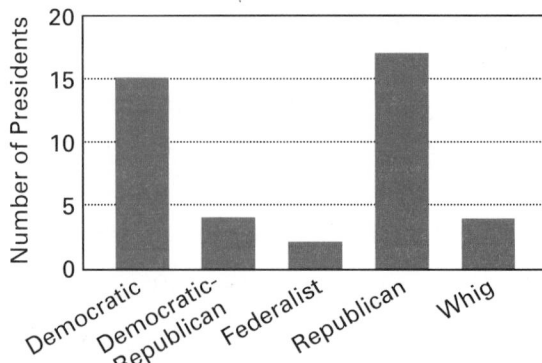

Presidents' Political Parties

Sometimes all of the data are crowded at the top end of the range. Sometimes a wide part of the range has no data. In these situations, you may want to "break" the scale.

Example 2

Make a bar graph of the data.

Lengths of the Great Lakes (through widest point)					
Lake	Erie	Huron	Michigan	Ontario	Superior
Length (mi)	241	206	307	193	350

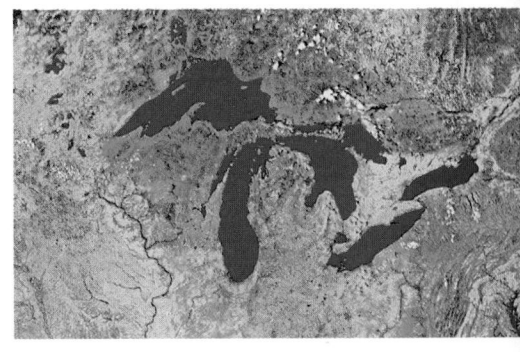

Since all of the data are 193 or greater, you may want to skip over the values between 0 and 193 by breaking the scale. If you want to show the actual heights of all the bars, however, use the entire scale beginning at 0, as in the right-hand graph.

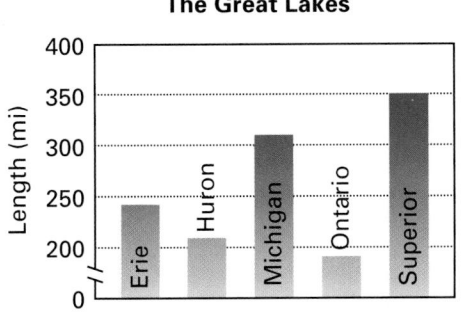

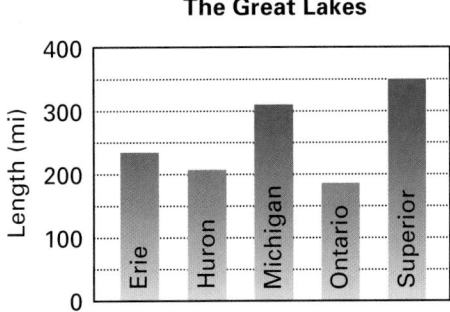

Try It

Make a bar graph of the data showing female Prime Ministers years in office.

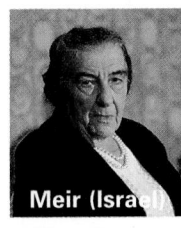

Meir (Israel)	Gandhi (India)	Thatcher (UK)	Brundtland (Norway)
Years in Office 5	18	11	13

Check | Your Understanding

1. How does the range affect the scale and intervals of a bar graph?

2. When should you use a broken scale on a bar graph? Give an example.

3. Is only one scale possible for a given bar graph? Explain.

Practice and Apply

1. **Getting Started** For each data set, give the range and choose the better interval to use for a bar graph.

   a. Data: 3, 6, 9, 12, 15, 16; interval of 2 or 10?

   b. Data: 55, 101, 120, 145; interval of 10 or 25?

2. **Social Studies** Many people consider Presidential burial grounds to be of important historical value. The first 20 Presidents were buried in the following states: Illinois (1), Kentucky (1), Massachusetts (2), New Hampshire (1), New York (3), Ohio (3), Pennsylvania (1), Tennessee (3), Vermont (5).

   a. What is the range of values in this set of data?

   b. Make a bar graph of the data.

3. **Science** Make a bar graph to show the calories burned each hour by a 150-pound person while doing an activity. Use a broken scale, if appropriate.

Lincoln's burial site

Bicycling	Mowing the Lawn	Raking Leaves	Walking

  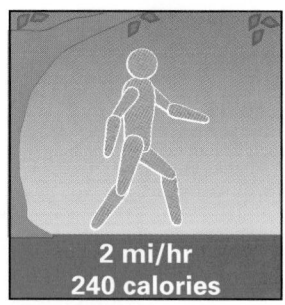

| 5.5 mi/hr 210 calories | 250 calories | 360 calories | 2 mi/hr 240 calories |

4. **Test Prep** What interval is used on this bar graph's scale?

   Ⓐ 5   Ⓑ 0

   Ⓒ 10   Ⓓ 15

National Political Conventions

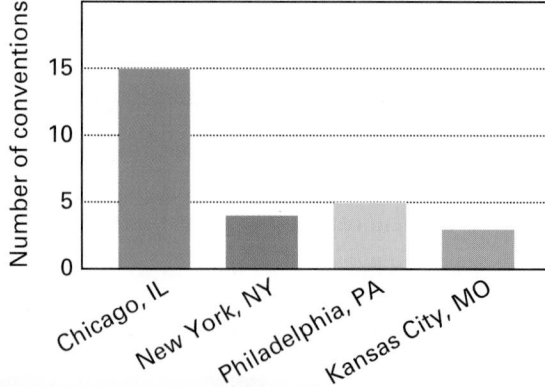

Problem Solving and Reasoning

5. Geography The graphs show the average temperatures of two of the coldest and two of the warmest cities in the United States.

Temperatures of U.S. Cities

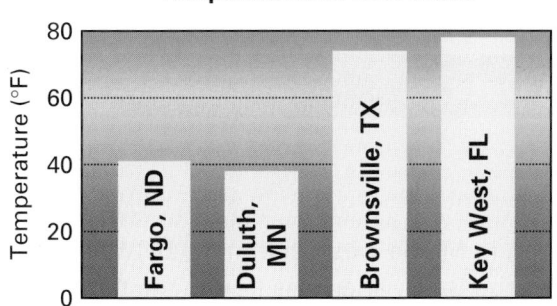

Temperatures of U.S. Cities

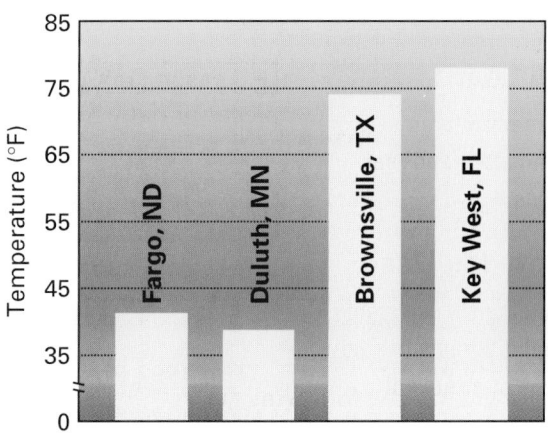

a. For each graph, give the range of values and the interval used on the scale.

b. Critical Thinking Compare the appearance of the two graphs. Could either graph be misleading? Explain.

c. Communicate Describe the shape of the data shown in the bar graphs.

6. Critical Thinking The bar graph was made from the following data.

a. Two of the bars have been drawn incorrectly. Which two have been drawn wrong? What is wrong about them?

b. The scale used in the graph is not convenient. What would be a better scale for this data?

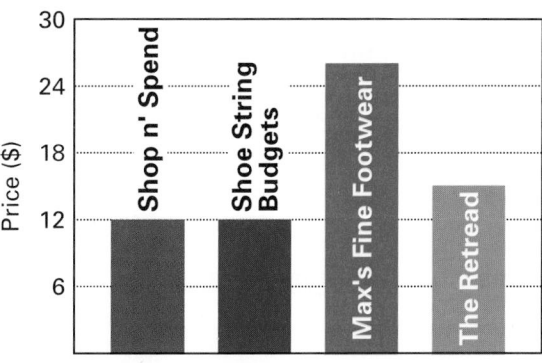

Sandal Prices

Price of a Pair of Sandals	
Shop'n'Spend	$10
Shoe String Budgets	$12
Max's Fine Footwear	$23
The Retread	$15

Mixed Review

Perform the appropriate operation. *[Previous course]*

7. 4678 + 3909

8. 12,439 + 58,002

9. 536,092 + 182,438

10. 9,346 + 16,724

11. 25,392 + 7,325

12. 36,382 + 945,217

13. 6329 − 2735

14. 51,027 − 38,021

15. 837,327 − 683,442

16. 7003 − 628

17. 23,422 − 9,431

18. 603,288 − 37,294

1-6 Stem-and-Leaf Diagrams

You'll Learn ...

■ to organize large sets of data into stem-and-leaf diagrams

... How It's Used

Paleontologists use stem-and-leaf diagrams to study the sizes of groups of dinosaurs.

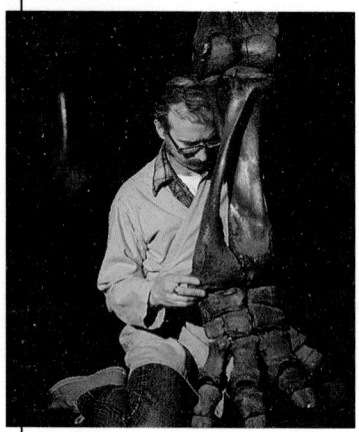

Vocabulary

stem-and-leaf diagram

▶ **Lesson Link** You've seen how a line plot helps to organize individual pieces of data. Sometimes, you need to organize data in intervals. ◀

Explore Ordering Data

The Maine Event

The 1992 Presidential election in Maine was a tight race between three candidates—Bill Clinton, George Bush, and Ross Perot. The table shows the total votes for each candidate in the 16 largest cities in Maine.

1992 Maine Election Results							
City	Clinton	Bush	Perot	City	Clinton	Bush	Perot
Auburn	5,025	3,653	3,964	Old Town	2,272	1,173	1,302
Augusta	4,657	3,003	3,002	Portland	19,510	8,660	6,910
Bangor	6,826	5,185	4,689	Rockland	1,192	1,081	1,059
Bath	1,988	1,630	1,458	Saco	4,000	2,769	2,303
Biddeford	4,945	2,533	2,717	Sanford	3,854	3,030	3,215
Brewer	1,788	1,907	1,625	So. Portland	5,933	3,999	2,734
Gardiner	1,391	1,054	1,115	Waterville	3,868	1,832	2,257
Lewiston	9,265	4,372	6,180	Westbrook	3,665	2,904	2,512

1. Order each candidate's 16 totals from greatest to least.

2. For each candidate, determine the strongest city and the weakest city.

3. Describe any voting patterns you see in the table.

George Bush (left), Ross Perot (center), and Bill Clinton (right)

A **stem-and-leaf diagram** is a graph that shows the shape of the data according to the data place values. The "leaf" of a number is usually the right-hand digit. The "stem" is the portion of the number to the left of the leaf.

Number		Stem	Leaf
47	→	4	7
710	→	71	0
8802	→	880	2
6	→	0	6

Example 1

Analyze the shape of the data in the table by making a stem-and-leaf diagram.

Draw two columns, and write the stems in the left column. Since all of the data are in the 40s, 50s, and 60s, you need only three stems: 4, 5, and 6. For every number, write the last digit (the leaf) in the right column on the same line as the matching stem.

Ages of 20th-Century Presidents at Inauguration			
42	51	56	55
51	54	51	60
62	43	55	56
61	52	69	64
46			

Stem	Leaf
4	2 3 6
5	1 6 5 1 4 1 5 6 2
6	0 2 1 9 4

Now redraw the diagram, ordering the leaves from least to greatest.

Stem	Leaf
4	2 3 6
5	1 1 1 2 4 5 5 6 6
6	0 1 2 4 9

Kennedy was inaugurated at age 43.

> **► History Link**
>
> Three Presidents have been elected even though they didn't receive the highest number of votes from the people: John Quincy Adams in 1824, Rutherford Hayes in 1876, and Benjamin Harrison in 1888.

The diagram shows that the data range from 42 to 69, that the most frequent age is 51, and that most Presidents were in their 50s when they took office. Note that, unlike most bar graphs and tally charts, a stem-and-leaf diagram groups data in intervals.

Try It

Make a stem-and-leaf diagram of the bowling scores.

130	90	141	128	133	142	113	148	105	93
118	130	133	100	124	146	97	108	126	115
136	144	114	101	93	108	95	143	128	141

It may be helpful to write down all of the stems before you begin to plot the leaves.

WHAT DO YOU THINK?

Catherine and Jamar need to plan a party for their community band. Before they decide on what kind of party to have, they want to see how the ages of the band members are distributed.

Community Band Member Ages									
21	34	16	26	41	21	9	34	19	11
20	39	24	18	21	59	32	14	32	41
14	21	36	43	27	26	16	28	13	20

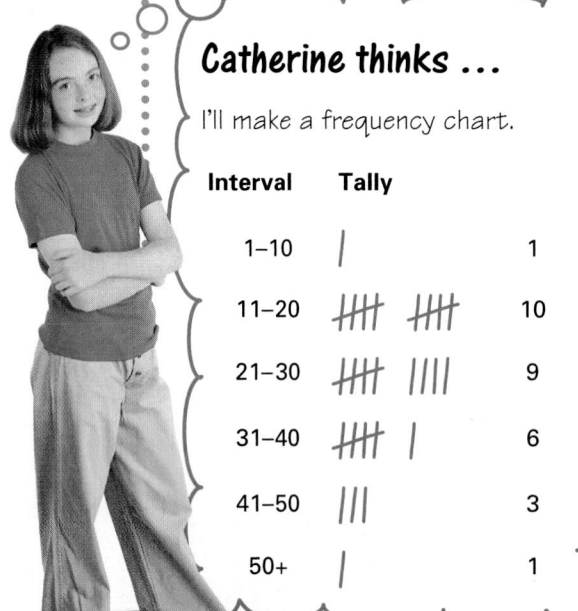

Catherine thinks ...

I'll make a frequency chart.

Interval	Tally	
1–10	I	1
11–20	‖‖ ‖‖	10
21–30	‖‖ ‖‖	9
31–40	‖‖ I	6
41–50	‖	3
50+	I	1

Jamar thinks ...

I'll make a stem-and-leaf diagram.

Stem	Leaf
0	9
1	1 3 4 4 6 6 8 9
2	0 0 1 1 1 1 4 6 6 7 8
3	2 2 4 4 6 9
4	1 1 3
5	9

What do you think?

1. What conclusions can Catherine and Jamar draw from their displays?

2. For what purposes could you use either display equally well? When might Jamar's display have an advantage over Catherine's? When might Catherine's display have an advantage over Jamar's?

Check Your Understanding

1. How is a stem-and-leaf diagram like a line plot? How is it different?

2. Why is a stem-and-leaf diagram helpful when trying to organize a large set of data?

1-6 Exercises and Applications

Practice and Apply

1. **Getting Started** Follow the steps to make a stem-and-leaf diagram of the data.

27, 38, 42, 18, 29, 40, 19, 10, 32, 47, 19, 36, 42

a. Use two columns. Write the stems from least to greatest. Write each leaf to the right of its stem.

Stem	Leaf
1	
2	
?	
?	

b. Redraw the stem-and-leaf diagram, with the leaves in order from least to greatest.

Stem	Leaf
1	
2	
?	
?	

2. **Science** Make a stem-and-leaf diagram from the data.

The ten fastest fish in the world (in miles per hour) include the following: sailfish, 68; blue shark, 43; swordfish, 40; marlin, 50; bluefin tuna, 46; wahoo, 41; tarpon, 35; bonefish, 40; yellowfin tuna, 44; tiger shark, 33.

3. **History** Make a stem-and-leaf diagram from the ages of the first 20 Presidents at death.

Presidents	Age	Presidents	Age	Presidents	Age
Washington	67	Van Buren	79	Buchanan	77
J. Adams	90	W. Harrison	68	Lincoln	56
Jefferson	83	Tyler	71	A. Johnson	66
Madison	85	Polk	53	Grant	63
Monroe	73	Taylor	65	Hayes	70
J. Q. Adams	80	Fillmore	74	Garfield	49
Jackson	78	Pierce	64		

Use the stem-and-leaf diagram for Exercises 4–7.

4. What is the range of the values?

5. What value appears most often?

6. What's the largest number in the data that's less than 50?

Stem	Leaf
2	1
3	0 0 4 4 7 8
5	0 2 2 2 2 3 3

7. **Test Prep** How many times was 53 a data item?
Ⓐ two   Ⓑ three   Ⓒ five   Ⓓ thirty-three

Problem Solving and Reasoning

Use the stem-and-leaf diagram for Exercises 8–10.

This stem-and-leaf diagram is based on the available amount of room in cubic feet in the car models of one manufacturer.

Stem	Leaf
0	7 8 8 8
1	3 3 3 3 3 3 3 3 3 3 6 6 7
2	0 0 0
3	3 3 3 3
6	9
8	2
9	1 2 6 6 6 8 8 9 9

1 cubic foot

8. **Communicate** How many numbers appear three times in the data? How can you tell?

9. **Critical Thinking** Why is there no 7 in the stem column?

10. **Journal** Describe the shape of the data. Explain how this graph could help consumers narrow their search for the best car.

This is a list of First Ladies and their ages when they became First Ladies. Use this list for Exercises 11–12.

First Ladies	Age	First Ladies	Age
Grace Coolidge	44	Lady Bird Johnson	50
Lou Hoover	53	Patricia Nixon	56
Eleanor Roosevelt	48	Betty Ford	53
Bess Truman	60	Rosalynn Carter	49
Frances Cleveland	21	Nancy Reagan	59
Mamie Eisenhower	56	Barbara Bush	64
Jacqueline Kennedy	31	Hillary Clinton	46

Frances Cleveland

11. **Critical Thinking** If you make a stem-and-leaf diagram of the data, will there be more leaves after the 4 stem or the 5 stem? Explain.

12. **Communicate** Why is the data for Frances Cleveland so unusual?

Mixed Review

Perform the appropriate operation. *[Previous course]*

13. 16×72 **14.** 35×28 **15.** 68×20 **16.** 44×91

17. $386 \div 2$ **18.** $483 \div 3$ **19.** $790 \div 5$ **20.** $987 \div 7$

At the beginning of this section, you read about a few of the shared characteristics of our presidents. The following exploration asks you to make decisions about how to display data about presidential characteristics.

Job Opportunity for Ambitious American!

The table gives data on the winners of presidential elections from 1900 to 1992 (Rep = Republican, Dem = Democrat).

President	Age	Party	Birth Month	Age of Vice President	Years in Office	Birth State
McKinley	54	Rep	January	43	4	OH
T. Roosevelt	42	Rep	October	53	7	NY
Taft	51	Rep	September	54	4	OH
Wilson	56	Dem	December	59	8	VA
Harding	55	Rep	November	49	2	OH
Coolidge	51	Rep	July	60	6	VT
Hoover	54	Rep	August	69	4	IA
F. Roosevelt	51	Dem	January	65	12	NY
Truman	60	Dem	May	72	8	MO
Eisenhower	62	Rep	October	40	8	TX
Kennedy	43	Dem	May	53	3	MA
Johnson	55	Dem	August	54	5	TX
Nixon	56	Rep	January	51	6	CA
Ford	61	Rep	July	66	2	NE
Carter	52	Dem	October	49	4	GA
Reagan	69	Rep	February	57	8	IL
Bush	64	Rep	June	42	4	MA
Clinton	46	Dem	August	45	4	AR

1. In addition to the presidents' last names, there are six sets of data. Chose three of the six sets. For each set, make either a frequency chart or a stem-and-leaf diagram. Explain why you chose the type of graph you used.

2. Choose one of your frequency charts or stem-and-leaf diagrams. If you drew a bar graph of this data, would your scale start at zero? Would it show any breaks? How large would each interval be?

3. Make the bar graph that you described for the previous question.

1. The data lists several people who ran for President and the number of Presidential elections they lost. Make a frequency chart and a line plot of the data. Describe the shape of the data.

Name	Elections Lost	Name	Elections Lost
William Bryan	2	Adlai Stevenson	2
Alton Parker	1	Richard Nixon	1
Eugene Debs	3	Gerald Ford	1
William Taft	1	Jimmy Carter	1
Theodore Roosevelt	1	John Anderson	1
Alfred Smith	1	Walter Mondale	1
Norman Thomas	3	Michael Dukakis	1
Herbert Hoover	1	George Bush	1
Thomas Dewey	2	Bob Dole	1

I know how to do #1-3, just 2 lazier 2 do it.

2. Make a bar graph of the data.

Cost of Private Piano Lessons (30 min—rounded to nearest $)			
Atlanta, GA	$16.00	Los Angeles, CA	$18.00
Chicago, IL	$18.00	Miami, FL	$19.00
Houston, TX	$16.00	New York, NY	$27.00

3. Make a stem-and-leaf diagram of the lengths of water birds in inches. Describe the shape of the data.
   15, 22, 15, 32, 23, 17, 18, 23, 19, 23, 23, 32, 24

Test Prep

On a multiple-choice test, you may need to match a set of data to a stem-and-leaf diagram. It may be helpful to first draw your own stem-and-leaf diagram, and then match that diagram to the choices provided.

4. Which stem-and-leaf diagram accurately represents the data set?
   47, 42, 59, 43, 53, 42, 38, 53, 55, 50, 61, 42, 41, 60, 57

Ⓐ
Stem	Leaf
3	8
4	1 2 2 2 3 7
5	0 3 3 5 7 9
6	0 1

Ⓑ
Stem	Leaf
3	8
4	1 2 2 3 3 7
5	0 3 3 5 7 9
6	0 1

Ⓒ
Stem	Leaf
3	8
4	1 2 2 2 3 7
5	0 3 3 3 7 9
6	0 1

Describing Data

will the REAL #1 athlete Please STAND UP?

Patricia Hoskins played women's college basketball for 4 years at Mississippi Valley State University. She played in over 100 games, and she scored thousands of baskets. On the average, she scored over 28 points per game. Was she the best women's college basketball player?

Sports fans spend a great amount of time and energy trying to determine who is the best athlete. This is complicated, because athletes don't always perform exactly the same in every game. In 1992, tennis pro Andre Agassi beat Pete Sampras at the French Open. One year later, Sampras beat Agassi at Wimbledon.

Every day, American newspapers publish thousands of statistics about athletes. If this data just piled higher and higher, no one would understand it. Fortunately, mathematics can turn huge amounts of data into a few easy-to-understand numbers. So baseball rankings, gymnastics scores, and soccer standings can all be turned into numbers that help determine who is #1.

1 What are other examples of numerical data about athletes?

2 Why is it so important to determine who is #1?

3 In what situations, other than sports, can you use mathematics to determine who is #1?

1-7 Median and Mode

You'll Learn ...

■ to calculate the median and the mode for a set of data

... How It's Used

Real estate agents use medians and modes when comparing the costs of houses for sale.

Vocabulary

median

mode

▶ **Lesson Link** You know how to organize data using a frequency chart, and how to show the shape of a data set using a line plot or a stem-and-leaf diagram. Now you will learn how to find single numbers that describe entire sets of data. ◀

Explore | The Middle and the Most

The Winning Pitch

The table gives the totals of the top 15 major league pitchers according to career wins.

Cy Young	511	Kid Nichols	361	John Clarkson	326
Walter Johnson	416	Pud Galvin	361	Don Sutton	324
Christy Mathewson	373	Tim Keefe	342	Nolan Ryan	319
Grover Alexander	373	Steve Carlton	329	Phil Niekro	318
Warren Spahn	363	Eddie Plank	327	Gaylord Perry	314

1. Get together with a partner. One person chooses a number from the data. The other person tries to guess which number the first person chose in as few guesses as possible. After each guess, the first person should say "too high," "too low," or "correct."

2. Play the game twice. Switch roles after the first game.

3. Which number is the best first number to guess? Why?

4. If your partner chose a number at random and you could only make one guess, which guess would be the best guess to make? Why?

Learn | Median and Mode

The **median** of a data set is the middle number when the data are listed from lowest to highest. If a set has two middle numbers, the median is the value halfway between the two middle numbers.

The **mode** of a data set is the item that occurs most often. If all items occur once, there is no mode. If several items occur "most often," each is a mode.

Example 1

The Long Beach State women's basketball team has won more games than any other major college women's basketball team. Find the median number of wins and the mode number of wins.

Long Beach State Win Totals (for 1986–1996)										
29	33	28	30	25	24	21	9	11	13	15

9 11 13 15 21 24 25 28 29 30 33   Order the totals.

9 11 13 15 21 [24] 25 28 29 30 33   Find the middle number.

The median is 24 wins. Since each number appears once, there is no mode.

Example 2

Twelve Houston babysitters were surveyed to find their hourly rates. Find the median and the mode of the data.

Babysitter Hourly Rates ($)		
4.00	3.30	3.25
3.00	3.75	3.25
3.15	3.50	3.00
3.75	3.75	3.60

To find the median, list the numbers in order.

3.00, 3.00, 3.15, 3.25, 3.25, 3.30, 3.50, 3.60, 3.75, 3.75, 3.75, 4.00

There are two middle numbers, $3.30 and $3.50. The median is the value halfway between, which is $3.40.

The mode is $3.75 because it appears more times than any other number.

Try It

Number of Stations on Longest Commuter Rail Systems in the United States								
134	108	18	126	62	101	181	27	158

a. Find the median of the data.   **b.** Find the mode of the data.

Check | Your Understanding

1. For any data set, which is bigger, the median or the mode? Explain.

2. Is the median of a data set always one of the numbers in the set? Is the mode? Explain.

Practice and Apply

1. [Getting Started] Find the median and the mode for each data set. The data are ordered from lowest to highest.

   a. $1, $2, $3, $4, $4, $5, $10, $10, $10

   b. 12, 12, 18, 19, 54, 54, 102

   c. 82, 82, 84, 85, 87, 88, 95, 98

   d. 300, 301, 302, 310, 313, 318

2. Geography Find the median and mode number of counties for the 11 western states shown in the map.

3. Geography Find the median number of counties for the 5 states surrounding Nevada.

4. Geography Find the median number of counties for the 6 states surrounding Utah.

Number of Counties per State

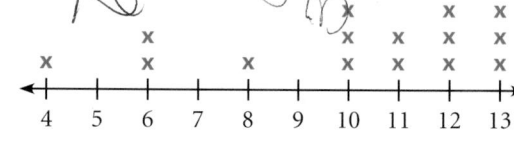

Washington 39
Montana 56
Oregon 36
Idaho 44
Wyoming 23
Nevada 16
Utah 29
Colorado 63
California 58
Arizona 15
New Mexico 33

Find the median and mode.

5.

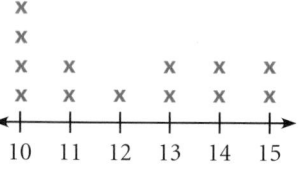

10 11 12 13 14 15

6.

Stem	Leaf
5	1 2 3
6	5 5 6 7 9
8	1 1 2 2 2 6 6
9	7 7

7.

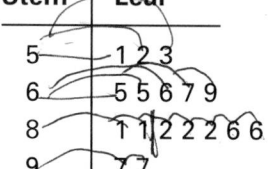

4 5 6 7 8 9 10 11 12 13

8. [Test Prep] Find the median and the mode of this data set: 25, 31, 28, 25, 21, 21, 32, 25, 32.

  Ⓐ 21 and 25   Ⓑ 25 and 32   Ⓒ 21 and 32   Ⓓ 25 and 25

Find the median and mode.

9. 15, 31, 45, 61, 13, 21, 31, 13, 20

10. 25, 26, 24, 21, 25, 21, 23, 21, 26, 21, 20

11. 9, 13, 7, 11, 12, 6, 8, 14

12. 20, 25, 21, 23, 22, 30, 28, 20, 23, 22, 21, 30, 29, 28, 28, 28, 30, 29, 20

13. 25, 16, 18, 20, 21, 24, 23, 28, 27, 26, 17, 18, 18, 28, 28, 27, 28, 27, 26

14. 23, 24, 24, 34, 30, 31, 32, 23, 24, 26, 27, 23, 23, 24, 24, 24, 34, 34

Make a line plot for each and then find the median and mode.

15. 6, 11, 12, 5, 7, 11, 6, 6, 10

16. 3, 0, 1, 0, 1, 3, 2, 2, 3, 1, 0, 3

Problem Solving and Reasoning

17. Critical Thinking Create a data set of 10 numbers with a median of 8 and a mode of 10.

18. Critical Thinking The following data lists the tennis players with the most Wimbledon titles. Laurence Doherty's data is missing. If the median of the data set is 13 and the modes are 10 and 13, what's the missing data?

Louise Brough	13	Suzanne Longlen	15
Margaret Court	10	Martina Navratilova	18
Laurence Doherty	???	William Renshaw	14
Doris Hart	10	Elizabeth Ryan	19
Billie Jean King	7	Helen Wills-Moody	12

Martina Navratilova

19.  Describe how to find the median of a set of data. Your description should explain what to do if the data set contains either an even or an odd number of values.

Mixed Review

Multiply. *[Previous course]*

20. 83 × 54   **21.** 29 × 76   **22.** 80 × 32   **23.** 91 × 98   **24.** 42 × 76

25. 302 × 18   **26.** 412 × 43   **27.** 520 × 63   **28.** 622 × 22   **29.** 928 × 52

30. 816 × 102   **31.** 792 × 653   **32.** 140 × 339   **33.** 469 × 203   **34** 515 × 934

35. What's the second highest selling type of shoe? *[Lesson 1-1]*

36. What's the difference between the sales in running shoes and golf shoes? *[Lesson 1-1]*

37. If the total sales equals 100 pairs, what's the number of sales for tennis shoes? *[Lesson 1-1]*

38. If each symbol represented 7 pairs of shoes, how many running shoes would have been sold?

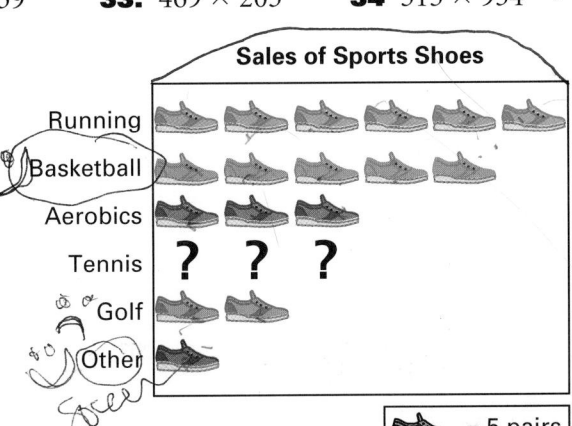

Sales of Sports Shoes
Running
Basketball
Aerobics
Tennis ? ? ?
Golf
Other
= 5 pairs

The Meaning of Mean

You'll Learn ...

■ to calculate the mean for a set of data

... How It's Used

Automobile manufacturers examine the mean dimensions of a person's body when designing an automobile.

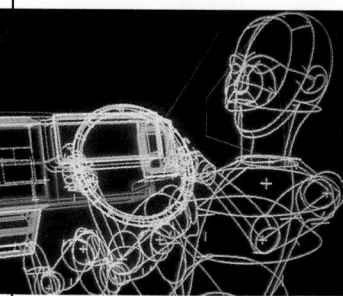

Vocabulary

mean

▶ **Lesson Link** You've learned to use the median and the mode of a data set to describe the data. Now you'll learn to find another such number that is often referred to as the *average*. ◀

Explore   The Mean

Let's Cut a Record

Materials: String, Scissors, Meter stick or Yard stick

Work in a group of at least four students.

1. Start at the end of a roll of string. Use the string to measure one student's arm length (shoulder to finger tip). Mark the arm length on the string. Beginning *at that mark,* measure the second student's arm length and mark that. Continue until all arms have been measured on the same string.

2. Cut the string at the last mark. You should now have a single length of string equal to the combined lengths of all the arms. Measure and record the total length of the string.

3. Cut the string into equal-length sections so that there are as many sections as there are members of your group. Measure and record the length of one section. What does the length of each section represent?

4. Does it make a difference which student gets measured first and which student gets measured last? Explain.

5. If you add a new person to your group and repeat Steps 1 through 3, will your final section be longer or shorter than the final section for your original group?

The **mean** of a data set is the sum of the items in the set divided by the number of items. The mean can also be called the *average*. To find the mean, add all the data values and divide by the number of values.

Remember

The sum of a set of numbers is the result of adding the numbers together. [**Previous course**]

Example 1

The Iditarod dogsled race crosses the Alaskan wilderness from Anchorage to Nome. Susan Butcher has won the race four times. Here are her 1983–1994 finishing positions. (She wasn't in the race in 1985.) Find the mean.

9, 2, 1, 1, 1, 2, 1, 3, 2, 4, 10

9 + 2 + 1 + 1 + 1 + 2 + 1 + 3 + 2 + 4 + 10 = 36   Add the items.

36 ÷ 11 = 3.272727...   Divide the sum by the number of items.

Susan Butcher's mean finishing position was 3.272727…. Sometimes the mean is a decimal value with several digits after the decimal point. Since real-world measurements aren't usually written with so many decimals, it's reasonable to use just the first two digits after the decimal. So, Susan Butcher's mean finishing position was 3.27.

Try It

a. Find the mean soccer ball price. $12.50, $16.00, $14.95, $19.00, $9.50

b. Find the mean number of soccer goals scored. 2, 3, 0, 1, 1, 2, 5, 0, 2, 1, 1, 0

The mean is sometimes referred to as the *equal sharing* number. If all the values in a data set are evened out so that they are all equal to each other and their total is still the same, then each value will be equal to the mean.

Check   Your Understanding

1. How is the mean different from the median? The mode?

2. Is the mean of a data set a member of the set? Explain.

Practice and Apply

Getting Started For each data set, find the mean by adding the numbers and then dividing the sum by the number of items.

1. $10, $10, $5, $1, $2, $5, $4, $3

2. 100, 85, 88, 98, 95, 87, 82, 83, 84

3. 5, 5, 5, 5, 5, 5, 5, 5

4. **Consumer** Find the mean amount of money spent by patrons at theaters.

   $8, $7, $10, $12, $8, $11, $8, $6, $9, $8, $10, $7, $7, $7

5. **Health** The data is the number of seconds it took Manuel to run the 100-meter dash. Find his mean time.

   10, 12, 15, 10, 11, 14, 13, 16, 10, 12, 10, 9, 13, 12, 11, 11

Find the mean of each set of data.

6.

Stem	Leaf
1	3 4 5
2	1 2 2 5 6
4	2 4 6 6
5	7 9

7.

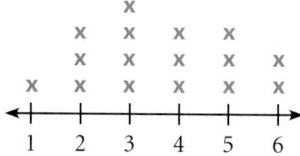

8. Find the mean, median, and mode.

NFL Teams That Have Played the Most Postseason Games (through 1995)			
Team	Games	Team	Games
Cowboys	49	Rams	33
'49ers	33	Raiders	36
Redskins	35		

9. **Test Prep** Which number is **not** the mean, median, or mode for the following data?

   6, 7, 7, 7, 6, 4, 4, 7, 2, 0

   Ⓐ 7　　　　　Ⓑ 5　　　　　Ⓒ 6　　　　　Ⓓ 50

Problem Solving and Reasoning

10. Critical Thinking Find the mean, median, and mode. Which one best describes the tennis players?

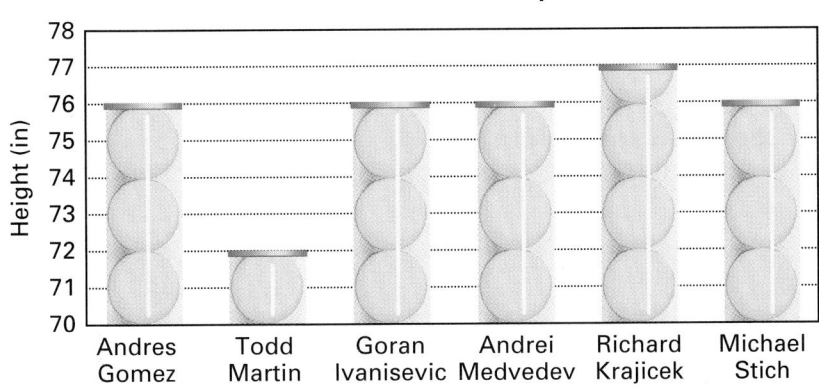

Famous Tennis Players

11. Critical Thinking Create a data set of five different numbers whose mean is 10. Explain your method.

13. Critical Thinking How does the mean of a data set change if you add a number to the data and the new number is exactly equal to the mean?

12. Choose a Strategy Suppose you have test scores of 92, 85, 86, and 90. What would you need to score on the next test to have a mean score of 90?

Problem Solving

STRATEGIES

- Look for a Pattern
- Make an Organized List
- Make a Table
- Guess and Check
- Work Backward
- Use Logical Reasoning
- Draw a Diagram
- Solve a Simpler Problem

Mixed Review

Divide. *[Previous course]*

14. 275 ÷ 5   **15.** 361 ÷ 7   **16.** 834 ÷ 9   **17.** 709 ÷ 8

18. 396 ÷ 11   **19.** 522 ÷ 13   **20.** 618 ÷ 15   **21.** 980 ÷ 20

22 384 ÷ 24   **23.** 616 ÷ 56   **24.** 996 ÷ 83   **25.** 736 ÷ 32

26. What is the difference between the weight of a rabbit and the weight of a snake? *[Lesson 1-2]*

27. About how many times taller than the snake bar does the elephant bar appear to be? *[Lesson 1-2]*

28. Do you think the graph is misleading? Explain. *[Lesson 1-2]*

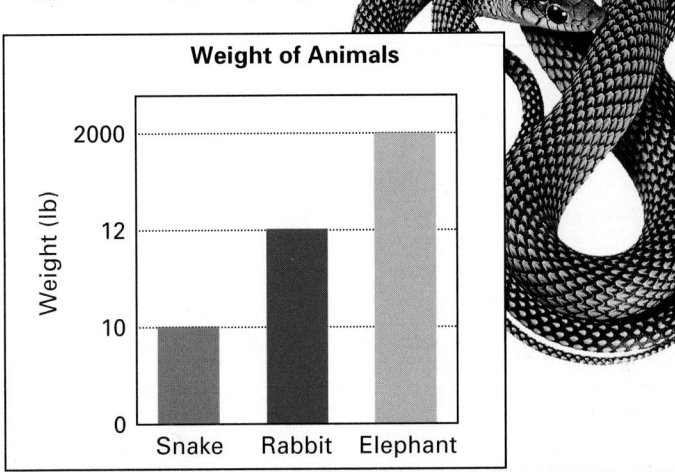

Weight of Animals

T E C H N O L O G Y

Using a Spreadsheet • Finding the median

Problem: What is the median for the given set of data?

You can use your spreadsheet to sort the data. This will help you find the median.

90	80	88	58	78	93	93	93	75	88	90	70
78	95	83	75	78	50	88	78	93	43	93	48
60	93	83	78	48	70	65	73	85	85	88

1 Type the data into column A. Check to make sure you have 35 numbers in the spreadsheet.

	A	B
1	90	
2	80	
3	88	
4	58	
5	78	
6	93	
7	93	
8	93	

2 Use the sort command to arrange the data from least to greatest. To do this, first highlight the data then select the sort command.

3 Using what you know about computing the median, find the median of the data.

Solution: The median of the data is 80.

TRY IT

a. What is the median of the first four columns of data?

b. What is the median of the top two rows of data?

ON YOUR OWN

► Use a spreadsheet to determine the median number of brothers and sisters your classmates have.

► How can the sort function of a spreadsheet help you find the mode?

► Is it possible to get a wrong answer when using a spreadsheet to find the median? Explain.

The Effects of Outliers

▶ **Lesson Link** You've learned about three numbers that you can use to describe a data set—the median, the mode, and the mean. Now you'll see how data items that are much different from the other items in the set can affect the median, the mean, and the mode. ◀

Explore | Outliers

Wayne's World

The Hart Trophy is awarded each year to the professional hockey player who is voted the most valuable in the National Hockey League. The table lists all but one of the players who won the Hart Trophy from 1974 to 1995.

1. Find the median, the mode, and the mean of the data.

2. The player who is not listed in the table is hockey legend Wayne Gretzky. Gretzky won the Hart Trophy nine times. Add Gretzky's data to the data set and recalculate the median, the mode, and the mean.

3. How does Gretzky's total affect the median? The mode? The mean?

Hart Trophy Winners 1974-95

Name	Trophies
Bobby Clark	2
Phil Esposito	1
Sergei Federov	1
Brett Hull	1
Guy Lafleur	2
Mario Lemieux	2
Eric Lindros	1
Mark Messier	2
Bryan Trottier	1

You'll Learn ...

■ to determine if an outlier affects the analysis of a data set

... How It's Used

Exercise researchers must check whether their data has been affected by outliers before they can use it to recommend new training procedures.

Vocabulary

outlier

Learn | The Effects of Outliers

An **outlier** is a number in a data set that is very different from the rest of the numbers. Outliers can have a big effect on the mean.

In the last lesson, you saw that the mean of a data set may represent the set well. For example, the mean of the daily high temperatures shown here is 91°F. Because the mean is close to all of the data, it represents the set well.

Daily High Temperatures (°F)	
Monday	88
Tuesday	94
Wednesday	94
Thursday	92
Friday	87

Suppose that on Saturday the temperature plunges to 55°F. Look what happens to the mean: 88 + 94 + 94 + 92 + 87 + 55 = 510

510 ÷ 6 = 85

The mean temperature of 85°F is *less than* five of the six data items. It has been pulled downward by the outlier, 55°F.

The table shows that the median is affected only slightly by the addition of the Saturday outlier. The mode hasn't changed.

	Mon–Fri	Mon–Sat
Mean	91	85
Median	92	90
Mode	94	94

You can see that a data set with an outlier is usually better represented by the median or the mode. The mean is often pulled too much toward the outlier to represent the set well.

Example 1

Find the median, mode, and mean of the data with and without the outlier.

Tallest Buildings in Las Vegas	
Building	**Height (ft)**
Vegas World Tower	1012
Fitzgerald Hotel	400
Landmark Hotel	356
Las Vegas Hilton	345

Without outlier

Median = 356
No mode
Mean: 400 + 356 + 345 = 1101
        1101 ÷ 3 = 367

With outlier

Median: 400 + 356 = 756
        756 ÷ 2 = 378
No mode
Mean: 400 + 356 + 345 + 1012 = 2113
        2113 ÷ 4 = 528.25

Try It

Find the median, mode, and mean with and without the outlier.

States with Most Indian Reservations							
State	AZ	CA	MN	NV	NM	WA	WI	SD
Number	23	96	14	19	25	27	11	9

Check | Your Understanding

1. Why doesn't the mode change when an outlier is added to a data set?

2. Would a high outlier and a low outlier affect a data set differently? Explain.

1-9 Exercises and Applications

Practice and Apply

Getting Started Identify the outlier in each data set.

1. 24, 24, 18, 56, 25, 12, 15, 22

2. 34, 28, 31, 34, 37, 2, 29, 21

3. 7, 6, 9, 10, 11, 6, 8, 11, 0, 10, 7, 8

4. 200, 225, 3000, 500, 325, 311

Identify the outliers in each data set.

5.

Stem	Leaf
0	3
1	0 0 0 1 1 5 8
2	1 3 3 8 9
3	0 0

6.

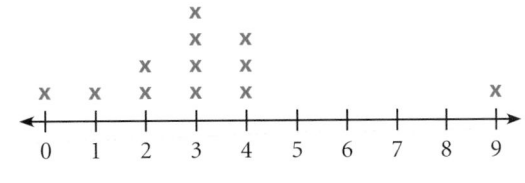

7.

Stem	Leaf
1	0 0 2 2 5
2	0 2 6 7
3	0 3 4 6
7	0

8. a. Find the mean, median, and mode with and without the outlier.

   b. Did the outlier affect the mode? The mean? The median? Which did it affect the most?

British Open Tournament Scores (1996)	
John Daly	282
Costantino Rocca	282
Michael Campbell	283
Steven Bottomley	283
Barry Lane	288

9. a. Find the mean, median, and mode with and without the outlier.

   b. Did the outlier affect the mode? The mean? The median? Which did it affect the most?

Dinah Shore Tournament Scores (1996)	
Nanci Bowen	285
Susie Redman	286
Brandie Burton	287
Sherri Turner	287
Meg Mallon	292

10. **Test Prep** Which has the greatest value for the following set of data, the mean, the median, the mode, or the outlier?

94, 88, 11, 90, 94, 92

Ⓐ mean Ⓑ median

Ⓒ mode Ⓓ outlier

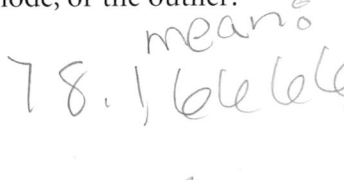

Problem Solving and Reasoning

11. The following table shows the number of games Michael Jordan has played with the Chicago Bulls.

Year	Games Played	Year	Games Played	Year	Games Played
1984–85	82	1988–89	81	1993–94	78
1985–86	???	1989–90	82	1994–95	17
1986–87	82	1991–92	82	1995–96	82
1987–88	82	1992–93	80		

a. Find the mean, median, and mode of the data provided. Ignore the entry for 1985–86.

b. During the 1985–86 season, Michael had an injury and played only 18 games. Add this outlier to the data and recompute the mean, median, and mode.

c. Communicate How do the outliers affect the mean? The median? The mode? Explain.

d. Critical Thinking Which number (the median, the mode, or the mean) is the best measure to use when describing the number of games Michael played each year? Explain.

Mixed Review

Perform the appropriate operation. *[Previous course]*

12. 234 + 5278   **13.** 5678 − 3991   **14.** 26 × 52   **15.** 307 ÷ 9

16. 43,675 + 2,344   **17.** 89,021 − 5,811   **18.** 329 × 86   **19.** 914 ÷ 30

20. How many women played in exactly three games? *[Lesson 1-3]*

21. One woman played in six games. How many hits did she get? *[Lesson 1-3]*

22. Does there appear to be a trend in the scatterplot? Explain. *[Lesson 1-3]*

Hits For Women's Softball Players

Number of hits (vertical axis: 1 2 3 4 5 6)
Number of games played (horizontal axis: 1 2 3 4 5 6)

Project Progress

Continue to work on the graphs and charts that show your data. If you find a large set of data about a single topic, you may want to calculate the median, the mode, and the mean of the data and include that in your report.

Problem Solving

Understand
Plan
Solve
Look Back

The article at the beginning of this section stated that "mathematics can turn huge amounts of data into a few easy-to-understand numbers." Since then, you've learned about three measures that can do this: the median, the mode, and the mean. Now you'll have a chance to use those numbers to decide which athlete is #1.

Will the Real #1 Athlete Please Stand Up?

Babe Ruth and Hank Aaron are two of baseball's most famous athletes. Both played for different teams and at different times. Is it possible to use statistics to determine who was the better athlete?

The following data represent the hits and home runs made by each player during the years he played for the teams shown.

Babe Ruth	New York Yankees (1920–1934)													
Hits	172	204	128	205	200	104	184	192	173	172	186	199	156	138	105
Home Runs	54	59	35	41	46	25	47	60	54	46	49	46	41	34	22

Hank Aaron	Milwaukee Braves (1954–1965)											
Hits	131	189	200	198	196	223	172	197	191	201	187	181
Home Runs	13	27	26	44	30	39	40	34	45	44	24	32

1. For each player, find the median, mode, and mean for both hits and home runs.

2. According to the statistics, who do you think was the better athlete? Write a paragraph explaining your reasoning.

3. Choose either the hits data or the home runs data. Draw a graph comparing the athletes' means, medians, and modes. The graph should help justify your decision of who is the better athlete.

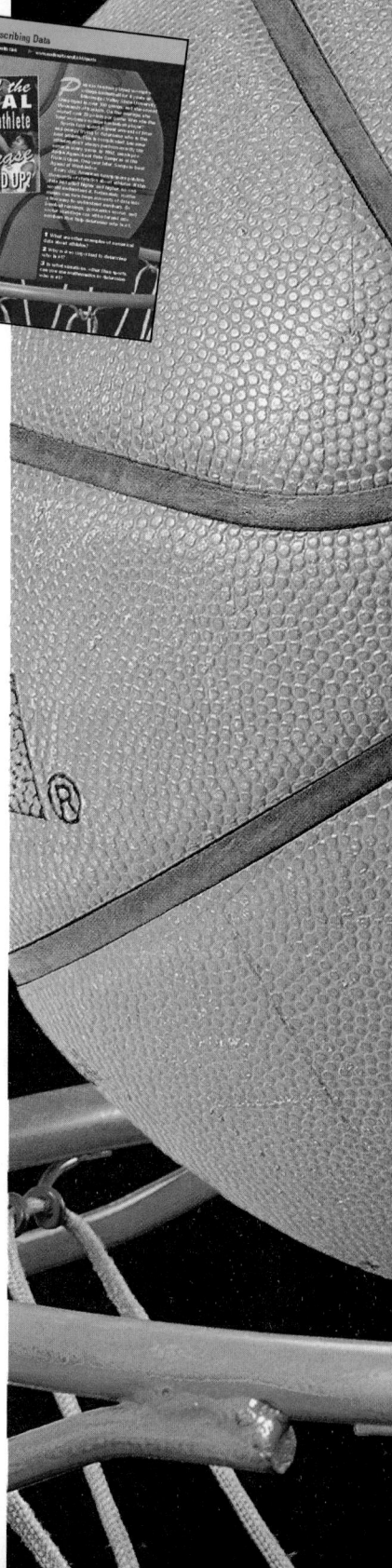

Find the mean, median, and mode of each set of data.

1. 1, 1, 5, 5, 7, 7, 9, 9, 8,
   1, 1, 3, 4, 5, 5, 6

   mode = 1, 5
   mean = 4.8125
   median = 5

2. *I know how 2 do this (#1-3)*

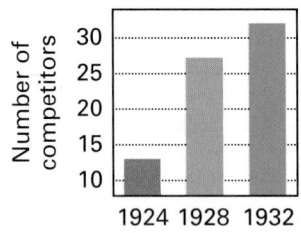

3.

Stem	Leaf
1	0 0 0 0 1 1 2 2 3 3 4
2	5 5 5 5

4. These graphs display data about female athletes in the Winter Olympics.

Female Competitors in Winter Olympics

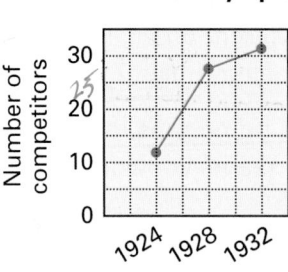

   a. How many women competed in the 1932 Winter Olympics? *31/32*

   b. The number of females increased between 1924 and 1928. By how much did it increase? *16*

   c. **Communicate** Could either graph be misleading? Explain. *yes, the bar graph*

5. **Communicate** Which measure—the mean, the median, or the mode—can be most affected by an outlier? Why? *mean, b/c*

6. Draw a bar graph for the data about the length in days of each country's school year: Hong Kong, 195; Japan, 244; Netherlands, 200; Scotland, 200; United States, 180. *I know how 2 do*

Test Prep

When you need to find the median and mode of a large set of data, a line plot can help you keep track of the data.

7. Which value is greater for the following set of data, the median or the mode?

   9, 10, 12, 11, 9, 13, 12, 10, 11, 10, 12, 11, 11, 10, 12, 11, 13, 15

   Ⓐ Median   Ⓑ Mode   Ⓒ The two are equal.

b/c if does not start w/ 0.

a really high # brings the mean up and vice versa

Box-and-Whisker Plots

You can show the shape of a data set with a box-and-whisker plot.

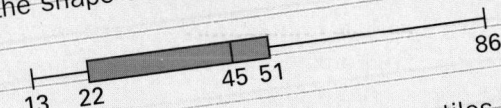

The box shows the median, 45, and the two quartiles at 22 and 51. The "whiskers" extend to the lowest and the highest values, 13 and 86.

To make a box-and-whisker plot for the data 9, 17, 18, 26, 36, 36, 37, 38, 45, and 55, first draw a line and label it with a number scale long enough to include all the numbers in the list. Mark the lowest and the highest numbers in the data set.

Calculate the median and the quartiles. The median is 36. The quartiles are the medians for the first and second half of the data. The quartiles are 18 and 38. Draw a box using the quartiles as the left and right ends. Label the quartiles.

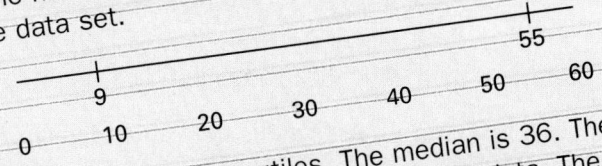

Draw and label a line at the median. Erase the numbers that indicate the scale and the lines to the left and right of the "whiskers".

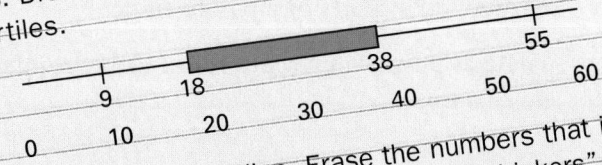

Try It
1. Draw a box-and-whisker plot for this data set: 35, 67, 22, 12, 90, 88, 55, 57, 11, 81.
2. If the box in a box-and-whisker plot is shorter than the whiskers, what does this tell you about the data set?
3. Is it possible for the median and a quartile to have the same value? Explain.

Chapter 1 Summary and Review

Graphic Organizer

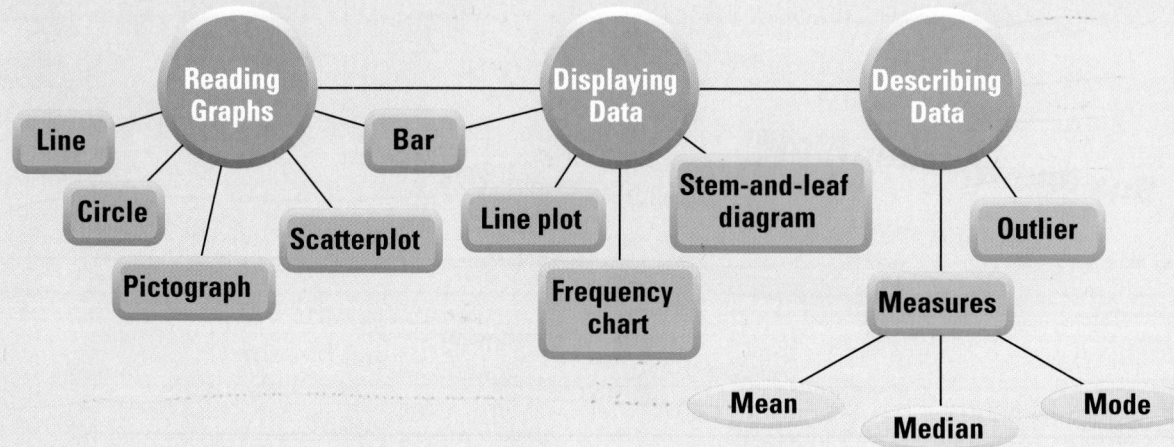

Section 1A Reading and Interpreting Graphs

Summary

- Data is represented in a **bar graph** by the height of each bar.

- In a **pictograph**, data is shown by symbols. A key tells the value of each symbol.

- Data is represented in a **line graph** by the heights of points on a line.

- In a **circle graph**, data is represented as parts of a whole circle.

- You can graph two sets of data as points on a **scatterplot**. If the points fall in a line, the scatterplot shows a **trend**.

Review

1. How many blue jackets were sold?

One Hundred Jackets Sold

Red — 10
Pale Blue — 16
Navy Blue — 41
Medium Blue — 23
Black — 10

2. About how far did the train travel in the first 3 hours?

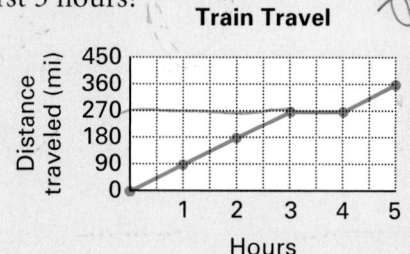

Train Travel

Section 1B Displaying Data

Summary

- Use **tally marks** to count data by type. Then organize them into a **frequency chart**.

- Use columns of ×'s to show the shape of the data in a **line plot**.

- Use **range** to help decide the **scale** and **intervals** needed to mark the **horizontal** and **vertical axes** of a bar graph.

- Use a **stem-and-leaf diagram** to see the distribution or shape of data in intervals.

Review

3. Use tally marks to make a frequency chart of campaign souvenirs.

4. Make a bar graph using the veto data for these presidents: Carter, 29; Ford, 66; Nixon, 42; L. B. Johnson, 30; and Kennedy, 21.

5. Describe the stems and leaves for a set of data containing all the even whole numbers less than 100.

Section 1C Describing Data

Summary

Three measures can help you describe a set of data.

- The **median** is the middle value of an ordered set of data.

- A **mode** is the number or numbers that appear most often in a set of data.

- The **mean** is the sum of the numbers in a data set divided by the number of numbers.

- An **outlier** is a data value that is far from the other data in the set.

Review

6. Find the median, mode, and mean for these home-run records: Aaron, 755; Williams, 521; Foxx, 534; Ruth, 714; Jackson, 563; Mays, 660; Robinson, 586; Killebrew, 573; Mantle, 536; Schmidt, 548; and McCovey, 521.

7. For any data set, which of the three measures is likely to be most affected by an outlier?

For Problems 1–6, match each description with a vocabulary word.

1. A number that is much larger or much smaller than any other number in a data set

2. A measure found by adding the data values and dividing by the number of values

3. A graph that shows a trend between two sets of data

4. A graph that is often used to see the shape of large sets of data in intervals

5. The middle value of a data set

6. A graph that usually shows change over time

a. Line graph
b. Mean
c. Scatterplot
d. Outlier
e. Median
f. Range
g. Stem-and-leaf diagram
h. Circle graph

7. Favorite sports and the number of millions of people who engaged in them in 1995: Walking, 71; Swimming, 60; Bicycling, 50; and Fishing, 56.

   a. Use the data to draw and label a bar graph.

   b. Find the mean of the data.

Use the data shown on the graphs to answer Exercises 8–13.

Stem	Leaf
0	2 5
1	2 3 5 6
2	2

8. Does the data show a trend? Explain.

9. Is there an outlier? If so, where?

10. What is the value of each symbol?

11. How many cars were washed?

12. What is the median value?

13. What is the mode?

Performance Task

At the end of the 1994–95 season, these colleges had the most bowl wins: Alabama, 27; University of Southern California, 24; Oklahoma, 20; Penn State, 19; and Tennessee, 19. Name the types of data displays you could use to show this information. Make at least two of these displays and explain how each helps you understand the data.

Performance Assessment

Choose one problem.

State of Recall

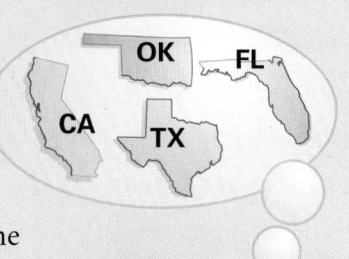

Use a watch or clock with a second hand. Ask at least 20 people to name as many states in the United States as they can in 30 seconds. Collect and record your data in a table. Make a line plot and a stem-and-leaf diagram of the data. Explain which chart gives a better picture of the data.

Let's Go Fly a Kite!

Here are the results from the Lakeside Kite Flying Contest.

Contestant	Height (m)	Contestant	Height (m)
Greg	233	Hassan	360
Tyron	212	Bill	274
Ku	272	Cassie	501
Manny	319	Ali	124
Charlene	275	Maria	286

Create a bar graph from this data. List five things that you can interpret from the bar graph.

It's My Party

Pizza Party

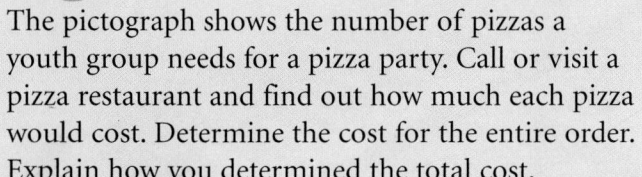

Large, one topping

Large, two toppings

Medium, one topping

Small, one topping

🍕 = 4 pizzas

The pictograph shows the number of pizzas a youth group needs for a pizza party. Call or visit a pizza restaurant and find out how much each pizza would cost. Determine the cost for the entire order. Explain how you determined the total cost.

As Time Goes By

Use a watch or clock with a second hand. Ask at least 20 people to esti-mate a minute. Record the data and find the mode, median, and mean. Explain which measure best describes the data, and discuss any outliers.

2 Connecting Arithmetic to Algebra

Arts and Literature Link
www.mathsurf.com/6/ch2/Arts

Science Link
www.mathsurf.com/6/ch2/science

Science

The "flash-to-bang" equation states how far away lightning struck. The number of seconds between the lightning and the thunder divided by 5 equals the distance in miles.

Arts & Literature

When you talk about art sales, you need to use large numbers. Vincent van Gogh's *Portrait du Dr. Gachet* sold for $75 million.

Entertainment

Billboard magazine uses this formula to rank songs on the Top 40 Chart: (copies sold × 0.4) + (number of radio plays × 0.6) = chart value.

Social Studies

Many cultures helped to develop algebra. The first definite use of algebra is Egyptian. The Greeks added the use of letters to represent unknown numbers. The Arabs added the number 0 to their study of algebra.

People of the World

People in China use an *abacus* to help them do arithmetic. Each column of beads in an abacus represents a place value, such as ones, tens, or hundreds. You can add, subtract, multiply, and divide numbers by moving the beads up and down.

KEY MATH IDEAS

Large numbers can be expressed using place values bigger than thousands.

Mental math strategies can be used to do math computation without pencil and paper or calculator.

When an exact answer isn't necessary, estimation strategies can be used to determine a reasonably close answer.

A variable is a mathematical symbol that represents an unknown value or set of values.

An equation is a mathematical sentence that can be used to represent real-world situations.

CHAPTER PROJECT

Problem Solving

Understand
Plan
Solve
Look Back

In this project, you will research how far you could travel in 24 hours. Begin by thinking about different ways you can travel, and the different types of information you would need to determine how far you could go.

Problem
Solving

Understand
Plan
Solve
Look Back

Problem Solving Focus

Finding Unnecessary Information

To solve real-life problems, you need to understand the available data. Some of the data is needed to find the answer, but usually not all of it. Identifying the information that will not help you answer the question is an important step in finding a solution.

For each problem, state which sentences do not include necessary information. For some problems, all the sentences may have necessary information.

1 The tallest mountain in the world, Mount Everest, is 29,028 feet high. It is located in Nepal. The second largest mountain, K2, is 778 feet shorter than Mount Everest. The third largest mountain, Kanchenjunga, is 28,208 feet high. What's the difference in elevation between K2 and Kanchenjunga?

2 In Antarctica, there are two mountains higher than 16,000 feet. There are ten mountains taller than 14,000 feet. There are exactly three mountains whose heights are between 15,000 and 16,000 feet. Their names are Shinn, Gardner, and Epperly. How many mountains are between 14,000 and 15,000 feet?

3 There are 50 tons of garbage on Mount Everest left by people who have climbed the mountain. 17 tons can be found in the South Col area, just below the summit. How many tons can be found on the rest of Mount Everest?

Greetings! from Planet Earth

Are we alone in the universe? Throughout history, people have searched the skies for the answer. In 1972, scientists took a more direct approach. They launched a space probe named *Pioneer 10.* Fourteen years later, *Pioneer 10* crossed the orbit of Pluto and became the first human-made object to leave our solar system.

Scientists use a variety of technologies to study the universe. Astronauts orbit Earth and land on the moon. Space stations and orbiting telescopes provide information that is impossible to get from Earth. Signals have been sent to distant stars describing who we are and inviting anyone who receives the message to visit.

In order to learn about and describe the universe, people have to use numbers much larger than hundreds, thousands, or even millions. Mathematics provides people with several tools for talking about large numbers conveniently and effectively. Meanwhile, *Pioneer 10* speeds toward a distant star called Ross 248. It should arrive in the year 34,600 unless it encounters something else first. Something, or someone …

1. Why will it take *Pioneer 10* over 32,000 years to reach the star Ross 248?

2. Why do people spend so much time and energy trying to find life in outer space?

3. Why do you need mathematics to learn about and describe things in the universe?

Reading and Writing Large Numbers

► **Lesson Link**
In the last chapter, you learned to display and interpret data. To display and interpret some kinds of data, you must be able to read and write extremely large numbers. ◄

You'll Learn ...

■ the place values of digits in numbers

■ to write numbers in standard form, word form, and number-word form

... How It's Used

Astronomers must be able to read and write huge numbers when studying the distance between planets.

Vocabulary

place value

Explore | **Large Numbers**

Mission Control, Do You Read Me?

You are the commander of a disabled spacecraft. Mission Control in Houston wants to know how far you are from Earth. Although you can hear Mission Control, they cannot hear you. Each time Mission Control guesses a distance, you must press one of the signal buttons.

Work with a partner. One of you should play the Spacecraft Commander, and the other, Mission Control.

1. The Spacecraft Commander should secretly pick a distance from 1 to 100 miles. Mission Control should try to guess the distance in as few guesses as possible. After each guess, the Spacecraft Commander should say "Too high," "Too low," or "Correct."

2. Switch roles. This time, the Spacecraft Commander should pick a distance from 1 to 1,000,000 miles.

3. Which game was easier? Why?

4. Which game would go faster, a game from 20 thousand to 50 thousand or a game from 20 million to 50 million? Why?

Learn | **Reading and Writing Large Numbers**

Every digit of a number has a **place value**. The place value tells you how much that digit represents. In 2364, the digit 3 represents 3 hundreds (or 300) because the 3 is in the hundreds place. In order to use large numbers, you need to know the names of large place values.

Place Value

hundreds	tens	ones	hundreds	tens	ones	hundreds	tens	ones	hundreds	tens	ones	hundreds	tens	ones
4	5	0	0	0	0	0	0	0	0	0	0	0	0	0
Trillions			Billions			Millions			Thousands			Ones		

Numbers can be written in three different forms.

Standard form: 45,000,000,000,000
Word form: forty-five trillion
Number-word form: 45 trillion

Examples

1 Find the place value of the 9 in Vega's diameter.

Vega's diameter is 2,5 $\boxed{9}$ 4,200 miles.

The 9 is in the ten-thousands place. It represents 9 ten-thousands, or 90,000.

2 Write Alpha Centauri's diameter in word form.

Write each number of trillions, billions, millions, thousands, and ones.

$\boxed{\text{1 million}}$ $\boxed{\text{37 thousands}}$ $\boxed{\text{700 ones}}$

1,000,000   037,000   700

one million,   thirty-seven thousand,   seven hundred

3 Write seven billion, forty thousand, two in standard form.   7,042,002

$\boxed{\text{billions}}$ $\boxed{\text{millions}}$ $\boxed{\text{thousands}}$ $\boxed{\text{ones}}$

7,   000,   040,   002 → 7,000,040,002

4 Write 36,000,000,000 in number-word form.

36,000,000,000 = 36 billion

Try It

a. Find the place value of the digit 1 in Arcturus's diameter.

b. Write the diameter of Arcturus in words.

c. Write five trillion, twenty billion, three hundred in standard form.

Diameters of Six Brightest Stars	
Name	**Diameter (mi)**
Sun	864,730
Sirius	1,556,500
Canopus	25,941,900
Alpha Centauri	1,037,700
Arcturus	19,888,800
Vega	2,594,200

▶ **Science Link**

The largest known star is Betelgeuse (BEE-tuhl-joos) in the constellation of Orion. Betelgeuse has a diameter of approximately 400,000,000 miles, about 500 times the diameter of the sun.

▶ **Language Link**

Scientists use the prefix *mega-* to indicate 1 million (as in *megabyte*) and the prefix *giga-* to indicate 1 billion (as in *gigabyte*).

1. How is each place value related to the one on the right?

2. Is there a name for every number, no matter how large? Explain.

2-1 Exercises and Applications

Practice and Apply

Getting Started Name the place-value position of the given digit in the number 31,480,725.

1. 5 ~~ones~~   **2.** 7 ~~hundreds~~   **3.** 8 ~~ten th.~~   **4.** 3 ~~ten #millions~~

5. 1 ~~millions~~   **6.** 4 ~~hund. thous~~   **7.** 0 ~~th.~~   **8.** 2 ~~tens~~

Write the number in words.

9. 30,080,705   **10.** 5,111,293,026   **11.** 8235   **12.** 9,303,946

13. 7098 ~~7thousand ninety-eight~~   **14.** 222   **15.** 56,056,560   **16.** 8,000,969,152,001

Science Write each planet's average distance from Earth in number-word form.

17. Mercury   **18.** Venus

19. Saturn   **20.** Uranus

21. Neptune   **22.** Pluto

Average Distance from Earth	
Planet	**Distance (mi)**
Mercury	93,000,000
Venus	141,500,000
Saturn	888,000,000
Uranus	1,779,500,000
Neptune	2,791,000,000
Pluto	3,653,500,000

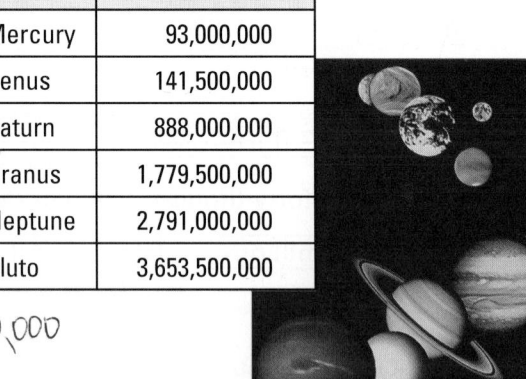

Write each number in standard form.

23. 52 million ~~52,000,000~~   **24.** 38 thousand

25. 560 million ~~560,000,000~~   **26.** 7 trillion ~~7,000,000,000,000~~

27. 9 thousand ~~9,000~~   **28.** 4 hundred ~~400~~

29. 321 thousand ~~321,000~~   **30.** 26 million ~~26,000,000~~

31. forty-two million, six thousand ~~42,006,000~~   **32.** eight hundred four thousand, two

33. nine trillion, twenty billion, thirty   **34.** four thousand, seven hundred five

35. eighty-one thousand, five hundred   **36.** three million, nine hundred

Complete.

37. 36,000 = 36 _thousand_

38. 42,000,006,000,000 = 42 million

39. 67,000,000,000 = 67 _billions_

40. 5,000,000,000 = 5 trillion

Science For each fact, write the number in word form and in number-word form.

41. The Cassini orbiter, designed to carry a probe, science instruments, and fuel into space, weighs 5655 kg.

42. Scientists can see more than 100,000,000,000 galaxies in the universe.

43. Neptune's mean distance from the sun is 2,798,800,000 miles.

44. As of 1995, American astronauts have spent over 17,715 hours in space.

Shannon Lucid.

45. **Test Prep** Select the standard form for four hundred thirty thousand, four hundred seven.

Ⓐ 43,047   Ⓑ 403,407   Ⓒ 430,047   Ⓓ 430,407

Problem Solving and Reasoning

46. **Communicate** Explain the difference between the two 7's in the number 737,459.

47. **Critical Thinking** When the planets are aligned, Earth has an approximate distance of 92,960,000 miles from the sun. Pluto has an approximate distance of 3,573,240,000 miles from Earth. What is the approximate distance between Pluto and the sun? Explain.

48. **Critical Thinking** Make a bar graph of a student's budget: $4 for bus, $5 for lunch, $3 for games. Then make a bar graph of a city's budget: $4 million for road maintenance, $5 million for salaries, $3 million for construction. How are the graphs similar? How are they different?

Mixed Review

Use the stem-and-leaf diagram for Exercises 49–50. *[Lesson 1-6]*

49. Identify the outlier.

50. How many digits are in each number of the data?

51. Find the mean of the data. Round to the nearest tenth. *[Lesson 1-8]*

1, 2, 7, 0, 3, 1, 0, 4, 2, 1, 0

Stem	Leaf
1	4
2	8 8 9
3	2 6 6 7
4	1 2 4 4 4 9

2-2 Rounding Large Numbers

You'll Learn ...

■ to round numbers using rules for rounding

■ to use common sense to round numbers in real-life situations

... How It's Used

Reporters round scientific data to make the stories accurate but easier to read.

Vocabulary

rounding

▶ **Lesson Link** In the last lesson, you learned how to read and write large numbers. Now you'll learn how to make large numbers easier to use. ◀

Explore | Rounding

Round and Round and Round It Goes

Pioneer 11 was launched on April 5, 1973. Twenty months later, three reports described the spacecraft's closest encounter with Jupiter.

1. Do any of the reported distances give *Pioneer 11*'s exact distance from Jupiter? How can you tell?

2. Why do the reports give three different distances?

3. Earlier in 1973, *Pioneer 10* came within 81,000 miles of Jupiter. To compare *Pioneer 11*'s performance with *Pioneer 10*'s, which of the three reported distances would you use?

4. A *Pioneer 11* engineer explained why there should be another Jupiter project: "We're getting closer each time. This time we were down to almost 25,000 miles." Why did the engineer use 25,000 miles instead of one of the distances in the reports?

> **NASA Press Release**
>
> Dateline: 12/2/74
> Contact: J.P. Richards
> NASA Public Relations
>
> Today, December 2, 1974, the space probe Pioneer 11 bypassed Jupiter at an altitude of 26,725 miles.

> **10A**
>
> ## Pioneer 11 Close to Jupiter
>
> **(UPI)** — The Planetary explorer Pioneer 11 was nearly 27,000 miles from Jupiter when it flew by yesterday.

> **Pioneer 11**
>
> Late in 1974, Pioneer 11 passed within 30,000 miles of the planet Jupiter.

Learn | Rounding Large Numbers

Large numbers can be difficult to work with. You don't always need to use the *exact* value of large numbers. You can often use numbers that are close to the exact value but easier to work with.

Rounding is one way to find a number that's more convenient. Rounding will give you the closest convenient number according to a given place value.

There are four steps involved in the rounding process.

67,683 to thousands		2,341 to hundreds
6 7 ,683	Find the place value.	2, 3 41
6 7 ,683	Look at the digit to the right.	2, 3 41
6 7 ,683 ↑ Add one	If this digit is 5 or greater, add 1 to the place-value digit. If it's less than 5, leave the place-value digit alone.	2, 3 41 ↑ Leave alone
68,000	Change the digits to the right to zeros.	2,300

Examples

According to the 1990 U.S. Census, there were 45,249,989 people in the 5-to-17 age group. Round the population to the given place.

1 millions | millions | | Leave the millions digit unchanged. |
$$\downarrow \; \downarrow$$
4 5, 2 4 9, 9 8 9   → round to 45,000,000

2 ten-millions | ten-millions | | Add 1 to the ten-millions digit. |
$$\downarrow \; \downarrow$$
4 5, 2 4 9, 9 8 9   → round to 50,000,000

Try It

Round 73,952 to the given place.

a. ten-thousands   **b.** thousands   **c.** hundreds

Sometimes it makes more sense to round up or round down, even if it means rounding to a number that's not the closest number.

Example 3

Danielle thinks her diving tank contains enough air for about a 47-minute dive. Since 47 rounds to 50, can she make a 50-minute dive?

No. Danielle can't afford to run out of air under water. Rounding up gives her a closer number, but common sense says she should round *down* to estimate the length of her dive.

DID YOU KNOW?

The 1990 census counted about 41 million students in public schools. At an average of about $4700 per student per year, the United States spends about $200 billion annually on public education.

1. Why is a rounded number easier to work with?

2. Describe one situation when you might purposely round up, and one when you might purposely round down.

2-2 Exercises and Applications

Practice and Apply

1. **Getting Started** Answer these questions to round 1,374,692 to the nearest ten-thousand.

   a. What is the digit to the right of the ten-thousands place?

   b. Is that digit greater than 5 or less than 5?

   c. Should you leave the ten-thousands digit the same or add 1 to it? Why?

   d. What is 1,374,692 rounded to the nearest ten-thousand?

Round to the given place.

2. 8,702; hundreds 8,700

3. 94,655; ten-thousands

4. 1,850,817,349; hundred-millions

5. 738; tens

6. 800,000,000,000; trillions

7. 3,886,000; hundred-thousands

8. 2,790,600,073,521; ten-billions

9. 22,900; thousands

10. Round 84,226,499,391 to the given place.

    a. hundreds   **b.** 10 thousands   **c.** 100 thousands   **d.** 10 billions

Science On August 29, 1989, the planetary explorer *Voyager 2* crossed Pluto's orbit and left the solar system. *Voyager 2* was 2,758,530,928 miles from Earth.

11. Write *Voyager 2*'s distance from Earth in words.

12. Round *Voyager 2*'s distance to the given place.

    a. hundred-thousands   **b.** ten-millions

    c. hundred-millions   **d.** billions

13. **Test Prep** Round ninety-seven thousand, five hundred forty-nine to the nearest thousand.

    Ⓐ 98,500   Ⓑ 98,000   Ⓒ 97,500   Ⓓ 97,500   Ⓔ 97,000

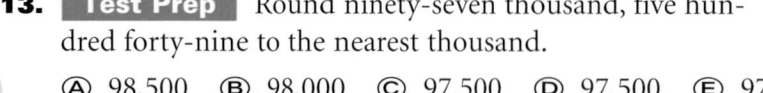

14. Estimation Arnold's car is about to run out of gas. He estimates that the car can go about 25 miles before this happens. The next gas station is 30 miles away. Should he try to make it to the next station? Explain your answer.

Problem Solving and Reasoning

15. Journal Make a list of everyday situations for which you must use exact numbers. Then make a list of everyday situations when you can use rounded numbers to approximate answers.

16. Critical Thinking While entering 1990 population data into a computer, a census worker mistakenly deleted digits from the populations of two Texas towns.

Borger
Elev: 3,050
Pop: 1_,675

Copperas Cove
Elev: 1,602
Pop: 2_,079

The worker remembered that both populations rounded to 20,000 to the nearest thousand. What could the two populations be? Explain why.

17. Communicate Claudia must reserve buses to take students to the Science Museum. She thinks that about 263 students will be going. Each bus holds 30 students. How many buses does she need? Why?

PROBLEM SOLVING 2-2

Mixed Review

Add. *[Previous course]*

18. 2672 + 2438 + 8616

19. 2107 + 596 + 5632

20. 759 + 6675 + 3219

21. 9820 + 423 + 890

Use the data to make a frequency chart and a line plot. *[Lesson 1-4]*

22. 48, 48, 49, 52, 53, 53, 53, 54

23. 101, 94, 96, 103, 98, 100, 100

Find the median, mode, and range. *[Lesson 1-7]*

24. 12, 2, 6, 10, 2, 10, 11

25. 32, 29, 22, 32, 30, 32

26. 44, 48, 31, 57

27. 108, 96, 108, 108, 96, 102, 102

Comparing and Ordering Numbers

You'll Learn ...

■ to compare and order large numbers

... How It's Used

Stock market traders must compare and order large numbers to determine which companies are the most successful.

▶ **Lesson Link**   You've learned to read, write, and round numbers. Now you will learn how to decide whether one number is greater than another. ◀

Explore Comparing and Ordering

Line Up—That's an Order!

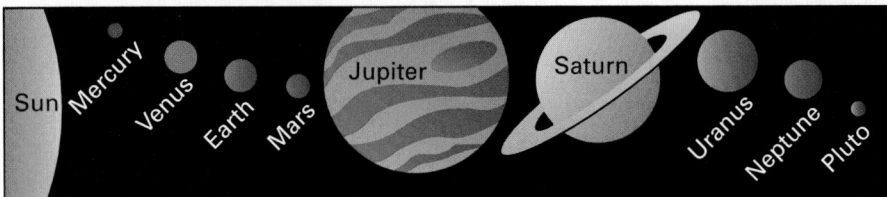

The chart lists eight U.S. space probes sent to the other planets in our solar system and how far the probes were from the sun when they visited the planets or crossed their orbits.

1. Match each probe and its distance with the planet it visited or the planetary orbit it crossed.

2. Explain how you determined which probe matched up with each planet.

3. Suppose a new planet is discovered between the orbits of Neptune and Pluto. Give its possible distance from the sun.

Probe	Distance (mi)
Mariner 2	sixty-seven million
Pioneer 10	500,000,000
Pioneer 10	4,000,000,000
Pioneer 11	3 billion
Mariner 10	forty million
Viking 1	150 million
Voyager 2	1,700,000,000
Voyager 1	one billion

MENTAL MATH

If two whole numbers have different numbers of digits, the number with more digits is greater.

Learn Comparing and Ordering Numbers

To compare two numbers with the same number of digits, start at the left and find the first place-value position that has different digits. The number with the larger digit is the larger number.

236,⬚4⬚12

236,⬚7⬚83

Since 7 is larger than 4, the second number is larger than the first

The symbols $>$ and $<$ are used to compare numbers. The symbol $>$ means "is greater than," and $<$ means "is less than."

Examples

1 Mount Shasta is 14,162 feet tall. Mount Russell is 14,086 feet tall. Compare the heights of these California mountains.

$\boxed{1}$4,162
$\boxed{1}$4,086 } The ten-thousands digits are equal. Move to the right.

1$\boxed{4}$,162
1$\boxed{4}$,086 } The thousands digits are equal. Move to the right.

14,$\boxed{1}$62
14,$\boxed{0}$86 } In the hundreds place, 1 is greater than 0.

14,162 > 14,086   Mount Shasta is taller than Mount Russell.

2 Order from least to greatest the three craters on the visible side of the moon.

227,000 < 234,000   Compare two at a time.
Schickard < Deslandres

234,000 < 303,000   Use the same symbol in
Deslandres < Bailly   the second comparison.

Craters on the Moon	
Name	**Diameter (m)**
Deslandres	234,000
Schickard	227,000
Bailly	303,000

The order is Schickard at 227,000 meters, Deslandres at 234,000 meters, and Bailly at 303,000 meters.

▶ **Science Link**

Craters are formed when meteors strike the surface of a planet or moon.

Try It

a. Order from least to greatest: 138,417; 146,416; 98,419.

b. The Belkovich crater is 198,000 meters in diameter. The Janssen crater is 190,000 meters in diameter. Compare the diameters of the two craters.

Check Your Understanding

1. Is it easier to compare large numbers when they are written in standard form or in word form? Why?

2. The first digit of a number is 7. Is the number greater than another number whose first digit is 6? Explain.

Practice and Apply

PRACTICE 2-3

Getting Started Compare the numbers, using > or < .

1. 277 ☐ 31   **2.** 5768 ☐ 924   **3.** 873 ☐ 2183   **4.** 327 ☐ 91

5. 64 ☐ 65   **6.** 158 ☐ 185   **7.** 448,119 ☐ 448,191

Order each group of numbers from least to greatest.

8. 77; 7,777; 777; 77,777

9. 5678; 5768; 5687

10. 57,000; 56,940; 56,490

11. 20,200; 22,000; 20,002

12. 20 million; 500 thousand; 1 billion

13. 10 hundred; 10 million; 1 trillion

14. 9 hundred; 901; nine

15. 62 thousand; 6 hundred; 29 billion

16. Measurement In almost 19 years, *Voyager 1* traveled 11,005,000,000 kilometers, and *Voyager 2* traveled 10,042,000,000 kilometers. Which spacecraft traveled farther?

17. **Test Prep** Choose the smallest number.

ⓐ 138,528   ⓑ 13,855   ⓒ 13,852   ⓓ 13,555

18. Logic Marisela, Luis, and Raymond are comparing their heights. Luis is 54 inches tall. Marisela is shorter than Luis but 2 inches taller than Raymond. Order the three students from shortest to tallest.

19. Geography The diameter of Earth at the equator is 7926 miles. The diameter from the North Pole to the South Pole is 7898 miles. Which diameter is greater?

20. Chance In the fall raffle at Oakdale Middle School, 4269 tickets were sold. In the winter raffle, 4629 were sold. In the spring raffle, 4962. Rank the raffles from easiest-to-win to hardest-to-win.

21. Geography List the cities in order from largest population to smallest: Rio de Janeiro, Brazil: 12,788,000; Buenos Aires, Argentina: 12,232,000; Calcutta, India: 12,885,000.

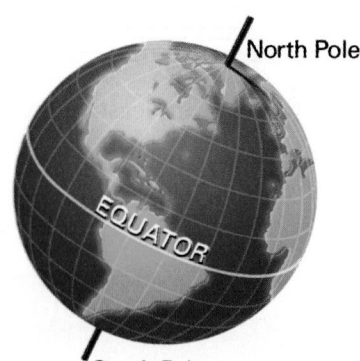

North Pole

EQUATOR

South Pole

22. Science The two most experienced space women are Shannon Lucid and Elena Kondakova. As of 1996, Lucid had spent 5354 hours in space. As of 1995, Kondakova had spent 2033 hours in space. Compare their hours in space, using > or <.

23. Science Indonesia has 268,356,000 acres of forest. Australia has 261,931,000 acres. Compare the two amounts, using > or <.

Elena Kondakova

Problem Solving and Reasoning

24. Critical Thinking Use the digits 7, 1, 5, 9, and 3 to write the largest and smallest possible 5-digit numbers. Each digit must be used exactly once. Use < or > to compare your answers.

The bar graph shows the five most populated metropolitan areas in the United States, according to the 1990 census. Use the data for Exercises 25–27.

25. Critical Thinking The populations of the five areas are 18,087,251; 6,253,311; 14,531,529; 8,065,633; and 5,899,345. Match each area with its population.

26. Critical Thinking The population of Jakarta, Indonesia, is greater than that of Chicago. How does Jakarta's population compare with that of San Francisco?

27. Communicate Can you tell how Jakarta's population compares with the population of Los Angeles? Why or why not?

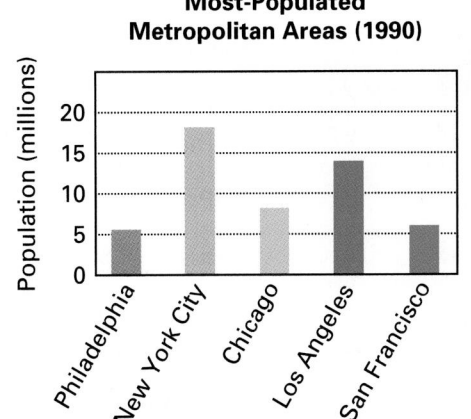

Most-Populated
Metropolitan Areas (1990)

Mixed Review

Add. *[Previous course]*

28. 4212 + 2590 + 3856

29. 22,386 + 6,911

30. 356,093 + 734,035

31. 160,577 + 64,444

32. 454,232 + 711,804

33. 560,380 + 479,120

34. 984,909 + 978,099

35. 328,040 + 288,045

36. 423,371 + 968,195

Find the mean. *[Lesson 1-8]*

37. 40, 34, 50, 39, 61, 34

38. 72, 92, 83, 47, 101

39. 123, 98, 112, 131, 121

40. 204, 342, 267, 412, 383, 439

Exponents

► **Lesson Link**
In this section, you have learned to round and compare large numbers. Now you will learn an easy way to write certain large numbers. ◄

You'll Learn ...

■ to use exponents to express numbers

■ to write expressions containing exponents in standard form

... How It's Used

Urban planners use exponents to predict how quickly the population of a city will grow.

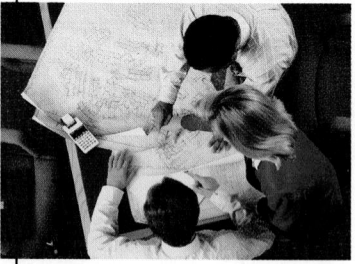

Vocabulary

factor

base

exponent

power

squared

cubed

Explore | **Repeated Multiplication**

One, Two, Three, Four ... Press!

Materials: Scientific calculator

1. Use only the numbers 1, 2, 3, and 4. On your calculator, press this sequence:

   1, 2, 3, or 4 $\boxed{y^x}$ 1, 2, 3, or 4 $\boxed{=}$.

   Record the numbers you pressed and the answer given by the calculator.

2. Repeat Step 1 as many times as necessary until you understand how the calculator finds the answer. Explain the calculator's method.

3. Predict each result. Then use your calculator to check your prediction.

   a. 2 $\boxed{y^x}$ 5 $\boxed{=}$ **b.** 6 $\boxed{y^x}$ 2 $\boxed{=}$ **c.** 10 $\boxed{y^x}$ 3 $\boxed{=}$

4. Find 3 $\boxed{y^x}$ 5 $\boxed{=}$ and 5 $\boxed{y^x}$ 3 $\boxed{=}$ on your calculator. Are the results the same? Why or why not?

Learn | **Exponents**

When you multiply numbers, each number is a **factor** of the result.

$$\overset{\text{Factors}}{\overset{\diagup\ \ |\ \ \diagdown}{2 \times 3 \times 5}} = 30$$

You can represent repeated multiplication of the same number by using exponential notation. The **base** is the number to be multiplied. The **exponent** is the number that tells how many times the base is used as a factor.

$$\underset{\underset{\text{5 factors}}{\uparrow}}{3 \times 3 \times 3 \times 3 \times 3} = 3^{\underset{\underset{\text{3 is the base}}{\uparrow}}{5}} \quad \overset{\downarrow \text{ 5 is the exponent}}{}$$

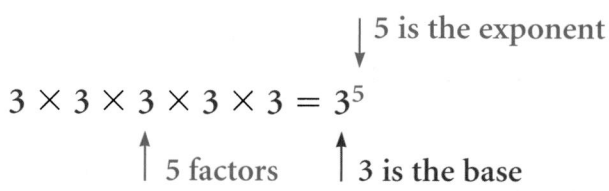

Numbers involving exponents can be written in three different forms.

Exponential notation: 9^4

Expanded form: $9 \times 9 \times 9 \times 9$

Standard form: 6561

When the base and exponent are small, you can use mental math or pencil and paper to convert numbers to standard form. Otherwise, use the $\boxed{y^x}$ key on your calculator:

$3 \times 3 \times 3 \times 3 \times 3 = 3 \boxed{y^x} 5 \boxed{=} 243$

Examples

1 Write $8 \times 8 \times 8 \times 8 \times 8 \times 8$ using exponents.

$8 \times 8 \times 8 \times 8 \times 8 \times 8 = 8^6$

2 Write 7^4 in expanded form.

$7^4 = 7 \times 7 \times 7 \times 7$

3 Write 5^3 in standard form.

$5^3 = 5 \times 5 \times 5 = 125$

4 When the space probe *Mariner 10* passed the planet Mercury in 1972, the probe was traveling about 19^4 mi/hr. Write 19^4 in standard form.

$19^4 = 19 \times 19 \times 19 \times 19 = 19 \boxed{y^x} 4 \boxed{=} 130{,}321$

Mariner 10's speed was about 130,321 mi/hr.

Try It

a. Write $12 \times 12 \times 12 \times 12$ using exponents.

b. Write 5^6 in expanded form.

c. Use mental math to change 9^2 to standard form.

d. Change 11^5 to standard form.

An exponent is also called a **power** . We read 3^6 as "3 raised to the sixth power," or simply "3 to the sixth power." The second and third powers have special names:

We read 5^2 as "5 to the second power," or 5 **squared** .

We read 8^3 as "8 to the third power," or 8 **cubed** .

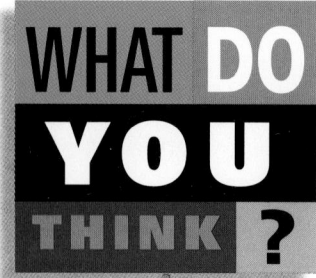

WHAT DO YOU THINK ?

In science class, Tyreka and Ricardo learned that the sun is about 10^8 miles from Earth. They want to evaluate 10^8.

Tyreka thinks ...

I'll use my calculator.

10 $\boxed{y^x}$ 8 $\boxed{=}$ 100,000,000

Ricardo thinks ...

$10^2 = 10 \times 10 = 100$, which is a 1 followed by two zeros.

$10^3 = 10 \times 10 \times 10 = 1,000$, which is a 1 followed by three zeros. Each time I multiply by 10, I add one zero to the product. Therefore, 10^8 is a 1 followed by eight zeros, or 100,000,000.

What do you think?

1. Whose method would you use to evaluate 10^{25}? Why?

2. What rule could Ricardo use to evaluate powers of 100?

Keep in mind that 8^3 and 8×3 do not have the same meaning.
8×3 represents repeated addition. It has the same value as $8 + 8 + 8$.
8^3 represents repeated multiplication. It has the same value as $8 \times 8 \times 8$.

$$8 \times 3 = 24, \text{ but } 8^3 = 512.$$

Check | **Your Understanding**

1. What is the advantage of using exponents to write numbers?

2. Is 3^7 the same as 7^3? Explain.

3. What happens to a number when you raise it to the first power?

2-4 Exercises and Applications

Practice and Apply

1. **Getting Started** Answer these questions to write
$4 \times 4 \times 4 \times 4 \times 4 \times 4 \times 4$ using an exponent.

  a. What number is the factor in the product?

  b. How many times is the number used as a factor?

  c. To write $4 \times 4 \times 4 \times 4 \times 4 \times 4 \times 4$ in exponential notation, what number should you use as the base? As the exponent?

  d. Write $4 \times 4 \times 4 \times 4 \times 4 \times 4 \times 4$ in exponential notation.

Write using exponents.

2. $5 \times 5 \times 5 \times 5$ **3.** $9 \times 9 \times 9 \times 9 \times 9$ **4.** $24 \times 24 \times 24$ **5.** 79×79

6. $20 \times 20 \times 20$ **7.** $7 \times 7 \times 3 \times 3$ **8.** $8 \times 8 \times 8 \times 4$ **9.** 36

Write in expanded form.

10. 4^3 **11.** 25^2 **12.** 11^6 **13.** 200^4 **14.** 13^5 **15.** 7^7

16. 10^{10} **17.** 3^4 **18.** 19^6 **19.** 5^9 **20.** 1^{10} **21.** 9^8

Write in standard form.

22. 6^2 **23.** 5^3 **24.** 10^4 **25.** 3^5 **26.** 13 squared

27. 1^{10} **28.** 7^5 **29.** 2^8 **30.** 15^4 **31.** 9 cubed

Science For each number in exponential notation, identify the base and exponent. Use a calculator and write each number in standard form.

32. In September of 1979, the space probe *Pioneer 11* approached within 114^2 miles of Saturn. The probe was traveling about 4^8 mi/hr. It collected data showing that Saturn's rings are about 11^5 miles wide.

33. Pluto, the planet farthest from the sun, orbits at a speed of about 8^6 miles per day. At this speed, it takes about 3^5 years to orbit the sun.

Saturn

Compare, using $<$, $>$, or =.

34. $2^3 \ \square \ 3^2$ **35.** $5^4 \ \square \ 5 \times 4$ **36.** $1^{12} \ \square \ 12^1$ **37.** $10^{15} \ \square \ 10^{16}$

38. **Test Prep** Track A is 3^7 yards long. Track B is three times longer than Track A. How long is Track B?

Ⓐ 3^8 Ⓑ 3^{21} Ⓒ 9^{21} Ⓓ 6^{14}

Problem Solving and Reasoning

39. Critical Thinking The number of bacteria cells in a biology experiment doubles every hour. After 1 hour there are 2 cells, after 2 hours there are 2×2 (or 4) cells, after 3 hours there are $2 \times 2 \times 2$ (or 8) cells, and so on.

a. Use exponents to write the number of cells after each of the first 10 hours of the experiment.

b. Write an expression in exponential notation for the number of cells after 50 hours.

40. Number Sense Find each number.

a. The number that equals 100 when it is squared

b. The number that equals 27 when it is cubed

41. Choose a Strategy What whole number, when raised to the fourth power, equals 1296?

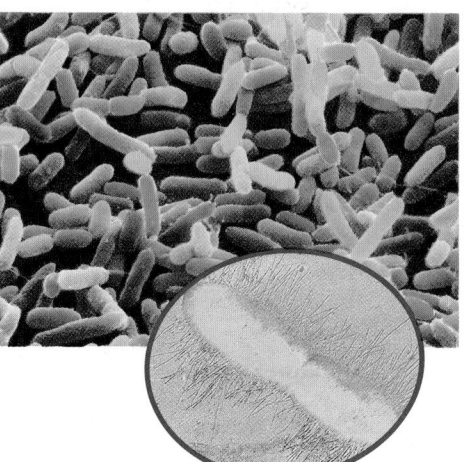

Problem Solving

STRATEGIES

- Look for a Pattern
- Make an Organized List
- Make a Table
- Guess and Check
- Work Backward
- Use Logical Reasoning
- Draw a Diagram
- Solve a Simpler Problem

Mixed Review

Multiply. *[Previous course]*

42. $2 \times 2 \times 2 \times 2$ **43.** $3 \times 3 \times 3 \times 3$

44. $4 \times 4 \times 4 \times 4$ **45.** $2 \times 3 \times 2 \times 3$

46. $2 \times 4 \times 2 \times 4$ **47.** $3 \times 4 \times 3 \times 4$

Add. *[Previous course]*

48. $13,427.00 + $46,212.00   **49.** $7295.63 + $1754.89

50. $824,788 + $567,673   **51.** $8,691,288 + $7,643,841

52. $372,150 + $517,720   **53.** $8,542,505 + $3,276,023

Project Progress

Choose six different ways that you could travel. For example, one of them might be by bicycle. For each method, determine how far you could travel in one hour.

Problem Solving

Understand
Plan
Solve
Look Back

Section 2A Connect

Our solar system has nine planets. As far as we know, the only planet in our solar system with intelligent life on it is Earth.

Planets are starting to be detected around other stars as well. One distant star known as PSR1257 + 12 is suspected of having planets orbiting it.

Greetings from Planet Earth

Current research indicates that there are two planets orbiting the star PSR1257 + 12. Let's call them Planet 1 and Planet 2.

The table gives the approximate distances of four of our planets from our sun, and of Planets 1 and 2 from PSR1257 + 12.

Distance from Local Star	
Planet	**Distance (km)**
Earth	148 million
Mars	228,260,860
Mercury	58,000,000
Venus	one hundred five million
Planet 1	52 million
Planet 2	eighty million

1. Suppose Planets 1 and 2 were in our solar system and the distances in the table were the distances from our sun. Make a sketch showing all six planets lined up beside our sun in their correct order. Label each planet with its name and its distance from the sun.

2. Make a list that states how far each planet is from Earth. (Assume that all of the planets are in a straight line.)

3. Make three lists of the distances from the sun from least to greatest. In the first list, round all the distances to the nearest million. In the second list, round to the nearest ten-million. In the third list, round to the nearest hundred-million. If you were writing a report about the planets, which list would you use? Why?

4. The farther from a star a planet is, the longer the planet takes to orbit the star. The orbital times in Earth days of the six planets listed in the table are approximately 5^4, 15^2, 3^4, 7^3, 8^2, and 10^2. Match each planet with the approximate time it takes to orbit its star.

Write each number in standard form. Then round that number to the place indicated.

1. 4^2; tens
2. 5^3; tens
3. 10^5; hundred-thousands
4. 8^4; thousands
5. 9^2; hundreds
6. 16^5; ten-thousands

7. **Science** The Russian space probe *Venera* measured the surface temperature of Venus as $2^5 \times 3^3$ degrees Fahrenheit.

   a. Give the temperature in standard notation.

   b. Without calculating, decide which is greater, $2^6 \times 3^3$ or $2^5 \times 3^4$. Explain how you made your decision.

Venus

The table lists the highest points on the seven continents.

8. Order the elevations from least to greatest.

9. Round the elevations to the nearest thousand.

10. **Journal** Compare ordering numbers to putting words in alphabetical order.

Continent	Elevation (ft)
Africa	19,340
Asia	29,028
Antarctica	16,864
Australia	7,310
Europe	18,510
North America	20,320
South America	22,834

Compare, using $<$, $>$, or $=$.

11. 9 million ☐ 9,000,000
12. 2^5 ☐ 2×5
13. 50,999 ☐ 51,000
14. 2080 ☐ two thousand eight
15. 3^2 ☐ 2^3
16. 47,350 ☐ 4,735

17. **Communicate** Juanita says that 1000 thousand is the same as 1 million. Seth says that there is no such number as 1000 thousand. Who is right? Explain.

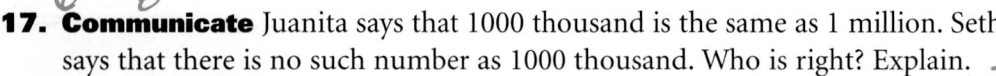

Test Prep

Find the area of a square by squaring the length of a side. Find the volume of a cube by cubing the length of a side.

18. Find the area of a square with a side of 5.
    ⓐ 10   ⓑ 25   ⓒ 32   ⓓ 50

19. Find the volume of a cube with a side of 6.
    ⓐ 36   ⓑ 64   ⓒ 216   ⓓ 729

First Class Collectibles

One hundred years ago, a boy received a letter with a 50¢ stamp on it. He threw away the envelope, but saved the letter to give to his grandchildren.

One hundred years ago, a boy received a letter and $500. He threw away the $500, but saved the letter to give to his grandchildren.

As strange as it may sound, the two stories above are the exact same story. If someone in 1898 saved a 50¢ Trans-Mississippi stamp, his or her grandchildren could sell it today for over $500. This may sound like a lot of money, but to someone who collects stamps, it might be worth it.

People collect all sorts of things, from autographs to automobiles. A good collector uses several skills when trying to assemble the best possible collection for the least amount of money. One of the most important skills to have is a good understanding of mathematics.

1. Why are some items in a collection more expensive than others?

2. How does having a good understanding of mathematics help you build a collection for the least amount of money?

2-5

Mental Math

▶ **Lesson Link** You've learned many ways to deal with one number, including rounding, graphing, and writing with exponents. Now you will learn some methods for operating on two or more numbers mentally. ◀

You'll Learn ...

■ to simplify problems mentally using patterns, the Distributive Property, compatible numbers, and compensation

... How It's Used

Waiters and waitresses use mental math to verify that the bills they give to their customers are correct.

Vocabulary

Distributive Property

Explore | Mental Math

Stamp of Excellence!

During the annual Carson Stamp Convention, the sponsors ran a contest. Each participant had to simplify the ten math problems below without using paper and pencil or a calculator. The top scorer won a collectible Vietnamese chameleon stamp.

a. 60×100 **b.** 37×16 **c.** $25 + 16 + 75$ **d.** $381 + 99$ **e.** $315 \div 12$

f. 19×4 **g.** $1200 \div 4$ **h.** $4 \times 25 \times 7$ **i.** 21×5 **j.** $498 + 795$

1. Which problems do you think nearly all your classmates could simplify correctly in their heads? Which could almost no one simplify correctly? Explain.

2. Rank the problems in order of difficulty, from easiest to hardest.

3. Explain how you would simplify the three easiest problems in your head.

4. For each of the three problems you chose, write a similar problem that could be simplified mentally using the same method. Trade problems with a partner and simplify each other's problems mentally.

Learn | Mental Math

It is often convenient to simplify math problems mentally. Here are several mental math techniques that are especially useful.

Compatible Numbers Compatible numbers are pairs of numbers that can be computed easily. Combine compatible numbers, and then combine what remains.

Patterns When multiplying numbers that end in zeros, multiply the non-zero parts and annex one zero to your answer for each zero in the problem. When dividing numbers that end in zeros, subtract the number of zeros in the divisor from the number of zeros in the dividend to find the number in the quotient.

Compensation Choose a number close to the number in the problem. Then adjust the answer to compensate for the number you chose.

The Distributive Property Break numbers into smaller numbers. Calculate using the smaller numbers, and then put your answers together.

Remember

The *Commutative Property* states that changing the order of addends or factors does not change the sum or product. For example, $4 \times 7 = 28$, and
$$7 \times 4 = 28.$$
[Previous course]

Examples

Simplify.

1 20×700

Use patterns:

$$2 \times 7 = 14$$

1 zero + 2 zeros = 3 zeros

$$20 \times 700 = 14,000$$

2 $5,400,000 \div 90$

Use patterns:

$54 \div 9 = 6$

5 zeros − 1 zero = 4 zeros

$5,400,000 \div 90 = 60,000$

3 $25 + 18 + 75$

25 and 75 are compatible because they are easy to add.

$$25 + 18 + 75 = (25 + 75) + 18$$
$$= 100 + 18 = 118$$

4 58×3

Since 58 is close to 60, you can use compensation:

$$58 \times 3 = (60 \times 3) - (2 \times 3)$$
$$= 180 - 6 = 174$$

Remember

The *Associative Property* states that changing the grouping of addends or factors does not change the sum or product. For example, $(5 + 3) + 7 = 15$, and
$$5 + (3 + 7) = 15.$$
[Previous course]

5 A collector offered to sell five World's Fair posters at $32 apiece. Use the Distributive Property to find the total cost.

$32 \times 5 = (30 + 2) \times 5$ Break 32 into 30 + 2.

$\quad = (30 \times 5) + (2 \times 5)$ Multiply each piece by 5.

$\quad = (150) + (10) = 160$ Add the pieces together.

Try It

Simplify.

a. 4000×300 **b.** $210,000 \div 700$ **c.** 61×3 **d.** $285 + 47 + 15$

e. $50 \times 2 \times 13$ **f.** $296 + 55$ **g.** 29×6 **h.** 102×7

1. Compatible numbers are numbers that are easy to add or multiply together. What are some pairs of compatible numbers for addition? For multiplication?

2. Why is it useful to be able to do arithmetic in your head?

2-5 Exercises and Applications

Practice and Apply

1. **Getting Started** Use patterns to simplify each problem.

   a. 60×4 **b.** 600×40 **c.** $6,000 \times 400$ **d.** $6,000 \times 4,000$

   e. $210 \div 3$ **f.** $2,100 \div 30$ **g.** $2,100 \div 300$ **h.** $21,000 \div 3,000$

Simplify.

2. 40×20 3. $251 + 314$ 4. $96 + 117$ 5. $4 \times 11 \times 25$

6. 24×2 7. $240 \div 6$ 8. $25 + 23 + 75$ 9. 49×3

10. $198 + 123$ 11. $2,500 \div 50$ 12. $68 + 31$ 13. $50 \times 2 \times 9$

14. 30×600 15. 31×4 16. $750 + 119 + 250$ 17. 99×7

18. 53×3 19. 89×6 20. $819 + 120$ 21. 700×5

22. $147 - 99$ 23. $250 \times 4 \times 35$ 24. $90 + 57 + 10$ 25. $9,000 \times 800$

26. $800 + 336 + 200$ 27. 58×5 28. $560,000 \div 80$ 29. $2,645 + 213$

30. $5,000 \times 18 \times 2$ 31. $461 - 295$ 32. 112×4 33. $1,800,000 \div 9,000$

34. $12,000 \times 300$ 35. 42×8 36. $79 + 98 + 3$ 37. $550 - 25$

38. $22 + 88$ 39. $84 - 34$ 40. $1,200,000 \times 500$ 41. 29×6

42. Marcie bought a movie poster for $4.45 plus $0.34 sales tax. Find the total cost of the poster.

43. At the Metropolitan Coin Fair, Robbie sold 99 coins from his collection of 876. How many coins did he have left?

44. **Science** The moon is about 240,000 miles from Earth. How long would it take you to fly to the moon at a speed of 40,000 miles per day?

45. Craig earns $5 per hour at his after-school job. One week he worked 21 hours. Find his total earnings for the week.

Use the bar graph to answer each question.

46. How many yards did Marcus swim?

47. How much farther did he swim in freestyle than butterfly?

48. **Test Prep** Simplify 48 × 6.

   Ⓐ 24   Ⓑ 72

   Ⓒ 288   Ⓓ 300

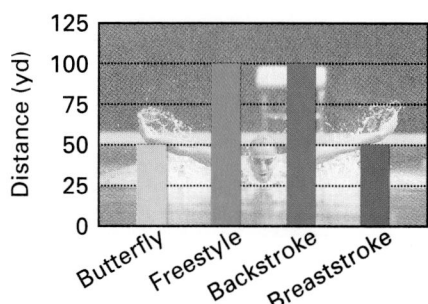

Marcus's Swimming Record

Problem Solving and Reasoning

49. **Journal** Explain the difference between using compatible numbers and compensation. Give examples to illustrate your answer.

50. **Communicate** Which problem is easier to simplify with mental math, 20 × 19 × 5 or 20 × 19 × 6? Explain your reasoning.

51. **Critical Thinking** Janet has $13.64, and she wants to buy a board game for $15.84. How much more money does she need? If the game goes on sale for $2.00 less, will she have enough money?

Mixed Review

Write in standard form. *[Lesson 2-1]*

52. six hundred forty-eight million, two hundred twenty-eight thousand, nine hundred seventy-three

53. three hundred thirty-five million, seven hundred twenty-eight thousand, six hundred forty-two

Write in words. *[Lesson 2-1]*

54. 467,987,382   **55.** 5,976,321,401   **56.** 5983   **57.** 3,093,002

Subtract. *[Previous course]*

58. 412 − 176   **59.** 91,233 − 17,974   **60.** 845,213 − 685,787

61. 6,329,432 − 3,654,987   **62.** 54,987 − 3,283   **63.** 94,040 − 32,804

64. 4,931,515 − 34,687   **65.** 7,237,802 − 5,091,465   **66.** 111,996 − 22,197

Estimating Sums and Differences

▶ **Lesson Link** You've learned to use mental math to find exact answers. In this lesson, you'll learn to estimate answers to addition and subtraction problems when you don't need exact answers. ◀

Explore **Estimating Sums and Differences**

A Penny for Your Thoughts

The table gives prices of 1913 Lincoln-head pennies from three mints in five different qualities. Prices are in dollars.

Mint	Good	Very Good	Fine	Very Fine	Extremely Fine
Denver	0.85	1.95	3.79	8.30	16.75
Philadelphia	0.49	0.65	1.19	2.75	9.20
San Francisco	5.15	6.65	7.45	11.19	24.95

1. Without using a calculator, try to find a set of four different pennies with a total cost that is as close to $30 as possible without going over $30. Keep trying until you find a set of four as close to $30 as possible.

2. Estimate how close your total is to $30. Explain how you made your estimates.

3. Find the total cost of your four pennies exactly. Compare your results with those of other students.

4. If you round two prices to estimate their sum, how can you be sure that your estimate does not exceed the actual sum?

5. Without using a calculator, how can you tell that the combined cost of the Denver and the San Francisco pennies in fine condition is greater than $11?

When you don't need an exact answer to a problem, you can estimate. When using *front-end estimation,* add or subtract using only the first digit of each number. Estimate the sum or difference of the remaining digits and add this to the first estimate. For a more accurate estimate, calculate using the first *two* digits.

Examples

1 Estimate 982 − 539 using one-digit front-end estimation.

$$\begin{array}{r} 982 \\ -\ 539 \\ \hline 400 \\ +\ 40 \\ \hline 440 \end{array}$$

Subtract the first digit in each number.
Add 40 because 82 − 39 is about 40.

2 Estimate using the first two digits: 23,745 + 54,881

$$\begin{array}{r} 23{,}745 \\ +\ 54{,}881 \\ \hline 77{,}000 \\ +\ 1{,}600 \\ \hline 78{,}600 \end{array}$$

Add the first two digits in each number.
Add 1,600 because 745 + 881 is about 1,600.

When adding several numbers that are approximately equal, use *clustering* to estimate the sum. Replace all of the numbers with a single number close to them that is easy to multiply. Then multiply.

Example 3

A scientist measured four strides of a dinosaur. Estimate the combined length of the four strides.

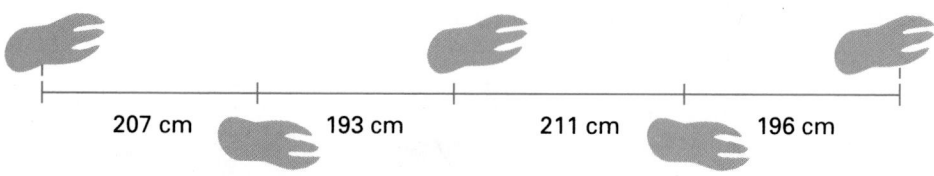

207 cm   193 cm   211 cm   196 cm

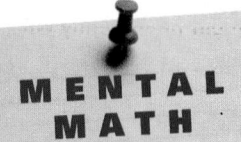

MENTAL MATH

When you add a group of equal numbers, you can use multiplication as a shortcut.

Each distance is approximately 200 cm.

$200 + 200 + 200 + 200 = 4 \times 200 = 800$

The dinosaur walked about 800 cm.

Try It

Estimate. **a.** 773 + 848   **b.** 6707 − 4559   **c.** 307 + 297 + 299

1. Describe some real-life addition and subtraction situations that require exact answers. Describe some where estimates are satisfactory.

2. Is front-end estimation the same as rounding and adding? Explain.

2-6 Exercises and Applications

Practice and Apply

1. **Getting Started** Simplify using one-digit front-end estimation, and then two-digit front-end estimation.

   a. $216 + 516$　　**b.** $3,006 - 1,811$　　**c.** $85,002 - 12,667$　　**d.** $880 + 110$

Estimate.

2. $555 + 429$

3. $489 + 495 + 976 + 503 + 515$

4. $7641 - 2578$

5. $98 + 107 + 95 + 97 + 103$

6. $49,245,209 + 53,923,831 + 54,902,756$

7. $873 - 549$

8. $3101 + 3054 + 2916$

9. $5,901,877 - 2,635,392$

10. $3409 + 7118$

11. $257 + 249 + 241 + 259$

12. $48,206 + 81,175$

13. $443,677 + 158,371 + 43$

14. $634,799 + 654 + 863,755$

15. $7621 + 8109 + 2117$

16. $14,651 + 23,977$

17. $9 + 11 + 13 + 8 + 7 + 12 + 9$

18. $21,529 + 40,783 + 377 + 16,403$

19. $8,715,739 + 9,849,129$

20. $891 + 677$

21. $1577 - 1328$

22. **Geography** The average depth of the Caribbean Sea is 8685 feet. The average depth of the South China Sea is 5419 feet. About how much deeper is the Caribbean Sea?

23. A picture frame measures 36 in. by 18 in. Estimate the distance around the outside of the frame.

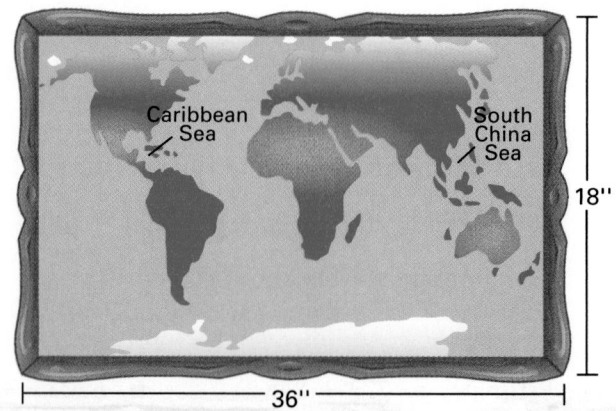

24. Literature The letter of the alphabet with the most entries in the *Oxford English Dictionary* is *s*, with 34,556 entries. The next is *c*, with 26,239, and then *p*, with 24,980.

a. Estimate the number of words in the dictionary that start with either an *s*, a *c*, or a *p*.

b. Estimate the difference between the number of words starting with *c* and the number of words starting with *p*.

Use the table for Exercises 25 and 26.

25. Give one-digit and two-digit front-end estimates for the total number of pennies made at the three mints.

26. Estimate how much more Philadelphia's total was than Denver's.

Mint	Number of Pennies Made
Denver	15,804,000
Philadelphia	76,532,352
San Francisco	6,101,000

27. **Test Prep** A bank has 2 million dollars. Suppose in one day $1,002,987 is taken out and $2,987,102 is deposited. Which estimate is closest to how much money the bank has at the end of the day?

    Ⓐ $1 million   Ⓑ $2 million   Ⓒ $3 million   Ⓓ $4 million

Problem Solving and Reasoning

28. Critical Thinking Erika estimated the sum of 299 + 298 + 297 as 900. Was her estimate high or low? Explain.

29. [Journal] Explain how to add a group of numbers using clustering. Give an example to illustrate your answer.

30. Communicate For 86,002 + 17,775, how much more accurate is two-digit front-end estimation than one-digit front-end estimation?

Mixed Review

Round to the given place value. *[Lesson 2-2]*

31. 6,967,243; hundred-thousand

32. 42,352,408; hundred

33. 423,855,211; hundred-million

34. 8,788,212,403; thousand

Subtract. *[Previous course]*

35. $823.44 − $127.58

36. $212,203 − $83,498

37. $62,148.67 − $45,746.23

38. $753,497.62 − $376,032.07

Estimating Products and Quotients

You'll Learn ...

■ to estimate products and quotients using rounding and compatible numbers.

... How It's Used

Chefs use estimation skills to determine about how much of an ingredient should be used in cooking.

▶ **Lesson Link**   In the last lesson, you learned convenient methods for estimating answers to addition and subtraction problems. Now you will learn two methods that work well with multiplication and division problems. ◀

Explore   **Estimating**
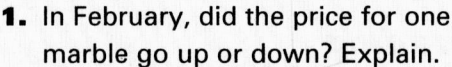

Cat's Eyes and Immies

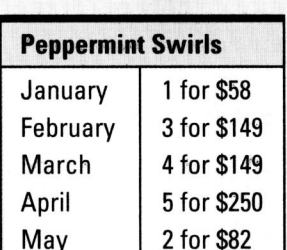

The Marbelous Marbles shop sells a rare type of marble known as a Peppermint Swirl. The price of this marble changes each month.

Answer the questions without using a calculator.

Peppermint Swirls	
January	1 for $58
February	3 for $149
March	4 for $149
April	5 for $250
May	2 for $82

1. In February, did the price for one marble go up or down? Explain.

2. In March, did the price for one marble go up or down? Explain.

3. In April, did the price for one marble go up or down? Explain.

4. In May, did the price for one marble go up or down? Explain.

5. In which month was the price the highest? Explain.

6. In which month was the price the lowest? Explain.

Remember

To round a number, look at the digit to the right of the place you want to round to. If the digit is 5 or greater, round up. If it is less than 5, leave the digit being rounded the same. **[Page 71]**

Learn   **Estimating Products and Quotients**

Like sums and differences, products and quotients can be estimated when you don't need exact answers. To estimate a product or quotient using *rounding*, round all numbers so that each contains only one nonzero digit. Then multiply or divide.

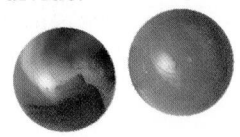

Examples

Estimate, using rounding.

1 429 × 16

429 × 16 ≈ 400 × 20   Round.

       = 8000

2 1170 ÷ 45

1170 ÷ 45 ≈ 1000 ÷ 50   Round.

          = 20

Remember

The symbol ≈ means "is approximately equal to." [Previous course]

Try It

Estimate, using rounding.

a. 84 × 279   **b.** 7912 ÷ 43

To estimate using *compatible numbers*, rewrite the problem using numbers that go together easily. Then multiply or divide.

Examples

3 Estimate 48 × 12 using compatible numbers.

48 × 12 ≈ 50 × 10 = 500

4 Ted scored 231 points during the 28-game basketball season. Estimate the average number of points he scored each game.

231 ÷ 28 ≈ 240 ÷ 30 = 8

He scored about 8 points per game.

Try It

Estimate, using compatible numbers.

a. 22 × 31   **b.** 553 ÷ 79

Check | Your Understanding

1. Would rounding and compatible numbers be good estimation strategies for addition and subtraction problems? Explain.

2. Explain two ways you could estimate 3177 ÷ 45.

2-7 Exercises and Applications

Practice and Apply

1. **Getting Started** Estimate, using rounding.

   a. 560 × 4   **b.** 7800 ÷ 22   **c.** 68 × 472   **d.** 9433 ÷ 300

   Estimate, using compatible numbers.

   e. 372 ÷ 56   **f.** 58 × 5   **g.** 8099 ÷ 8   **h.** 27 × 4286

Estimate.

2. 183 ÷ 21
3. 7111 × 7888
4. 327 ÷ 64
5. 488 × 53
6. 4522 ÷ 92
7. 9 × 11 × 17
8. 11 × 23 × 98
9. 777 ÷ 38
10. 217 × 308
11. 207 × 6 × 15
12. 24,111 ÷ 84
13. 54 × 82
14. 4270 ÷ 38
15. 2803 ÷ 24
16. 1895 ÷ 463
17. 463 × 719
18. 5 × 26 × 12
19. 175 ÷ 28
20. 425 ÷ 59
21. 51 × 14 × 19
22. 358 ÷ 7
23. 149 ÷ 4
24. 29 × 41
25. 19 × 4 × 7
26. 248 × 5 × 8
27. 23,714 ÷ 522
28. 185 × 29
29. 200,000 ÷ 720
30. 2733 ÷ 71
31. 103 ÷ 54
32. 3625 ÷ 581
33. 5 × 9 × 2457

34. Tracy collects old sheet music. In a bin at a flea market, she found 19 songs priced at $4.95 apiece. Estimate the total cost of the music.

35. **Industry** Flight 777 carries 54 passengers, each with 2 suitcases. Each suitcase weighs, on average, 36 pounds. If the airplane was built to carry 5000 pounds of luggage, is the flight over or under its limit?

36. **Social Science** The *Yomiuri Shimbun* in Japan is the daily newspaper with the highest circulation, at 8,700,000 papers per day. If one day's papers were distributed evenly among Japan's four islands, about how many newspapers would be on each island?

37. **Measurement** There are 5280 feet in a mile and 12 inches in a foot. Estimate the number of inches in a mile.

38. Carlos has been offered $825 for his collection of 19 model train cabooses. He wants to get an average of at least $40 per caboose. Should he accept the offer? Explain how he can use estimation to decide.

39. **Test Prep** Choose the best estimate for 5,985 × 89.

    Ⓐ 4,000,000   Ⓑ 450,000   Ⓒ 540,000   Ⓓ 600,000

Problem Solving and Reasoning

40. **Critical Thinking** You are stacking 105-lb boxes on a freight elevator. A sign on the elevator says, "Do not exceed 1000 pounds total." What is the maximum number of boxes you can stack on the elevator? Explain your reasoning.

41. **Journal** List two situations where it is better to have an exact answer than an estimate, and explain why.

42. **Choose a Strategy** Leslie won some money in a contest. After spending $12 on a CD, almost $34 on new bicycle tires, and about $16 on a pair of pants, she has about $15 left over. Estimate how much money Leslie won. Explain your answer.

> **Problem Solving**
> ## STRATEGIES
> - Look for a Pattern
> - Make an Organized List
> - Make a Table
> - Guess and Check
> - Work Backward
> - Use Logical Reasoning
> - Draw a Diagram
> - Solve a Simpler Problem

Mixed Review

Compare. Use > or <. *[Lesson 2-3]*

43. 2156 ☐ 2157   **44.** 324,265,129 ☐ 324,264,872   **45.** 19,667 ☐ 190,675

46. 3189 ☐ 3891   **47.** 267 ☐ 627   **48.** 134,256 ☐ 134,265

Order the numbers from least to greatest. *[Lesson 2-3]*

49. 1023; 10; 356; 1009; 383   **50.** 22,456; 122,802; 21,904; 122,501

Multiply. *[Previous course]*

51. 20 × 607   **52.** 50 × 505   **53.** 60 × 304   **54.** 70 × 801

55. 14 × 18   **56.** 26 × 21   **57.** 60 × 52   **58.** 83 × 57

59. 12 × 12   **60.** 21 × 25   **61.** 63 × 34   **62.** 99 × 99

Order of Operations

► **Lesson Link** You've learned how to work with arithmetic problems with one operation. Now you'll learn how to simplify problems using several operations. ◄

You'll Learn ...

■ to use order of operation rules to solve arithmetic problems

... How It's Used

Cashiers must use the same rules to calculate prices that involve sales tax, discounts, and coupons.

Vocabulary

order of operations

► **Technology Link**

To find out if your calculator follows order of operation rules, press 2 [+] 3 [×] 4 [=]. If the answer is 14, the calculator follows the rules.

Explore | Order of Operations

The Calculators That Didn't Always Agree

David Hicks collects calculators and has a calculator museum on the World Wide Web. One of his calculators is an early HP-01 calculator watch from the 1970s. Another is the HP 9820, one of the first algebraic calculators. Each calculator processed arithmetic problems in a different way.

1. Sometimes the calculators gave different answers because each one did a different part of the problem first. For each problem, determine which operation each calculator did first.

Problem	HP-01	HP 9820
$3 + 4 \times 5$	35	23
$2 + 8 \times 6$	60	50
$9 \times 4 - 8$	28	28
$6 + 15 \div 3$	7	11
$20 - 16 \div 4$	1	16
$42 \div 7 + 3$	9	9

2. Using your answers, explain which operation the HP-01 calculator watch does first.

3. Using your answers, explain which operation the HP 9820 calculator does first.

4. Predict the values that each calculator gave for each expression:

    a. $50 - 10 \div 2$ **b.** $12 \times 6 - 3$ **c.** $14 + 21 \div 7$ **d.** $20 + 5 \times 3$

Learn | Order of Operations

The value of an expression that involves several operations depends on the order in which you perform the operations. Suppose you wanted to simplify $9 + 6 \div 3$. You could add first or divide first.

Adding first:	$9 + 6 = 15$
Now divide:	$15 \div 3 = 5$

Dividing first:	$6 \div 3 = 2$
Now add:	$9 + 2 = 11$

Mathematicians use parentheses to show which part of the problem should be done first. But some problems don't have parentheses. To make sure everyone gets the same answer for a problem, mathematicians use a set of rules known as the **order of operations** .

ORDER OF OPERATIONS

1. Simplify inside parentheses.

2. Simplify exponents.

3. Multiply and divide from left to right.

4. Add and subtract from left to right.

Examples

Simplify.

1 $7 \times (3 + 2)$

$$7 \times (3 + 2) = 7 \times 5 \qquad \text{Simplify inside parentheses first.}$$
$$= 35 \qquad \text{Multiply.}$$

2 5×3^2

$$5 \times 3^2 = 5 \times 9 \qquad \text{Simplify exponents first.}$$
$$= 45 \qquad \text{Multiply.}$$

3 $12 + 5 \times 4$

$$12 + 5 \times 4 = 12 + 20 \qquad \text{Multiply first.}$$
$$= 32 \qquad \text{Add.}$$

4 $16 \div 2 \times 9$

$$16 \div 2 \times 9 = 8 \times 9 \qquad \text{Do left part first.}$$
$$= 72 \qquad \text{Do right part.}$$

Try It

Simplify.

a. $28 - 12 \div 4$ **b.** $36 \div 12 \div 3$ **c.** $19 - 4^2$ **d.** $8 \times (10 - 4)$

Check Your Understanding

1. Why do you need the order of operation rules to compute $20 + 5 \times 3$?

2. Give a real-world example of something you could do in several ways that people have agreed to do the same way.

Practice and Apply

P | E | M | D | A | S

1. [Getting Started] State which operation should be performed first.

a. $36 - (29 \times 102)$ **b.** $(62 + 45) \times 58$ **c.** $119 \div 26 - 13$ **d.** $8^7 - 132$

e. $(36 - 29) \times 102$ **f.** $62 + 45 \times 58$ **g.** $119 \div (26 - 13)$ **h.** $(8 - 132)^7$

Simplify each expression.

2. $25 - 10 \div 5$ **3.** $14 + 7 \times 6$ **4.** $30 \times 6 + 2$ **5.** $50 \div 5 - 2$

6. $32 \div 8 \div 4$ **7.** $2 \times 4 \times 6$ **8.** $15 \div 3 \times 5$ **9.** $9 \times 6 \div 2$

10. $10 - 8 - 2$ **11.** $(10 - 8) - 2$ **12.** $10 - (8 - 2)$ **13.** $(6^2 + 4) \times 3$

14. $50 \div 5^2$ **15.** $6^2 - 9$ **16.** $(4 + 5)^2$ **17.** $10^2 \times 3$

18. $6^2 - 2 \times 6$ **19.** $2^3 + 8 \div 4$ **20.** $7^2 - 4^2 \times 3$ **21.** $9 - (4 - 1)^2$

22. $4 \times (5 - 3)$ **23.** $(8 + 7) \div 3$ **24.** $6 \times (9 - 4)^2$ **25.** $(7 + 3)^2 \div 5$

26. $32 - 6 + 5 \times 4$ **27.** $40 + 18 \div 2 - 16$ **28.** $45 \div 9 - 21 \div 7$ **29.** $144 \div 9 \div 8 \div 2$

Use mental math to evaluate.

30. $30,000 - 5,000 \times 4$ **31.** $6 + 48,000,000 \div 800,000$ **32.** $60 \times 4 \div 3 + 19$

33. $5,000 + 400 \times 8$ **34.** $60 + 60 \div 60$ **35.** $200 - 200 \div 20$

Insert parentheses to make each statement true.

36. $2 \times 3 + 6 = 18$ **37.** $20 \times 15 - 2 = 260$ **38.** $4 + 4^2 \div 5 = 4$ **39.** $2 \times 6^2 - 8 = 56$

40. $6 + 8 \div 2 = 10$ **41.** $12 + 10 \div 11 = 2$ **42.** $5 \times 4 \div 2 = 10$ **43.** $5 + 4 \div 3 = 3$

44. Number Sense Find an arithmetic expression equal to 9 that contains the following operations.

a. Addition and division

b. Subtraction and division

c. Addition, multiplication, and an exponent

45. [Test Prep] Danielle bought 3 pairs of earrings on sale. They normally sell for $4.50 each. Which expression describes the final amount of her purchase?

Ⓐ $(4.50 \times 3) - 1.00$ Ⓑ $(4.50 - 1.00) \times 3$ Ⓒ $(3 - 1.00) \times 4.50$

$1 off each pair

46. **Test Prep** The dance committee needs 3 balloons at each of 15 tables. They also need 50 balloons for each of the four walls of the room. For other decorations, they need 35 balloons, and the committee will order 10 extra balloons. Which is the correct order of operations?

ⓐ $3 + 15 + 50 + 4 + 35 + 10$ ⓑ $3 \times 15 + 50 \times 4 + 35 + 10$

ⓒ $3 \times 15 + 50 \times 4 + 35 \times 10$ ⓓ $3 + 50 \times 15 + 4 + 35 \times 10$

47. Joy bought four snow globes at $7.00 each. She used a $2.00 coupon. After the coupon, the tax came to $1.96. Joy's father paid half of the final cost. Write an expression that describes the situation and equals the total money Joy paid.

Problem Solving and Reasoning

48. **Critical Thinking** A painter said that a wall measured "twenty plus ten squared" square feet. Explain two possible meanings of the comment. Using the order of operations, what is the correct mathematical meaning of what the painter said?

49. **Critical Thinking** You order a large pizza, three large drinks, and a bag of apples. You split the cost evenly with three friends. What order of operations would you use to find out how much each person should pay?

Mixed Review

Simplify. *[Lesson 2-4]*

50. 30^2 **51.** 10^5 **52.** 3^3 **53.** 4^6 **54.** 27^3 **55.** 14^4

Express in exponential notation and simplify. *[Lesson 2-4]*

56. $8 \times 8 \times 8 \times 8$ **57.** $2 \times 2 \times 2 \times 2 \times 2 \times 2 \times 2$ **58.** $4 \times 4 \times 4 \times 4$

Multiply. *[Previous course]*

59. 127×489 **60.** $856 \times 45,625$ **61.** $28,598 \times 67,204$ **62.** $123,087 \times 765,294$

Project Progress

Once you know how far you can travel in an hour for each of your six methods, estimate how far you could travel in 24 hours. Save your estimates. Then calculate the exact amount you could travel in 24 hours.

Problem Solving

Understand
Plan
Solve
Look Back

Numerical Patterns

▶ **Lesson Link** You have seen how number sense can help you solve arithmetic problems. Now you'll learn how to use number sense to identify and extend numerical patterns. ◀

You'll Learn ...

■ to identify and continue numerical patterns based on addition and subtraction

... How It's Used

Marine biologists use numerical patterns when determining the times for high tides and low tides.

Explore | Numerical Patterns

Gridlock!

Materials: Hundred charts, Colored pencils or markers

1. For each list of numbers, color in all the list's numbers in a different hundred chart.

List A: 1, 3, 5, 7, 9, 11, 13, 15, 17, 19, 21

List B: 5, 8, 11, 14, 17, 20, 23, 26, 29, 32

List C: 97, 86, 75, 64, 53

List D: 100, 99, 98, 97, 96, 95, 94, 93, 92, 91

2. For each hundred chart, if you continued to color numbers in the same pattern, would the number 44 be colored? Explain.

3. Make a pattern of your own like the ones shown. Color in a hundred chart, and then write a list of all the numbers less than 50 in your pattern.

4. Trade lists with a partner. Ask the partner to determine if a certain number greater than 50 will be in your pattern.

Learn | Numerical Patterns

A numerical pattern is a list of numbers that occur in some predictable way. Numerical patterns can be used to describe real-world things, such as population growth and the decay of materials. They can also be used to generate art such as fractals, which are complex math pictures created by repeating a simple math pattern.

Introduction to Algebra

▶ **Science Link**   ▶ **www.mathsurf.com/6/ch2/oceans**

JOURNEY TO THE BOTTOM OF THE SEA

O ceanographers use many tools to study the ocean, such as scuba equipment, diving spheres, remote controlled robots, and mathematics. What do we know about life under the sea?

1 Compare the pressures at 500 ft and 1,000 ft; at 3,200 ft and 6,400 ft; at 1,000 ft and 10,000 ft. What patterns do you see? Do you think it's possible to predict the pressure at any depth? Explain.

2 Why do darkness, coldness, and pressure increase as you descend farther into the ocean?

500 ft Most familiar fish and mammals live near the surface. Pressure about 220 lb/in^2.

1,000 ft Sharks, whales, octopus, and squid venture this depth. Pressure about 440 lb/in^2.

2,300 ft Lower limit for light. All creatures below this point live in total darkness. Pressure about 1,000 lb/in^2.

3,200 ft Some fish here have large eyes for seeing in the dark. Others make their own light. Pressure about 1,400 lb/in^2.

6,400 ft Fish here are gelatin-like. Many are blind. Pressure about 2,800 lb/in^2.

10,000 ft Water temperature only a few degrees above freezing. Little food, a few simple organisms. Pressure about 4,400 lb/in^2.

35,840 ft Deepest point in ocean. Temperature below freezing. Pressure about 15,800 lb/in^2.

Variables and Expressions

► **Lesson Link** You've learned to work with arithmetic expressions like 3×25, where both numbers are known. In this lesson, you'll learn how to work with expressions with one unknown number. ◄

You'll Learn ...

- the difference between a variable and a constant
- to evaluate expressions

... How It's Used

Accountants use variables to represent how much money a certain investment will return over time.

Vocabulary

variable

constant

expression

Explore **Operations and Patterns**

Mining Your Own Business

The ocean is a treasure trove of dissolved materials. For example, a volume of sea water the size of a 30-story building contains about $400 worth of dissolved gold. Suppose you have invented a way to recover the gold from a building-size volume of water for $250.

1. Complete the table to show how much money you can make processing gold from ocean water.

Number of Building-Size Volumes	Value of Gold	Processing Cost	Profit
1	$400	$250	$150
2			
3			
4			
5			
10			
20			
50			
100			

2. How did you find each value in the second column? The third column? The fourth column?

3. Find the values in each column for 1 million building-size volumes of water.

Learn | Variables and Expressions

A **variable** is a quantity that can change or vary. Water temperature is a variable because it changes from hour to hour. Mathematicians use letters to represent variables.

A quantity that does not change is a **constant**. The freezing temperature of water at sea level is a constant. It is always 32 degrees Fahrenheit.

An **expression** is a mathematical phrase involving constants, variables, and operation symbols. There are different ways to represent different operations.

Addition	Subtraction	Multiplication	Division
$8 + x$	$8 - x$	$8x$	$\frac{8}{x}$

If you know the values of the variable, you can evaluate the expression by replacing the variable with each value. This is known as substituting a value for the variable.

DID YOU KNOW?

x is the letter that mathematicians use most often for a variable, but you can use any letter to represent a variable.

Examples

Evaluate the expression for $x = 1, 2,$ and 3.

1 $x + 5$

x	$x + 5$
1	$1 + 5 = 6$
2	$2 + 5 = 7$
3	$3 + 5 = 8$

2 $11 - x$

x	$11 - x$
1	$11 - 1 = 10$
2	$11 - 2 = 9$
3	$11 - 3 = 8$

3 $4x$

x	$4x$
1	$4 \times 1 = 4$
2	$4 \times 2 = 8$
3	$4 \times 3 = 12$

4 $\frac{12}{x}$

x	$\frac{12}{x}$
1	$12 \div 1 = 12$
2	$12 \div 2 = 6$
3	$12 \div 3 = 4$

▶ **Technology Link**

Calculator buttons use variables to represent the number in the display. For example, the $\boxed{x^2}$ button will square the number in the display.

Try It

Evaluate the expression for $x = 3, 4,$ and 5.

a. $7x$　　　　**b.** $15 - x$　　　　**c.** $\frac{60}{x}$　　　　**d.** $x + 23$

1. What is the advantage of using a variable to represent a number?

2. How many quarters are there in *m* dollars? How many pennies?

2-10 Exercises and Applications

Practice and Apply

1. **Getting Started** State whether the quantity should be represented by a variable or a constant.

   a. Number of days in January   **b.** Price of a calculator

   c. Number of students in a school   **d.** Number of inches in a foot

   e. Number of people in a state   **f.** Number of giraffes in a herd

2. Complete the table.

x	x + 1	2x	18 ÷ x	
1	1 + 1 = 2	2+1=2	18÷1=18	1 − 1 = 0
2	2+1=3	2x2=4		2 − 1 = 1
3	3+1=4	3x2=6	18 ÷ 3 = 6	3 − 1 = 2

Evaluate each expression for x = 2, 3, and 4.

3. $x + 7$ **4.** $12 - x$ **5.** $6x$ **6.** $\dfrac{24}{x}$ **7.** $12 + x$ **8.** $6x$

9. $8x$ **10.** $x - 1$ **11.** $15 + x$ **12.** $11x$ **13.** $\dfrac{36}{x}$ **14.** $\dfrac{x}{1}$

Evaluate each expression for x = 3, 5, and 9.

15. $20 - x$ **16.** $9x$ **17.** $\dfrac{45}{x}$ **18.** $36x$ **19.** $x + 3$ **20.** $x + 12$

21. x **22.** $\dfrac{135}{x}$ **23.** $x + x$ **24.** $1x$ **25.** x^2 **26.** x^3

Evaluate each expression for x = 2, 4, and 7.

27. $\dfrac{56}{x}$ **28.** $x - 2$ **29.** $3x$ **30.** $\dfrac{28}{x}$ **31.** $5x$ **32.** $8x$

33. $4x$ **34.** $16 - x$ **35.** $27 + x$ **36.** $39 + x$ **37.** $x + 12$ **38.** $\dfrac{x}{1}$

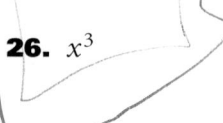

Complete each table.

39. History In 1776, there were 13 stars on every United States flag.

Number of Flags	Number of Stars
1	
2	
3	
4	
w	

40. Science An average blue whale eats 9000 pounds of food each day.

Amount of Food (lb)	Number of Days
63,000	
81,000	
126,000	
f	

41. **Test Prep** Choose the expression that would generate the given data.

Ⓐ $b + 6$ Ⓑ $4b$
Ⓒ $2b$ Ⓓ $b - 8$

b	Data
2	8
4	10
6	12

Problem Solving and Reasoning

42. **Journal** Explain the meaning of $7x$ and explain how to evaluate $7x$ for $x = 3$ and $x = 4$.

43. **Critical Thinking** Match the situation to the correct expression.

a. Fingers on t hands (including thumbs) **i.** $t - 5$

b. Price of a $\$t$ CD with a $5 coupon **ii.** $5t$

c. Price of a $\$t$ sweater with $5 tax **iii.** $t + 5$

44. **Communicate** Which of the following expressions will always have the same solution, no matter what you choose for x? Explain.
$x + 3,\quad 5 - x,\quad 0x$

Mixed Review

Estimate. *[Lesson 2-6]*

45. $1567 + 5408$ **46.** $21,805 + 79,502$ **47.** $45,405 - 9,826$

48. $4305 - 1875$ **49.** $3615 + 2778$ **50.** $31,618 - 17,611$

Choose the numbers that can be divided by the first number with no remainder.
[Previous course]

51. $8 \ (28, 64, 8, 739, 384, 502)$ **52.** $4 \ (26, 552, 450, 482, 116, 74)$

53. $6 \ (17, 24, 30, 51, 67, 74)$ **54.** $9 \ (21, 37, 45, 55, 82, 93)$

Writing Expressions

You'll Learn ...

■ to translate phrases and situations into mathematical expressions

... How It's Used

Expressions allow veterinarians to compare the growth rates of animals.

Vocabulary

sum

difference

product

quotient

▶ Lesson Link You've learned how to evaluate expressions. Now you will learn how to translate word problems into the language of constants, variables, and expressions. ◀

Explore | Writing Expressions

Mister Ree Stories

Late last night Mister Ree wrote a test consisting of four word problems. Unfortunately, he was so tired when he finished that he mistakenly tossed the problems into his waste basket. This morning, all he can find are his solutions:

$$15 + 13 = 28 \qquad 140 - 60 = 80 \qquad 12 \times 5 = 60 \qquad 48 \div 4 = 12$$

1. For each solution, write a word problem that has that solution. You may not use the words *add, subtract, multiply,* or *divide,* or any forms of these words. Instead, think of a situation that leads naturally to the use of each operation.

2. Share your problems with the class. Help your teacher compile a list of situations in which you can use each arithmetic operation.

Remember

The numbers that you multiply together to get a product are called *factors* of the product.
[Page 78]

Learn | Writing Expressions

Some words in English can be translated into specific mathematical operations.

Word	Definition	Numerical Expression	Variable Expression
Sum	The result of adding numbers	$3 + 5$	$6 + x$
Difference	The result of subtracting numbers	$8 - 24$	$y - 10$
Product	The result of multiplying numbers	2×9	$5b$
Quotient	The result of dividing numbers	$20 \div 5$	$\dfrac{a}{2}$

To translate situations that don't use these words, you need to choose an operation that is appropriate for the situation. It may be easier to choose an operation if you first replace the variable with a number.

Examples

Write as an expression.

1 What is the product of 20 and *k*?

Product means multiplication.

20*k*

2 What is the difference of *g* and 6?

Difference means subtraction.

$g - 6$

3 Mae bought *b* bananas and ate 3. How many does she have?

If Mae bought 10 bananas and ate 3, she'd have 7 bananas, because $10 - 3 = 7$. The operation to use is subtraction.

$b - 3$

4 Tanisha had a 200-page book about the *Titanic*. She read *p* pages each day. How many days did it take to read the book?

If Tanisha read 10 pages each day, it would take 20 days, because $200 \div 10 = 20$. The operation to use is division.

$$\frac{200}{p}$$

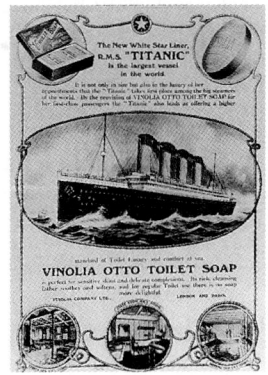
Try It

Write as an expression.

a. What is the sum of *c* and 8?

b. What is the quotient of *n* and 9?

c. Rafael raked *r* bags of leaves. Nicole raked 5 bags. How many bags of leaves were raked altogether?

d. Jake ran *x* laps every day for 7 days. How many laps did he run?

Check | Your Understanding

1. Other than *sum, difference, product,* and *quotient,* what words suggest addition? Subtraction? Multiplication? Division?

2. Give a situation suggested by each expression: $10 - n$; $\frac{y}{24}$; $50p$.

Practice and Apply

Getting Started Match the description to the expression.

1. A number plus 5
2. 5 take away a number
3. 5 into x groups
4. A number 5 times

A. $x + 5$
B. $x - 5$
C. $5 - x$

D. $5x$
E. $\dfrac{5}{x}$
F. $\dfrac{x}{5}$

Write the phrase as an expression.

5. q times 10
6. Half of h
7. d times 6

8. j and 2 more
9. s minus 3
10. 52 smaller than d

11. v multiplied by 20
12. z doubled
13. y decreased by 3

14. w divided by 3
15. 5 less than n
16. r to the third power

Write an expression to answer each question.

17. What is the difference of n and 4?
18. What is 8 more than x?

19. If x students are organized into equal teams of 8, how many teams are there?

20. There are 12 groups with p penguins in each group. How many penguins are there?

Write the problem as an expression.

North Pole

Quito, Ecuador

EQUATOR

21. **Fine Arts** The German composer Ludwig van Beethoven wrote s more symphonies than his countryman Johannes Brahms. Brahms wrote four symphonies. How many did Beethoven write?

22. **Health** An orange has 62 calories. It has c fewer calories than a nectarine. How many calories does a nectarine have?

23. **Science** The temperature at the North Pole was 146 degrees Fahrenheit cooler than the temperature in Quito, Ecuador. The temperature in Quito was t degrees. What was the temperature at the North Pole?

24. Literature Author Jules Verne's fictional submarine, the *Nautilus*, traveled 20,000 leagues under the sea. Let m leagues equal 1 mile. How many miles did the *Nautilus* travel?

25. Geography Lake Michigan covers about 22,278 square miles. Lake Iliamna in Alaska covers only m miles. How much larger is Lake Michigan?

26. **Test Prep** Thirty-six people at a picnic equally shared a watermelon weighing p pounds. Choose the expression to use to find the weight of each share.

Ⓐ $\dfrac{36}{p}$ 　　　Ⓑ $\dfrac{p}{36}$

Ⓒ $p \times 36$ 　　Ⓓ $36p$

Carmen Lomas Garza, "Sandia/Watermelon" 1986. Gouache painting. Collection of Dudley D. Brooks & Tomas Ybarra-Frausto, New York, NY.

Problem Solving and Reasoning

27. 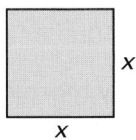 **Journal** Choose an operation (addition, subtraction, multiplication, or division) and describe three situations that require that operation.

28. Communicate For each expression, write a situation that the expression might describe.

$n - 60;\ 60n;\ \dfrac{60}{n};\ n + 60$

29. Critical Thinking Write an expression for the distance around each square.

a.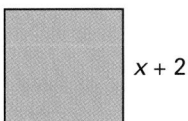

b.

c.

$x + 3$

Mixed Review

Estimate. *[Lesson 2-7]*

30. 103×64 　　**31.** $63{,}880{,}204 \div 80{,}129$ 　　**32.** 8212×779 　　**33.** 495×508

34. $52{,}305 \div 4{,}967$ 　　**35.** $112{,}635 \div 52{,}175$ 　　**36.** 633×490 　　**37.** $123 \div 41$

Divide. *[Previous course]*

38. $154 \div 7$ 　　**39.** $1464 \div 12$ 　　**40.** $627 \div 33$ 　　**41.** $20{,}097 \div 63$

42. $210 \div 5$ 　　**43.** $624 \div 8$ 　　**44.** $2470 \div 10$ 　　**45.** $56{,}316 \div 13$

2-12 Using Equations

► Lesson Link In the last lesson, you learned how to write expressions where the final answer was unknown. Now, you'll learn how to write expressions where the answer is known. ◄

You'll Learn ...
- what an equation is
- to determine if an equation is true or false

... How It's Used

Meteorologists use equations to convert temperatures between the Fahrenheit and Celsius measuring systems.

Vocabulary

equation

► Science Link

Fish that live a mile below sea level have unusual traits that help them survive. These can include flat, uncrushable bodies and glow-in-the-dark skin.

Explore | Using Equations

Tanks for the Anemones!

Wolf eel

Bat ray

Leather sea star

Gopher rockfish

On Monday afternoon, four staff members at the Bay City Aquarium made these changes in the central aquarium.

- Leon tripled the number of leather sea stars. Now there are 30.
- Val removed 4 bat rays. Now there are 7.
- Rico added 5 gopher rockfish. Now there are 13.
- Wendy took out half of the wolf eels. Now there are 10.

The list gives the number of each type of fish on Monday morning, before any changes were made.

1. Which is the number of leather sea stars? How can you tell?

2. Which is the number of bat rays? How can you tell?

3. Which is the number of gopher rockfish? How can you tell?

4. Which is the number of wolf eels? How can you tell?

5. Choose a type of fish and write your own question like one of these. Switch questions with a partner and discuss the answers.

Monday Morning
8
10
55
20
13
11
7

An **equation** is a mathematical sentence that uses an equal sign, =, to show that two expressions are equal. An equation can be either true or false.

$5 + 7 = 12$ is true. $16 - 6 = 12$ is false.

$30 \div 5 = 6$ is true. $3 \times 5 = 35$ is false.

An equation with a variable can also be true or false, depending on the value of the variable.

If $x = 5$, $x + 6 = 11$ is true.   If $x = 12$, $x + 6 = 11$ is false.

Examples

Is the equation true for the given value of the variable?

1 $5y = 40$, $y = 8$

$5 \times 8 \stackrel{?}{=} 40$ Substitute 8 for y.

$40 = 40$ Multiply.

The equation is true.

2 $r + 20 = 35$, $r = 10$

$10 + 20 \stackrel{?}{=} 35$ Substitute 10 for r.

$30 \neq 35$ Add.

Since $10 + 20$ does not equal 35, the equation is false.

Try It

Is the equation true for the given value of the variable?

a. $\frac{30}{z} = 3$, $z = 6$ **b.** $h - 12 = 24$, $h = 12$ **c.** $5 + d = 5$, $d = 0$

Like expressions, equations can be used to model real-world situations. For example, the recommended depth for recreational diving is 130 feet. If you dive d feet and you have 50 more feet before you reach the limit, you could model this as $d + 50 = 130$.

▶ **Science Link**

The deepest point on Earth is in the Mariana Trench in the Pacific Ocean. It is more than 10 kilometers below sea level. The highest point, Mount Everest, is less than 9 kilometers above sea level.

Check | Your Understanding

1. What are the differences between an equation and an expression?

2. Does every equation have a variable? Explain.

Practice and Apply

1. **Getting Started** State if the equation is true or false.

    a. $3 + 10 \overset{?}{=} 13$ **b.** $16 - 12 \overset{?}{=} 6$ **c.** $12 + 5 \overset{?}{=} 18$ **d.** $16 - 12 \overset{?}{=} 4$ **e.** $63 + 3 \overset{?}{=} 69$

    f. $20 \times 6 \overset{?}{=} 130$ **g.** $15 \div 3 \overset{?}{=} 5$ **h.** $27 \div 9 \overset{?}{=} 4$ **i.** $6 \times 16 \overset{?}{=} 96$ **j.** $3 \times 7 \overset{?}{=} 21$

Is the equation true for the given value of the variable?

2. $8 + r = 17, r = 9$ **3.** $16 - x = 7, x = 12$ **4.** $w - 23 = 2, w = 19$

5. $5h = 25, h = 5$ **6.** $s + 45 = 52, s = 7$ **7.** $10y = 30, y = 3$

8. $\dfrac{15}{q} = 5, q = 5$ **9.** $22y = 24, y = 2$ **10.** $\dfrac{w}{12} = 2, w = 24$

11. $12 \times t = 48, t = 4$ **12.** $v - 13 = 16, v = 29$ **13.** $9 \times 3l = 28, l = 3$

14. $\dfrac{14}{u} = 25, u = 7$ **15.** $45m = 3, m = 1$ **16.** $\dfrac{0}{n} = 0, n = 30$

17. $\dfrac{e}{3} = 7, e = 21$ **18.** $\dfrac{42}{p} = 24, p = 2$ **19.** $1k = 2, k = 2$

Write an equation for each situation.

20. Mary had f oranges and gave 1 to Byron. She had 3 oranges left.

21. Jarrod bought 12 snacks and shared them equally among p people. Each person got 3 snacks.

22. Nigel has 2 green shirts, b blue shirts, and 3 white shirts. He has a total of 8 shirts.

23. **Geography** King George Falls in Guyana is 1600 ft high. Angel Falls in Venezuela is x ft higher than King George Falls. Angel Falls is 3212 ft high.

24. **Geography** One trail at Takkakaw Falls in Canada is f ft long. Edward walked the trail at a rate of 550 ft/hr. It took him 3 hours.

25. Mona bought $84 worth of computer supplies and paid d dollars in sales tax. The total came to $88.

26. Sheena bought r rolls of film at $4 per roll and paid $60.

North Pole

Venezuela

EQUATOR

Angel Falls, Venezuela

27. Super Sports is selling a Grand Slam baseball bat for $75. The same bat is on sale at Scoreboard for b. You can save $26 dollars if you buy the bat at Scoreboard.

28. **Test Prep** Diana cut an orange into s equal slices. She ate 6 slices and had 2 slices left. Choose the correct equation to model the problem.

    Ⓐ $s + 6 = 2$ Ⓑ $s - 6 = 2$ Ⓒ $6s = 2$ Ⓓ $6 - s = 2$

Problem Solving and Reasoning

29. Choose a Strategy Franz and Jenna built a rectangular tree-house. The north and south walls were each f feet long. The east and west walls were $f + 2$ feet long. The total distance around the treehouse was 24 feet. Was the north wall 6 feet long? Explain.

30. Critical Thinking For an addition equation like $2 + x = 5$, how many values will make the equation true? Explain.

31. [Journal] Explain why an equation is either true or false, but an expression is neither true nor false. Give examples in your answer.

32. Communicate Juan states that $x \times 0 = 4$ will always be false, no matter what value is put in for the variable. Do you agree? Explain.

Problem Solving
STRATEGIES
• Look for a Pattern
• Make an Organized List
• Make a Table
• Guess and Check
• Work Backward
• Use Logical Reasoning
• Draw a Diagram
• Solve a Simpler Problem

Mixed Review

Write each multiplication equation as a division equation using the same numbers. *[Previous course]*

33. $5 \times 111 = 555$ **34.** $40 \times 30 = 1200$ **35.** $32 \times 48 = 1536$ **36.** $77 \times 8 = 616$

37. $42 \times 13 = 546$ **38.** $31 \times 31 = 961$ **39.** $23 \times 86 = 1978$ **40.** $18 \times 98 = 1764$

Write each division equation as a multiplication equation using the same numbers. *[Previous course]*

41. $64 \div 8 = 8$ **42.** $2100 \div 700 = 3$ **43.** $32 \div 4 = 8$ **44.** $99 \div 9 = 11$

45. $3528 \div 56 = 63$ **46.** $4402 \div 71 = 62$ **47.** $1044 \div 12 = 87$ **48.** $2025 \div 45 = 45$

Evaluate the expression for $x = 1, 2,$ and 3. *[Lesson 2-10]*

49. $12 + x$ **50.** $3x$ **51.** $\dfrac{36}{x}$ **52.** $x - 1$ **53.** $6x$

54. $7x$ **55.** $\dfrac{30}{x}$ **56.** $8 - x$ **57.** $x + 7$ **58.** $5x$

Solving Equations

▶ **Lesson Link**   You have learned how to find out if a given value for a variable will make an equation true. Now you will learn how to find the value that will make an equation true. ◀

Explore | Solving Equations

Turning the Tables

1. Copy the tables, and evaluate the expressions with the given values.

x	x − 3
3	
5	
6	
10	

x	$\frac{24}{x}$
1	
2	
3	
4	

2. Copy the tables, and find the values for the variable that will provide the given values for the expressions.

x	x + 7
	10
	14
	19
	31

x	2x
	6
	14
	28
	42

3. Explain how you found the values in the first column.

Learn | Solving Equations

Most real-world situations that involve equations with variables do not provide you with a value to check in the equation. Sometimes you need to find the exact value that will make an equation true. This is known as solving the equation.

Number sense can help you solve equations. Think of equations as questions where the variable is read as "What number?" For example, $z + 5 = 7$ can be read as "What number plus 5 equals 7?" Use mental math to answer the question.

Examples

Solve each equation.

1 $w + 13 = 20$

$w + 13 = 20$	Read as "What number plus 13 equals 20?"
$\mathbf{7} + 13 = 20$	Use mental math.
$20 = 20$ ✓	Check to see that the equation is true.

w is equal to 7.

2 $x - 10 = 14$

$x - 10 = 14$	Read as "What number minus 10 equals 14?"
$\mathbf{24} - 10 = 14$	Use mental math.
$14 = 14$ ✓	Check to see that the equation is true.

x is equal to 24.

3 $9y = 180$

$9y = 180$	Read as "What number times 9 equals 180?"
$9 \times \mathbf{20} = 180$	Use mental math.

y is equal to 20.

4 Karen divided her diving time into 25-minute periods. There were 4 periods all together. How many minutes did she spend diving?

$\dfrac{z}{25} = 4$	Write an equation.
$\dfrac{z}{25} = 4$	Read as "What number divided by 25 equals 4?"
$\dfrac{\mathbf{100}}{25} = 4$	Use mental math.

She spent 100 minutes diving.

Try It

Solve. **a.** $a + 7 = 22$ **b.** $b - 12 = 51$ **c.** $5c = 110$ **d.** $\dfrac{d}{4} = 12$

Check | Your Understanding

1. Can x have any value in $x + 5$? Can x have any value in $x + 5 = 7$? Explain.

2. How can you use mental math to help solve an equation?

Practice and Apply

Getting Started Use mental math to determine if the value of the variable must be greater than 6 or less than 6.

1. $r + 5 = 10$ **2.** $q - 3 = 6$ **3.** $12 - w = 8$ **4.** $3r = 6$ **5.** $6 \times t = 24$

6. $\dfrac{28}{i} = 7$ **7.** $p - 16 = 32$ **8.** $12 + d = 29$ **9.** $\dfrac{f}{7} = 14$ **10.** $g \times 10 = 80$

Find the given value of x that makes the equation true.

11. $x + 7 = 9$ $x = 1, 2, 3,$ or 4 **12.** $x - 5 = 4$ $x = 7, 8, 9,$ or 10

13. $2x = 16$ $x = 2, 4, 6,$ or 8 **14.** $x - 3 = 2$ $x = 5, 6, 7,$ or 8

15. $3 + 5 = x$ $x = 2, 5, 8,$ or 15 **16.** $\dfrac{x}{2} = 6$ $x = 2, 4, 6,$ or 12

17. $\dfrac{x}{5} = 2$ $x = 5, 10, 15,$ or 20 **18.** $\dfrac{18}{x} = 3$ $x = 6, 12, 15,$ or 18

Find the values for the variable that will provide the given values for the expressions.

19.

n	$n - 12$
	10
	14
	19
	31

20.

n	$\dfrac{n}{12}$
	10
	14
	19
	31

Solve the equation.

21. $5j = 30$ **22.** $12 + l = 18$ **23.** $9k = 54$ **24.** $z + 3 = 37$

25. $19 - v = 13$ **26.** $8b = 64$ **27.** $\dfrac{72}{n} = 9$ **28.** $\dfrac{m}{4} = 21$

29. $z - 38 = 42$ **30.** $d + 4 = 37$ **31.** $\dfrac{100}{g} = 20$ **32.** $5p = 150$

33. $21 + k = 30$ **34.** $w - 30 = 80$ **35.** $\dfrac{r}{2} = 84$ **36.** $37 - x = 15$

37. **Test Prep** Choose the correct value for x if $12x = 120$.

   (A) 0   (B) 10   (C) 100   (D) 1000

Write an equation for each situation and then solve it.

38. Geography The top three gold-producing countries produce 1171 tonnes (metric tons) of gold. South Africa produces 584 tonnes. Australia produces 256 tonnes. The United States produces u tonnes. How much does the United States produce?

39. The French submarine *Nautile* can dive to 20,000 ft. Diving at x ft/hr, it takes 20 hours to reach the maximum depth. How fast must the *Nautile* dive to reach that depth?

40. Geography The largest desert in the world is the Sahara Desert, which covers 3,500,000 square miles. The second largest desert, the Australian Desert, is d square miles, 2,030,000 less than the Sahara. How big is the Australian Desert?

Practice and Problem Solving

41. Critical Thinking If the average depth of the Arctic Ocean is tripled, the result is 114 meters more than 3000 meters. The equation $3x - 114 = 3000$ models this situation. Find the average depth of the Arctic Ocean.

42. Communicate Jamie wanted to use her calculator to find the value of x that makes $56x + 716 = 5140$. Describe how to do it.

43. Critical Thinking Suppose $a + b = 10$. If the value of a increases by 2, how must the value of b change so that the equation is still true?

Mixed Review

Write each addition equation as a subtraction equation with the same numbers. *[Previous course]*

44. $22 + 8 = 30$ **45.** $49 + 151 = 200$ **46.** $25 + 34{,}567{,}890 = 34{,}567{,}915$

Write each subtraction equation as an addition equation with the same numbers. *[Previous course]*

47. $53 - 10 = 43$ **48.** $163 - 57 = 106$ **49.** $180{,}000 - 21{,}000 = 159{,}000$

Project Progress

For each of your six methods, refer to your calculations of how far you could travel in 24 hours. Evaluate whether or not your calculations are reasonable. For an unreasonable answer, how could you adjust it to be more reasonable?

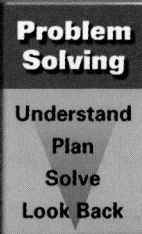

Problem Solving

Understand
Plan
Solve
Look Back

TECHNOLOGY

Using a Spreadsheet   Using Guess and Check

Problem: What values for x and y will make these two equations true at the same time: $x - y = 25$ and $xy = 150$?

You can use your spreadsheet to set up two formulas that will help you use the "guess and check" method to find the values.

	A	B	C
1	x		
2	y		
3			
4	x − y		
5	xy		
6			
7			

1 Enter the information into the spreadsheet as shown.

	A	B	C
1	x	50	
2	y	25	
3			
4	x − y	25	
5	xy	1250	
6			
7			

2 In cell B4, enter the formula =B1−B2. In cell B5, enter the formula =B1*B2.

	A	B	C
1	x	40	
2	y	15	
3			
4	x − y	25	
5	xy	600	
6			
7			

3 Enter values into cell B1 for x and cell B2 for y so that the answer for $x - y$ is 25.

4 Change your values for x and y until $x - y = 25$ and xy is 150. If the answer for xy is too high, choose smaller values for x and y. If the answer for xy is too low, choose bigger values for x and y.

Solution: The answer is $x = 30$ and $y = 5$.

	A	B	C
1	x	30	
2	y	5	
3			
4	x − y	25	
5	xy	150	
6			
7			

TRY IT

a. Find a solution for $x + y = 36$ and $\frac{x}{y} = 5$.

b. Find a solution for $xy = 24$ and $\frac{x}{y} = 24$.

ON YOUR OWN

▶ Why do you think the multiplication formula uses an "*" and not an "×" for multiplication?

▶ When going from a bad guess to a better guess, why is it important to change the values for both x and y?

▶ Is it faster to find a solution for x and y with a spreadsheet or without a spreadsheet? Explain.

126

On January 23, 1960, Jacques Piccard and Donald Walsh used a diving vessel called a bathyscaphe to descend nearly 7 miles into the deepest part of the Pacific Ocean. Their descent was the deepest ever made by humans. Such adventures are dangerous and costly. Much of today's deep-sea research is done by robots called ROVs, for "remotely operated vehicles."

Journey to the Bottom of the Sea

The fearsome angler fish makes its home in the ocean at a depth of around 3000 feet. An oceanography research team wants to rent an ROV and try to get photos of an angler fish. The price for renting ROV-1 is the number of minutes plus $545. The price for renting ROV-2 is $5 per minute. The team has limited funds and must find the best possible deal.

1. For each ROV, write an expression you can use to determine the total rental cost for x minutes.

2. Make a table showing the total cost of each ROV for 30 minutes, 60 minutes, 90 minutes, and so on up to 240 minutes (4 hours).

3. Which ROV should the team rent? Explain your reasoning.

4. Suppose the team had exactly $3000 to spend on ROV rental. For how long could they rent each ROV?

5. An angler fish swam up to the ROV, and the team took several excellent photos. Total ROV rental time was 127 minutes. The budget coordinator was pleased to find that the team had paid the lowest possible rent. Which ROV did the team rent? Explain.

127

Section 2C Review

ex. #10 = eg. yes =

State whether the quantity should be represented by a variable or a constant.

1. The height of Mount McKinley *C*

2. The value of an old comic book *V*

Write the situation as an expression.

3. *d* divided by 4   *d ÷ 4*   **4.** 16 less than *g*   *G − 16*   **5.** *m* times 16   *m × 16*   **6.** 4 added to *h*   *4 + h*

7. The Carson family evenly distributed *d* dollars to 17 different charities.   *17 ÷ d*

Estimate.

8. $35,677 + 23,898$ **9.** 21×451 *20 × 500 = 10,000*   **10.** $5302 - 3926$ **11.** $6022 \div 99$ *6000 ÷ 100 = 60*

Simplify.

3 + 14 = 17   *7 + 10 = 17*   *3 + 25 = 28*   *22 × 10 = 220*

12. $3 + 7 \times 2$ **13.** $14 \div 2 + 10$ **14.** $3 + 5^2$ **15.** $(10 + 12) \times 10$

16. $t + 6, t = 7$ *13*   **17.** $\dfrac{24}{b}, b = 6$ *A*   **18.** $8w, w = 9$ *72*   **19.** $j - 11, j = 23$ *12*

Is the equation true for the given value of the variable?

20. $\dfrac{14}{q} = 2, q = 7$ *C*   **21.** $9y = 24, y = 2$ **22.** $w - 1 = 13, w = 13$

Solve.

23. $6 + x = 28$ *22*   **24.** $\dfrac{x}{5} = 15$ *75*   **25.** $9x = 45$ *x = 5*   **26.** $x - 3 = 27$ *x = 30*

27. Geography The Humber Estuary Bridge in the United Kingdom is 4626 feet long. Round this to the nearest thousand.   *5000 ft*

Test Prep

You can solve equations by substituting given values to see which value makes the equation true.

28. Find the value of *x* that gives a true equation: $\dfrac{x}{4} = 6$

ⓐ 2   ⓑ 10

ⓒ 24   ⓓ 4096

29. Find the value of *x* that gives a true equation: $\dfrac{48}{x} = 8$

ⓐ 40   ⓑ 384

ⓒ 8   ⓓ 6

Triangular and Square Numbers

Because one, three, six, and ten dots can be arranged in triangles, they are called triangular numbers.

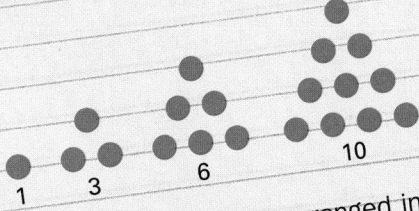

One, four, nine, and sixteen dots can be arranged in squares, so they are called square numbers.

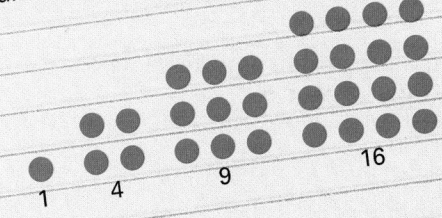

Try It

1. Name and sketch the next two triangular numbers.

2. Name and sketch the next two square numbers.

3. Other than 1, name the smallest number that can be shown as both a triangular number and a square number.

4. Describe a pattern for determining the first ten triangular numbers without using a drawing.

5. Describe a pattern for determining the first ten square numbers without using a drawing.

Graphic Organizer

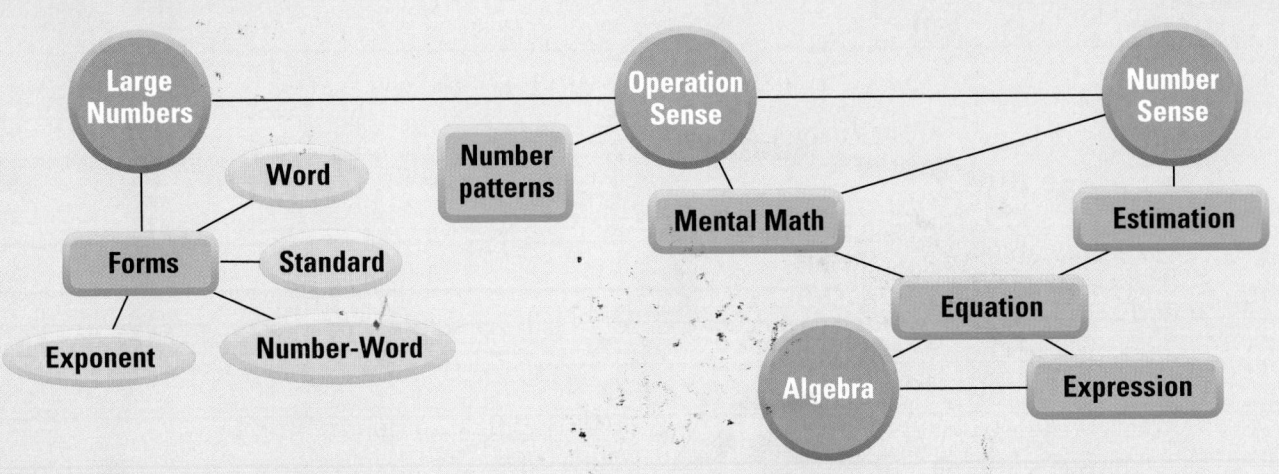

Section 2A Making Sense of Large Numbers

Summary

- The value of each digit in a number is found in a **place-value** chart.

- Numbers can be written in standard form, word form, or number-word form.

- Two or more numbers used as multipliers are called **factors**.

- In **exponential notation**, an **exponent** tells how many times to use the **base** as a factor.

Review

imp. for this item to write
twenty-nine million, can tell you
One ... code

1. Find the place value of 6 in 336,870. *endus.*

2. Write 29,158,647 in word form.

3. Round 29,158,647 to the given place: *@ 29,160,000* *@ 29,000,000*

4. Use > or < to compare 129,058,647 to 129,186,000. *this is not clear* *<*

   a. ten-thousands   **b.** millions

5. Order from least to greatest:

   4,567,238; 40,098,001; 4,067,338 *2 3 1*

6. Give the base and exponent of 5^9.

7. Write 7^3 in expanded form. *7·7·7 = 343*

8. Write 8 squared in exponential notation.

9. Write each in standard form:

   a. 4^2 **b.** 2 cubed   **c.** 10^4 **d.** 9^1 **e.** 11 to the second power

4·4 = 16   *2·2·2 = 8*   *10·10·10·10 = 10000*   *9·*   *11·11 = 132*
121

Section 2B Number Sense and Operation Sense

Summary

- Patterns, compatible numbers, compensation, and the Distributive Property can be used to do problems mentally.

- When an exact answer is not necessary, you can use front-end estimation, clustering, rounding, and compatible numbers to estimate an answer.

- Using the order of operations helps everyone get the same answer.

Review

Use mental math to solve each problem.

10. $48 + 52 + 220 + 80$

11. 6×204

12. 900×1000

13. $420{,}000 \div 600$

14. Estimate, using front-end estimation.

    a. $681 - 357$ **b.** $8564 + 2312$

15. Estimate, using compatible numbers.

    a. $442 \div 92$ **b.** 73×12

Use the order of operations to solve each problem.

16. $44 \div 4 - 2$

17. $(6 + 7) \times 9^2 \div 3$

Find the next three numbers for each pattern.

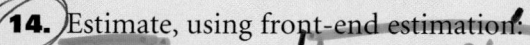

18. $64, 57, 50, 43, 36, \ldots$

19. $36, 51, 66, 81, 96, 111, \ldots$

Section 2C Introduction to Algebra

Summary

- A **variable** is a quantity that can change or vary.

- An **expression** contains constants, variables, and operation symbols.

- An **equation** shows that two expressions are equal.

Review

20. Evaluate $6x$ for $x = 2, 3,$ and 4.

21. Evaluate $11 - x$ for $x = 7, 8,$ and 9.

22. Write an expression for the quotient of m and 11.

23. Is the equation $4x + 3 = 31$ true for $x = 7$? For $x = 9$?

24. Solve for x.   **a.** $x - 8 = 53$ **b.** $\frac{x}{4} = 29$

Chapter 2 Assessment

1. a. Write 10^5 in standard form.   **b.** Write 10^5 in number-word form.

[handwritten: 10·10·10·10·10 =100,000] [handwritten: 100 thousand]

2. A stamp collector counted 31 New Zealand, 36 Canadian, 33 French, and 28 British stamps. Estimate the total number of stamps he had. *[handwritten: 130 stamps]*

3. Use > or < to compare Dallas's 1990 census of 1,006,877 to Detroit's census of 1,027,974. *[handwritten: <]*

4. Round 34,578 to the hundreds place. *[handwritten: 34,600 34,600]*

5. Find the value of $2m$ for $m = 1, 2,$ and 3.

6. Find the product of 35 times 10 cubed.

7. Evaluate $m - 2$ for $m = 5, 6,$ and 7.

8. Evaluate $m + 19$ for $m = 5, 6,$ and 7.

9. Is 5^2 the same as 5×2? Explain. *[handwritten: No, $5^2 = 5 \times 5 = 25$, $5 \times 2 = 10$]*

Explain how you would solve each problem using mental math.

10. 49×2 *[handwritten: 50 =100]*

11. $4800 \div 60$ *[handwritten: 80]*

12. $76 + 17 - 6$ *[handwritten: 80+20-6 100-6=94]*

13. 4×206 *[handwritten: 4×200 800]*

Estimate each answer.

14. 286×43 *[handwritten: 300 12,000]*

15. $35,782 \div 3,939$ *[handwritten: 36,000 9 4000]*

16. $426 \div 69$ *[handwritten: 420÷70=6]*

For each pattern, find the next three numbers.

17. $6, 8, 12, 18, 26, \ldots$

18. $10, 7, 4, 9, 6, 3, 8, \ldots$

Write an expression for each situation.

19. The distance around the box.

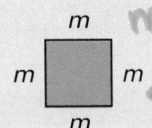

[handwritten: m, m, m, m, 4m]

20. Submarine *A* dived 1600 ft less than submarine B. How deep did submarine A dive? *[handwritten: B-1600 = ?]*

Find the value of the variable that makes the equation true.

21. $\dfrac{d}{6} = 20$ *[handwritten: d=4]*

22. $c + 32 = 37$ *[handwritten: c=5]*

23. $9y = 108$ *[handwritten: y=12]*

24. $y - 7 = 42$ *[handwritten: y=49]*

Performance Assessment

Not all the mathematical ideas found in this chapter are shown on the graphic organizer on page 130. Revise the organizer. Make it larger by including at least ten other ideas you have used to solve problems in this chapter. Label your new ideas correctly. Make sure that any ideas that you connect on your organizer are connected in their use in solving problems.

Multiple Choice

Choose the best answer.

1. Choose the largest number. *[Lesson 2-3]*

   (A) 207,135,528   (B) 271,105,528

   (C) 271,130,528   (D) 207,150,528

2. For the data 25, 22, 24, 20, 29, 21, 36, 23, 25, which has the lowest value, the mean, median, mode, or the outlier? *[Lesson 1-9]*

   (A) mean   (B) median

   (C) mode   (D) outlier

3. Calculate 224×4. *[Lesson 2-5]*

   (A) 886   (B) 8816

   (C) 844   (D) 896

4. Jessie has started doing sit-ups. If she does 2 the first day and each day does 2 times as many as the day before, how many will she do on the third day? *[Lesson 2-4]*

   (A) 2^6 (B) 2^3

   (C) 2^5 (D) 3^2

5. How many times was 26 a data item? *[Lesson 1-6]*

   (A) 2

   (B) 5

   (C) 3

   (D) not here

Stem	Leaf
0	1 2 6 6 6 7
1	0 6 7 8 8
2	5 6 6 7 7 8

6. Choose the next number in the pattern. 180, 173, 184, 177, 188, ... *[Lesson 2-9]*

   (A) 200   (B) 181

   (C) 196   (D) 234

7. Choose the best estimate for $4,235 + 9,608 + 9,342$. *[Lesson 2-6]*

   (A) 13,800   (B) 22,400

   (C) 20,700   (D) 23,000

8. What interval would be best to use for a bar graph's scale with this data? Cars, 175; Trucks, 290; Vans, 98; and Jeeps, 60 *[Lesson 1-5]*

   (A) 25   (B) 32

   (C) 70   (D) 55

9. Simplify $14 + (9 - 3)2 \div 2$. *[Lesson 2-8]*

   (A) 32   (B) 25

   (C) 17   (D) not here

10. Round three million, six hundred eighty-four to the nearest thousand. *[Lesson 2-2]*

    (A) 3,684, 000   (B) 3,006,840

    (C) 3,001,000   (D) 3,000,684

11. Estimate $472 \div 63$. *[Lesson 2-7]*

    (A) 7   (B) 10

    (C) 41   (D) 80

12. Manuel's dog has a litter of puppies. He gives three puppies away and has two left. Choose the correct equation to model the problem. *[Lesson 2-12]*

    (A) $p = 3 - 2$ (B) $2 - p = 3$

    (C) $p - 3 = 2$ (D) $3 - p = 2$

13. In a pictograph, each fish symbol represents 5 million fish. How many millions of fish do 7 symbols represent? *[Lesson 1-1]*

    (A) 7.5 million   (B) 35 million

    (C) 12 million   (D) not here

14. Evaluate the expression $\frac{144}{x}$ for $x = 2, 3,$ and 4. *[Lesson 2-10]*

    (A) 146, 147, 148   (B) 72, 46, 36

    (C) 142, 141, 140   (D) 72, 48, 36

15. Choose the correct value for x if $8x = 120$. *[Lesson 2-13]*

    (A) 960   (B) 128

    (C) 15   (D) 12

3 Decimals

→ Entertainment Link
www.mathsurf.com/6/ch3/ent

→ Social Studies Link
www.mathsurf.com/6/ch3/social

Social Studies

The Aztecs are credited as one of the first cultures to use the number 0. Without this digit, our current base 10 system wouldn't be possible.

People of the World

In Europe, a comma is used in place of a decimal point. The number 42.37 in the United States would be 42,37 in Europe.

Entertainment

In 1988, Carl Lewis won the Olympic gold medal for the 100-meter dash by completing the race in 9.92 seconds.

BRIOCHETTE
3,50 F

CHAUSSON AUX POMMES
4,90 F

BOSTOCK
5,50 F

Arts & Literature

In *The Gift of the Magi*, O. Henry stated "One dollar and eighty-seven cents. That was all. And sixty cents of it was in pennies." He never explained how this was possible.

Science

The Richter scale uses decimals to measure earthquake intensity. A 1.3 earthquake is recorded but not felt. A 6.1 earthquake destroys buildings. Earthquakes above 7.9 cause total destruction.

KEY MATH IDEAS

Decimal numbers can be used to describe numbers that are in between whole numbers.

Decimal place values, such as tenths and hundredths, describe amounts that are smaller than 1.

Decimal numbers can be rounded to the nearest place value in the same way that whole numbers can.

Decimal numbers can be added and subtracted like whole numbers when the decimal points of the numbers are lined up.

You can multiply and divide decimal numbers as if they were whole numbers, but you need to pay special attention to where the decimal point is placed in the answer.

CHAPTER PROJECT

Problem Solving

Understand
Plan
Solve
Look Back

In this project, you will investigate your own personal budget by analyzing how much money you spend over a certain period of time. Begin by estimating how much you spend per week on food, travel, and entertainment.

135

Problem Solving Focus

Reading the Problem

When you are trying to understand a problem and you are stuck, it sometimes helps to answer simpler questions about the problem. Thinking about the information that has been given can sometimes help you decide upon a new strategy for solving the problem.

Read each problem, and answer the questions about the problem.

1 According to the American Veterinary Medical Association, 31 out of every 100 households in America have pet cats. The average number of cats per household is 2. If there are an estimated 57,000,000 pet cats in America, how many homes are there in America?

a. What is the problem about?

b. What is the problem asking for?

c. About how many pet cats are there in America?

d. If an average neighborhood had 600 homes in it, how many of those homes would have cats?

e. Write and answer a question of your own.

2 One year the American Kennel Club had 126,393 registered Labrador Retrievers. There were also 42,621 Dalmatians, 46,129 Dachshunds, and 39,947 Pomeranians. Was the combined number of Dalmatians, Dachshunds, and Pomeranians bigger or smaller than the number of Labrador Retrievers?

a. What is the problem about?

b. What is the problem asking for?

c. How many Dalmatians were registered?

d. Were there more Dachshunds or more Pomeranians?

e. Write and answer a question of your own.

Decimal Concepts

▶ Science Link   ▶ www.mathsurf.com/6/ch3/spiders

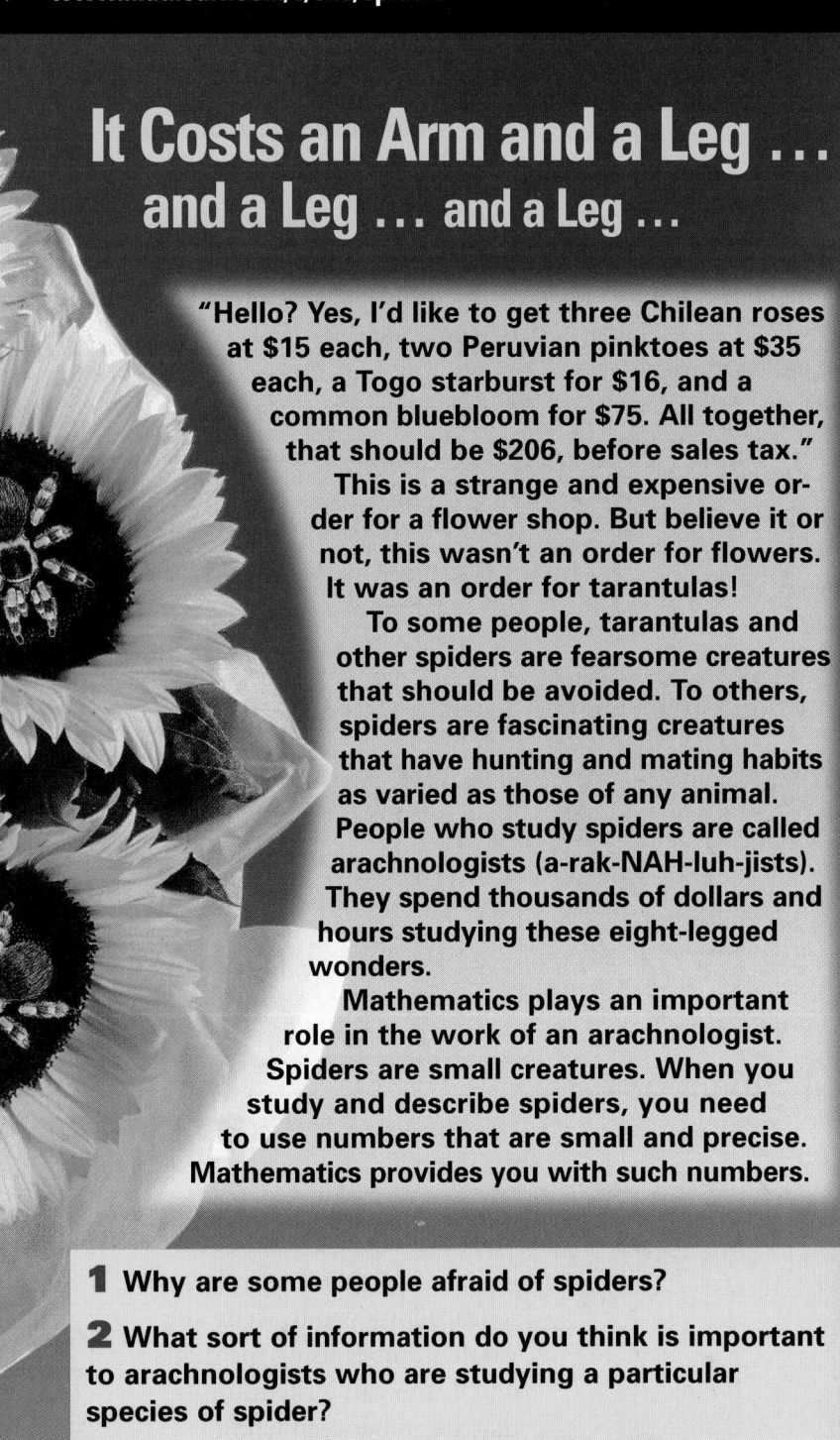

It Costs an Arm and a Leg …
and a Leg … and a Leg …

"Hello? Yes, I'd like to get three Chilean roses at $15 each, two Peruvian pinktoes at $35 each, a Togo starburst for $16, and a common bluebloom for $75. All together, that should be $206, before sales tax."

This is a strange and expensive order for a flower shop. But believe it or not, this wasn't an order for flowers. It was an order for tarantulas!

To some people, tarantulas and other spiders are fearsome creatures that should be avoided. To others, spiders are fascinating creatures that have hunting and mating habits as varied as those of any animal. People who study spiders are called arachnologists (a-rak-NAH-luh-jists). They spend thousands of dollars and hours studying these eight-legged wonders.

Mathematics plays an important role in the work of an arachnologist. Spiders are small creatures. When you study and describe spiders, you need to use numbers that are small and precise. Mathematics provides you with such numbers.

1 Why are some people afraid of spiders?

2 What sort of information do you think is important to arachnologists who are studying a particular species of spider?

3 Why do you need to use small numbers when studying spiders?

137

Decimal Notation

▶ **Lesson Link**
In Chapter 2, you learned to name and write whole numbers. Now you'll see how to name and write numbers that are not whole numbers, especially numbers between 0 and 1. ◄

You'll Learn ...

■ how to write numbers in decimal notation

■ how to represent decimal numbers using a grid model

... How It's Used

Seismologists use decimal numbers to describe the amount of energy released in an earthquake. Measurements are taken off of seismographs and translated into amount of energy.

| **Explore** | Decimal Notation |

What's the Name of That Place?

Materials: Calculator

	Hundreds	Tens	Ones		
Arithmetic Form	100 ÷ 1	10 ÷ 1	1 ÷ 1	1 ÷ 10	1 ÷ 100
Fraction Form	$\frac{100}{1}$				
Calculator Form					

1. Use a calculator and your knowledge of patterns to complete the table.

2. Add one more column to the right of the table, and fill in the column so that it continues the pattern.

3. The names of the three columns to the right are "Tenths," "Hundredths," and "Thousandths." Explain the reasons for these names.

4. How are the columns to the right of the "Ones" similar to the columns to the left of the "Ones"? How are they different?

| **Learn** | Decimal Notation |

The place-value system of ones, tens, hundreds, thousands, and so on, allows you to write any whole number using the digits 0 to 9. You can write numbers that are in between whole numbers by using a decimal point and place values that are smaller than ones.

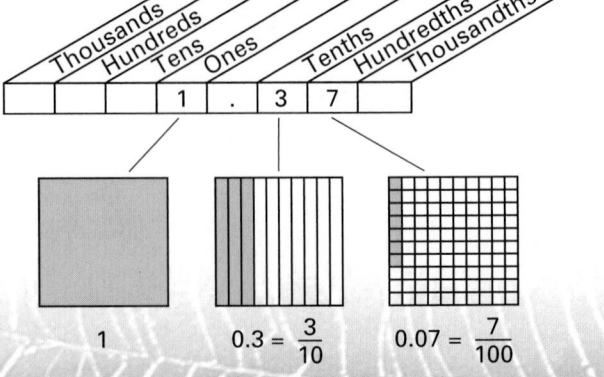

Examples

1 What decimal number does the grid represent?

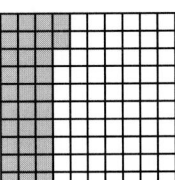

The grid represents 0.32

2 Draw a grid to represent 0.7.

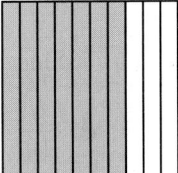

3 Write one and twenty-one thousandths in decimal form.

one and twenty-one thousandths = 1.021

4 A desert tarantula measures 6.94 cm in length. Write this in word form.

6.94 = six and ninety-four hundredths.

▶ **Science Link**

Desert tarantulas seldom bite people. Their venom is usually no more dangerous than a bee sting.

Try It

What decimal numbers does each grid represent?

a.

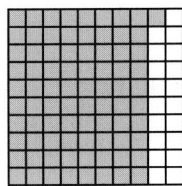

b.

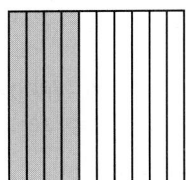

Represent in grid form.   **c.** 0.2   **d.** 0.13

Write in word form.   **e.** 3.051   **f.** 0.171   **g.** 0.47   **h.** 8.1

Write in standard form.   **i.** nine hundredths

j. two and one hundred one thousandths

Study TIP

All the place values smaller than one have names that end in *ths*.

Check Your Understanding

1. How many tenths are in a whole? How many hundredths? How many thousandths?

2. How many hundredths are in a tenth?

3. Why is the United States money system referred to as a decimal system?

EVEN

Practice and Apply

1. **Getting Started** Write each fraction as a decimal.

    a. $\dfrac{6}{10}$ **b.** $\dfrac{43}{100}$ **c.** $\dfrac{312}{1000}$ **d.** $\dfrac{9}{10}$ **e.** $\dfrac{97}{1000}$ **f.** $\dfrac{8}{100}$

What decimal number does each grid or set of grids represent?

2.
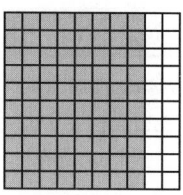

3.
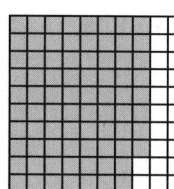

4.
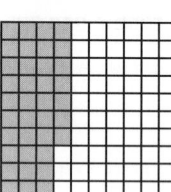

5.

Draw a grid to represent each decimal.

6. 0.7   **7.** 0.18   **8.** 0.5   **9.** 0.99   **10.** 0.67   **11.** 0.37

For Exercises 12–17, write the number as a decimal.

12. fifty-one hundredths

13. one and sixty-seven thousandths

14. three and forty-two hundredths

15. eight hundredths

16. one hundred sixty-seven thousandths

17. two tenths

18. **History** The ancient Greeks discovered that a person's height from the floor to the waist is about sixty-two hundredths of the total height. Write this number as a decimal.

19. **Science** The average body length of a dust mite is fifteen thousandths of an inch. Write this number as a decimal.

20. **Science** The earth revolves around the sun once every three hundred sixty-five and twenty-four hundredths of a day. Write this number as a decimal.

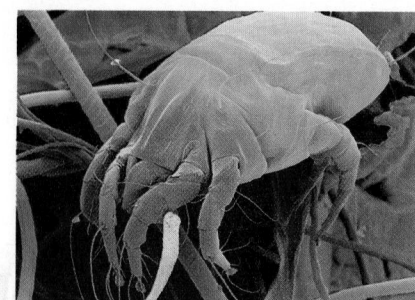

Write the decimal in word form.

21. 0.67   **22.** 0.075   **23.** 8.611   **24.** 5.09   **25.** 12.006   **26.** 0.4

27. Sports In 1988 Florence Griffith-Joyner broke the women's world record in the 100-meter dash with a time of 10.48 seconds. Write her time in word form.

28. Health Eighteen baked snack crackers contain 0.5 grams of saturated fat and 1.5 grams of unsaturated fat. Write both decimal numbers in word form.

29. [**Test Prep**] Choose the decimal form for two and twenty-nine hundredths.

Ⓐ 229.00   Ⓑ 2.29

Ⓒ 2.029   Ⓓ 0.229

Problem Solving and Reasoning

30. Communicate Draw a grid that represents 0.4. Then draw a grid that represents 0.40. Explain the similarities and differences between the two grids.

31. Critical Thinking Jarvis made a four-digit number with 0, 3, 6, and 8. The number was smaller than 5 but bigger than 1. What could his number be? Explain.

32. [Journal] Why does a place-value chart not have a column for "oneths"?

33. Critical Thinking How many numbers are there between 1.01 and 1.10? Explain.

Mixed Review

For each data set, make a frequency chart and a line plot. *[Lesson 1-4]*

34. 3, 4, 7, 9, 10, 4, 6, 3, 10, 3, 6, 5, 12, 3, 5, 8, 7

35. 20, 50, 70, 80, 40, 100, 30, 60, 70, 70, 70, 80, 30, 20, 50, 10, 50

Evaluate each expression for the given values of the variable. *[Lesson 2-10]*

36. $g + 13$; $g = 2, 3, 4$ **37.** $d - 10$; $d = 21, 18, 15$ **38.** $3k$; $k = 4, 6, 10$

39. $\frac{r}{2}$; $r = 2, 16, 22$ **40.** $5p$; $p = 2, 6, 7$ **41.** $20 - b$; $b = 3, 5, 19$

Simplify. *[Previous course]*

42. $286 + 312$ **43.** $618 - 202$ **44.** 200×317 **45.** $606 \div 202$

46. $792 + 488$ **47.** $931 - 575$ **48.** 497×101 **49.** $956 \div 478$

3-2

Rounding Decimals

You'll Learn ...

■ how to round decimal numbers

■ how to measure length with a metric ruler

... How It's Used

Architects use decimal measurements when drawing blueprints.

▶ **Lesson Link** In the last chapter, you rounded whole numbers in order to estimate answers. You can round decimals for the same purpose. ◀

Rounding decimals is often useful when you are measuring lengths. Three units often used to measure length are the meter, the centimeter, and the millimeter. The meter (m) is about the distance from the floor to a doorknob. A centimeter (cm) is $\frac{1}{100}$ of a meter. A millimeter (mm) is $\frac{1}{1000}$ of a meter.

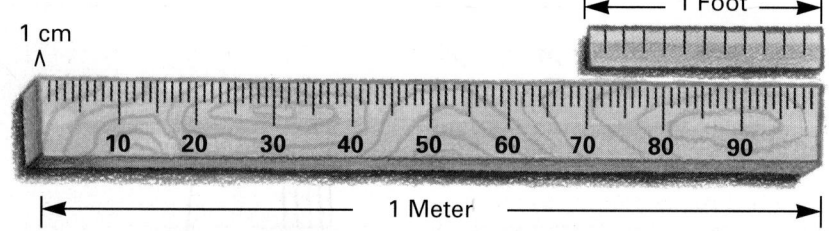

| 1 Foot |
| 1 cm |
| 10 20 30 40 50 60 70 80 90 |
| 1 Meter |

Explore | Rounding Decimals

It's a Toss Up!   Materials: Meterstick, Masking tape, Cotton balls

Play the following game in groups of 2 to 4.

1. Put a length of tape 1 meter long on the floor. Mark one end 0 and the other end 1.

2. Stand at the 0 end of the tape. Estimate whether a cotton ball that you toss will land closer to 0 or to 1. Toss the ball. Give yourself a point if your estimate was right. Everyone should take four turns, making an estimate each time.

3. Using the meterstick, draw nine lines on the tape to divide it into ten equal sections. Label each new line with a decimal number (0.1, 0.2, 0.3, up to 0.9). Take four turns again, this time estimating to the nearest tenth. Score one point for each correct estimate.

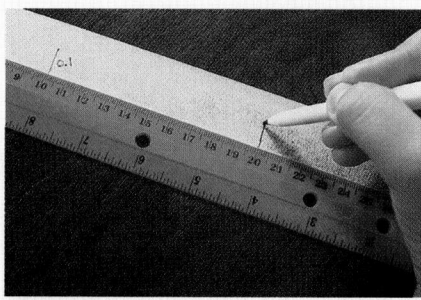

4. In which round did you score the most points? Why?

5. Which would be easier, a game where you had to hit 0.5, or one where you had to hit a number closer to 0.5 than to either 0 or 1? Why?

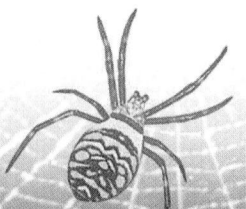

Recall that you can *round* numbers when you want to estimate an answer, or when you don't need as precise a measurement as the one you are given.

> To round a number, look at the digit to the right of the place you want to round to. If the digit is 5 or greater, round up. If it is less than 5, round down.

Remember

Rounding is a method of finding an estimate that's the *closest* to a given place value.

[Page 71]

Examples

1 A scale on a microscope slide allows a biologist to estimate lengths to the nearest hundredth of a centimeter. A spider egg measures 0.1347 cm in length. Find the biologist's estimate of the egg's length.

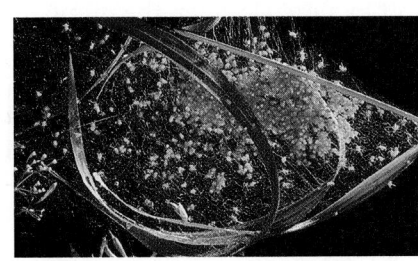

0.1⌐3⌐47   Find the place value.
  ↑ hundredths

0.1⌐3⌐47   Look at the digit to the right. If it is 5 or greater, add 1 to the place-value digit. If it's less than 5, leave the place-value digit alone.

0.13   Drop the digits to the right of the place value.

The length is approximately 0.13 cm.

2 A baseball player's batting average is rounded to the nearest thousandth. In 1924, Rogers Hornsby of the St. Louis Cardinals achieved the highest batting average in modern baseball history: .4235074. What was his average rounded to the nearest thousandth?

       ↓ This is the thousandths place.
0.42⌐3⌐5074
          ↑ The digit to the right is 5 or greater.
            Add 1 to the thousandths place.

Hornsby's batting average was 0.424.

Science Link

Spiders are not insects, although they are invertebrates, or animals without spines. They belong to a separate class of arthropods called Arachnida.

Try It

Round to the given place.

a. 0.846, tenths   **b.** 7.045, hundredths   **c.** 3.461825, thousandths

d. A spitting spider can squirt a sticky substance on a prey that is up to 1.905 cm away. What is this distance rounded to the nearest tenth?

You can use a metric ruler to measure the length of an object in centimeters. Most objects do not equal an exact number of centimeters, so centimeter measurements are usually rounded to the nearest centimeter, or the nearest tenth of a centimeter.

Example 3

What is the length of the pencil to the nearest centimeter and the nearest tenth of a centimeter?

On a metric ruler, the numbered divisions represent centimeters. The tip of the pencil is between the 10 mark and the 11 mark, and it is closer to the 11 mark. To the nearest centimeter, the pencil is 11 cm long.

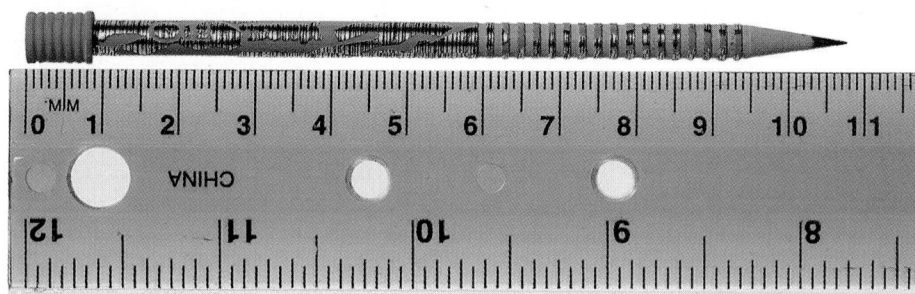

Problem Solving TIP

When measuring with a ruler, make sure one edge of the object being measured lines up with the 0-mark on the ruler.

On a metric ruler, each centimeter is divided into ten sections. Each section is one tenth of a centimeter. The tip of the pencil is between the 10.7 mark and the 10.8 mark, but closer to the 10.8 mark. To the nearest tenth of a centimeter, the pencil is 10.8 cm long.

Try It

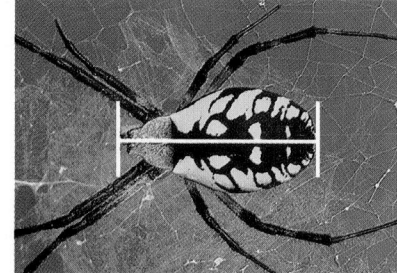

a. Measure the length of the spider's body to the nearest centimeter and the nearest tenth of a centimeter.

b. Measure the length of the "Check Your Understanding" bar to the nearest centimeter and the nearest tenth of a centimeter.

Check Your Understanding

1. How is measuring to the nearest centimeter on a metric ruler like rounding?

2. How is rounding to thousands similar to rounding to thousandths? How is it different?

Practice and Apply

1. | Getting Started | Round to the nearest whole number.

   a. 0.78   **b.** 2.65   **c.** 3.34   **d.** 0.11   **e.** 1.49   **f.** 2.22

Round to the underlined place value.

2. 10.6_7_4   **3.** 5._8_1   **4.** 56.0_9_8   **5.** 0.47_1_5   **6.** 11._9_9   **7.** 4._3_45

8. 904.8_4_6   **9.** 0.10_0_2   **10.** 0.28_0_2   **11.** 33._4_56   **12.** 8.9_2_8   **13.** 16.1_2_87

14. 4._0_02   **15.** 7.3_0_06   **16.** 26.9_0_3   **17.** 88._3_   **18.** 4._6_7   **19.** 7._3_42

20. 52.0_9_   **21.** 8._2_03   **22.** 7.3_9_21   **23.** 0.789_3_   **24.** 3.01_9_1   **25.** _5_6.82

26. Science The largest sea spider ever found was 75 cm long from leg to leg. The smallest sea spider measures only 0.1 cm. Round the length of the smallest sea spider to the nearest centimeter.

27. Estimation Jonathan has discovered a trail of ants on his porch. Each ant is about 0.93 cm long, and he guesses there are almost 1000 of them. Estimate how long the ant trail is.

28. | Test Prep | Round 182.9807 to the nearest hundredth. Choose the correct answer.

   Ⓐ 182.98   Ⓑ 182.981   Ⓒ 183   Ⓓ 200

Measurement Measure each object's height to the nearest centimeter and tenth of a centimeter.

29.    **30.** 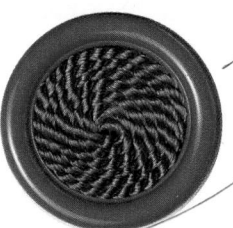   **31.**

HMS

6   *Jamar Bayless*

GRADE   SIGNATURE

32.    **33.**

Measurement Measure each object's length to the nearest centimeter and millimeter.

34.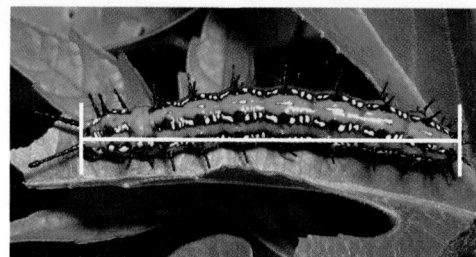

35.

Problem Solving and Reasoning

36. Critical Thinking Form a decimal out of the digits 1, 2, 4, 6, and 8, so that the decimal will round up if rounded to the nearest tenth but stay the same if rounded to the nearest hundredth. You do not need to use all five digits.

37. Communicate Explain why 4.95 rounded to the nearest tenth is 5.0.

38. Communicate Carlos says that the number 5.9999999 will round up to the same answer, no matter what place you round to. Is he right? Explain.

39. Journal   Why is a measurement always an estimate?

40. Critical Thinking Wendell and Terry both rounded the number 3.4682. Wendell says that he rounded the number up. Terry says that he rounded the number down. To what place value might the number have been rounded by Wendell? By Terry? Explain.

Mixed Review

For each set of data, draw a bar graph. *[Lesson 1-5]*

41. Number of Juice Cans Sold

Apple	28
Grape	24
Orange	37
Cranberry	21

42. Number of Telephones in House

None	1
One	4
Two	12
Three or more	6

For each situation, write an expression. [Lesson 2-11]

43. Elaine ate 12 crackers, and then she ate k more. How many crackers did Elaine eat?

44. Carlos worked for five days. He earned w dollars each day. How many dollars did Carlos earn?

T E C H N O L O G Y

Using a Spreadsheet • Formatting Decimal Data

Problem: Given the data below, what's the average number of customers per day rounded to the nearest whole number?

You can use spreadsheets to analyze large amounts of data, and you can also use them to make the data look the way you want it to look.

1 Enter the information about the number of customers served at a hotdog stand into the spreadsheet as shown:

	A	B	C	D	E	F	G
		Mon	Tue	Wed	Thu	Fri	
1		Mon	Tue	Wed	Thu	Fri	
2	8:00 – 10:00	23	36	67	90	35	
3	10:00 – 12:00	25	4	78	21	47	
4	12:00 – 2:00	79	67	89	87	14	
5	2:00 – 4:00	2	43	55	43	56	
6	4:00 – 6:00	15	56	90	53	23	
7	6:00 – 8:00	45	32	66	14	23	
8							
9	Average						
10							

2 In cell B9, enter the formula = average(B2:B7). This will calculate the Monday average.

	A	B	C	D	E	F	G
1		Mon	Tue	Wed	Thu	Fri	
2	8:00 – 10:00	23	36	67	90	35	
3	10:00 – 12:00	25	4	78	21	47	
4	12:00 – 2:00	79	67	89	87	14	
5	2:00 – 4:00	2	43	55	43	56	
6	4:00 – 6:00	15	56	90	53	23	
7	6:00 – 8:00	45	32	66	14	23	
8							
9	Average	32	40	74	51	33	
10							

3 Copy the formula across the row to column F.

4 Use the format command to format the averages to show no places after the decimal.

Solution: The averages, rounded to the nearest whole number, are 32, 40, 74, 51, and 33.

TRY IT

a. If the data was about ounces of ketchup used, you might want to see the data to the nearest tenth. Format the averages to show tenths.

b. If the data was about money collected, you might want to see the data to the nearest hundredth. Format the averages to show hundredths.

ON YOUR OWN

▶ Name a situation where it might make sense to round a number to the nearest thousandth.

▶ If a number in a spreadsheet is 700, can you tell how many places it's been rounded to?

▶ What other ways can you format numbers in a spreadsheet?

3-3

Comparing and Ordering Decimals

You'll Learn ...

■ how to compare and order decimals

... How It's Used

Sports officials must compare race times in decimals to determine who won a race.

▶ **Lesson Link** You know how to compare and order large numbers. You can use similar methods to compare and order decimal numbers. ◀

Explore Comparing and Ordering Decimals

Doing It by the Book

Libraries use the Dewey decimal system to arrange nonfiction books. Books are arranged in order of their Dewey decimal numbers. These books are arranged in the correct order, but the labels have fallen off.

154.6 Library	595.79 Library	759.9492 Library

595.1 Library	595.4 Library	796.357 Library	912 Library	341.23 Library	796.48 Library

1. Match each label to the correct book.

2. Explain how you decided which label matched each book.

3. If a new book was added between *The United Nations* and *The Mystery of Dreams,* what could its Dewey decimal number be?

▶ **Literature Link**

The Dewey decimal system breaks all subjects down into ten categories: reference, psychology, religion, social sciences, language, pure science, applied science, the arts, literature, and history.

Learn Comparing and Ordering Decimals

When you *annex* zeros to the right of a decimal number, you do not change the value of the number.

$4.37 = 4.370 = 4.3700 = 4.37000$

Decimals are easy to compare when they have the same number of digits after the decimal point. Annexing zeros can help you do this.

148 *Chapter 3 • Decimals*

Examples

1 Compare 0.5 and 0.07.

0.50 ☐ 0.07   Annex zeros.

0.5 > 0.07

2 Compare 32.207 and 32.3.

32.207 ☐ 32.**3**00   Annex zeros.

32.207 < 32.3

Try It

Use > and < to compare the pairs of decimals.

a. 2.8 ☐ 2.45   **b.** 0.67 ☐ 0.067   **c.** 12.71 ☐ 12.2   **d.** 5 ☐ 5.2

When you have to order several decimal numbers, using a number line may be faster than annexing zeros.

On a number line, the farther to the right a number is, the greater it is. The farther to the left a number is, the smaller it is.

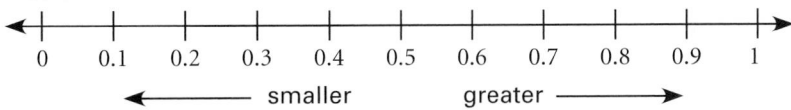

Example 3

Every spider leg is made of seven segments. Kim measured the lengths of the segments in a golden huntsman spider leg. Order the lengths from least to greatest.

Segment Length (cm)		
0.9	0.881	0.804
0.892	0.87	
0.85	0.876	

On a number line, the interval from 0 to 1 can be divided into tenths, hundredths, and (if needed) thousandths. Then, each decimal value can be located.

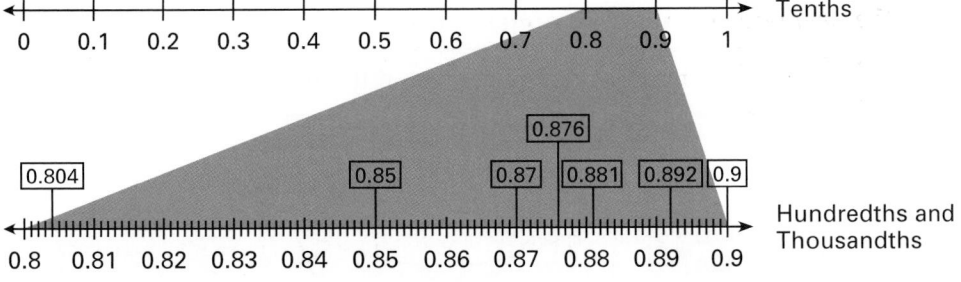

▶ **Science Link**

Unlike most spiders, the golden huntsman does not spin an organized web. Instead, it walks in slow search of its prey.

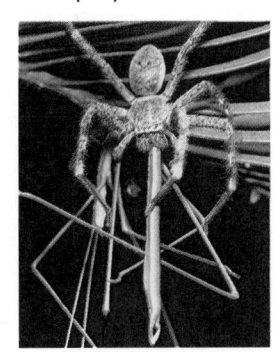

The segment lengths from least to greatest are 0.804, 0.85, 0.87, 0.876, 0.881, 0.892, and 0.9.

Try It

Order from least to greatest: 1.74, 1.08, 1.009, 1.725, 1.6

WHAT DO YOU THINK?

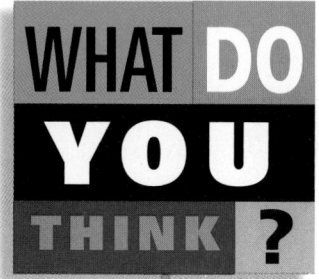

Maritess and Aaron want to rank these earthquakes in order of their measure on the Richter scale.

Earthquakes Around the World		
1755	Lisbon, Portugal	8.75
1906	San Francisco, USA	8.3
1950	Assam, India	8.7
1977	Indonesia	8
1985	Mexico City	8.1

Maritess thinks ...

I'll annex zeros and compare the numbers.

$$8.75 = 8.75$$
$$8.3 = 8.30$$
$$8.7 = 8.70$$
$$8 = 8.00$$
$$8.1 = 8.10$$

The order is 8, 8.1, 8.3, 8.7, 8.75.

Aaron thinks ...

I'll locate the measurements on a number line.

8 8.1 8.2 8.3 8.4 8.5 8.6 8.7 8.8 8.9 9

The order is 8, 8.1, 8.3, 8.7, 8.75.

What do you think?

1. Which method would you prefer to use? Why?

2. Would both methods work equally well if the measurements went to thousandths? Explain.

Check Your Understanding

1. If 35 is greater than 4, why is 0.4 greater than 0.35?

2. Name two numbers between 1.52 and 1.53.

3. You are given two decimal numbers, and you need to decide which one is bigger. Which part of the number should you look at first? Why?

Practice and Apply

1. **Getting Started** Annex zeros to the numbers so that they have the same number of digits after the decimal point.

   a. 0.276 and 0.28   **b.** 1.45 and 1.3492   **c.** 1.67 and 1.679   **d.** 0.3 and 0.4783

Use >, <, or = to compare each pair of numbers.

2. 0.193 ⬚> 0.187   **3.** 7.32 ⬚ 7.320   **4.** 52.1 ⬚< 52.16   **5.** 2.1 ⬚ 1.94

6. 5.07 ⬚< 5.16   **7.** 8.600 ⬚ 8.6   **8.** 21.7 ⬚> 21.07   **9.** 3.04 ⬚ 3.1

10. 66.77 ⬚< 67.77   **11.** 34.21 ⬚ 35.19   **12.** 98.23 ⬚< 98.3   **13.** 6.9 ⬚ 6.96

14. 4.6 ⬚= 4.60   **15.** 5.03 ⬚ 5.30   **16.** 30.10 ⬚< 30.11   **17.** 0.02 ⬚ 0.20

Science Use the graph for Exercises 18–20. The lengths of the spiders, in no particular order, are 0.872, 0.989, 0.83, 0.746, and 0.675 inches.

18. How long is the golden-silk spider?

19. How long is the turret spider?

20. How long is the wolf spider?

Web-Weaving Spider

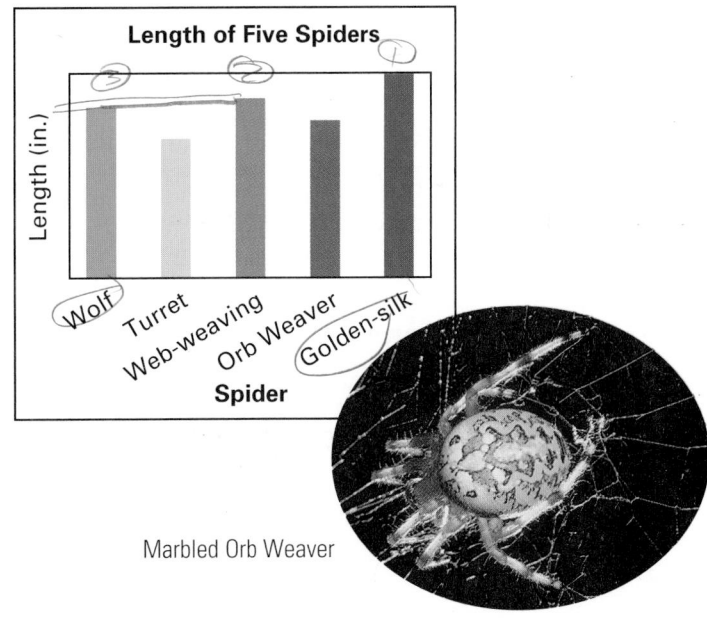

Marbled Orb Weaver

Order from least to greatest.

21. 27.948, 27.939, 27.946

22. 0.53, 0.534, 0.538

23. 1.23, 2.64, 1.5

24. 11.066, 11.0666, 11.66

25. 2.96, 2.84, 3.02

26. 0.1147, 0.217, 0.1146

27. 31.7, 31.07, 3.107, 30.17, 310.7

28. 2.12, 2.22, 1.22, 1.21, 2.21, 1.11

29. **Test Prep** Choose the group of numbers where the value of each decimal number is the same.

Ⓐ 0.5, 0.50, 0.500   Ⓑ 0.50, 0.05, 0.5   Ⓒ 0.005, 0.050, 0.0500

30. The chart shows the finishing times for a swimming race. Who came in first, second, and third?

Swimmer	Time (sec)
Gabe	32.01
Raul	31.84
Josh	31.92

31. The track coach measured the running strides of her distance runners. Sue's stride was 1.34 m, Angela's was 1.41 m, and Temeca's was 1.4 m. The coach chose the two runners with the longest strides to run the 800-meter race. Whom did she choose?

Problem Solving and Reasoning

32. Critical Thinking Letti's time in the 50 m freestyle was clocked to the thousandths place but rounded to 25.69 seconds. Give a possible slower time that would round to 25.69. Give a possible faster time that would round to 25.69. Explain.

33. Communicate Write a number that has a thousandths place and is between 8.75 and 8.739. Explain how you chose the number.

34. Communicate Joel says 7.49 is greater than 7.6 because 49 is greater than 6. Explain why Joel's statement is incorrect.

Mixed Review

For the given data, make a stem-and-leaf diagram. *[Lesson 1-6]*

35. 51, 42, 68, 32, 60, 61, 36, 49, 30, 47, 48, 61, 32, 44, 50, 52, 63, 51

36. 7, 9, 10, 13, 12, 11, 6, 4, 7, 3, 6, 10, 13, 16, 13, 11, 10, 7, 11, 8, 4, 11, 19

State whether each equation is true for the given value. *[Lesson 2-12]*

37. $4x = 28$; $x = 7$ **38.** $25 - y = 20$; $y = 15$ **39.** $12 + p = 20$; $p = 16$

Project Progress

Start to keep a record of all of the things that you spend money on. For each item, note when you spent the money, what you paid for, and how much it cost.

Problem Solving

Understand
Plan
Solve
Look Back

Scientific Notation

▶ **Lesson Link**   You've seen that numbers can be extremely large or small. Now you'll see how to use exponents, which you studied in the last chapter, to make writing large numbers easier. ◀

Recall that an *exponent* tells you how many times a number, the *base*, has been used as a factor.

$8 \times 8 \times 8 \times 8 \times 8 = 8^5$

Base: 8   **Exponent:** 5

Read: "8 to the 5th *power*."

Explore   Scientific Notation

Lots of Naughts   **Materials:** Scientific calculator

1. Copy the table below. Continue the table for even exponents of 10 from 2 to 16. Use $\boxed{y^x}$ to find how the calculator displays numbers given in exponent form. Example: To find 10^2, use 10 $\boxed{y^x}$ 2 $\boxed{=}$.

Exponent Form	Number of Factors of 10	Calculator Display	Number of Zeros in Standard Form
10^2	2	100	2
10^4	4	10000	4

2. How does the number of zeros compare with the exponent?

3. Why doesn't the calculator display 1,000,000,000,000 for 10^{12}?

4. How would a calculator display 100,000,000,000,000,000,000?

You'll Learn ...

■ how to represent numbers in scientific notation

... How It's Used

Chemists use scientific notation to describe how cells grow over time.

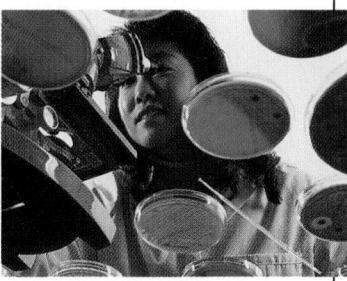

Vocabulary

scientific notation

▶ **Science Link**

Arachnophobia (a-rak-nuh-FOH-bee-uh) is the fear of spiders.

Learn   Scientific Notation

Spiders first appeared on Earth 350,000,000 years ago. Numbers like 350,000,000 can be hard to work with because they have so many zeros. Scientists use **scientific notation** as an easier way to write these numbers. A number in scientific notation is written as the product of a number greater than or equal to 1 but less than 10 and a power of 10.

To convert a number from scientific notation to standard form, move the decimal point to the right the same number of places as the power.

Scientific notation   **Standard form**

$$3.5 \times 10^8 = 350{,}000{,}000 \; \leftarrow \; \begin{array}{l} \textbf{3.5 with decimal point} \\ \textbf{moved 8 places to the right.} \end{array}$$

To convert a number from standard form to scientific notation, write the number as the product of two factors.

- The first factor is a number greater than or equal to 1 but less than 10.

- The second factor is a power of 10 in exponent form.

Standard form   **Scientific notation**
$$26{,}800 = \qquad 2.68 \times 10^4$$

| number with one digit before the decimal ↑ | ↑ power of 10 in exponent form |

Examples

1 Write 5.133×10^7 in standard form.

The exponent is 7. The decimal in the decimal number must be moved 7 places to the right.

$$5.133 \times 10^7 = 51{,}330{,}000$$

2 Write 437,000,000 in scientific notation.

$437{,}000{,}000 = 4.37 \times \underline{?}$ Write decimal factor.

The first factor must be a number with one digit to the left of the decimal. For 437,000,000, the first factor is 4.37.

The second factor is a power of 10. The exponent equals the number of places the decimal point moves to the left. For 437,000,000, it moves 8 places. The power of 10 is 10^8.

$$437{,}000{,}000 = 4.37 \times 10^8$$

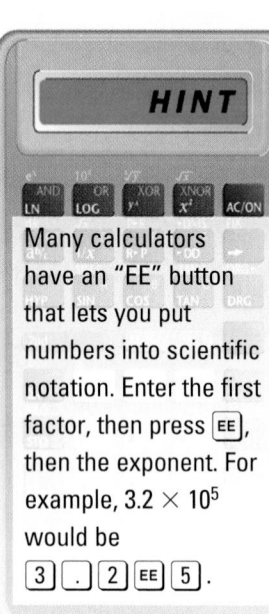

HINT

Many calculators have an "EE" button that lets you put numbers into scientific notation. Enter the first factor, then press $\boxed{\text{EE}}$, then the exponent. For example, 3.2×10^5 would be

$\boxed{3}\,\boxed{.}\,\boxed{2}\,\boxed{\text{EE}}\,\boxed{5}$.

Try It

Write in standard form.   **a.** 3×10^4 **b.** 9.062×10^{10}

Write in scientific notation.   **c.** 52,000   **d.** 1,740,000,000

Most calculators show scientific notation with an E (for exponent) instead of a power of 10. For example, 7.55 E 14 has the same meaning as 7.55×10^{14}, or 755,000,000,000,000.

1. Is 10^3 equal to 1000? Explain.

2. What advantages does scientific notation have over standard notation? What disadvantages does it have?

3-4 Exercises and Applications

Practice and Apply

1. **Getting Started** Write the missing exponent.

    a. $47,000 = 4.7 \times 10 \underline{?}$ **b.** $800,000 = 8 \times 10 \underline{?}$ **c.** $5380 = 5.38 \times 10 \underline{?}$

Write each number in standard form.

2. 8.3×10^3

3. 7.5×10^4

4. 6.7×10^6

5. 2×10^5

6. 6.89×10^4

7. 8.89×10^6

8. 2.3×10^2

9. 2.459×10^{12}

10. 1.02×10^2

11. 4.456×10^{11}

12. 2.405×10^{14}

13. 6.9×10^9

14. 7×10^{12}

15. 3.7×10^5

16. 2.33×10^4

17. 5.7×10^7

18. **Science** The adult human body contains 5×10^{13} cells. Write this number in standard form.

19. **Science** Scientists believe there may be 5×10^4 to 1×10^5 kinds of spiders. Write both numbers in standard form.

20. **Science** Large female spiders can lay more than 2×10^3 eggs at one time. Write this number in standard form.

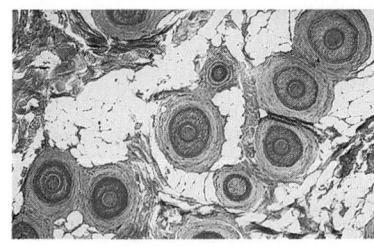

Write each number in scientific notation.

21. 5,000

22. 3,200

23. 160,000

24. 4,700,000

25. 7,900,000,000

26. 99,000,000,000

27. 51 million

28. 3 billion

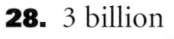

29. 6 trillion

30. 47,000

31. 500

32. 32,000,000

33. **Science** In some species, newborn spiders travel to other areas by making parachutes out of their silk thread. Sailors more than 12,000,000 feet out at sea have seen these "flying" spiders. Write the number in scientific notation.

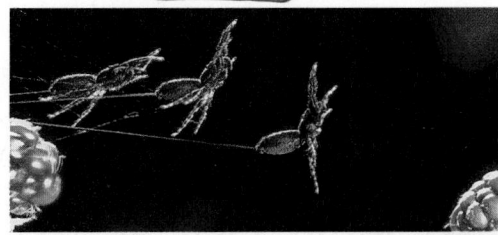

34. Social Science According to the *World Almanac*, there were 5.7 billion people on Earth in 1995. Write this number in scientific notation.

35. **Test Prep** Choose the correct scientific notation for 58,000,000.

Ⓐ 5.8×10^5　　Ⓑ 58×10^5　　Ⓒ 5.8×10^6　　Ⓓ 5.8×10^7

36. Science Complete the table.

Planet	km from Sun in Scientific Notation	km from Sun in Standard Form	km from Sun in Number-Word Form
Mercury	5.8×10^7		
Venus		110,000,000	
Earth			150 million
Mars	2.3×10^8		

Problem Solving and Reasoning

37. Communicate Explain why the correct scientific notation for 361,000 is 3.61×10^5, not 361×10^3.

38. **Journal** How is the number of zeros at the end of 45,000,000,000 related to the exponent in 4.5×10^{10}?

39. Critical Thinking What would be the standard form of 3.65×10^0? Explain.

40. Choose a Strategy In 1993, the U.S. Post Office released a large number of stamps picturing Elvis Presley. In scientific notation, the exponent is 8. The decimal factor has three digits, all of them odd. It's greater than 5.13, less than 5.19, and all the digits are different. How many Elvis Presley stamps were issued in 1993?

Problem Solving

STRATEGIES

- Look for a Pattern
- Make an Organized List
- Make a Table
- Guess and Check
- Work Backward
- Use Logical Reasoning
- Draw a Diagram
- Solve a Simpler Problem

Elvis Presley
Graceland Mansion
3764 Elvis Presley Blvd.
Memphis, TN 38116

Mixed Review

Find the median and the mode for the given data. *[Lesson 1-7]*

41. Number of minutes spent brushing teeth: 5, 7, 5, 3, 12, 8, 6, 8, 10, 11, 7

42. Number of left-handed students in each class: 3, 0, 2, 1, 1, 0, 2, 2, 0, 2

Solve. *[Lesson 2-13]*

43. $5h = 50$　　**44.** $m - 13 = 20$　　**45.** $20 + k = 32$　　**46.** $\dfrac{36}{b} = 6$

Section 3A Connect

In this section, you've seen how to use decimals to write numbers between whole numbers, as well as numbers in scientific notation. Now you will use this knowledge to plan a spider exhibit.

It Costs an Arm and a Leg ... and a Leg ... and a Leg ...

The local zoo is planning a new exhibit on spiders. The curator of the zoo wants you to help plan the exhibit for orb weavers. Most orb weavers spin spiraling orb webs on support lines that stretch out from the center. The table lists information on six types of orb weavers found in North America.

Name of Spider	Habitat	Length of Male Body (cm)	Length of Female Body (cm)
Barn spider	Barns, caves, mines	3.81	4.445
Shamrock spider	Meadows, woods	1.17	3.556
Garden spider	Gardens	2.413	3.175
Marbled orb weaver	Meadows, shrubs	2.405	3.558
Golden-silk spider	Shaded woods, swamps	1.016	5.969
Silver argiope	Fields, gardens	1.143	3.56

1. Order the spiders by (a) length of male and (b) length of female.

2. Choose one spider. If males were placed end-to-end, about how many would fit along a meterstick? How many females would fit along a meterstick? Explain how you made your estimate.

3. The curator expects 4.5×10^4 people to visit the exhibit during the first year. The staff arachnologist expects 2.3×10^5 people. Who is expecting more people? Explain.

Section 3A Review

all

Write each as a decimal.

26.5   *.63*

1. $\frac{7}{10}$ *.7*   **2.** $\frac{49}{100}$ *.49*   **3.** twenty-six and five-tenths   **4.** sixty-three hundredths

Measurement Measure each length to the nearest centimeter.

5.

6.

Round to the underlined place value.

7. 0.1<u>4</u>   **8.** 0.3<u>5</u>1   **9.** 2.4<u>1</u>7   **10.** 0.08<u>1</u>3   **11.** 6.<u>9</u>68   **12.** 1.98<u>2</u>7

0.1   *.35*   *2.42*   *.081*   *07.0*   *1.183*

13. Technology Computer memory is measured in bytes. The three usual measures are kilobytes (KB: 10^3 bytes), megabytes (MB: 10^6 bytes), and gigabytes (GB: 10^9 bytes).

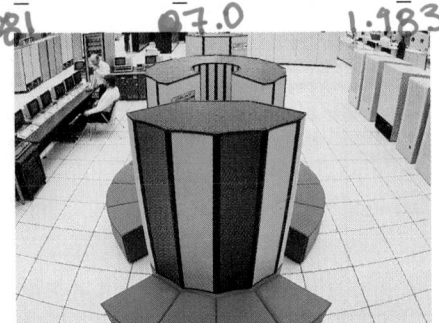

a. Write each measure of bytes in standard form.

b. A Cray Computer has 2.4 gigabytes of memory. Write the number in scientific notation.

Write each number in standard form.

14. 7×10^3 **15.** 1.2×10^8 ✓**16.** 2.92×10^5 **17.** 5.6×10^5 **18.** 1×10^{11}

Write each number in scientific notation.

✓**19.** 45 billion   **20.** 480,000   **21.** 6,780,000   **22.** 63 trillion

23. 60,000,000   **24.** 320,000   **25.** 56,900   **26.** 41 thousand

Test Prep

Remember that in scientific notation, a number with a large exponent is bigger than a number with a small exponent.

27. Which of the following statements is true?

Ⓐ $3.4 \times 10^5 > 4.7 \times 10^3$ Ⓑ $3.4 \times 10^5 = 4.7 \times 10^3$ Ⓒ $3.4 \times 10^5 < 4.7 \times 10^3$

Getting Your Money's Worth

Bicycle wanted.
Willing to pay 70,500
Turkish lira.

I'm looking to buy a used bicycle. Can pay 3 Egyptian pounds.

I have 770 South Korean won. You have a used bicycle for sale.
Let's trade!

Used bicycle needed desperately! Looking to spend 10 Austrian shillings.

Which person would you be willing to sell your bicycle to? Don't be too quick to sell to any of them. They're all offering less than one American dollar!

Just as many different languages are spoken throughout the world, many different types of money are used throughout the world. Each type of money, or currency, has a different value, and those values change. One year, an American dollar might be equal to 200 Japanese yen. The next year, that same American dollar might be worth 300 yen, or 100 yen.

People need to understand how to work with decimal numbers to make good decisions about money. Would you rather sell your camera for 4000 South African rands or 4000 Russian rubles? That depends on whether the camera is worth $1000, or 84¢.

1 What are the names of units of currency other than the American dollar?

2 Why don't all the countries of the world agree on a single type of money?

3 How does understanding decimal numbers help you to work with money?

Estimating with Decimals

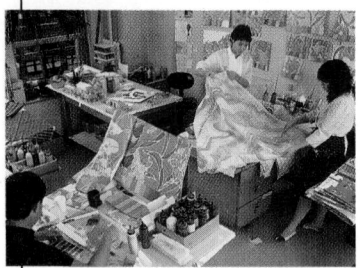

▶ **Lesson Link**   In the last chapter, you used several ways to estimate sums, differences, products, and quotients with whole numbers. Now you'll use some of those same methods to estimate with decimals. ◀

Explore   Estimating with Decimals

Miso, Dal, and Apple Pie

Here's the menu for International Night at North Side Middle School:

1. Decide whether you can buy each meal for the given price. You may not use paper and pencil or a calculator. Instead, estimate the sum. There are no tips or sales tax.

   A. Miso soup, dal, lasagna, apple pie: $11

   B. Tabouli salad, stuffed zucchini, sauerbraten: $7

   C. Egg rolls, chicken molé, halava: $8

   D. Tabouli salad, stuffed grape leaves, lasagna, pound cake: $10

2. For each meal, state whether you are "certain," "somewhat certain," or "not certain" that you made the correct decision.

Learn   Estimating with Decimals

You can use *rounding* to estimate sums and differences with decimals. Most of the time, people round decimal values to the closest whole number. To be more accurate, they round to the closest tenth.

Example 1

While vacationing in Australia, Tanya saw a poster for $4.50 and a shirt for $14.95 that she wanted to buy. She had $20. Was it enough?

$4.50 → $5.00
$14.95 → $15.00   Round each number to the nearest dollar.
          $20.00   Add.

The cost was about $20. Since Tanya rounded up, the actual sum is less than the estimate. Tanya had enough to buy the poster and the shirt.

You can also use rounding to estimate a decimal product or quotient. Rounded numbers may not be easier to use than the original numbers.

$$36.95 \div 7.39 = ?$$
$$\downarrow \qquad \downarrow$$
$$37 \div 7 = ?$$

For that reason, *compatible numbers* often work better for estimating decimal products and quotients.

Examples

2 Estimate 9.88×23.15.

9.88 → 10
23.15 → 23   Choose numbers compatible for multiplying.

$10 \times 23 = 230$

3 Estimate $158.75 \div 28.95$.

158.75 → 150
28.95 → 30   Choose numbers compatible for dividing.

$150 \div 30 = 5$

Try It

Estimate each sum, difference, product, or quotient.

a. $14.63 + $19.26   **b.** $58.37 - 22.84$ **c.** 67.52×9.18 **d.** $47.13 \div 6.4$

Check Your Understanding

1. How can you decide whether a decimal estimate is high or low?

2. Some problems involving decimals require an exact answer. For others, an estimate is good enough. Give an example of each.

Practice and Apply

1. **Getting Started** Choose the better estimate.

   a. 5.417 × 8.53; 40 or 50

   b. 124.93 ÷ 5.17; 20 or 25

   c. 39.76 − 30.02; 10 or 15

   d. 0.53 + 3.6029; 5 or 7

Estimate each sum, difference, product, or quotient.

2. $31.27 + $18.52
3. $5.93 − $3.68
4. $4.98 × 9
5. 39.43 ÷ 8
6. 10.581 − 1.203
7. 6.53 + 2.48
8. 15.391 − 8.67
9. 62.3 × 4.9
10. 27.32 × 4.09
11. $7.84 × 28
12. 30.49 ÷ 4.7
13. 31.23 ÷ 5.1
14. 35.617 + 0.816
15. 89.632 − 47.32
16. 14.32 × 2.26
17. 36.26 + 36.7
18. $8.47 − $1.26
19. 1.628 × 82.09
20. 23.42 + 89.67
21. 27.83 × 62.9
22. 65.298 + 14.83
23. $102.36 ÷ 48.2
24. 63.501 − 3.999
25. 37.32 ÷ 5.99
26. 0.756 + 63.5
27. 93.278 × 86.059
28. 12.89 − 10.432
29. 45.01 × 16.3
30. 67.8425 + 13.67
31. 321.8 ÷ 28.45
32. $19.59 − $5.95
33. 54.69 ÷ 11.9

Number Sense Use the picture for Exercises 34 and 35.

34. About how many CDs could you buy with $40? With only $20?

35. One week the music store sold 35 copies of the "Cry of the Loons" CD. Estimate how much money the store collected from those sales.

36. **Test Prep** Choose the best estimate of 675.324 + 24.9645.

    Ⓐ 675   Ⓑ 699

    Ⓒ 700   Ⓓ 725

37. A recipe required 18.5 ounces of pineapple. Raphael had three and a half 5.4-ounce cans. Did he have enough pineapple for the recipe?

38. Karima had $50. She looked at a coat for $34.99 and a pair of shoes for $17.45. Did she have enough money for both items?

39. Health Carlos's dad uses a pedometer to determine how far he walks. He walked 16.4 km in 5 days. Estimate about how far he went each day.

Problem Solving and Reasoning

40. Critical Thinking Joe used estimation to solve these problems. For each problem, explain how Joe might have arrived at his estimate.

    a. $0.78 + 0.39 \approx 1.2$

    b. $0.45 \times 0.6 \approx 0.24$

    c. $\$21.16 - \$12.41 \approx \$10$

41. Communicate Bev estimated $71.69 \div 8.51$ to be about 9. Write a note to Bev to explain why 9 is not a good estimate. What is a better estimate?

42. Critical Thinking You bought four pairs of pants at the same price. Based on rounding, your estimate of the total cost was $40 before tax.

    a. If you rounded to the nearest dollar, what is the maximum price for each pair? Explain.

    b. If you rounded to the nearest dollar, what is the minimum price? Explain.

43.  Describe a situation involving money where it makes more sense to round up than down. Describe a situation involving money where it makes more sense to round down.

Mixed Review

Find the mean of each set of data. *[Lesson 1-8]*

44. 135, 136, 132, 137, 130, 131, 135   **45.** 72, 68, 55, 62, 70, 69, 57, 72

Write each fraction as a decimal. *[Lesson 3-1]*

46. $\dfrac{78}{100}$ **47.** $\dfrac{32}{100}$ **48.** $\dfrac{3}{10}$ **49.** $\dfrac{789}{1000}$ **50.** $\dfrac{560}{1000}$ **51.** $\dfrac{5}{100}$

Project Progress

Take your expenses and group them into categories. For example, you might have a category for "food." Total the amount of money spent in each category.

Problem Solving

Understand
Plan
Solve
Look Back

Adding and Subtracting Decimal Numbers

You'll Learn ...

■ how to add and subtract with decimals

... How It's Used

Pilots have to add decimal amounts to determine how far they've flown.

▶ **Lesson Link**   In the last lesson, you estimated the solutions to problems involving decimals. Now you will find sums and differences exactly. ◀

Explore | **Adding and Subtracting Decimal Numbers**

Square Dance

Materials: Hundreds grids, Colored pencils

Adding Decimals

- Color the tenths for the first number.
- Color the tenths for the second number.
- Color the hundredths for the first number.
- Color the hundredths for the second number.
- Describe the number modeled in the grid.

$$\begin{array}{r} 0.14 \\ +\ 0.67 \\ \hline 0.81 \end{array}$$

1. Model these problems.

   a. $0.35 + 0.42$ **b.** $0.63 + 0.20$ **c.** $0.16 + 0.77$ **d.** $0.85 + 0.07$

Subtracting Decimals

- Color the first number.
- Cross out the second number from the first number.
- Describe the amount left over in the grid.

$$\begin{array}{r} 0.75 \\ -\ 0.36 \\ \hline 0.39 \end{array}$$

2. Model these problems.

   a. $0.68 - 0.27$ **b.** $0.93 - 0.40$

   c. $0.52 - 0.19$ **d.** $0.88 - 0.49$

3. In the problem $0.07 + 0.03 = 0.10$, the numbers being added both have hundredths. When you add them together, why are there no hundredths in the answer?

4. In the problem $0.52 - 0.08 = 0.44$, how can you take eight hundredths away from the first number when the first number only has a "2" in the hundredths place?

Learn   Adding and Subtracting Decimal Numbers

When you add, you must make sure you're adding tenths to tenths, hundredths to hundredths, and so on. To do this, line up the decimal points. Then add as if you were adding whole numbers.

Example 1

Add 1.7 and 2.49.

Estimate: 2 + 2 = 4.

Line up the decimal points.

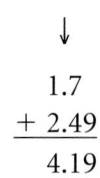

$$
\begin{array}{r}
1.7 \\
+\ 2.49 \\
\hline
4.19
\end{array}
$$

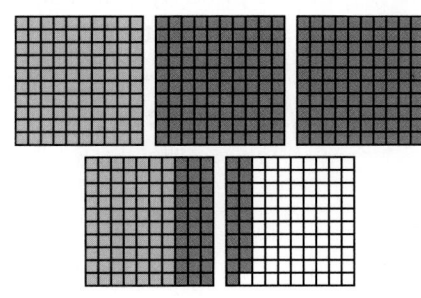

Use the same plan when subtracting decimals. Line up the decimal points, and then subtract as if you were subtracting whole numbers. Annex zeros if the second number has more digits after the decimal than the first.

Example 2

The United Kingdom uses a decimal currency based on the *pound* (£). Paul has £1.8. Edmund has only £1.38. How many more pounds does Paul have?

Subtract to find the difference.

Estimate to tenths: 1.8 − 1.4 = 0.4.

Line up the decimal points.

$$
\begin{array}{r}
1.80 \\
-\ 1.38 \\
\hline
0.42
\end{array}
$$
Annex zeros.

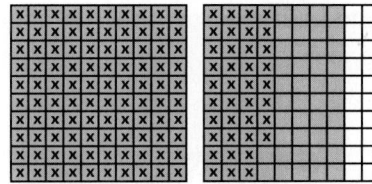

Paul has £0.42 more than Edmund.

Remember

Annexing zeros to the right of a decimal number does not change the value of the number.
[Page 148]

Try It

Find the sum or difference.

a. 4.631 + 3.986   **b.** 8.592 − 4.635   **c.** 5.6 + 1.973   **d.** 7.3 − 4.45

You may want to check your answer to a decimal subtraction problem. You can do this by adding the second number in the subtraction problem to the answer. The sum should be the first number in the problem.

The Sports Center in Vancouver, Canada, sells Crown croquet sets for $34.70. The Athletic Club sells them for $49.85. A Sports Center ad claims that they beat the Athletic Club's price by $25. Van and Lauren want to know if the claim is correct.

Van thinks . . .

I'll subtract.

$$\begin{array}{r} 49.85 \\ -\ 34.70 \\ \hline 15.15 \end{array}$$

The claim is wrong.

Lauren thinks . . .

I'll estimate by rounding 49.85 to 50 and 34.70 to 35.

50 − 35 = 15. My estimate is close to the actual difference.

The claim is wrong.

What do you think?

1. Which method would you use to verify the claim? Why?

2. How did Lauren know that her estimate was close to the actual difference?

Check | Your Understanding

1. Why is it important to line up the decimal points when adding or subtracting decimal numbers?

2. How can you check to see if you have added or subtracted two decimal numbers accurately?

Practice and Apply

1. **Getting Started** Choose the equation that the grid models.

a.

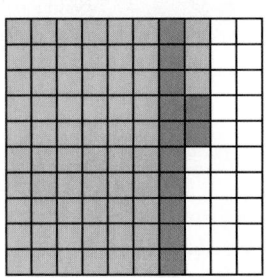

i. $0.63 + 0.12 = 0.75$

ii. $0.63 + 0.21 = 0.51$

b.

i. $0.80 - 0.28 = 0.99$

ii. $0.80 - 0.19 = 0.61$

c.

i. $0.06 + 0.04 = 0.10$

ii. $0.06 + 0.04 = 1.00$

Simplify.

2. $3.56 + 8.75$

3. $94.716 - 47.81$

4. $34.982 - 8.52$

5. $8.2 + 0.2$

6. $7.5 - 0.492$

7. $\$25 - \$13.75$

8. $23.05 + 67.06$

9. $12.904 + 13$

10. $3.06 + 4.902$

11. $78.234 - 12.0056$

12. $14 - 7.95$

13. $0.001 + 0.06$

14. $3.2 - 1.2$

15. $\$38 - \$27.99$

16. $74.008 + 1.021$

17. $11.6 + 2.78$

18. $54.81 + 54.81$

19. $506 - 63.8178$

20. $60.49 - 44.72$

21. $34.8 + 6.89$

22. $700.01 - 34.906$

23. $93.952 - 89.005$

24. $7960 + 3245$

25. $10.678 + 5$

26. $\$4.26 + \$32.07 + \$0.52$

27. $6.3 + 7.23 + 29.1$

28. $50 + 2.852 + 13.6$

29. $\$72.61 + \$1.45 + \$2.51$

30. $4.5 + 2.78 + 30.01$

31. $7.8 + 80 + 16.87$

32. **Consumer** One day, 1 Japanese yen was worth 0.0098 U.S. dollars. The same day, a Swedish krona was worth 0.1297 U.S. dollars.

   a. How much more was the krona worth than the yen?

   b. On the same day, 1 Thai baht was worth 0.0398 U.S. dollars. How much U.S. money equals one baht plus one yen?

33. **Test Prep** Sam has 0.25 cup of milk, 0.333 cup of water, and 0.01 cup of vanilla. When he mixes the ingredients, how much liquid does he have?

   Ⓐ 0.359 cup   Ⓑ 1.143 cups

   Ⓒ 0.55 cup   Ⓓ 0.593 cup

PRACTICE 3-6

34. Model trains come in various sizes. G-gauge track is 5.3975 cm wide. O-gauge track is 3.175 cm wide. N-gauge track is 0.79375 cm wide.

a. How much wider is G-gauge track than O-gauge track?

b. How much wider is O-gauge track than N-gauge track?

Problem Solving and Reasoning

35. **Critical Thinking** You and your friend won a radio contest and get to be DJs for part of a day. You must put together a 15-minute segment of consecutive songs chosen from the list. No more than 2 minutes can be left at the end of the set.

a. Which songs would you pick?

b. How much time would the songs use?

c. How much time do you have left at the end of your segment?

d. What is the maximum number of songs that you could choose to fill 15 minutes?

36. **Critical Thinking** Use each of the digits 0–9 exactly once. Make two decimal numbers whose sum is close to 2 and whose difference is close to 1.

SONGS	TIME
Born in the USA (Bruce Springsteen)	4.65 min
On Bended Knee (Boyz II Men)	5.48 min
Old Time Rock and Roll (Bob Seger)	3.21 min
I Only Want To Be With You (Hootie and the Blowfish)	3.76 min
Are You Ready For This? (B2 Unlimited)	3.77 min
YMCA (Village People)	3.48 min

37.  Explain the similarities and differences between adding and subtracting whole numbers and adding and subtracting decimal numbers.

Mixed Review

Find the mean, median, and modes with and without the outlier. *[Lesson 1-9]*

38. 45, 46, 47, 42, 45, 50, 50, 115

39. 23, 68, 19, 22, 19, 20, 21, 20

40. 10, 10, 10, 12, 12, 11, 11, 11, 18

41. 42, 38, 39, 40, 41, 37, 2, 35, 35

Round to the given place value. *[Lesson 3-2]*

42. 0.273, hundredths

43. 5.998, thousandths

44. 62.73, tenths

45. 34.5, ones

46. 2.006, hundredths

47. 0.156, tenths

Solving Decimal Equations: Addition and Subtraction

▶ **Lesson Link** You've used mental math to solve equations involving whole numbers. Now you'll use the same method to solve addition and subtraction equations involving decimals. ◀

Explore Missing Lengths

Where in the World ...?

These diagrams show the measurements of two sides of a triangle. The total distance around the triangle is also given.

Distance = 19.8
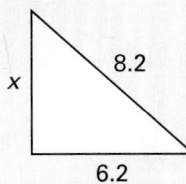

Distance = 16.2
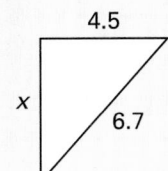

Distance = 19.3
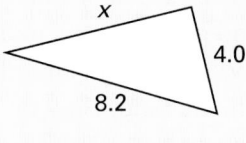

Distance = 14.7
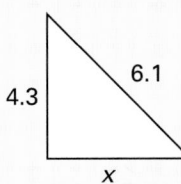

Distance = 23.3
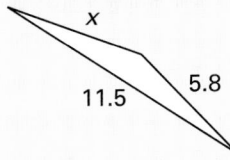

Distance = 27.6
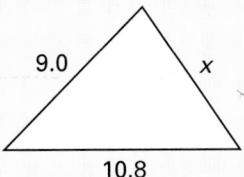

You'll Learn ...
■ to solve equations that involve adding and subtracting decimals

... How It's Used

Store managers use decimal equations to determine how much to subtract from the price of an item on sale.

Value of x   5.0   4.3   6.0   5.4   7.1   7.8

1. Match each diagram to the correct value of x.

2. Choose one diagram and write an equation using addition that describes the diagram.

3. Choose a different diagram and write an equation using subtraction that describes the diagram.

4. Can each diagram be described with both an addition equation and a subtraction equation? Explain.

Recall that you can solve addition and subtraction equations with whole numbers using mental math. You can also solve equations with decimals in the same way.

Examples

1 Solve $x + 2.3 = 3.4$.

$x + 2.3 = 3.4$ Read as "What number plus 2.3 equals 3.4?"

$\mathbf{1.1} + 2.3 = 3.4$ Use mental math.

$3.4 = 3.4 ✓$ Check to see that the equation is true.

The value of x is 1.1.

2 Jean planned to hike the Mount Wolf trail. The first day, she hiked 8 miles. The second day, she reached the end of the trail, where a sign stated the trail was 10.6 miles long. How far did she hike the second day?

Let x = the distance Jean hiked the second day.

$8 + x = 10.6$ Read as "What number plus 8 equals 10.6?"

$8 + \mathbf{2.6} = 10.6$ Use mental math.

$10.6 = 10.6 ✓$ Check to see that the equation is true.

Jean hiked 2.6 miles the second day.

> **Problem Solving TIP**
>
> You can also solve the problem by using subtraction to work backwards. What is $10.6 - 8$?

Try It

Solve each equation. **a.** $x + 9.4 = 19.5$ **b.** $n - 0.5 = 10.1$

c. $j + 7.1 = 12.2$ **d.** $p - 2.0 = 0.2$

Check | Your Understanding

1. Would you solve $4.3 + x = 7.7$ the same way you'd solve $x + 4.3 = 7.7$? Explain.

2. Give a real-world problem modeled by $n - 2.5 = 15.3$.

Practice and Apply

1. **Getting Started** State if each equation is true or false for $h = 1.4$.

    a. $h - 1.3 = 0.1$ **b.** $h + 2.4 = 4.0$ **c.** $0.6 + h = 2.0$ **d.** $5.8 - h = 3.4$

Solve.

2. $11.6 - b = 8.3$ **3.** $0.12 + d = 0.52$ **4.** $\$75.40 + n = \$100$

5. $x + 5.7 = 13.8$ **6.** $y - 10.1 = 60$ **7.** $u + \$12.60 = \$14.97$

8. $25.001 - n = 24$ **9.** $w + 7.4 = 35.6$ **10.** $p - 4.01 = 15.08$

11. $1.12 + a = 2.34$ **12.** $0.06 - v = 0.02$ **13.** $c + 14.99 = 15.01$

14. $e + 4.35 = 10.5$ **15.** $\$16.75 + f = \$20$ **16.** $g + 8.7 = 10.1$

17. $i - 42.7 = 45$ **18.** $j + 0.088 = 0.099$ **19.** $m - 0.035 = 0.053$

20. $r + 32.45 = 62.78$ **21.** $3.43 - w = 1.11$ **22.** $k + \$66.45 = \$76.90$

23. $100.7 - z = 40.7$ **24.** $l - 682 = 0.251$ **25.** $t + 1.33 = 2$

Geometry Given the distance around the shape, find the length of the unknown side.

26. Total distance: 25.5 m

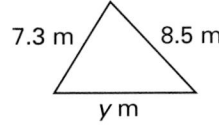

7.3 m   8.5 m

y m

27. Total distance: 40 cm

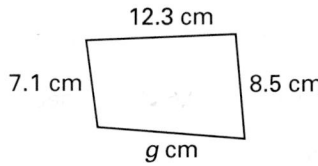

12.3 cm

7.1 cm   8.5 cm

g cm

28. **Operation Sense** Jorge won a cash prize in a contest. He donated half of the money to his Boy Scout troop. Then he spent $19.49 on a computer game and put the rest, $30.51, into his savings account. How much money did he win?

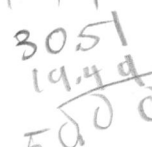

29. **Test Prep** Choose the correct value for x: $x + 2.91 = 4.01$.

    Ⓐ 1.1   Ⓑ 2.9

    Ⓒ 2.11   Ⓓ 6.92

Career When a store buys something at one price and then sells it at a higher price, the difference in prices is called the *profit.* For Exercises 30 and 31, write and solve an equation for the situation.

30. A store owner obtained a jacket for $46.25 and sold it for $66.75. What was the profit?

31. A pair of tennis shoes cost the store owner $26.49. She wants to make a profit of $18.50. What should the selling price be?

Problem Solving and Reasoning

32. Critical Thinking In West Lafayette, the fine for a speeding ticket in dollars is $32.62 + x$, where x is the miles per hour over the speed limit.

   a. What is the fine for going 38.6 mi/hr in a 25 mi/hr school zone?

   b. Ed was fined $50.50 for speeding in this school zone. How fast was he traveling?

33. Communicate Study the pattern:

$$x + 3.2 = 9.2$$
$$x + 6.4 = 12.4$$
$$x + 9.6 = 15.6$$

   a. What is the value of x?

   b. What are the next three equations in this pattern?

   c. Invent your own pattern using addition of decimals and $x = 8$.

34. Critical Thinking Maurice has 30 m of fence to make a rectangular dog run. The width can only be 3.75 m because of the shape of his yard. What is the maximum length of the dog run?

35. Choose a Strategy Brandi, Molly, and Leah have a total of $4.25. Brandi has a dollar more than Molly. Brandi has twice as much as Leah. How much money does each girl have?

Problem Solving
STRATEGIES

• Look for a Pattern
• Make an Organized List
• Make a Table
• Guess and Check
• Work Backward
• Use Logical Reasoning
• Draw a Diagram
• Solve a Simpler Problem

Mixed Review

Order from least to greatest. *[Lesson 3-3]*

36. 4.663, 4.664, 4.65

37. 0.123, 0.672, 1.784

38. 32.5, 32.67, 32.495

Write each number in word form. *[Lesson 2-1]*

39. 560,326,700,000

40. 4,983,228

41. 2,892,000,362,421

42. 763,218

In this section, you've seen that many countries use different types of money. In order to convert one kind of money to another, you need to know the *exchange rate*. You'll have a chance to use exchange rates— and your knowledge of decimals—to plan a trip to five nations.

Getting Your Money's Worth

Country	Basic Unit	Value of One Unit in U.S. Dollars ($)	Number of Units One U.S. Dollar Will Buy
Belgium	Franc	0.03258	30.693
Chile	Peso	0.00243	410.80
China	Yuan	0.12038	8.3071
Colombia	Peso	0.00096	1046.50
India	Rupee	0.02802	35.695
Indonesia	Rupiah	0.00043	2340.70
Ireland	Punt	1.62054	0.61708
Nigeria	Naira	0.01264	79.10
Pakistan	Rupee	0.02807	35.6189
Switzerland	Franc	0.82816	1.2075

1. List five countries from the table that you would like to visit.

2. You plan to spend $200 U.S. in each country. Estimate the amount of each country's money you will get in exchange for your $200 U.S.

3. After your trip, you have 3 units of each country's money left to exchange for U.S. dollars. For each country, state how much the 3 units are worth in U.S. dollars. Round to the nearest cent.

4. How much of the $1000 you started with did you spend?

Section 3B Review

Measurement Estimate the height to the nearest tenth of a centimeter.

1.

2.

3.

Write each number in decimal form.

4. thirty-five hundredths

5. two and five tenths

6. sixty-four thousandths

7.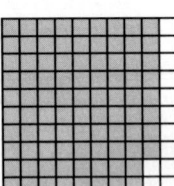

8.

9.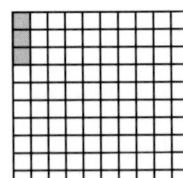

10.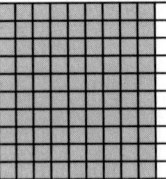

Simplify.

11. $4.5 + 23.9$

12. $8.65 - 4.2$

13. $3.05 + 2.111$

14. $6.01 - 2.222$

Geometry Find the distance around the shape.

15.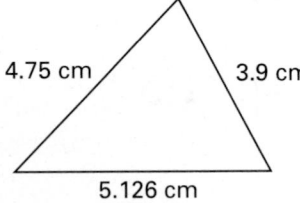

4.75 cm   3.9 cm

5.126 cm

16.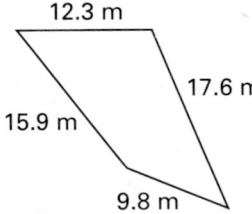

12.3 m

17.6 m

15.9 m

9.8 m

Solve.

17. $x - 7.2 = 16.85$

18. $y + 12.52 = 19.37$

19. $9.8 + n = 27.3$

Test Prep

Estimation can help to confirm that you've done the problem correctly as well as help eliminate unreasonable answers.

20. Choose the correct answer for $9.56 + 5.77$.

Ⓐ 0.1533   Ⓑ 1.533   Ⓒ 15.33   Ⓓ 153.3

REVIEW 3B

Multiplying and Dividing with Decimals

Trials and Trails

Imagine that your family is driving from Missouri to Oregon.

"Dad, how long until we get to Oregon?"

"About two months."

"Can we ride inside the car today?"

"Don't be silly. If we do that, where will we put our stuff?"

"We're out of food."

"If we walk quickly, we should be at the next store tomorrow. Ask Mom for a vinegar drink."

"We left Mom in Nebraska when she got sick."

Does this sound like an odd conversation?

If you replace the word car with wagon, it could be an ordinary conversation for pioneers on the Oregon Trail.

In the 1800s, more than a quarter of a million people traveled this dangerous trail to the western United States. They faced disease and harsh weather while walking this 2000-mile trail with nothing more than a wagon and a team of oxen. Fortunately, those early pioneers had one advanced tool at their disposal: mathematics.

1 How is a trip from Missouri to Oregon different today than it was in the 1800s?

2 Why do you think so many people in the 1800s chose to move west, even though the journey was so difficult?

3 How could mathematics help pioneers in the 1800s?

Multiplying a Whole Number by a Decimal

You'll Learn ...

■ how to multiply a whole number by a decimal

... How It's Used

Civil engineers multiply with decimals to find how much weight a bridge can support.

▶ **Lesson Link**   You know how to multiply whole numbers, and you know how to add decimals. Now you'll multiply a whole number by a decimal. ◀

Explore Multiplying a Whole Number by a Decimal

You Too Can Be a Model Student!

Materials: Hundreds squares, Colored pencils

Multiplying a Whole Number by a Decimal

- Color the tenths for the decimal number. Do this as many times as the whole number.

- Color the hundredths for the decimal number. Do this as many times as the whole number.

$$\begin{array}{r} 0.41 \\ \times\ \ 3 \end{array}$$

- Describe the number modeled in the grid.

1. Model these problems.

a. 2×0.30	**b.** 3×0.14	**c.** 4×0.44	**d.** 6×0.27
e. 7×0.09	**f.** 5×0.20	**g.** 9×0.22	**h.** 0×0.68

2. When you multiply a whole number by a decimal less than one with tenths and no hundredths, does your answer have tenths? Hundredths? Why?

3. When you multiply a whole number by a decimal less than one with hundredths and no tenths, does your answer have tenths? Hundredths? Why?

4. When you multiply a decimal and a whole number, is your answer larger than the whole number or smaller than the whole number?

Learn Multiplying a Whole Number by a Decimal

Recall that multiplication is repeated addition. Multiplying a whole number by a decimal is the same as repeatedly adding the decimal to itself the same number of times as the whole number.

Example 1

Multiply 2.5 × 3.

One way to find the product is to add 2.5 three times:

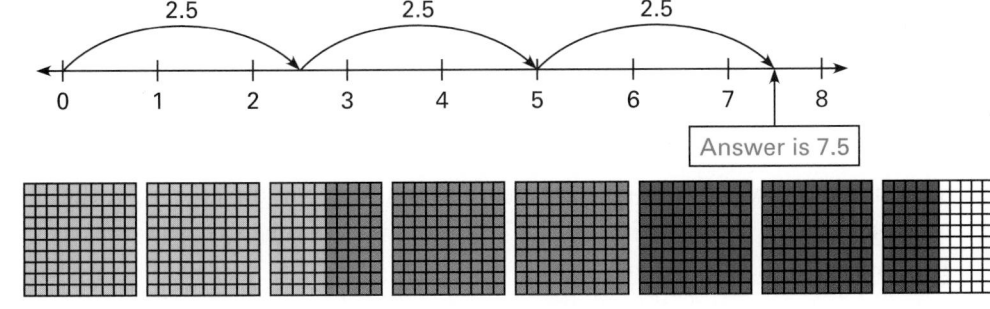

Answer is 7.5

2.5 × 3 = 7.5

You can use arithmetic to multiply a whole number by a decimal. Multiply as though you were multiplying two whole numbers. Then count the number of digits after the decimal in the decimal factor. Place the decimal in the answer so that the answer has the same number of digits after the decimal.

$$\begin{array}{r} 43 \\ \times\ 0.27 \\ \hline 301 \\ 86\ \ \\ \hline 11.61 \end{array}$$

M E N T A L   M A T H

You can also use the Distributive Property. Add the whole numbers three times: 2 + 2 + 2 = 6. Add the decimal parts three times: 0.5 + 0.5 + 0.5 = 1.5. Add 6 and 1.5 to get 7.5.

Example 2

On the Oregon Trail, each family member over 10 years of age was given 1.5 cups of beans per day. When the Conyers family traveled the trail in 1852, all seven members were over 10. How many cups of beans did the family eat each day?

$$\begin{array}{r} 1.5 \\ \times\ 7 \\ \hline 105 \end{array}$$ Multiply as for whole numbers.

There is one digit after the decimal in the decimal factor, 1.5.

The product should have one digit after the decimal → 10.5.

The family ate 10.5 cups of beans per day.

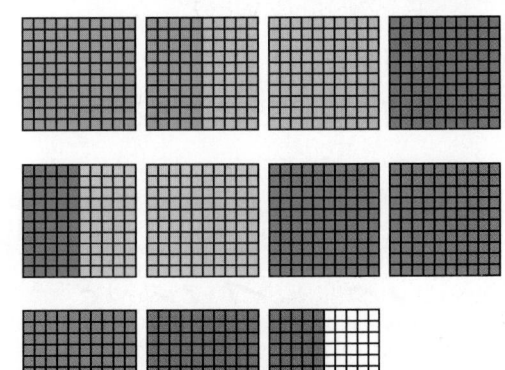

► **History Link**

People were always searching for faster ways to travel west. During the California gold rush of 1849, some people took ships across the Gulf of Mexico to the Isthmus of Panama. They crossed the land to the Pacific Ocean and took another ship up to California.

Example 3

Multiply 4.71 × 23.

Estimate: 4.71 × 23 ≈ 5 × 25 = 125

$$
\begin{array}{r}
4.71 \\
\times\ 23 \\
\hline
1413 \\
942 \\
\hline
10833
\end{array}
$$

Since there are two digits after the decimal in the decimal factor 4.<u>71</u>, the product is 108.<u>33</u>. The estimate of 125 confirms that this is reasonable.

Remember

If you annex zeros to the end of a decimal, you do not change its value. **[Page 148]**

Use these shortcuts to multiply a number by 10, 100, or 1000:

- To multiply by 10, move the decimal point one place to the right.
- To multiply by 100, move the decimal point two places to the right.
- To multiply by 1000, move the decimal point three places to the right.

   You may need to annex zeros to the number if there aren't enough places to move the decimal to the right.

Example 4

▶ History Link

Mailing letters in the 1800s by Pony Express was expensive. It cost $10 to mail a 1-ounce letter. For the same price, you could buy 100 pounds of bacon.

Pony Express riders carried mail in a leather saddle bag called a *mochila*. A rider normally carried about 1000 letters, each weighing 0.6 oz. Find the weight of the mail in a mochila.

0.6 × 1000 = ?

↓ Annex zeros so you can move the decimal point.

0.600 = 600

↑ Move decimal point three places to the right.

The weight was about 600 oz.

Try It

Multiply. **a.** 1.2 × 4   **b.** 0.6 × 7   **c.** 9.813 × 12   **d.** 0.62 × 100

Check | Your Understanding

1. Which is greater, 5 × 0.03 or 5 × 0.003? Explain.

2. A number has three places after the decimal. If you multiply the number by 100, how many decimal places will the product have?

3-8 Exercises and Applications

Practice and Apply

1. **Getting Started** Choose the equation that the grid models.

a.

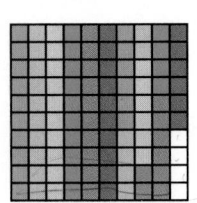

i. $6 \times 0.16 = 0.96$

ii. $5 \times 0.16 = 0.80$

b.

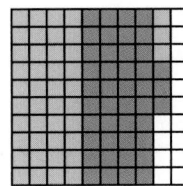

i. $2 \times 0.19 = 0.38$

ii. $2 \times 0.43 = 0.86$

c.

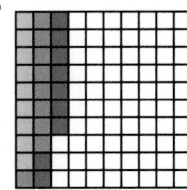

i. $3 \times 0.09 = 0.27$

ii. $6 \times 0.03 = 0.18$

Insert a decimal in each answer to make the equation true.

2. $76.89 \times 23 = 176847$

3. $4 \times 8.53 = 3412$

4. $5.6 \times 72 = 4032$

5. $3.004 \times 8 = 24032$

6. $9 \times 3.33 = 2997$

7. $14 \times 62.345 = 87283$

Multiply.

8. 10×3.578

9. 100×3.578

10. 1000×3.578

11. 8.7×6

12. 13.9×7

13. 143×6.1

14. 448×0.2

15. $\$86.15 \times 7$

16. $\$6.85 \times 19$

17. 415×0.031

18. 5.283×46

19. 8.07×10

20. 100×74.4

21. 3.85×1000

22. 10×0.059

23. $\$25.39 \times 100$

Oregon Trail

24. In 1843, in Independence, Missouri, Teresa bought 6 chocolate bars for her family. Each bar was 0.8 oz. How many ounces did she buy?

25. In 1847, at St. Joseph, Missouri, Reuben sold bushels of dried apples for $1.50 a bushel. How much would 4 bushels cost?

PRACTICE 3-8

26. History Salt was a valuable possession to the travelers of the Oregon Trail. It improved the taste of the food and took little space to store. According to the graph, how much salt did the Olsen family use on July 4?

Salt Used in Early July

Salt Used (lb) vs. Date in July

27. **Test Prep** Choose the correct answer for 5.69×29.

Ⓐ 1.6501   Ⓑ 16.501

Ⓒ 165.01   Ⓓ 16,501

28. History A wagon train on the Oregon Trail averaged 17.3 miles per day across the plains. How far did it get in a week?

Problem Solving and Reasoning

29. Critical Thinking Jamie wants to buy 5.4 feet of wood for a bookshelf. The wood costs $3 a foot, and Jamie has $17.50. Does he have enough for all the wood he wants? Explain.

31. Communicate Compare the products of 231×6, 23.1×6, and 2.31×6. Explain where the decimal is in each answer.

32. Communicate You meet someone along the trail who never learned how to multiply. He wants to buy 6 wagon wheels from you at $2.75 each. How would you explain to him that $6 \times \$2.75 = \$16.50$?

30. Choose a Strategy Andrea drinks 54.3 ounces of milk every week. She also drinks a 6-ounce can of orange juice and 8 glasses of water every day. If she drinks 544.3 ounces of liquid in a week and every glass of water is the same size, how big is each glass of water?

Problem Solving

STRATEGIES

• Look for a Pattern
• Make an Organized List
• Make a Table
• Guess and Check
• Work Backward
• Use Logical Reasoning
• Draw a Diagram
• Solve a Simpler Problem

Mixed Review

Order each group of numbers from least to greatest. *[Lesson 2-3]*

33. 34,890,000; 34,891,000; 34,790,001

34. 784,983; 784,982; 785,984

Write each number in standard form. *[Lesson 3-4]*

35. 5.54×10^3 **36.** 7.92×10^7 **37.** 1.42×10^4 **38.** 1.397×10^{10}

39. 9.28×10^5 **40.** 7×10^{12} **41.** 1.932×10^6 **42.** 2.54×10^8

Multiplying a Decimal by a Decimal

▶ **Lesson Link** You know how to multiply a whole number by a decimal. Now you'll multiply a decimal by a decimal, using the same method for placing a decimal point in a product. ◀

You'll Learn ...

■ how to multiply a decimal times a decimal

... How It's Used

Firefighters multiply decimals to determine how much water a hose can spray at a given pressure for a given amount of time.

Explore Multiplying a Decimal by a Decimal

Hunting for Hundredths

Materials: Hundreds squares, Colored pencils

Multiplying a Decimal by a Decimal

- Color the first number vertically.
- Color the second number horizontally.
- Describe the section in the grid where the two numbers overlap.

$$\begin{array}{r} 0.3 \\ \times\, 0.4 \\ \hline 0.12 \end{array}$$

1. Model these problems.

   a. 0.3 × 0.2   **b.** 0.6 × 0.6   **c.** 0.8 × 0.3   **d.** 0.4 × 0.7

   e. 0.9 × 0.5   **f.** 0.5 × 0.2   **g.** 0.7 × 0.1   **h.** 0.6 × 0.0

2. If you multiply two decimals that only go to tenths, does your answer only go to tenths? Explain.

3. When you multiply two decimal numbers between zero and one, is your answer bigger than both, smaller than both, or bigger than one but smaller than the other?

Learn Multiplying a Decimal by a Decimal

Multiplying a decimal by a decimal is similar to multiplying a decimal by a whole number. Multiply the two numbers as if they were whole numbers. The product of a decimal multiplication problem should have the same number of decimal places as the sum of the number of decimal places in both factors.

$$\begin{array}{r} 4.3 \\ \times\, 2.7 \\ \hline 3\,0\,1 \\ 8\,6 \\ \hline 11.6\,1 \end{array}$$

Study TIP

During a test or quiz, estimating the answer can help you determine if the answer is reasonable.

Examples

1 Multiply: 4.8×2.3

Estimate: $5 \times 2 = 10$

$$
\begin{array}{rl}
4.8 & \text{1 decimal place} \\
\times\ 2.3 & \text{1 decimal place} \\
\hline
144 & \\
96 & \\
\hline
11.04 & \text{2 decimal places}
\end{array}
$$

2 Multiply: 0.064×3.7

Estimate: $0.06 \times 4 = 0.24$

$$
\begin{array}{rl}
0.064 & \text{3 decimal places} \\
\times\ 3.7 & \text{1 decimal place} \\
\hline
448 & \\
192 & \\
\hline
0.2368 & \text{4 decimal places}
\end{array}
$$

Use these shortcuts to multiply a number by 0.1, 0.01, or 0.001:

- To multiply by 0.1, move the decimal point one place to the left.
- To multiply by 0.01, move the decimal point two places to the left.
- To multiply by 0.001, move the decimal point three places to the left.

You may have to annex zeros in order to move the decimal point.

annexed zeros

$5.47 \times 0.001 = 0.00547$

Examples

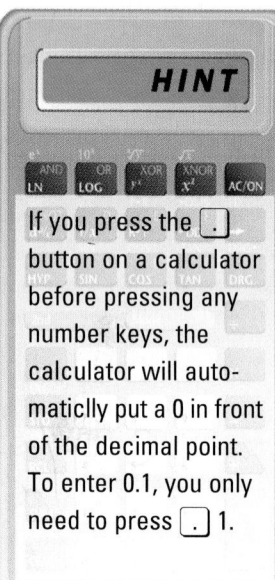

HINT

If you press the [.] button on a calculator before pressing any number keys, the calculator will automatically put a 0 in front of the decimal point. To enter 0.1, you only need to press [.] 1.

3 Multiply: 21×0.1

$$21 \times 0.1 = 2.1$$

4 Multiply: 6×0.001

$$6 \times 0.001 = 0.006$$

Try It

Multiply.

a. 0.4×23.6 **b.** 52.4×2.8 **c.** 0.009×4.1

d. 5677×0.01 **e.** 210×0.001 **f.** 6×0.1

Check   **Your Understanding**

1. Which is greater, 6.2×0.4 or 6.2×0.04? Explain.

2. When you multiply a number by 0.1, will the result be greater or less than the number? Explain.

3. How is multiplying a decimal by a decimal similar to multiplying two whole numbers?

3-9 Exercises and Applications

Practice and Apply

1. **Getting Started** Choose the equation that the grid models.

a.

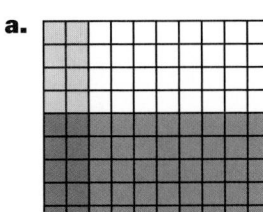

i. $0.2 \times 0.6 = 0.12$

ii. $0.3 \times 0.5 = 0.15$

b.

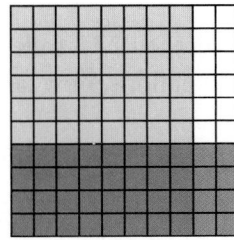

i. $0.8 \times 0.4 = 0.32$

ii. $0.8 \times 0.4 = 0.032$

c.

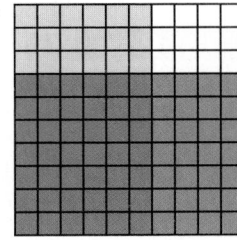

i. $0.6 \times 0.7 = 4.2$

ii. $0.6 \times 0.7 = 0.42$

Insert a decimal in each answer to make the equation true.

2. $0.57 \times 0.102 = 05814$

3. $4.17 \times 0.23 = 09591$

4. $1.9 \times 13.2 = 2508$

5. $1.567 \times 5.23 = 819541$

6. $4.09 \times 1.2 = 4908$

7. $65.1 \times 65.1 = 423801$

Multiply.

8. 0.1×75.4

9. 0.01×6.8

10. 0.001×265.3

11. 0.65×0.01

12. 97.8×0.1

13. 4.25×0.001

14. 4.2×6.3

15. 5.8×6.7

16. 9.7×0.6

17. 5.4×4.3

18. 0.29×0.4

19. 1.3×0.42

20. 2.07×0.03

21. 6.24×8.7

22. 0.08×6.5

23. 9.37×0.08

24. 10.2×0.4

25. 0.31×2.5

26. 0.4×0.18

27. 0.92×4.6

Estimate first. Then solve.

28. In 1863, at Fort Kearny, Nebraska, ging-ham cloth sold for $0.25 a yard. Mrs. Parks bought 16.5 yards to make clothes for her family. How much did she spend on cloth?

29. In 1863, emigrants could buy rice for $0.11 per pound in Chimney Rock, Nebraska. The Wilson's barrel could hold 19.25 pounds. How much did it cost to fill the barrel?

Compare, using <, >, or =.

30. 79.1×0.1 ☐ 79.1×0.01 **31.** 0.001×12.5 ☐ 0.01×12.5

32. 2.4×0.134 ☐ 0.24×0.134 **33.** 15.2×0.38 ☐ 1.52×3.8

34. Health Ava read on the wrapper that a candy bar had 12.5 g of fat. One gram of fat gives you 9.4 calories. How many calories from fat are in the candy bar?

35. **Test Prep** The Lyau's new car averaged 27.3 miles per gallon on a recent trip. If the gas tank holds 16.5 gallons, how far can they go on a tank of gas?

Ⓐ 4.5 miles   Ⓑ 45.04 miles   Ⓒ 450.45 miles   Ⓓ 4504.5 miles

36. Measurement Joel decided that his wrapping string should be 42.6 times longer than the piece shown here. How long should his string be?

Problem Solving and Reasoning

37. Critical Thinking Explain why $0.4 \times 0.2 \neq 0.8$.

38. Communicate Explain why multiplying numbers by 1000 moves the decimal to the right, and multiplying by 0.001 moves the decimal to the left.

39.  Imagine you are on the Oregon Trail in 1845. Write a problem that you might encounter on the trail that you can solve by multiplying two decimals.

Mixed Review

Simplify each expression, using the correct order of operations. *[Lesson 2-8]*

40. $50 - 10 \div 2$ **41.** $72 \div 9 - 1$ **42.** $6 \times 5 \times 3$ **43.** $4^2 \times 2 - 3$

44. $3 \times (8 - 6)$ **45.** $4 \div 2 - 0^6$ **46.** $50 \div 10 \times 4$ **47.** $(3 \times 4)^2 - 1$

Estimate each sum, difference, product, or quotient. *[Lesson 3-5]*

48. $65.79 + 12.56$ **49.** $7.67 - 5.33$ **50.** 7.87×10.06 **51.** $12.29 \div 4.47$

52. $72.593 + 3.485$ **53.** $21.09 - 11.06$ **54.** $55.88 \div 10.48$ **55.** 9.5×3.667

Dividing by a Whole Number

▶ **Lesson Link** In the first lesson in this section, you worked with multiplication problems with decimal answers. Now you will learn to do division problems with decimal answers. ◀

Explore Dividing by a Whole Number

Strip Mining

Materials: Tenths strips

Dividing by a Whole Number

- Color the first number.
- Break the first number down into equal groups. The number of groups should equal the second number.
- Describe one group in the grid.

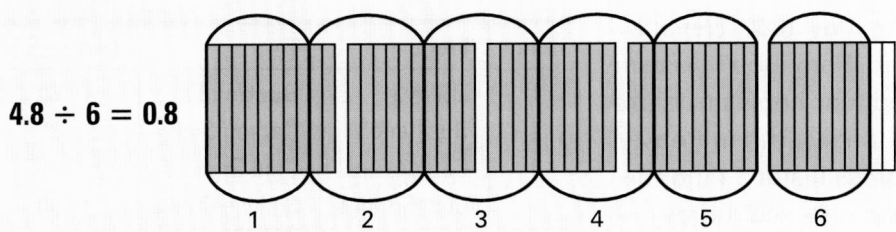

$4.8 \div 6 = 0.8$

1   2   3   4   5   6

1. Model these problems.

  a. $2.0 \div 5$ **b.** $2.1 \div 3$ **c.** $2.4 \div 4$ **d.** $3.5 \div 7$

2. Does $2.4 \div 3$ have the same answer as $3 \div 2.4$? Explain.

3. How is dividing a decimal by a whole number similar to dividing a whole number by a whole number?

You'll Learn ...

■ how to divide a decimal number by a whole number

... How It's Used

Dieticians divide decimal numbers to determine the amount of protein a person should eat per day.

Vocabulary

dividend

divisor

quotient

Learn Dividing by a Whole Number

When you divide one number by another, the number being divided is the **dividend**. The number you divide by is the **divisor**. The answer is the **quotient**.

When you divide by a whole number, you break the dividend into groups of equal size.

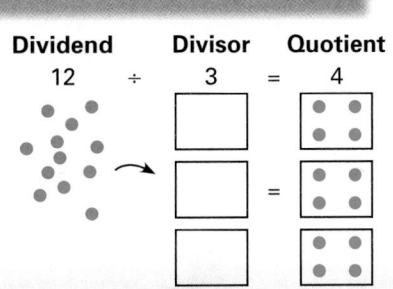

Dividend   Divisor   Quotient

12   ÷   3   =   4

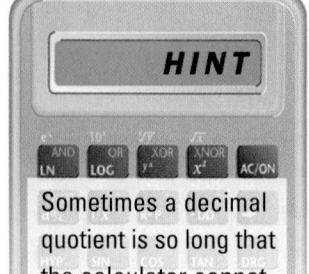

HINT

Sometimes a decimal quotient is so long that the calculator cannot show the entire number. In that case, the calculator may round the quotient to a shorter number.

When you have a decimal dividend, divide as if you were dividing whole numbers. Then place a decimal point in the quotient directly above the decimal point in the dividend.

```
        2.53
   27)68.31
      54
      143
      135
        81
        81
```

Examples

1 Divide: 153.92 ÷ 32

Estimate: 150 ÷ 30 = 5

```
        4.81
   32)153.92
      128
      259
      256
       32
       32
```

2 Divide: 427.8 ÷ 6

Estimate: 420 ÷ 6 = 70

```
       71.3
   6)427.8
     42
     07
      6
     18
     18
```

Remember

The mean is the result of dividing the sum of a set of numbers by the number of numbers in the set. **[Page 47]**

3 In May 1860, Nevada rider "Pony Bob" Haslam used four horses to make the longest run in Pony Express history. Find the mean distance run by each horse.

Horse	From	To	Distance (mi)
1	Friday's	Buckland's	60
2	Buckland's	Carson Sink	35
3	Carson Sink	Cold Springs	37
4	Cold Springs	Smith's Creek	30

Total distance = 60 + 35 + 37 + 30 = 162.
Add distances and divide by 4 to find the mean.

Mean = 162 ÷ 4

Estimate: 160 ÷ 4 = 40

```
       40.5
   4)162.0   ← Annex a zero.
     16
     020
      20
```

The mean distance run by each horse was 40.5 miles.

Use these shortcuts to divide a number by 10, 100, or 1000:

- To divide by 10, move the decimal point one place to the left.

- To divide by 100, move the decimal point two places to the left.

- To divide by 1000, move the decimal point three places to the left.

Recall that multiplying by powers of 10 that are less than 1, such as 0.1, 0.01, and 0.001, also moves the decimal place to the left.

Example 4

The table gives the estimated world population at two times 100 years apart. What is the average increase in population per year?

World Population (estimated)	
Year (A.D.)	Population
1900	1,600,000,000
2000	6,261,000,000

$$6,261,000,000$$
$$- 1,600,000,000$$
$$4,661,000,000$$

The total increase in 100 years is about 4,661,000,000.

To find the average increase per year, divide by 100:

$$4,661,000,000 \div 100 = 46610000.00$$

The average annual population increase is about 46,610,000.

Try It

Divide.

a. $154.4 \div 8$ **b.** $20.47 \div 23$ **c.** $8.029 \div 74$

d. $26.2 \div 100$ **e.** $3.012 \div 1000$ **f.** $45 \div 10$

DID YOU KNOW?

The world population is currently increasing faster than 1 person per second. In the time it takes to read this, more than 25 babies will have been born worldwide.

Check Your Understanding

1. If you divide a number with three places after the decimal by a whole number, how many decimal places are in the answer? Explain.

2. Dividing by 10 is the same as multiplying by 0.1. Explain. Can you think of other pairs of powers of 10 where dividing by one of them is the same as multiplying by the other?

3. How can you use multiplication to check a quotient?

Practice and Apply

1. **Getting Started** Choose the equation that the grid models.

a.

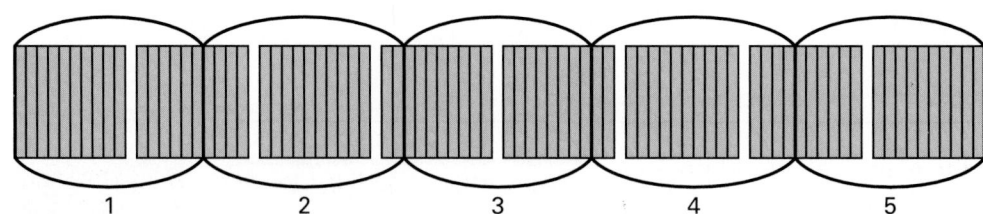

$$1 \quad 2 \quad 3 \quad 4 \quad 5$$

i. $8 \div 5 = 1.6$ **ii.** $8 \div 5 = 16$

b.

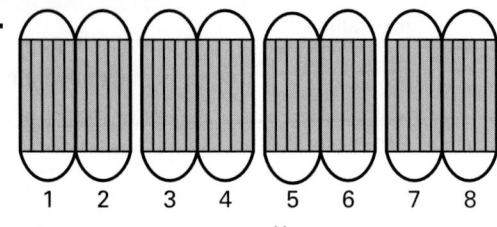

$$1 \quad 2 \quad 3 \quad 4 \quad 5 \quad 6 \quad 7 \quad 8$$

i. $4 \div 8 = 0.5$ **ii.** $40 \div 8 = 5$

c.

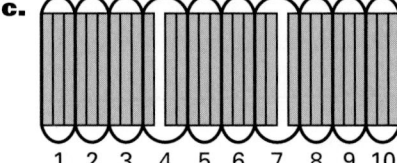

$$1 \; 2 \; 3 \; 4 \; 5 \; 6 \; 7 \; 8 \; 9 \; 10$$

i. $3 \div 10 = 0.3$ **ii.** $30 \div 10 = 3$

Insert a decimal in each answer to make the equation true.

2. $24.36 \div 6 = 406$ **3.** $287.63 \div 49 = 587$ **4.** $0.475 \div 5 = 095$

5. $99.4 \div 100 = 994$ **6.** $4.96 \div 10 = 0496$ **7.** $25.8 \div 1000 = 0258$

Divide.

8. $27.24 \div 6$ **9.** $13.932 \div 9$ **10.** $987.6 \div 12$ **11.** $133.414 \div 41$

12. $49.92 \div 16$ **13.** $0.104 \div 8$ **14.** $341.6 \div 56$ **15.** $2.856 \div 34$

16. $15.25 \div 61$ **17.** $9.92 \div 8$ **18.** $615.34 \div 10$ **19.** $945.25 \div 19$

20. $40.24 \div 8$ **21.** $382.092 \div 17$ **22.** $0.126 \div 7$ **23.** $56.88 \div 3$

24. $3.534 \div 6$ **25.** $2.035 \div 5$ **26.** $37.5 \div 3$ **27.** $4.69 \div 7$

28. Along the Oregon Trail, the trader's post in Fort Laramie, Wyoming, sold a 16-pound box of beef jerky for $5.92. What was the cost per pound?

29. **Health** The emigrants used lard for their cooking oil. Fifteen grams of lard have 141 calories. How many calories are in 1 gram?

188 *Chapter 3 • Decimals*

30. Maria spent $13.50 buying her class 30 ice cream bars. How much did each bar cost?

31. Measurement The distance between Fort Boise, Idaho, and Oregon City is 413 mi. On the emigrant's map, the distance was 3 in. How many miles does an inch on the map represent?

32. **Test Prep** Choose the correct solution to 24.501 ÷ 3.

Ⓐ 0.0816 Ⓑ 0.816 Ⓒ 8.167 Ⓓ 81.67

Problem Solving and Reasoning

33. **Journal** Explain why dividing a number by 100 is the same as multiplying by 0.01.

35. Critical Thinking In a whole-number division problem, both divisor and dividend are whole numbers. What kind of whole-number division problems have whole-number answers, and what kind of whole-number problems have decimal answers?

36. Communicate Suppose you are on the Oregon Trail in 1848. Invent a problem you would solve by dividing a decimal by a whole number.

34. Critical Thinking In a gymnastic competition, Dominique scored 9.5, 9.6, 9.5, 9.4, 9.7, and 9.6. Kim scored 9.5, 9.4, 9.6, 9.7, 9.7, and 9.5. Who had the higher average score? Explain.

Mixed Review

Find the next three numbers in each pattern. [Lesson 2-9]

37. 55, 60, 61, 66, 67, 72, …

38. 2, 4, 8, 16, 32, …

39. 38, 37, 35, 32, 28, …

40. 31, 39, 30, 38, 29, 37, …

41. 45, 42, 39, 36, …

42. 79, 82, 86, 91, 97, …

Simplify. [Lesson 3-6]

43. 49.02 + 3.05

44. 56.75 − 46.25

45. 0.267 − 0.26

46. 19.31 + 21.4

47. 6.98 − 3.45

48. $23.40 − $16.22

49. 5.847 + 1.152

50. 14.23 + 6.28

Project Progress

Draw a bar graph of the data you have collected about your expenses. Decide how to scale your bar graph to best show your data. Label each bar clearly, and make sure the height matches the dollar amount it represents.

Problem Solving

Understand
Plan
Solve
Look Back

Dividing by a Decimal

You'll Learn ...

■ how to divide decimal numbers by decimal numbers

... How It's Used

Pharmacists divide by decimals to determine how to best fill prescriptions for medicine.

▶ **Lesson Link**   In the last section, you divided by a whole number when the dividend is a decimal. Now you'll build on that skill by dividing by a decimal. ◀

Explore   Dividing by a Decimal

Divided We Stand

Materials: Tenths grid

Dividing by a Decimal

- Color the first number.
- Break the first number down into groups. Each group should be as large as the second number.
- Describe the number of groups in the grid.

$2.8 \div 0.7 = 4$

1. Model these problems.

   a. $3.0 \div 0.3$ **b.** $4.5 \div 0.9$ **c.** $4.2 \div 0.7$ **d.** $3.6 \div 0.6$

   e. $2.4 \div 0.8$ **f.** $2.5 \div 0.5$ **g.** $2.6 \div 0.1$ **h.** $1.2 \div 0.1$

2. When you divide a number by a decimal less than 1, is your answer smaller or larger than the number you started with?

3. In the problem $3.0 \div 0.6 = 5.0$, which number represents the number of groups? Which number represents the size of the groups?

Learn   Dividing by a Decimal

Dividing by a decimal is like dividing by a whole number. When you divide by a decimal, you break the dividend into groups of equal size.

The model illustrates the quotient of $2.5 \div 0.5$. There are 5 equal-size groups of 0.5 in 2.5. Therefore, $2.5 \div 0.5 = 5$.

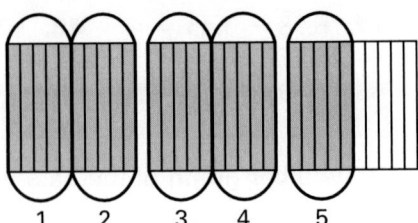

A problem with a decimal divisor can be difficult to solve. But, you can change the problem to one without a decimal divisor. Notice that when you multiply the dividend and the divisor by the same number, the quotient stays the same.

	Dividend	÷	Divisor	=	Quotient
	6	÷	2	=	3
Multiply dividend and divisor by 10 }	60	÷	20	=	3
Multiply dividend and divisor by 100 }	600	÷	200	=	3
Multiply dividend and divisor by 1000 }	6000	÷	2000	=	3

When you have a decimal divisor, multiply both divisor and dividend by a power of 10 that will make the divisor a whole number.

$$2.618 ÷ 0.34 = 261.8 ÷ 34.$$

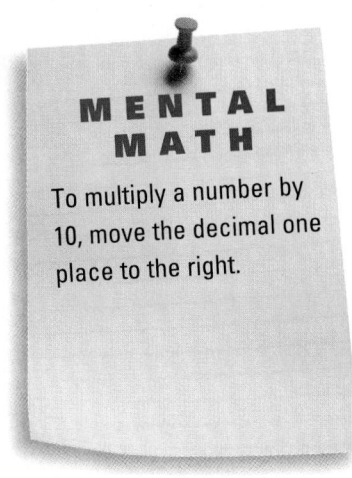

MENTAL MATH

To multiply a number by 10, move the decimal one place to the right.

▶ **History Link**

Pioneers who couldn't complete the Oregon Trail before winter would often die from the harsh weather and lack of food.

Examples

1 Find the quotient: 5.76 ÷ 1.6

$$5.76 ÷ 1.6 = 57.6 ÷ 16.$$ Multiply dividend and divisor by 10 to make the divisor a whole number.

```
      3.6
16)57.6    Divide.
   48
   96
   96
```

The quotient is 3.6.

2 The Caldwells traveled the Oregon Trail in 1870. They traveled 2212 miles in 126.4 days. Find the mean daily distance.

Mean distance = $22120. ÷ 1264.$ Multiply dividend and divisor by 10 to make the divisor a whole number.

```
         17.5
1264)22120.0    Divide.
     1264
     9480
     8848
      6320
      6320
```

The mean daily distance was 17.5 miles.

17.5 MILES PER DAY

WHAT DO YOU THINK?

Peter and Sonia wanted to buy 30 ounces of trail mix for a 3-day hike. Trail mix sells for $0.26 per ounce, or 32.5-ounce packages for $7.15. Which is the better buy?

Peter thinks ...

I'll divide the cost of the package by the weight to determine the price per ounce.

$7.15 \div 32.5 = 71.5 \div 325$

$$
\begin{array}{r}
.22 \\
325\overline{)71.50} \\
\underline{650} \\
650 \\
\underline{650}
\end{array}
$$

The package sells for $0.22 an ounce. This is a lower price per ounce. The package is a better buy.

Sonia thinks ...

I'll find the cost of 30 ounces at the price per ounce.

$$
\begin{array}{r}
0.26 \\
\times \quad 30 \\
\hline
0 \\
+ \ 780 \\
\hline
7.80
\end{array}
$$

2 decimal places

2 decimal places

30 ounces would cost $7.80, which is more than the package. The package is the better buy.

What do you think?

1. Which method would be easier to do with mental math? Paper and pencil? A calculator?

2. How could Peter check to see that his arithmetic was correct? How could Sonia check to see that her arithmetic was correct?

Check | Your Understanding

1. Write two decimal division problems with the same quotient as 20 ÷ 2.5.

2. Why is the answer to a division problem smaller than the dividend when you divide by a whole number, but bigger when you divide by a decimal between 0 and 1?

Practice and Apply

1. **Getting Started** Choose the equation that the grid models.

a.

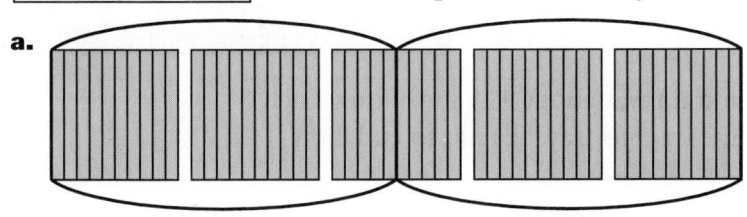

    i. 50 ÷ 25 = 2

    ii. 5 ÷ 2.5 = 2

b.

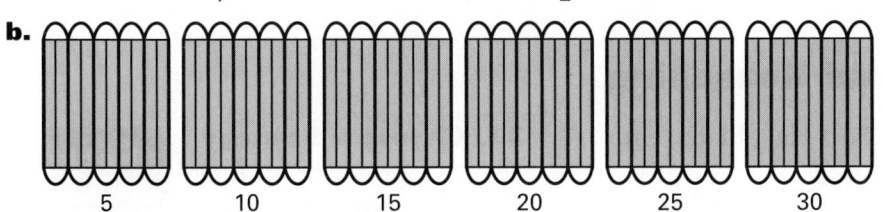

    i. 60 ÷ 20 = 30

    ii. 6 ÷ 0.2 = 30

c.

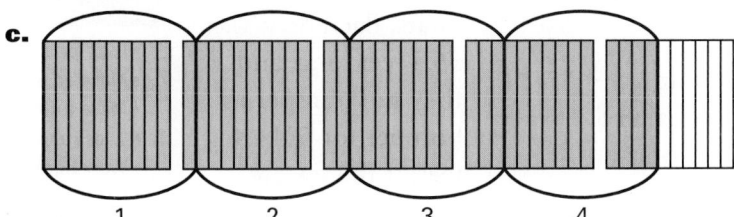

    i. 4.4 ÷ 1.1 = 4

    ii. 44 ÷ 11 = 33

Insert a decimal in each answer to make the equation true. Annex zeros if necessary.

2. 10.58 ÷ 2.3 = 46   **3.** 2.24 ÷ 0.8 = 28   **4.** 6.12 ÷ 1.8 = 34

5. 0.0036 ÷ 0.009 = 4   **6.** 98.6 ÷ 2.9 = 34   **7.** 45.505 ÷ 9.5 = 479

Divide.

8. 0.685 ÷ 2.74   **9.** 9.483 ÷ 8.7 = 1.09   **10.** 0.8449 ÷ 0.71   **11.** 2.4 ÷ 0.3 = 8.0

12. 0.104 ÷ 0.08   **13.** 0.427 ÷ 6.1   **14.** 0.804 ÷ 0.4   **15.** 5.49 ÷ 0.9 = 6.1

16. 422.1 ÷ 60.3   **17.** 69.09 ÷ 7   **18.** 126.28 ÷ 8.2   **19.** 13.3666 ÷ 6.89

20. 0.3321 ÷ 4.1   **21.** 50.4 ÷ 1.2   **22.** 6.89 ÷ 1.3   **23.** 2.59 ÷ 0.7 = 3.7

24. 6.684 ÷ 0.06   **25.** 3.48 ÷ 5.8   **26.** 87.4 ÷ 0.38   **27.** 2.5 ÷ 0.005 = 500.0

28. **Health** A pharmacist has 808.4 g of a generic medicine. She must fill capsules with 37.6 g of the medicine per capsule. How many capsules can she fill?

PRACTICE 3-11

29. History In the early 1850s, "Wind Wagon Thomas" invented a wind wagon that was half sailboat and half wagon. The wind wagon would have taken 133.5 days to travel 1968.4 miles. About how fast did the wind wagon travel?

30. The Figueroas traveled 501.5 miles on 15.4 gallons of gas. How many miles per gallon did they get, to the nearest tenth?

31. | **Test Prep** | The Smith's wagon train was about 98.98 feet long. Each wagon was about 9.8 feet long. If the wagons traveled end to end, how many wagons were in the train?

Ⓐ 10   Ⓑ 10.1   Ⓒ 11   Ⓓ 100

Problem Solving and Reasoning

32. Critical Thinking In Fort Hall, Idaho, emigrants could buy 10 pounds of candles for $2.50 or 100 pounds of sugar for $12.50. Which item costs less per pound?

34. **Journal** Explain what numbers you can divide by to get a quotient smaller than the dividend and what numbers you can divide by to get a quotient larger than the dividend.

33. Choose a Strategy Manuel was counting the lights on parade floats. Each float was 36.4 feet long, and they ran bumper to bumper for 5314.4 feet. If there were 150 lights on each float, how many lights did he count?

> **Problem Solving**
> **STRATEGIES**
>
> • Look for a Pattern
> • Make an Organized List
> • Make a Table
> • Guess and Check
> • Work Backward
> • Use Logical Reasoning
> • Draw a Diagram
> • Solve a Simpler Problem

35. Communicate Remember that multiplying by 0.1, 0.01, and 0.001 moves the decimal to the left. Explain what dividing by 0.1, 0.01, and 0.001 does. Show an example of each.

36. Critical Thinking Find the next three numbers in the pattern, and explain what the pattern is:
32, 16, 8, 4, 2, 1, 0.5, 0.25, 0.125, …

Mixed Review

Write each number in expanded form. *[Lesson 2-4]*

37. 15^3 **38.** $8^3 \times 2^4$ **39.** $7^3 \times 8^2$ **40.** 29^2 **41.** 34^9 **42.** 6^{11}

43. 1^5 **44.** 2^5 **45.** 3^6 **46.** $4^8 \times 6^7$ **47.** 10^9 **48.** 12^5

Solve. *[Lesson 3-7]*

49. $e + 4.5 = 12.6$ **50.** $\$20 + f = \$22.55$ **51.** $3.9 = g + 2.7$

52. $i - 98.6 = 38.3$ **53.** $j + 0.5 = 1.8$ **54.** $m - 0.056 = 0.077$

Solving Decimal Equations: Multiplication and Division

▶ **Lesson Link** | In the last section, you used mental math to solve addition and subtraction equations involving decimals. Now you'll use mental math again to solve multiplication and division equations involving decimals. ◀

Explore | Multiplication and Division Equations

"Sorry, Shopping Carts Haven't Been Invented Yet!"

The table lists prices of items that pioneers could buy in 1850 in Independence, Missouri, before setting out on the Oregon Trail. The people named actually traveled the Oregon Trail.

- Sarah York said, "I bought 3 of the same item for $9. The price for each item was *v*."

- Henderson Luelling said, "I bought 2 of the same item for $3.40. The price for each item was *w*."

- Narcissa Whitman said, "I paid $0.75 for *x* pounds of rice."

- Peter Burnett said, "I bought 100 of the same item for $15. The price for each item was *y*."

- Randolph Marcy said, "I paid $18 for *z* yards of cloth."

... How It's Used

Sailors use decimal equations to determine how fast to travel to reach a given port on a given day.

ITEM	COST ($)
Beans	1.50/bushel
Blanket	1.70
Bucket	0.30
Cloth	0.25/yard
Corn Meal	0.17/lb
Flour	3.00/sack
Lard	0.10/lb
Rice	0.15/lb
Salt	0.02/lb
Tent	15.00
Tools	4.50/set

1. Write an equation that represents each pioneer's statement.

2. For each pioneer, list the item purchased, the individual price, and how many items were purchased.

3. Make up a problem involving a pioneer on the Oregon Trail and a price given in the table. Have another student solve your problem.

Learn   Solving Multiplication and Division Equations

You can solve multiplication and division equations with decimals using mental math and number sense. Use mental math to determine the digits in the answer. Then, use number sense to determine where the decimal should be placed.

Examples

1 Solve: $\frac{x}{3} = 0.5$

$\frac{x}{3} = 0.5 \quad \rightarrow \quad \frac{x}{3} = 5$ Think of the numbers as whole numbers. Read as "What number divided by 3 equals 5?"

$\frac{15}{3} = 5$ Use mental math.

$\frac{1.5}{3} = 0.5$ Since there is one digit after the decimal in 0.5, there should be one digit after the decimal in 1.5.

x is equal to 1.5.

▶ **History Link**

Traveling the Oregon Trail was expensive. Few poor people made the journey because they could not afford the supplies.

2 At Fort Laramie, many emigrants sold their furniture for 0.2 times what they paid for it, just to lighten their wagons. If a family sold a dresser for $3.80, what did they pay for it originally?

Let p = the original price of the dresser.

$0.2p = 3.80 \rightarrow 2p = 380$ Think of the numbers as whole numbers. Read as "What number times 2 equals 380?"

$2 \times \mathbf{190} = 380$ Use mental math.

$0.2 \times \mathbf{19.0} = 3.80$ There are two decimal places in 3.80 and only one in 0.2. There should be one decimal place in 19.0.

The original price of the dresser was $19.00.

"Pilgrims on the Plains", sketched by Theo. R. Davis

Try It

Solve each equation.

a. $3j = 2.1$ **b.** $0.4w = 2.4$ **c.** $\frac{t}{5} = 1.1$ **d.** $\frac{f}{0.7} = 0.7$

Check   Your Understanding

1. How does number sense help you to solve decimal equations?

2. Give a real-world problem modeled by $0.5x = 3.5$.

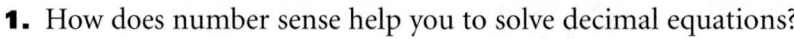

Practice and Apply

EVEN

1. **Getting Started** Which of the given values of x will make the equation true?

   a. $0.024x = 24$; 0.001 or 1000

   b. $\dfrac{450}{x} = 4.5$; 100 or 1000

   c. $8.5 \div x = 85$; 0.1 or 10

   d. $78.34x = 7.834$; 1 or 0.1

$\dfrac{6}{90} = x$

Solve.

2. $0.5d = 0.045$

3. $\dfrac{e}{3} = 0.21$

4. $\dfrac{t}{9} = 0.07$

5. $0.7r = 35$

$\dfrac{b}{6} = 90$

6. $0.9g = 72$

7. $1.6w = 0.032$

8. $\dfrac{p}{0.02} = 4.4$

9. $\dfrac{s}{1.07} = 107$

10. $9b = 8.1$

11. $\dfrac{u}{1.5} = 30$

12. $0.09k = 0.063$

13. $\dfrac{q}{5} = 2.5$

$\dfrac{.15}{9} = 6$

14. $\dfrac{p}{0.3} = 11$

15. $0.6h = 3.6$

16. $0.4m = 0.004$

17. $0.8n = 0.056$

18. $\dfrac{s}{0.07} = 0.4$

19. $\dfrac{v}{6} = 1.8$

20. $1.2z = 0.144$

21. $8k = 0.64$

22. $1.1a = 0.066$

23. $\dfrac{j}{0.7} = 0.2$

24. $\dfrac{f}{10} = 1.13$

25. $\dfrac{u}{0.4} = 0.05$

For Exercises 26–31, set up an equation and solve.

$= 36$

$.6x = 36$

26. Along the Oregon Trail, the Spikle family left Fort Boise with 36 kilograms (kg) of flour. They divided it into bags of 0.6 kg. How many bags did they have?

27. The Carlson family spent several days hiking through the Rocky Mountains. Every day, they hiked 8.3 miles. At the end of the vacation, they had hiked a total of 83 miles. How many days did they hike? *9*

28. Helen put several stamps on a large envelope. She placed 6 stamps of equal value on the envelope. The stamps together were worth $0.90. How much was each stamp worth?

29. A chemist conducting an experiment took a package of salt and split the contents into nine even groups. Each group weighed 0.08 kilograms. How much salt was in the original package?

PRACTICE 3-12

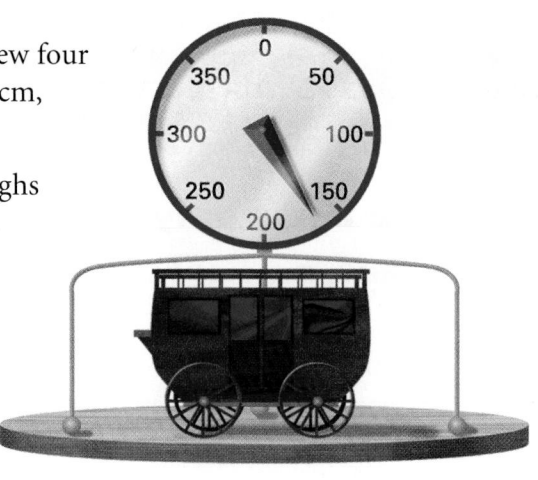

30. **Science** In a 2-week science experiment, a corn plant grew four times as much as a bean plant. If the corn plant grew 6.0 cm, how much did the bean plant grow?

31. A wagon weighs 165.3 kg. Carrying riders, the wagon weighs 465 kg. What is the weight of the riders?

32. **Test Prep** The mass of Object A is 25 grams. The mass of Object B is 77.5 grams. Choose the correct equation, where x is the mass of Object A.

  Ⓐ $3.1x = 77.5$ Ⓑ $77.5x = 3.1$

  Ⓒ $\dfrac{3.1}{x} = 77.5$ Ⓓ Not here

Problem Solving and Reasoning

33. **Choose a Strategy** Traders used the Santa Fe Trail to take manufactured goods from Kansas City to Santa Fe and return with gold, silver, furs, and wool. The wagons averaged 6.5 miles per hour over the 800-mile trail. They could travel 7 hours per day. How many days would it take the traders to make a round trip from Kansas City?

34. **Communicate** Write an equation involving decimal multiplication or division where the answer is 12.

35. **Journal** Explain the difference between the expression $0.3x$ and $0.3x = 2.1$.

> **Problem Solving**
> ## STRATEGIES
> - Look for a Pattern
> - Make an Organized List
> - Make a Table
> - Guess and Check
> - Work Backward
> - Use Logical Reasoning
> - Draw a Diagram
> - Solve a Simpler Problem

Mixed Review

Use the Calories in a Meal graph to answer each question. *[Lesson 1-1]*

36. What is the total number of calories for this meal?

37. Which part of the meal has the most calories?

38. How many combined calories are in the shake and the dessert?

Calories in a Meal

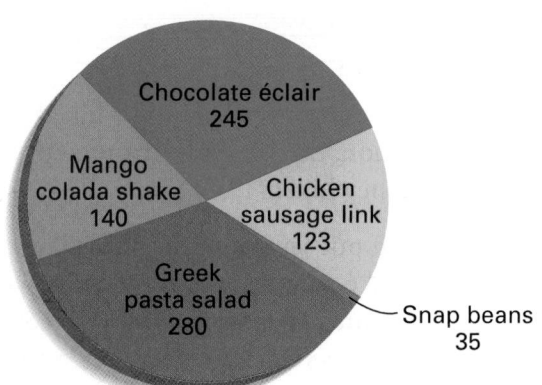

Multiply. *[Lesson 3-8]*

39. 1.45×6 40. 4.07×3 41. 5×4.36

42. 83×1.2 43. 51×1.06 44. 3.8×5

Section 3C Connect

In this section, you've learned about the historic Oregon Trail. In recent years, new trails have been built for the enjoyment of hikers and backpackers. One of the best known is the John Muir Trail, a 209.8-mile path through California's Sierra Nevada Mountains.

Trials and Trails

You and some friends are planning a 3-day backpacking trip on the John Muir Trail. You want to hike one of the two trail sections shown in these "profiles."

Dollar Lake to Lake Marjorie

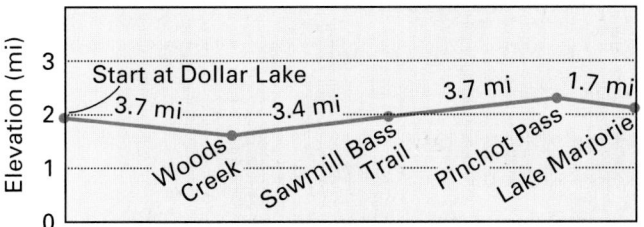

Lower Trinity Lake to Lyell Pass

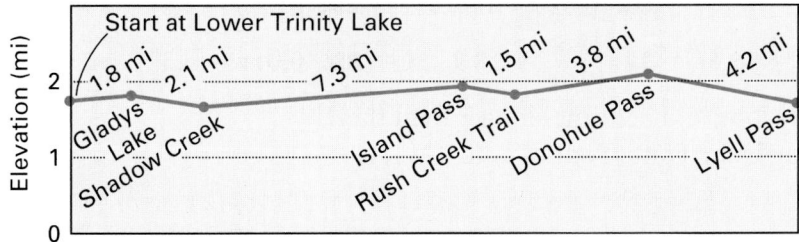

1. Find the length of each trail. Then calculate how long it will take you to hike each trail if you average 2.4 mi/hr.

2. Hiking uphill and downhill takes extra time. Each vertical mile uphill adds 2.5 hr onto the time you calculated in Question 1. Each vertical mile downhill adds 1.5 hr onto the time you calculated in Question 1. Use the vertical scale to estimate the up and down mileage of each trail section. Revise the total trail time you calculated in Question 1.

3. You plan to rest, on average, 0.25 hr for every hour of hiking time. Revise your total trail time again, this time adding rest time.

4. Which trail sections would you choose for a 3-day hike? Explain.

199

Write the number in standard form.

1. 5.6×10^6 **2.** 3.78×10^3 **3.** 4×10^8 **4.** 7.3×10^{11}

5. 1.22×10^5 **6.** 1.6×10^{12} **7.** 1.6×10^{10} **8.** 3.94×10^7

Simplify.

9. 4.7×5 **10.** $2.4 \div 0.4$ **11.** 625×0.4 **12.** 3.04×0.3

13. $12.6 + 8$ **14.** $45.89 + 6.7$ **15.** $80.05 - 20.03$ **16.** $0.06 - 0.057$

17. $6.73 - 4.69$ **18.** $31.06 - 29$ **19.** $167.55 + 143.2$ **20.** $16.79 + 4.01$

21. $259.2 \div 72$ **22.** $3.68 \div 0.08$ **23.** 6.65×0.42 **24.** $0.264 \div 0.24$

25. Students at Washington Middle School formed a hiking club. On Saturdays, they hiked 9.1 km, 8.3 km, 12.4 km, 9.6 km, and 14.5 km. What was the average length of a hike for the club?

Solve.

26. $1.2t = 3.6$ **27.** $\dfrac{u}{6} = 23.7$ **28.** $0.02b = 0.4$ **29.** $0.11n = 5.5$

30. $\dfrac{w}{5.7} = 14.8$ **31.** $s - 7.91 = 16.4$ **32.** $\dfrac{t}{0.08} = 18.9$ **33.** $0.01v = 8.3$

34. The Mississippi River is 2340 miles long and 3.2 times longer than the Platte/South Platte River. How long is the Platte/South Platte River, to the nearest tenth of a mile?

35. A store has Oregon Trail trading cards marked at seven for $2.50. How much does one card cost?

Test Prep

Determining the number of decimal places in the answer can help eliminate wrong answers.

36. Subtract: $72.967 - 12.973$

    Ⓐ 58.994   Ⓑ 59.994

    Ⓒ 589.94   Ⓓ 599.94

37. Add: $32.409 + 3.864$

    Ⓐ 35.273   Ⓑ 36.273

    Ⓒ 70.049   Ⓓ 71.049

REVIEW 3C

Binary Numbers

The number system used most often is the base 10 system. It is called the base 10 system because there are ten digits in the system: 0, 1, 2, 3, 4, 5, 6, 7, 8, and 9. Every place value in the base 10 system, such as hundreds, thousands, and millions, is a power of 10.

Most computers don't use the base 10 system. They use the base 2 system, which is also known as the binary system. In the binary system, there are only two digits: 0 and 1. Every place value is a power of 2.

Base 10	Base 2	Base 10	Base 2	Base 10	Base 2
0	0	3	11	6	110
1	1	4	100	7	111
2	10	5	101	8	1000

Try It

1. What are the binary numbers for the base 10 numbers 9 through 16?

2. What are the base 10 numbers for these binary numbers?
   a. 10001   **b.** 10100   **c.** 10111   **d.** 11111

3. In base 10, the first eight powers of 2 are 2, 4, 8, 16, 32, 64, 128, and 256. How do you write the first eight powers of 2 in the binary system?

4. In base 10, the number 0.1 means one-tenth. In the binary system, what do you think 0.1 means? Explain.

Chapter 3 Summary and Review

Graphic Organizer

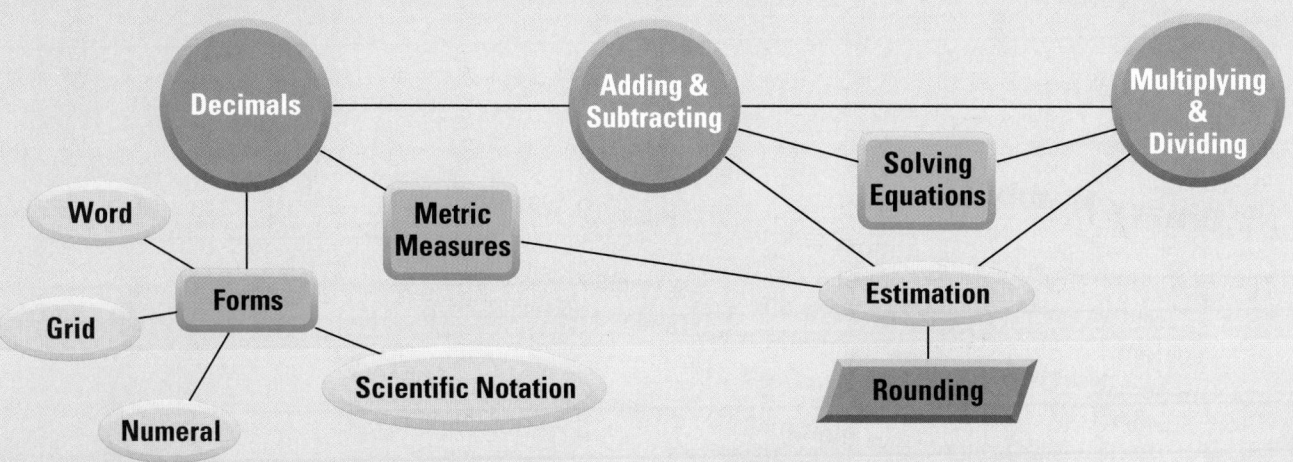

Section 3A Decimal Concepts

Summary

■ Decimals can be represented in word, number, or grid form.

■ Place values for decimal numbers mirror place values for whole numbers. Use place value to write, order, and compare numbers that are between two whole numbers.

■ Annexing zeros or using a number line can help you order and compare decimals.

■ Scientific notation is a way to write large numbers in a shorter form. A number in scientific notation has two factors: a number between 1 and 10, and a power of 10.

Review

1. Show each number in decimal form.

  a. 25 hundredths

  b.

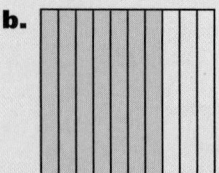

2. Round to the nearest tenth:

  a. 5.63   **b.** 0.77

3. Compare using > or <:

  a. 2.31 ☐ 2.13   **b.** 0.08 ☐ 0.6

4. Write in standard form:

  a. 7.16×10^4 **b.** 3.95×10^5

Summary

- Use rounding and mental math to estimate decimal sums, differences, products, and quotients.

- Before adding or subtracting decimals, line up the decimal points in the numbers. This will ensure that the place values in the first number are in line with the same place values in the second number.

Review

5. Estimate and then add $493.76 + 235.6$.

6. Estimate and then subtract $336.8 - 74.523$.

7. Add $2.76 + 33.9 + 29.26$.

8. Compare $(7.2 - 2.8)$ to 4.876.

9. A quarter measures 24.3 mm across. A dime measures 17.9 mm across. How many more millimeters across is the quarter?

10. Solve.

    a. $t + 3.2 = 7.8$

    b. $k - 7 = 6.5$

Section 3C Multiplying and Dividing with Decimals

Summary

- To multiply with decimals, multiply as if the numbers were whole numbers. The number of digits after the decimal point in the answer should be the same as the total number of digits after any decimal points in the factors.

- To divide with decimals, multiply the divisor and dividend by the power of 10 that makes the divisor a whole number. Then divide, and place a decimal point in the quotient directly above the decimal point in the dividend.

- When multiplying by 10, 100, or 1000, or dividing by 0.1, 0.01, 0.001, move the decimal point the appropriate number of places to the right.

- When dividing by 10, 100, or 1000, or multiplying by 0.1, 0.01, 0.001, move the decimal point the appropriate number of places to the left.

Review

11. Estimate and then multiply 2.3×56.

12. Estimate and then divide $53 \div 4$.

13. Estimate and then multiply 0.47×1.9.

14. Estimate and then divide $11.22 \div 5.1$.

15. Multiply 45.33×0.001.

16. Multiply 7.51×100.

17. Divide $367 \div 1000$.

18. Solve $9m = 27.9$.

Chapter 3 Assessment

1. What place value is to the left of the hundred-thousandths place?

2. Write three hundred and thirty-six hundredths in standard form.

3. One way nails are sized is by their gauge, or thickness. Order these nails from least to greatest according to their gauge in millimeters: 3.76, 3.05, 3.43, 3.33.

4. Name two numbers between 2.007 and 2.009.

5. There are an estimated 103,000 species of bees and wasps. Write this number in scientific notation.

6. A parsec is a unit of distance used in astronomy that is equal to 3.08×10^{13} km. Write this distance in standard notation.

Estimate and then simplify.

7. $17.32 - $5.76
8. 4.9967 + 3.021
9. 382.8 ÷ 8.7
10. 2.8 × 0.93

11. One kind of scale measures temperature in units called kelvins. The boiling point of gold is at 1074 K, and the boiling point of water is 700.852 K lower. Find the boiling point of water.

Multiply or divide.

12. 3.45 × 0.001
13. 0.87 ÷ 0.01
14. 7 ÷ 0.25

Solve.

15. $m + 4.2 = 6.9$
16. $\frac{x}{100} = 10,000$
17. $12.3a = 36.9$

Write an equation for each exercise and solve it.

18. What is the difference in size between a wheel 52.52 mm across and one 42.5 mm across?

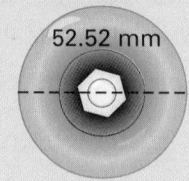

52.52 mm

19. A sonora blue butterfly measures 2.1 cm long. A waved sphinx moth measures 8.4 cm long. How many times longer is the moth than the butterfly?

Performance Task

A textbook measures 20.7 cm wide, 26.1 cm long, and 2.8 cm high. What is the greatest number of books a shipping department can pack into a carton 55 cm wide, 65.3 cm long, and 30 cm high? You may draw sketches to help you decide how to pack the books.

Performance Assessment

Choose one problem.

Kangaroo Patterns

3.65	3.25	2.85	2.45
10.85			
	17.65		
25.25		24.45	

In the grid, the numbers in every row form decimal patterns. To "hop" from one number to the next, you must always add or subtract the same number. The numbers in every column also form decimal patterns. Find the patterns and fill in the missing values.

Photo Possibilities

Choose two of the photos. Write a short word problem for each. One problem must use decimals. Each problem must be related to the subject of the photo. Write equations for each problem and solve them.

Worldly Costs

A fast-food chain sells hamburgers in several countries. The price in U.S. dollars of a large hamburger is listed below.

Switzerland	$4.80	Israel	$3.00
Sweden	$3.87	Denmark	$4.40
Germany	$3.22	France	$3.41
Argentina	$3.00	Belgium	$3.50

Construct a graph of the data to help someone visually compare the prices. Then write a paragraph explaining why the type of graph you chose is the best type for comparing the data.

An Exponential Challenge

Write each of the numbers and expressions shown as a single number in standard form. If you add the numbers in each row, which row will have the largest sum?

Team	Round 1	Round 2	Round 3
A	23×10^2	$6^2 - 3 + 5^3$	0.547×10^4
B	$15^3 + 5^2$	0.03×10^5	$3^3 - 4^2 + 24^1$
C	$7^6 \div 7 \text{ cubed}$	7 squared	0.007×10^6

4 Measurement

Social Studies

The ancient Incas used knotted rope called quipus to determine how large fields were, and how much tax to charge them.

Science

A meter was originally known as $\frac{1}{10,000,000}$ the distance from the Earth's equator to the North Pole.

Arts & Literature

Jules Verne stated in *20,000 Leagues Under the Sea*, "When the temperature dropped below 5° Celsius or 23° Fahrenheit, all the Nautilus would be covered with ice." However, 5° Celsius is 41° Fahrenheit.

Entertainment

The area of a standard football field is 57,600 ft². A football field could hold about 7 baseball diamonds, 20 tennis courts, or 1280 ping-pong tables.

People of the World

The great wall of China, built by the ancient Chinese, covers so much area that it is visible from outer space.

KEY MATH IDEAS

The metric system and the standard system provide different types of units for measuring length, mass, weight, and capacity.

The area of a shape is the amount of the space that the shape covers.

You can calculate the areas of a square, rectangle, parallelogram, or triangle if you know the base, the height, and the appropriate formula.

The area of a circle can be determined by using a special number known as π (pi).

CHAPTER PROJECT

Problem Solving

Understand
Plan
Solve
Look Back

In this project, you will design a miniature golf course. Begin by thinking about the sorts of shapes and kinds of obstacles you want to put in your golf course that will make it challenging to get a hole-in-one.

Finding Unnecessary Information

A problem often provides you with many numbers. Some of the numbers are needed to solve the problem, but not always all of them. To understand a problem, you may need to identify which numbers are unnecessary.

Problem Solving Focus

For each problem, state which numerical information is necessary, and which is unnecessary. Some problems may not have any unnecessary information.

1 A craft named *Lunik 2* was the first man-made object to land on the moon. It was launched from the former USSR on September 12, 1959. It landed on the Moon on September 14, 1959. How long did the flight take?

2 The Grimaldi Crater has a diameter of 138 miles, or 222 kilometers. The Janssen Crater has a diameter of 118 miles, or 190 kilometers. What's the difference in miles between the diameters of these two craters?

3 The first artificial satellite, *Sputnik 1*, was launched on October 4, 1957. The second, *Sputnik 2*, was launched November 3, 1957. How many days later was *Sputnik 2* launched?

4 In 1961, Yuri Gagarin became the first man in space when he orbited the Earth once. Gherman Titov orbited the Earth 17 times in the *Vostok II*. John Glenn was the first American astronaut in space. He orbited the Earth 64 times in 1962. All together, how many orbits did these first three astronauts make?

One Person's Trash is Another Person's . . .

Study these lists of words:

Column A

Broken tire treads
Empty tin cans
Used license plates
Old hub caps
Burned-out light bulbs
Cement bags

Column B

Dolls
Dust pans
Headdress jewels
Sandals
Briefcases
Artistic sculptures

1 Match each of the "garbage" items in Column A with its recycled version in Column B.

2 Why is it important to produce less garbage, and to reuse and recycle it?

3 How is mathematics used in the management of garbage?

All of the items in Column A seem like garbage. All of the items in Column B seem like useful things. To the people at the Museum of International Folk Art, they seem the same.

The Museum of International Folk Art is in Santa Fe, New Mexico. The curators there have studied how people take garbage and turn it into something useful, pleasant, or fun.

Every day, the world produces tons of trash. We must find ways to reduce the amount of trash we create, to reuse things before throwing them away, and to recycle the things we treat like garbage. We may not have much time on our hands, but we do have one thing on our side … mathematics!

Perimeter

► **Lesson Link**
You know how to add decimals and whole numbers. Now you will apply those skills to find the distance around geometric figures. ◄

You'll Learn ...

■ to find the perimeter of a geometric figure

... How It's Used

Homeowners calculate a perimeter when building a fence for their yard.

Vocabulary

perimeter

Explore | Perimeter

Watching the Side Lines

The chart below is based upon a row of triangles with equal sides of 4 units. The chart lists the distance around one triangle, two triangles, and so on.

NUMBER OF TRIANGLES	SKETCH	DISTANCE AROUND OUTSIDE
1	4 △ 4 / 4	12
2	4 / 4 ◢◣ 4 / 4	
3		
4		
5		
10	—	
100	—	

1. Copy and complete the chart. Don't sketch the last two figures.

2. The distance around a triangle is 12 units. Why doesn't the distance around the figure go up by 12 units when you add a new triangle?

3. What would the distance around the outside be for the first five rows if the figure was a square measuring 4 units on each side?

Learn | Perimeter

The distance around the outside of a figure is known as the **perimeter** . To determine the perimeter of a geometric figure, you add the lengths of each side.

Example 1

Find the perimeter.

The perimeter equals

12.5 cm + 18.3 cm + 20 cm, or 50.8 cm.

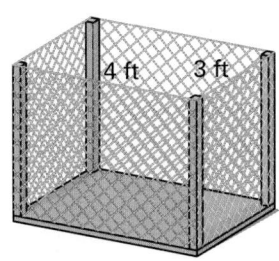

Sometimes, a figure does not give all the side lengths. You can often determine the length of an unlabeled side by looking at the opposite side.

Remember

When adding decimals, line up the decimal points. This helps you to be sure that you are adding digits with the same place value.

[Page 165]

Examples

2 Antwon wants to build a composter out of 1-yard high wire mesh. He wants it to be a rectangle with the front measuring 4 ft and the right side 3 ft. How much 1-yard high wire mesh does he need?

The composter has the shape of a rectangle. If the front is 4 ft, the back is also 4 ft. If the right side is 3 ft, the left side is also 3 ft.

Perimeter = 4 + 3 + 4 + 3, or 14 ft

Antwon needs 14 ft of 1-yard high wire mesh.

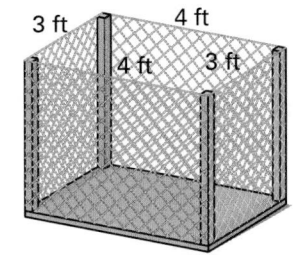

▶ **Science Link**

Composting allows organic garbage such as peels and grass to break down quickly and naturally. This leaves more room in landfills to store the garbage that cannot be recycled or broken down quickly.

3 Find the perimeter.

The bottom side is equal to the top two sides. Since the top two sides are 8 and 15, the bottom is 23.

The smallest side plus 7 is equal to 10. The smallest side is therefore 10 − 7, or 3.

Perimeter = 15 + 3 + 8 + 10 + 23 + 7, or 66

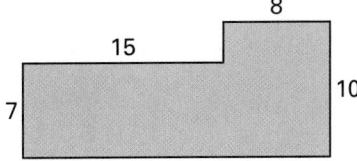

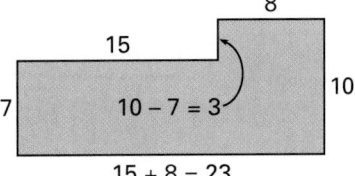

Try It

Find each perimeter.

a.

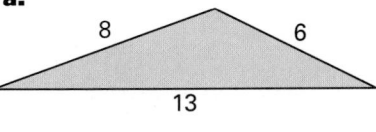

b.

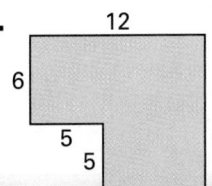

WHAT DO YOU THINK?

Larry and Catherine run laps around the school playground. The playground is 290 feet long and 150 feet wide. They want to know how many laps it takes to equal 5280 feet, or 1 mile.

Larry thinks . . .

I'll sketch the shape of the playground and label all four sides.

P = length + width + length + width

P = 290 + 150 + 290 + 150

P = 880

The perimeter of the playground is 880 feet.

$5280 \div 880 = 6$

It takes 6 laps to equal a mile.

```
        290 ft
      ┌─────────┐
150 ft│         │150 ft
      └─────────┘
        290 ft
```

Catherine thinks . . .

I'll add the length and width of the rectangle. I know there are two lengths and widths, so I will multiply the sum by 2 to find the perimeter.

Perimeter = $2 \times (290 + 150)$
= $2 \times (440)$
= 880

The perimeter of the playground is 880 feet.

$5280 \div 880 = 6$

It takes 6 laps to equal a mile.

What do **you** think?

1. Which method would you prefer if the lengths were decimals?

2. How does each method prevent the mistake of using only one length and width?

Check Your Understanding

1. If you know the length of one side of a square, how can you use multiplication to find the perimeter? Explain.

2. If one figure has a larger perimeter than another, does the first figure have to have more sides than the second? Explain.

4-1 Exercises and Applications

Practice and Apply

Getting Started Use mental math to find each perimeter.

1.
40 cm
50 cm | 50 cm
40 cm

2.
18 in.
12 in.
10 in.

3.
25 in.
25 in. | 25 in.
25 in.

4.
65 yd
35 yd | 35 yd
65 yd

Find each perimeter.

5.
2 cm
2 cm

6.
16 ft
22 ft

7.
6 in. | 5 in.
5 in.

8.
0.3 km
0.1 km
0.19 km
0.2 km

Find the lengths of each unknown side.

9.
15 in.
a
b
16 in.
7 in.
18 in.

10.
c | 30
25 | e
d | 50
20
70

11.
f
21 mm
g | 22 mm
5 mm
34 mm

12. Kristin wants to put organic garbage in a compost pile. She staked out a triangular area on the ground that has two sides of 6 and 8 feet. If the perimeter of the pile is 21 feet, how long is the third side?

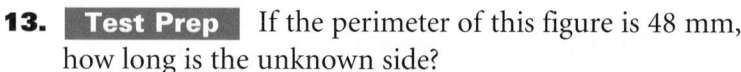

PROBLEM SOLVING 4-1

13. **Test Prep** If the perimeter of this figure is 48 mm, how long is the unknown side?

Ⓐ 3 mm Ⓑ 5 mm

Ⓒ 6 mm Ⓓ None of these

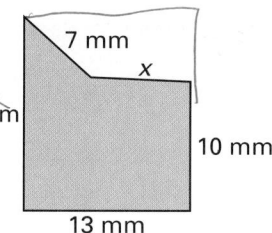

14. Major league baseball diamonds have 90 feet between bases. Little League baseball diamonds have 60 feet between bases. Find the difference in running distance for a home run on the two diamonds.

Problem Solving and Reasoning

15. **Critical Thinking** The students of Twin Creeks Middle School planted a rectangular garden. Thirty-six feet of decorative material was used for the border. Sketch two possible figures for the garden. Explain your sketches.

16. **Journal** If the length and width of a rectangle are doubled, is the perimeter also doubled? Explain.

17. **Communicate** Explain the steps needed to find the unknown side of a triangle if the other two sides are 7 inches and 9 inches, and the perimeter is 30 inches.

Mixed Review

For Exercises 18–20, use the Reaction Time graph. *[Lesson 1-1]*

18. At what age is the reaction time slowest for females? For males?

19. What is the difference between male and female reaction times at age 50?

20. What do you think the reaction times for 70-year-old females will be?

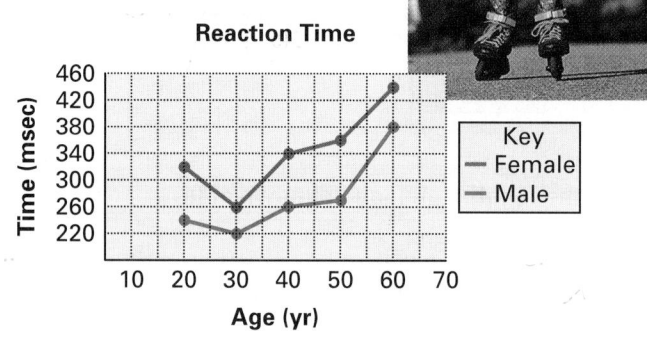

Reaction Time

Write in scientific notation. *[Lesson 3-4]*

21. 56,000 22. 72,300,000 23. 2 trillion 24. 6 thousand

25. 1,600 26. 48 billion 27. 94,560,000 28. 874,870,000,000

Project Progress

Draw sketches of the first four golf holes. Make the shapes interesting and challenging but keep the sides straight. Using a ruler, measure the perimeters in cm. If 1 cm = 2 feet, are your sketches a reasonable size?

Problem Solving

Understand
Plan
Solve
Look Back

Converting in the Metric System

▶ Lesson Link You know the decimal system is based on 10. Now you will use metric measurement, which is also based on 10. ◀

Explore Converting in the Metric System

Super Powers of 10

Materials: Calculator

1. Using a calculator, copy and complete the chart.

÷ 1000	÷ 100	÷ 10	Base Unit	× 10	× 100	× 1000
	0.05	0.5	5	50	500	
		1.7	17	170		
			2.1			
			0.55			
			36.7			

2. If these were the next three lines in the chart, what would be the values of *a*, *b*, and *c*? Explain.

		0.0045			*a*	
b				270		
	0.00021					*c*

3. How could you fill out the chart without using a calculator?

4. If the numbers 0.034 and 34,000 were in the same row, how many columns would be in between them? How can you tell?

You'll Learn ...

■ to measure using the metric system and to convert units within that system

... How It's Used

Endodontists convert units in the metric system when selecting tools to perform root canals.

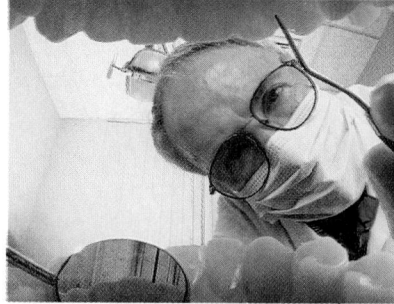

Vocabulary

metric system

meter

gram

liter

kilo-

centi-

milli-

Learn Converting in the Metric System

The **metric system** is a system of measurements used to describe how long, how heavy, or how big something is. The base unit for measuring length is the **meter** . The base unit for measuring mass is the **gram** . The base unit for measuring volume is the **liter** .

▶ History Link

The meter was originally defined as $\frac{1}{10,000,000}$ of the distance from the equator to the North Pole. It took the French from 1792 to 1798 to measure and calculate this distance. Today's satellites confirm that their measurements were only off by 0.2 mm.

The metric system also uses prefixes to describe amounts that are much larger or smaller than the base unit. The prefixes used most often are **kilo-**, meaning 1000; **centi-**, meaning $\frac{1}{100}$; and **milli-**, meaning $\frac{1}{1000}$.

	Name	Abbreviation	Number of Base Units	Approximate Comparison
Length	**Kilo**meter	km	1000	10 city blocks
	Meter	m	1	Half the height of a door
	Centimeter	cm	$\frac{1}{100}$	Length of a raisin
	Millimeter	mm	$\frac{1}{1000}$	Width of a period at the end of a sentence
Mass	**Kilo**gram	kg	1000	Mass of a cantaloupe
	Gram	g	1	Mass of a raisin
Volume	Liter	L	1	Half a large bottle of soda
	Milliliter	mL	$\frac{1}{1000}$	Half an eyedropper

The prefixes allow you to choose a convenient unit when something is too large or too small to be easily measured in meters, grams, or liters.

▶ Science Link

Glass never wears out. It can be recycled forever.

Example 1

Complete. Use the abbreviation for the most appropriate metric unit.

Height of a single-serving bottle: 17 _____

Since length (height) is being measured, the base unit should be the meter. Since a bottle is about 17 raisins tall, the appropriate unit is centimeters, abbreviated as cm. The height is 17 cm.

Try It

Complete. Use the abbreviation for the most appropriate metric unit.

a. Length of a marathon route: 42 _____

b. Width of a thumbnail: 1.5 _____

c. Mass of a dog: 15 _____

d. Amount of water in a small fishbowl: 2 _____

To convert a unit in the metric system, you multiply or divide by a power of 10. The table below lists the powers of 10 to use when converting.

÷ 1000	÷ 100	÷ 10	Base Unit	× 10	× 100	× 1000
Kilo-	Hecto-	Deka-	Meter	Deci-	Centi-	Milli-
			Gram			
			Liter			
× 1000	× 100	× 10	Base Unit	÷ 10	÷ 100	÷ 1000

Examples

2 The Danville Stroller Derby is 5 km long. How many meters is that?

The first unit given is kilometers. To convert from kilometers to meters, you multiply by 1000.

5 km × 1000 = 5000 m

3 60,000 cm = _____ km

First, to convert from centimeters to meters, you divide by 100. Then, to convert meters to kilometers, you divide by 1000.

60,000 cm ÷ 100 = 600 m

600 m ÷ 1000 = 0.6 km

Remember

A shortcut for multiplying by 1000 is to move the decimal point three places to the right. **[Page 178]** A shortcut for dividing by 1000 is to move the decimal point three places to the left. **[Page 187]**

Try It

Convert.

a. 7.36 km = _____ m   **b.** 0.008 L = _____ mL   **c.** 325 g = _____ kg

Number sense can help determine if a conversion is reasonable. When converting to a larger unit, your answer gets smaller. When converting to a smaller unit, your answer gets larger. For example, if you have a given distance in millimeters, it will take fewer centimeters to equal that same distance.

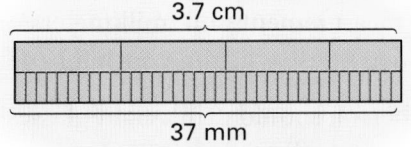

3.7 cm

37 mm

Check | Your Understanding

1. How are kilograms and kilometers similar? How are they different?

2. Can any measure in milliliters be converted to liters? Can any measure in milligrams be converted to meters? Explain.

4-2 Exercises and Applications

Practice and Apply

Getting Started **For each pair of measurements, choose the larger.**

1. 1 meter, 1 kilometer   **2.** 1 kilogram, 1 gram   **3.** 1 centimeter, 1 meter

4. 1 liter, 1 milliliter   **5.** 1 centimeter, 1 millimeter   **6.** 1 kilometer, 1 millimeter

For Exercises 7–12, name an appropriate metric unit of measure.

7. Weight of a 6th grader

8. Amount of water in a swimming pool

9. Distance from New York to Washington, DC

10. Amount of water in a raindrop

11. Weight of an aluminum can

12. Height of a stack of daily newspapers read in one month

Convert.

13. 90 g = ☐ kg   **14.** 32.6 mm = ☐ m   **15.** 0.1 L = ☐ mL

16. 5.3 m = ☐ mm   **17.** 7.88 mL = ☐ L   **18.** 1 m = ☐ cm

19. 0.0042 kg = ☐ g   **20.** 3 L = ☐ mL   **21.** 5 g = ☐ kg

22. 25 kg = ☐ g   **23.** 13.1 cm = ☐ mm   **24.** 8 mL = ☐ L

25. 2.67 km = ☐ cm   **26.** 18 cm = ☐ m   **27.** 42.9 kg = ☐ g

28. Career Which measurement unit, millimeters or meters, would an optometrist use when measuring patients' eyes?

29. Estimation A person should drink eight glasses of water every day. Estimate if this is more than or less than 1 liter.

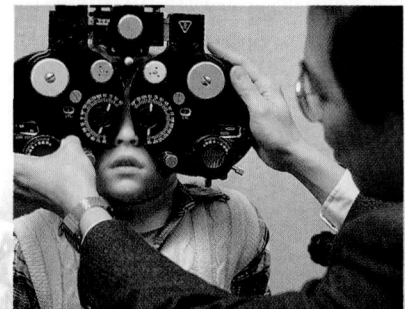

30. Every year, a person creates 163,300 grams of food and yard waste. Convert this amount to kilograms.

31. **Test Prep** In the 1996 Summer Olympics, Michael Johnson broke a world track record with a time of 19.32 seconds. Which distance did he most likely run?
Ⓐ 2 meters Ⓑ 200 meters
Ⓒ 200 liters Ⓓ 20 kilometers

32. Newspapers make up the largest part of trash in landfills. A 30.48 cm stack of newspapers weighs about 15.87 kg. Convert the measurements to meters and grams.

Problem Solving and Reasoning

33. **Communicate** State the perimeter of a square whose sides are each 12 cm in millimeters, centimeters, and meters. Explain your reasoning.

Problem Solving TIP

Draw a diagram.

34. **Journal** Describe a situation in which you would use liters and one in which you would use milliliters. Explain why each measurement is appropriate.

35. **Critical Thinking** Robert and his granddaughter Bailey built a playhouse. The foundation of the playhouse was a 1.86 m-by-95 cm rectangle. What was the perimeter of Bailey's playhouse? Explain.

36. **Critical Thinking** As part of a statistics experiment, seven students measured the approximate distance around a bus token. Find the average measurement rounded to the hundredths of a cm. Explain your reasoning.

Jon	3.6 cm
Diane	34.2 mm
Wu-Lin	3.4 cm
Shelly	3.8 cm
Truc	37.5 mm
Mary	32.1 mm
Jason	3.5 cm

Mixed Review

Write in standard form. *[Lesson 2-1]*

37. one hundred three **38.** 8 trillion **39.** 45 billion **40.** two thousand, five

41. forty-five thousand, six hundred twelve **42.** one million, sixty-one thousand, twenty-two

Write each fraction as a decimal. *[Lesson 3-1]*

43. $\frac{55}{100}$ **44.** $\frac{2}{10}$ **45.** $\frac{67}{1000}$ **46.** $\frac{532}{1000}$ **47.** $\frac{4}{10}$

48. $\frac{9}{10}$ **49.** $\frac{2}{100}$ **50.** $\frac{10}{10}$ **51.** $\frac{8}{1000}$ **52.** $\frac{99}{100}$

Using Conversion Factors

You'll Learn ...

■ to convert units within the customary system of measurement

... How It's Used

Chefs convert units in the customary system when preparing meals for a large number of people.

Vocabulary

inch

foot

yard

mile

ounce

pound

quart

gallon

conversion factor

▶ **Lesson Link** You have learned how to use the metric system of measurement. Now you will learn how to use the customary system of measurement for length, mass, and volume. ◀

Explore   Using Conversion Factors

Go to the Head of the Table!

Materials: Calculator

1. Each column of numbers in the table below is the result of taking the base number and multiplying or dividing it by some factor. For each column, determine the factor used.

÷ ???	÷ ???	Base	× ???	× ???
2	1,760	3,520	10,560	126,720
5	4,400	8,800	26,400	316,800
7	6,160	12,320	36,960	443,520
		14,080		

2. What are the missing values in the bottom row of the chart?

3. For each column in the table below, determine the factor used.

÷ ???	÷ ???	Base	× ???	× ???
35.2	352	3,520	35,200	352,000
88	880	8,800	88,000	880,000
123.2	1,232	12,320	123,200	1,232,000
		14,080		

4. What are the missing values in the bottom row of the chart?

5. In which chart is it easier to go from one column to the next? Why?

The customary system is another system of measurement used in the United States to describe how long, how heavy, or how big something is. The customary system does not use a base unit and prefixes. Each unit has a separate name.

	Name	Abbreviation	Approximate Comparison
Length	Inch	in.	Length of half a thumb
Length	Foot	ft	Length of adult male foot
Length	Yard	yd	Length from nose to outstretched fingertip
Length	Mile	mi	Length of 16 city blocks
Weight	Ounce	oz	Weight of birthday card
Weight	Pound	lb	Weight of three apples
Volume	Quart	qt	Amount in a medium container of milk
Volume	Gallon	gal	Amount in a small bucket

DID YOU KNOW?

There is more than one type of ounce. For example, Avoirdupois ounces are used to measure solid things. Fluid ounces are used to measure liquid things.

Inches can be abbreviated with quotation marks: 15" means 15 inches. Feet can be abbreviated with an apostrophe: 21' means 21 feet.

Example 1

Complete. Use the abbreviation for the most appropriate customary unit.

Height of a plastic water bottle: 11 _____

Since length is being measured, the customary unit should be inches, feet, yards, or miles. Since a bottle is about 11 half-thumbs, the appropriate unit is inches, which is abbreviated "in."

Try It

Complete. Use the abbreviation for the most appropriate customary unit.

a. Length of a marathon route: 26 _____

b. Weight of a dog: 45 _____

c. Amount of water in a small fishbowl: 2 _____

▶ Science Link

Plastics of different types cannot be recycled together. In order to help sort plastics, bottle manufacturers label the plastic type on the bottle. Polyethylene terephthalate, one of the most common types, is labeled "1 PET" or "1 PETE."

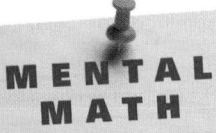

MENTAL MATH

When dividing a number with several zeros at the end, you can divide the whole number part and annex the zeros to your answer.

The customary system is not based on powers of 10. In order to convert from one unit to another, you need to know the **conversion factor**, or the number of units that another unit is equal to.

Length	Weight	Liquid Capacity
1 foot = 12 inches	1 pound = 16 ounces	1 gallon = 4 quarts
1 yard = 3 feet		
1 mile = 5280 feet		

To convert to a smaller unit, *multiply* by the appropriate conversion factor. The unit in the answer is smaller, so the number of units will be bigger. To convert to a larger unit, *divide* by the appropriate conversion factor. The unit in the answer is bigger, so the number of units will be smaller.

Examples

2 The average adult in the United States generates 8 pounds of newspaper garbage in a month. How many ounces is this?

One pound equals 16 ounces. Pounds are being converted to smaller units, so the number of pounds should be multiplied by the conversion factor.

$8 \times 16 = 128$ ounces

3 An oil company can re-refine 62 gallons of new oil from every 400 quarts of recycled oil. 400 quarts is equal to how many gallons?

One gallon equals 4 quarts. Quarts are being converted to larger units, so the number of quarts should be divided by the conversion factor.

$400 \div 4 = 100$ gallons

Try It

Convert. **a.** 7 gal = _____ qt **b.** 64 oz = _____ lb **c.** 2 mi = _____ ft

Check | Your Understanding

1. Is it easier to convert in the metric or the customary system? Why?

2. How can you tell when to multiply by a conversion factor and when to divide by a conversion factor?

Practice and Apply

Getting Started Convert to feet.

1. 36 inches   **2.** 24 inches   **3.** 96 inches   **4.** 144 inches   **5.** 60 inches

Convert.

6. 496 ounces = ☐ pounds   **7.** 252 inches = ☐ feet   **8.** 15 pounds = ☐ ounces

9. 36 feet = ☐ yards   **10.** 4 feet = ☐ inches   **11.** 2 pounds = ☐ ounces

12. 48 quarts = ☐ gallons   **13.** 12 yards = ☐ feet   **14.** 10,560 feet = ☐ miles

15. 24 pounds = ☐ ounces   **16.** 9 gallons = ☐ quarts   **17.** 4 miles = ☐ feet

18. 192 inches = ☐ feet   **19.** 21,120 feet = ☐ yards   **20.** 44 quarts = ☐ gallons

21. Number Sense You can double the height of a 2-year-old child to get an estimate of how tall he or she will be as an adult. Grant is 2 years old and 36 inches tall. How tall will he be as an adult? Give the answer in feet and in inches.

22. Patti made this drawing to help her remember the conversion factor for quarts and gallons.

   a. How many quarts are in a gallon?

   b. How many quarts are in 4 gallons?

   c. How many gallons are in 32 quarts?

1 gallon

23. History Many people recycle aluminum cans. An ordinary paper grocery bag holds about 1.5 pounds of crushed aluminum cans. How many ounces is that?

24. Order the following distances from shortest to longest distance: 2 miles; 15,840 feet; 63,360 inches; 7,040 yards.

25. | Test Prep | To change 16 quarts into gallons, you should

    Ⓐ multiply by 2.   Ⓑ multiply by 4.   Ⓒ divide by 2.   Ⓓ divide by 4.

26. To perform well on the balance beam, a gymnast must always be aware of the length of the beam. The length of the balance beam at the Olympic Games is 96 inches, and it is 4 inches wide. How many feet long is the balance beam?

Problem Solving and Reasoning

27. Critical Thinking

    a. Estimate how many heights in the table are between 5 and 6 feet.

    b. Convert the heights in the table to feet. How close was your estimate?

Name	Height (in.)
Allison	53
Clive	57
Alberto	60
Maurice	63
Tanya	72

28. Communicate Explain how to convert 30 inches to feet.

29. Communicate There are 12 inches in a foot and 5280 feet in a mile. What is the conversion factor between inches and miles? Explain.

30. Critical Thinking There are 16 ounces in a pound. You can use the equation $16x = y$ to convert ounces to pounds or pounds to ounces. Which variable is ounces and which is pounds? Explain.

Mixed Review

For Exercises 31–33, use the scatterplot. *[Lesson 1-3]*

31. What was the highest score? Who received it?

32. What was the speed of person B?

33. If another person, G, scored a 45, between which two scores was that score?

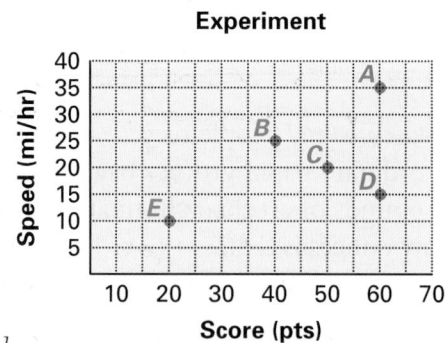

Experiment

For Exercises 33–38, order from least to greatest. *[Lesson 3-3]*

34. 0.77, 0.7777, 1.77, 0.777   **35.** 1.34, 1.06, 1.36, 1.66   **36.** 55.64, 0.564, 5.64, 5.06

37. 0.678, 0.0349, 0.982, 0.56   **38.** 3.005, 3.011, 3.002, 3.01   **39.** 67.1, 68.3, 66.3, 67.4, 67.5

In this section you've learned how to calculate perimeters and how to convert from one type of unit to another. Now you'll use this knowledge to decide on the most efficient route for a recyclables collection truck.

One Person's Trash Is Another Person's …?

Materials: Ruler, Colored pencils/pens

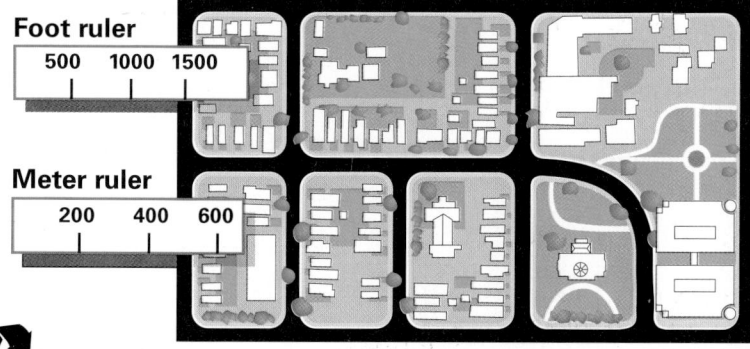

1. You need to determine the shortest possible route a recyclables truck can take to pick up recyclable material from all the buildings on the neighborhood map. Trace a copy of the map and label the route you think is best.

2. On another sheet of paper, trace the "foot ruler" and the "meter ruler" above. Use these rulers to measure the length of your route in feet and in meters.

3. Convert your measurement from feet to miles. If a truck can travel 150 miles on one tank of gas, how many neighborhoods could it collect recyclables from? Explain how you calculated your answer.

4. Convert your measurement from meters to kilometers. How many kilometers would a truck need to travel to collect recyclables from 20 neighborhoods? Explain how you calculated your answer.

225

REVIEW 4A

For Exercises 1–5, find each perimeter. Give the answer in centimeters.

1.

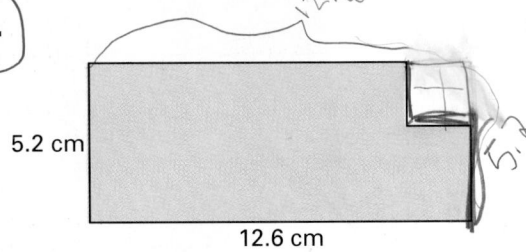

5.2 cm

12.6 cm

2.

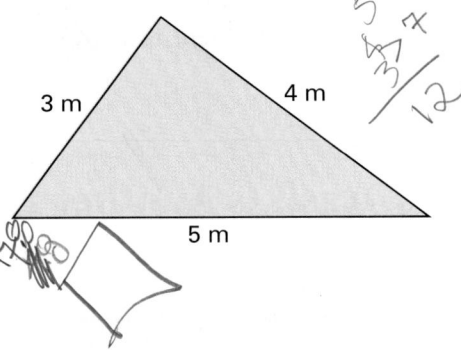

3 m   4 m

5 m

3. A square with a side length of 7.8 meters

4. A 6-sided figure with all sides 6.8 mm long

5. An 8-sided figure with half of the sides 32 m and half 48 m

For Exercises 6–10, find each perimeter. Give the answer in feet.

6.

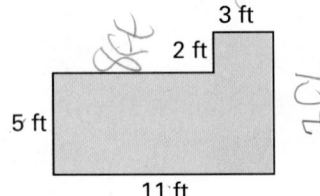

3 ft
2 ft
5 ft
11 ft

7.

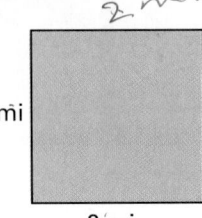

2 mi

2 mi

8. A triangle with sides of 6, 8, and 8 feet

9. A square with 5-yard sides

10. A rectangle where three of the sides are 12, 18, and 12 inches

Convert.

11. $8 L = \square$ mL

12. $1963.7 g = \square$ kg

13. $38 km = \square$ mm

14. 128 ounces $= \square$ pounds

15. 116 quarts $= \square$ gallons

16. 180 feet $= \square$ inches

Test Prep

You can convert from meters to kilometers by moving the decimal 3 places.

17. Convert 394.2 meters to kilometers.

   Ⓐ 0.3942 km   Ⓑ 3.942 km   Ⓒ 39.42 km   Ⓓ 394200 km

The Monster that Ate MINNESOTA

It's larger than seven football fields!

Every day, it swallows more than 100,000 people!

It stretches over 4.2 million square feet of the town of Bloomington, Minnesota!

Has King Kong returned? Is Godzilla on another rampage? Not exactly. These words don't describe a monster—they describe a shopping mall. Specifically, they describe the Mall of America, the largest U.S. mall. It's about 34 times bigger than the average U.S. mall.

Constructing a mall is a complex task. Designers have to decide exactly how big each of the many rooms, stores, and hallways is going to be. Geometry, one of the branches of mathematics, helps designers determine the area of objects such as malls. With mathematics, it's possible to describe how big something will be before it's ever built.

1 Why do people build malls?

2 What information must a designer know before planning a mall?

3 Why is it important to know the size of every room in a building before you start building it?

227

4-4 Area of Squares and Rectangles

You'll Learn ...
■ to find the area of squares and rectangles

... How It's Used
Employees at art stores must work with area when framing and putting protective glass on a customer's purchase.

Vocabulary
area

square inch

square centimeter

base

height

right angle

▶ **Lesson Link** You have calculated the distance around the outside of squares and rectangles. Now you'll calculate the amount of surface they cover. ◀

Explore Area of Squares and Rectangles

Grid Lock
Materials: Transparent 100-grids

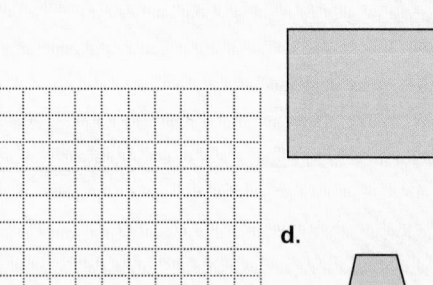
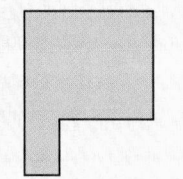
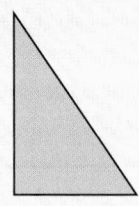
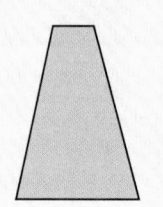
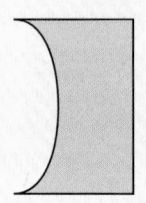
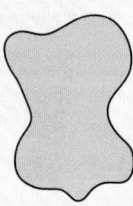

1. The grid contains 100 small squares. Estimate the number of small squares it takes to cover each gray figure.

2. When you have written all your estimates, get a transparent copy of the grid. Place it on top of each figure, and record the actual number of squares needed to cover the figure. For some figures, you may still need to make an estimate.

3. For which figure was your estimate without the grid closest to your measurement with the grid? Why was your estimate so accurate?

4. For which figure was your estimate without the grid furthest from your measurement with the grid? Why was your estimate so inaccurate?

5. Why were some of your measurements with the grids still estimates?

The **area** of a figure is the amount of surface it covers. Area is usually measured by the number of unit squares of the same size that fit into the figure.

Example 1

Which rectangle has a bigger area?

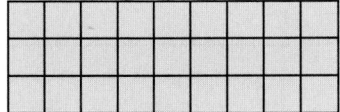 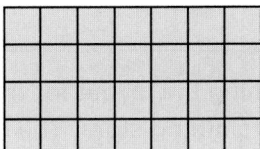

The first rectangle contains 27 squares. It has an area of 27 square units.
The second rectangle contains 28 squares. It has an area of 28 square units.

The second rectangle has a bigger area.

If a figure is labeled with inches, the area is expressed in **square inches** (in^2). A square inch is a square whose sides measure 1 inch. A **square centimeter** (cm^2) is a square whose sides measure 1 centimeter. A figure without labels is measured in square units (units^2).

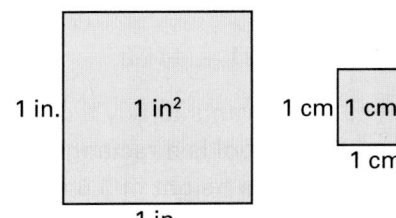

1 in.   1 in^2 1 cm | 1 cm^2
1 in.   1 cm

Example 2

Each square shown on the wall is a square meter. How much wallpaper would you need to cover the wall?

There are 20 squares in the rectangle. You would need 20 m^2 of wallpaper.

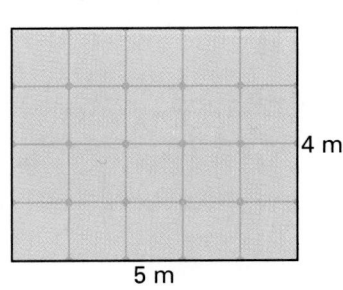

4 m

5 m

Try It

Find the area of each figure. Use the appropriate unit.

a.
7 in.
2 in.

b.
3 cm
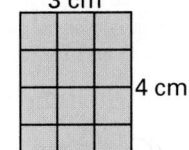
4 cm

c.
7 ft
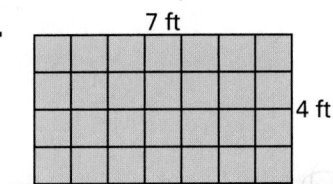
4 ft

You can determine the area of a square or rectangle without counting the squares inside by using a formula.

The **base** of a square or rectangle is the distance across the bottom. The **height** is the distance along a side. A **right angle** is an angle as wide as the corner of a page. The height of a shape always forms a right angle with the base.

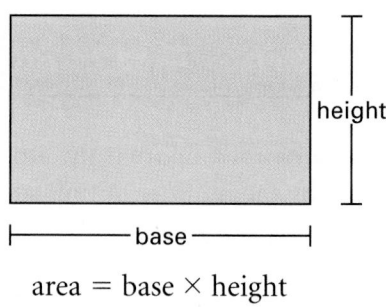

height

base

area = base × height

Examples

3 Karen is designing the layout for the customer area of her clothing store. The area is a square. Each side is 21 ft long. How big is the customer area?

The base and height of the customer area are both 21 ft.

Base × height = area

$21 \times 21 = 441$ ft^2

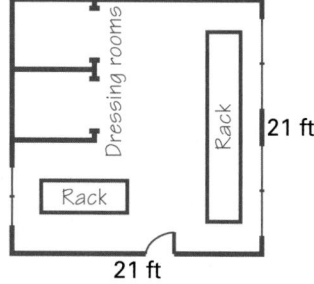

Dressing rooms

Rack

21 ft

Rack

21 ft

Problem Solving TIP

When multiplying with decimals, check your answer to make sure the number of digits after the decimal point in the product are the same as the total number of digits after the decimal points in the factors.

4 Jaymo wants to buy a cover for his pool. The pool is a rectangle with a base of 9 m and a height of 5.5 m. How big will the cover need to be?

Base × height = area

$9 \times 5.5 = 49.5$ m^2

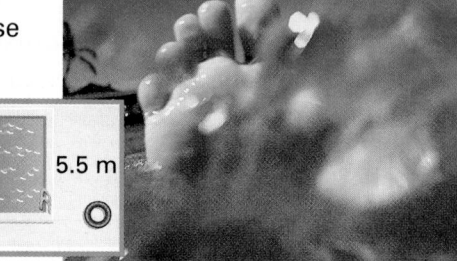

5.5 m

9 m

Try It

Find each area.

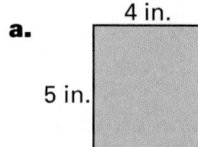

a.
4 in.
5 in.

b.
12 cm
4.5 cm

c.
14 yd
2 yd

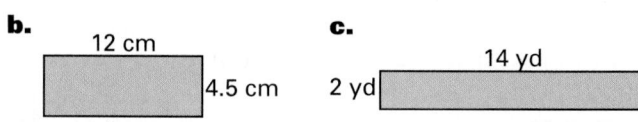

Check Your Understanding

1. For a given rectangle, if you switch the numbers for base and height, do you get a different area? Explain.

2. Why is area usually measured with squares, and not some other figure?

YOU ARE HERE

Practice and Apply

Getting Started Find each area.

1.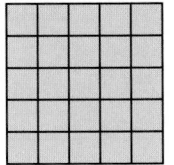

2.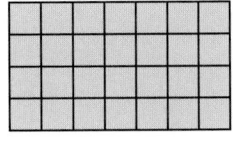

3.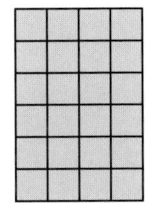

4.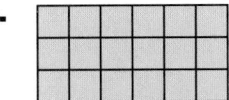

Find the missing measurement for each rectangle.

5. Area = 48 cm^2

Base = 2 cm

Height = ?

6. Area = 12.96 ft^2

Base = ?

Height = 7.2 ft

7. Area = ?

Base = 3 ft

Height = 9 ft

8. Area = 28.8 in^2

Base = ?

Height = 9.6 in.

9. Area = ?

Base = 0.8 km

Height = 1.5 km

10. Area = 33 yd^2

Base = 6 yd

Height = ?

11. Area = ?

Base = 12 mm

Height = 11 mm

12. Area = 300 in^2

Base = 30 in.

Height = ?

13. **Test Prep** Cristina's painting is 2 feet tall. What else must she know to calculate how many square feet the painting occupies?

Ⓐ The number of paintings on the wall

Ⓑ The length of the room

Ⓒ The width of the painting

Ⓓ The height of the ceiling

Find the area of each figure.

14. Rectangle with base 3 and height 6

15. Square with side 2 cm

16. Rectangle with sides 4 and 12 in.

17. Square centimeter

Johnson, William H.. "Man in a Vest," 1939–40. National Museum of American Art, Smithsonian Institute, Gift of the Harmon Foundation.

18. **Geometry** For the dance fundraiser, Janet and Paul need a piece of tarp to cover and protect the gym floor. The floor is 90 by 100 feet. What size rectangular tarp is needed?

19. **Fine Arts** *Man in a Vest*, painted by William H. Johnson, is 30 inches tall and 24 inches wide. Find the area of the painting.

Use the scatterplot for Exercises 20–22.

20. What is the area of each rectangle?

21. Which rectangle is also a square? How can you tell?

22. What is the area of the rectangle with a height of 3 inches?

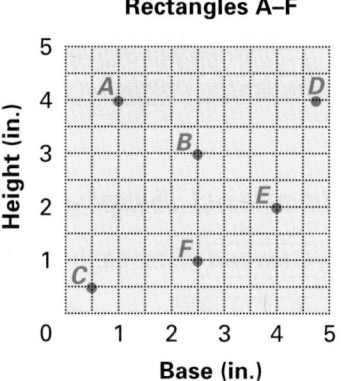

Rectangles A–F

Problem Solving and Reasoning

23. Critical Thinking Use the map of the shopping mall to answer these questions. Each colored area shows a different store.

   a. What is the area of the largest store? Explain.

   b. The annual rent for each store is $35 per ft². Find the range of rental costs. Explain your method.

24. Communicate A rectangle has an area of 120 cm². How many possible base/height pairs are there? Explain.

25. Critical Thinking The perimeter of a rectangular bookstore is 220 ft, and its length is 50 ft. What is the annual rent for the bookstore if the rent is $20 per square foot each year? Explain.

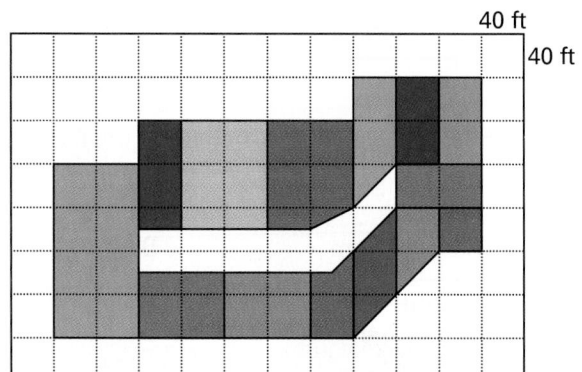

Mixed Review

For Exercises 26–28, use the stem-and-leaf diagram. *[Lesson 1-6]*

26. What is the range of values?

27. Is the median or the mean of the data larger? Explain.

28. What is the largest number in the data that is less than 25?

Stem	Leaf
0	9
1	2 5 6 6 7 9
2	1 1 2 3 5 7 7 8 8
4	0 0 1

Estimate each sum, difference, product, or quotient. *[Lesson 3-5]*

29. $67.29 + 3.01$ **30.** $14.76 \div 6.12$ **31.** 13.546×1.68 **32.** $0.886 - 0.324$

33. $52{,}395 \div 9{,}546$ **34.** $\$16.34 - \$5.49$ **35.** $87.003 + 56.31$ **36.** 23.3×4.37

Area of Parallelograms

▶ **Lesson Link** You know how to find the area of squares and rectangles. Now you will learn how to find the area of parallelograms. ◀

Explore   Area of Parallelograms

Is It Still the Same?

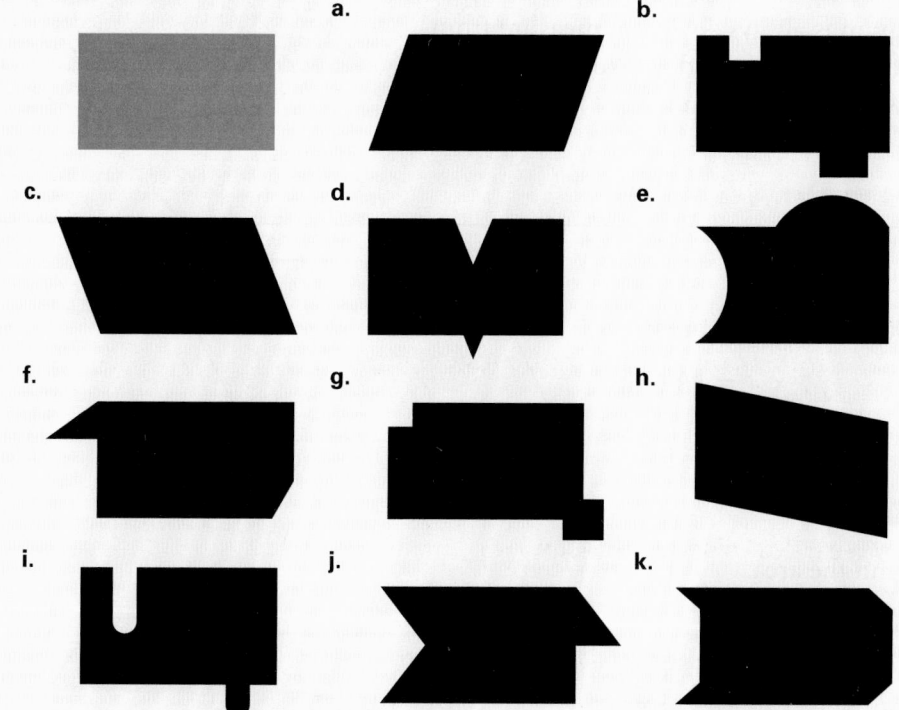

a. b. c. d. e. f. g. h. i. j. k.

1. State whether the area of each black figure is equal to, more than, or less than the area of the red rectangle. Explain your reasoning.

2. Can two different figures have the same area? Explain.

3. If you cut a piece from a figure and attach it to another side of the figure, does it still have the same area? Explain.

You'll Learn ...

■ to find the area of parallelograms

... How It's Used

City planners must calculate area when planning parking structures for public use.

Vocabulary

parallelogram

A **parallelogram** is a four-sided figure whose opposite sides are parallel.

A parallelogram has the same area as a rectangle of equal base and height. You can cut a triangle-shaped piece from one side of a parallelogram and move it to the other side to form a rectangle.

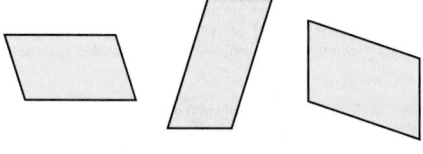

To find the area of a parallelogram, use the same formula for the area of a rectangle: base × height = area. The height of a parallelogram is always a vertical measure from the base, not a slanted measure. It is usually shown as a dashed line.

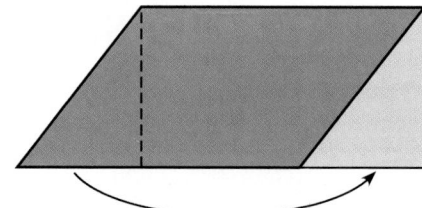

Study TIP

Parallel lines are straight lines that never meet, just like the two l's next to each other in the word *parallel*.

Example 1

Find the area.

Base × height = area

$7 \times 4 = 28$ units^2

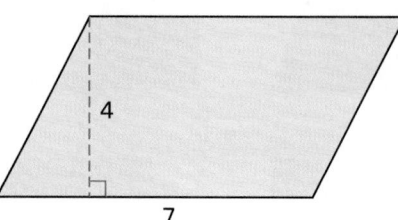

4

7

Try It

Find the area.

a.

b.

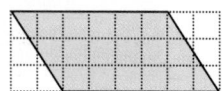

6 mm

33 mm

Check · Your Understanding

1. Can every parallelogram be changed into a rectangle by moving a section? Explain.

2. Can every four-sided figure be changed into a rectangle by moving a section? Explain.

YOU ARE HERE

Practice and Apply

Getting Started Find each area.

1.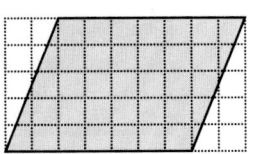

2.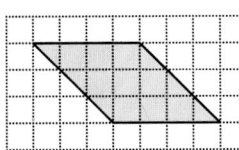

3.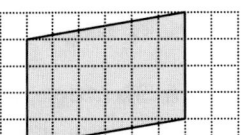

Find each area.

4.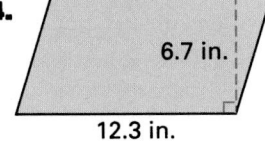
6.7 in.
12.3 in.

5.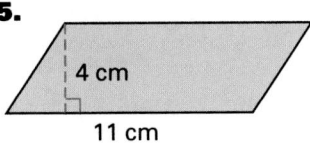
4 cm
11 cm

6.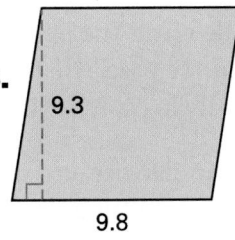
9.3
9.8

7.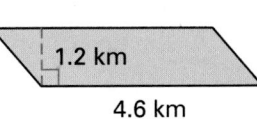
1.2 km
4.6 km

8.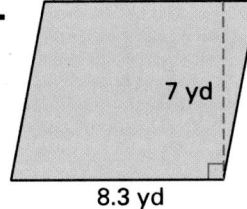
7 yd
8.3 yd

9.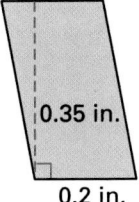
0.35 in.
0.2 in.

10.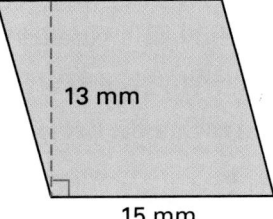
13 mm
15 mm

11.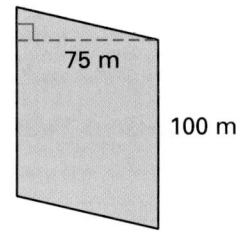
75 m
100 m

Find each area if b is the base and h is the height of a parallelogram.

12. $b = 20$, $h = 6$

13. $b = 12$ yd, $h = 7$ yd

14. $h = 25$ ft, $b = 25$ ft

15. $h = 14.7$ cm, $b = 18.1$ cm

16. $h = 13.2$ m, $b = 0.5$ m

17. $b = 1000$ km, $h = 1000$ km

18. **Test Prep** Choose the correct units for the area of a figure.

    Ⓐ Centimeters   Ⓑ Meters

    Ⓒ Square centimeters   Ⓓ Feet

19. **Geography** The state of Tennessee is shaped roughly like a parallelogram. Its northern border is about 442 miles long and the shortest distance between the northern and southern borders is about 115 miles. Estimate the area of Tennessee.

20. Patterns Jaspar drew a parallelogram with a base of 2 cm and a height of 2 cm. He drew another with base 2 cm and height 4 cm and a third with base 2 cm and height 8 cm. If Jaspar continues drawing parallelograms in this pattern, what will the area of the sixth figure be?

21. Geometry At some malls, parking spots are shaped like parallelograms. If a spot is 3.1 meters wide and 4.7 meters long, what is its area?

Problem Solving and Reasoning

22. Choose a Strategy Violet wants to add parallelograms to the design of her Native American drum. Each parallelogram should be about 36 square inches. If she wants the height to be four times longer than the base, what should the height of each parallelogram be? Explain.

23. 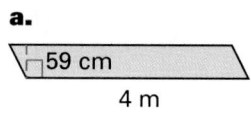 Describe the similarities and differences between a 2 cm by 4 cm rectangle and a parallelogram with base 2 cm and height 4 cm.

24. Communicate Which figure has the larger area, a rectangle with a base of 50 and a height of 20, or a parallelogram with a base of 50 and a slanted side of 20? Explain.

25. Critical Thinking Find each area. Explain your reasoning.

a.
59 cm
4 m

b.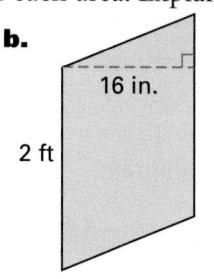
16 in.
2 ft

c.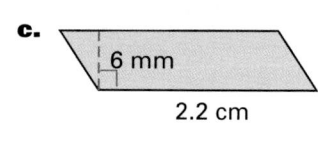
6 mm
2.2 cm

d.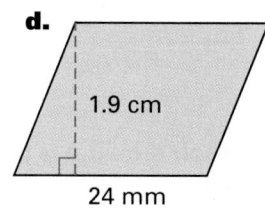
1.9 cm
24 mm

> **Problem Solving**
> ## STRATEGIES
> • Look for a Pattern
> • Make an Organized List
> • Make a Table
> • Guess and Check
> • Work Backward
> • Use Logical Reasoning
> • Draw a Diagram
> • Solve a Simpler Problem

Mixed Review

Write in standard form. *[Lesson 2-4]*

26. 5^9 **27.** 3^4 **28.** 9^5 **29.** 12^2 **30.** 2^6 **31.** 4^3

32. 10^{13} **33.** 1^{29} **34.** 6^1 **35.** 8^7 **36.** 20^2 **37.** 7^8

Simplify. *[Lesson 3-6]*

38. $108.93 - 72.41$ **39.** $0.5678 + 1.3452$ **40.** $6.25 + 7.36$ **41.** $238.14 - 5.67$

42. $1.5 + 0.5$ **43.** $2.3 + 4.5$ **44.** $87.003 - 56.31$

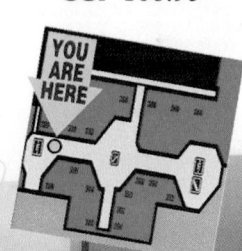

Area of Triangles

▶ **Lesson Link** You know how to find the area of several types of four-sided figures. Now you will find the area of a triangle. ◀

You'll Learn ...
■ to find the area of a triangle

... How It's Used

Carpet layers calculate areas in order to determine how much carpet they need.

Explore Area of Triangles

Size Wise

Materials: Dot paper

Area of Rectangle	Sketch	Area of Corner-to-Corner Triangle
1		$\frac{1}{2}$
2		
3		
4		
5		
6		
7		
8		
9		
10		
11		
12		

1. Copy the chart on dot paper. For each row, sketch one rectangle that has the given area. Some rectangles can be sketched in more than one way.

2. On each sketch, shade in a triangle that goes from one corner of the rectangle to the opposite corner. Estimate the area of the triangle.

3. Describe any patterns you see in comparing the areas of the rectangles and the areas of the corner-to-corner triangles.

4. For a rectangle with an area of 50 square units, what do you think the area of the corner-to-corner triangle would be? Explain.

Learn | Area of Triangles

The area of a triangle equals half the area of a rectangle whose base and height are the same as the triangle's. You can find the area of a triangle by calculating the area of the rectangle that surrounds it and dividing that in half. You can also use the area formula for a triangle.

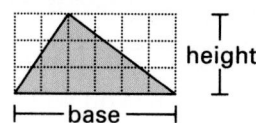

base × height ÷ 2 = area

Remember

When you divide a number by a number that doesn't go into the first number evenly, you get a decimal answer. The decimal point in the quotient should be placed directly above the decimal point in the dividend. **[Page 186]**

Examples

1 Find the area.

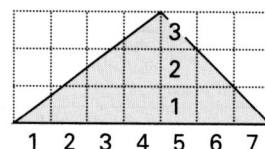

There are 7 squares across the base. The triangle is 3 squares tall.

base × height ÷ 2 = area

7 × 3 ÷ 2 = 10.5 units^2

2 Find the area.

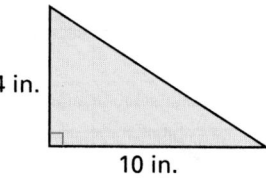

6.4 in.

10 in.

base × height ÷ 2 = area

10 × 6.4 ÷ 2 = 32 in^2

3 Devon wants to make a kite that measures 4 ft high and 5 ft at the base. How much fabric does she need?

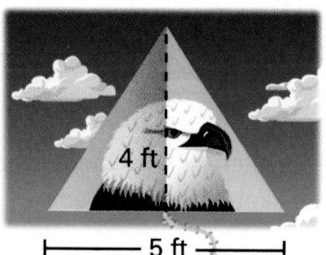

4 ft

5 ft

base × height ÷ 2 = area

5 × 4 ÷ 2 = 10

Devon needs 10 ft^2 of fabric.

► **History Link**

Kites are the oldest form of aircraft.

Try It

Find the area.

a.
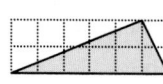

b.
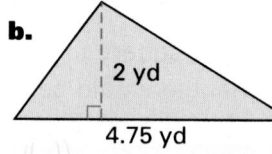
2 yd
4.75 yd

c.
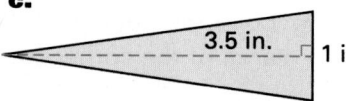
3.5 in. 1 in.

YOU ARE HERE

Sonia and Aaron are building the set for a play about ancient Egypt. They need to paint a large cardboard triangle to look like an Egyptian pyramid. The triangle measures 14 ft wide by 8 ft high. They have enough paint for about 60 square feet of cardboard. Do they have enough paint?

Sonia thinks ...

I'll imagine there's a rectangle around the triangle. I'll find the area of the rectangle and cut it in half.

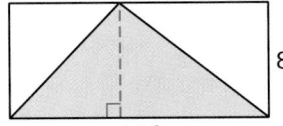

Area of a rectangle = base × height

$$= 14 \times 8$$
$$= 112 \text{ ft}^2$$

Half of 112 is 56. The cardboard is 56 square feet, so we have enough paint.

Aaron thinks ...

I'll use the area formula for a triangle.

Area of a triangle = base × height ÷ 2

$$= 14 \times 8 \div 2$$
$$= 56 \text{ ft}^2$$

The area is 56 ft². We have enough paint.

What do you think?

1. What information did Sonia and Aaron need to solve the problem?

2. Would Sonia and Aaron's answer change if the estimate of enough paint for 60 square feet was an overestimate? Explain.

Check Your Understanding

1. Why do you need to divide by 2 when finding the area of a triangle?

2. Do two triangles with the same height have the same area?

Practice and Apply

Getting Started Find the area of each triangle.

1.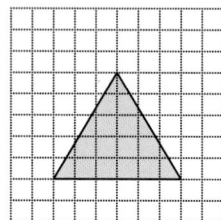

2.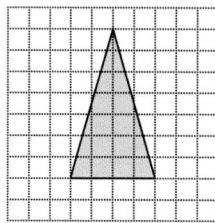

3.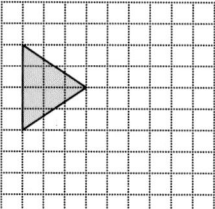

Find the area of each triangle.

4.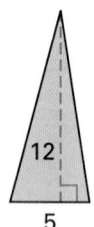

12
5

5.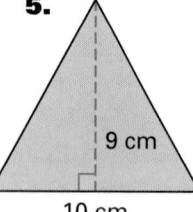

9 cm
10 cm

6.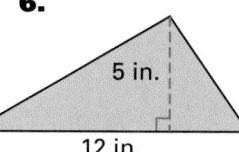

5 in.
12 in.

7.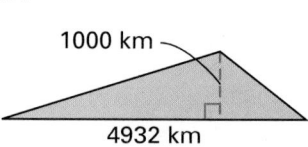

1000 km
4932 km

8.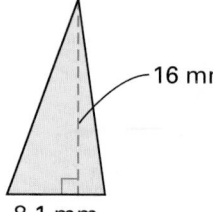

16 mm
8.1 mm

9.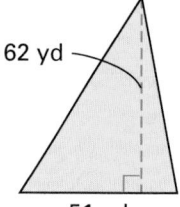

62 yd
51 yd

10.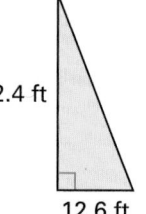

32.4 ft
12.6 ft

11.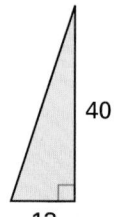

40
13

12. Geography The Bermuda Triangle is a region in the Atlantic Ocean where ships and airplanes are reported to have mysteriously disappeared since the 1940s. Use the diagram to find the area of the Bermuda Triangle.

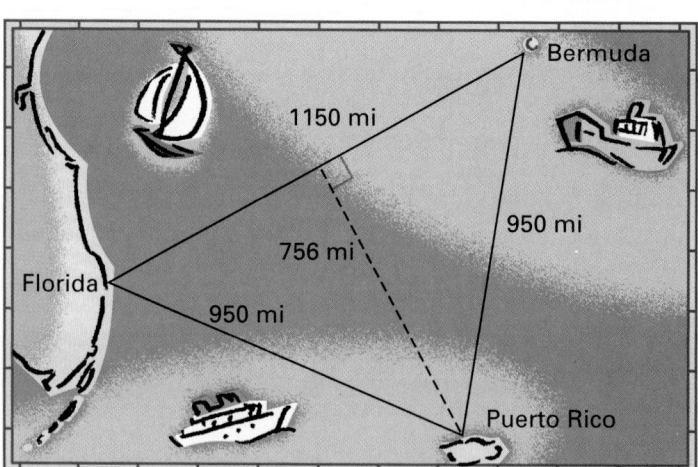

Bermuda
1150 mi
950 mi
756 mi
Florida
950 mi
Puerto Rico

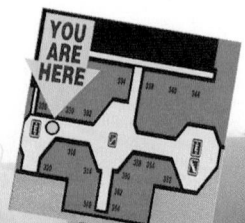

Find the area if _b_ is the base and _h_ is the height of a triangle.

13. $b = 6$ in., $h = 9$ in.

14. $b = 62$ ft, $h = 3$ ft

15. $h = 9$ in., $b = 7$ in.

16. **Test Prep** Find the area of the triangle.

Ⓐ 11.25 in^2

Ⓑ 15.4 in^2

Ⓒ 62.7 in^2

Ⓓ None of these

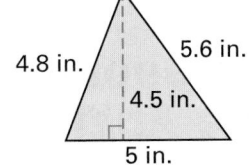

4.8 in.   5.6 in.

4.5 in.

5 in.

Problem Solving and Reasoning

17. Critical Thinking The central plaza of a shopping mall has four triangular flower beds. Each bed has a base of 60 inches and a height of 48 inches. If one plant can be planted every 4 square inches, how many are needed to fill the flower beds? Explain.

18. Communicate Describe how you can find the area of a regular pentagon, a figure with five equal sides, if you know how to find the area of triangles.

19. **Journal** A triangular plot of land has a base of 1 mile and an area of 1 square mile. Explain how they can both have a measure of 1.

Mixed Review

For Exercises 20–22, use the Shucked Oysters graph. *[Lesson 1-1]*

20. How many select oysters are in a pint?

21. How many more very small oysters than counts oysters are there in a pint?

22. Which size oyster gives the most number per pint?

Write each expression using exponents. *[Lesson 2-4]*

23. $6 \times 6 \times 6 \times 6 \times 6$

24. $435 \times 435 \times 435$

25. $7 \times 7 \times 7 \times 7$

26. $5 \times 5 \times 9 \times 9 \times 9$

27. $10 \times 10 \times 10 \times 10$

28. $1 \times 1 \times 1 \times 1 \times 1 \times 1$

29. $3 \times 3 \times 3 \times 3 \times 8$

30. 68×68

Project Progress

Return to your rough sketches and calculate the area of your golf holes. Make sure that at least two holes use rectangles and at least two holes use triangles in their shapes.

Problem Solving

Understand
Plan
Solve
Look Back

TECHNOLOGY

Using Dynamic Geometry Software • Finding the Sum of the Angles inside a Quadrilateral

Problem: How can you determine the sum of the angles inside every quadrilateral, or four-sided polygon?

You can use dynamic geometry software to determine the sums of the angles inside a four-sided polygon. At first, the investigation will focus only on convex polygons. These are polygons with no "dents".

❶ Using your geometry software draw a four-sided figure. Do **not** draw a figure with a "dent", like this one.

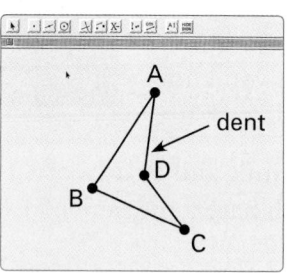

❷ Use the measure tool to measure the angles.

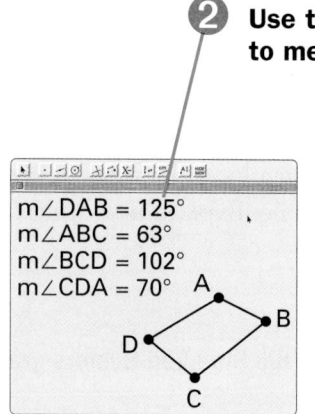

m∠DAB = 125°
m∠ABC = 63°
m∠BCD = 102°
m∠CDA = 70°

❸ Use the calculator feature of the software to find the sum of the measures of the angles.

❹ Without creating a dent, stretch the figure to see if the sum changes.

Solution: The sum of the angles inside a quadrilateral is 360°.

ON YOUR OWN

TRY IT

a. Find the sum of the angles inside a five-sided figure.

b. Find the sum of the angles inside a six-sided figure.

▶ Predict the sum of the angles inside a seven-sided figure. Explain your prediction. Draw a seven-sided figure with the software and check to see if your guess was correct.

▶ Write a rule or formula that predicts the sum of the inside angles for any figure, no matter how many sides it has.

▶ Draw a four-sided concave polygon—a polygon that has a "dent" in it. Is the sum of the interior angles different for this type of polygon? Explain.

In this section you learned how to find the area of squares, rectangles, parallelograms, and triangles. Now you will use your knowledge of area to decide how to design your own shopping mall.

The Monster That Ate Minnesota!

Materials: Ruler, Colored pencils or markers

1. You need to design a mini-mall that meets the following conditions:

   a. It must have at least six stores.

   b. It must have a central area with benches and a fountain. Customers can walk through the area from store to store.

   c. It must have restrooms and an elevator to a restaurant on the roof.

   d. Its area must be at least 1800 m².

2. Use a cm ruler to make a diagram of your mall. In one color, label the length of each line in centimeters. In a different color, label the length that each wall will be when the mall is built. Assume that 1 cm on your diagram equals 2 m of wall.

3. Calculate the area for each store, the central area, the restrooms, and the elevator. Your calculations should be in square meters. Write these areas on your diagram.

REVIEW 4B

Find the area of each figure.

1.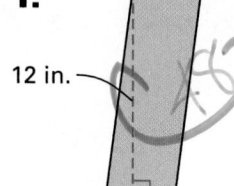

12 in.

4 in.

2.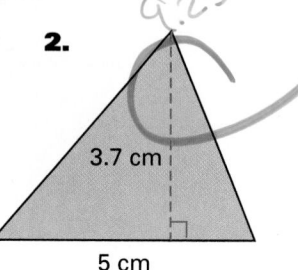

9.25 cm²

3.7 cm

5 cm

3.

.935 yd²

1.1 yd

0.85 yd

4.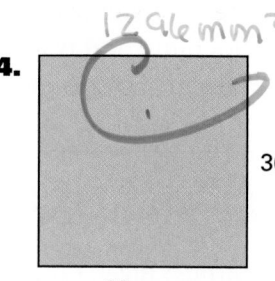

12.96 mm²

36 mm

36 mm

5. Number Sense Bob wants to cover his patio with tiles. The patio measures 12.5 by 7.5 feet. If Bob has 100 tiles that each measure 1 foot by 1 foot, does he have enough to cover the patio? yes

12.5
7.5

6. History The game of shuffleboard started as a small board game in which coins were shoved onto a scoring pattern. Cruise ships enlarged the game into a deck game for passengers. What is the area of the large triangle on a single shuffleboard court? 27 ft²

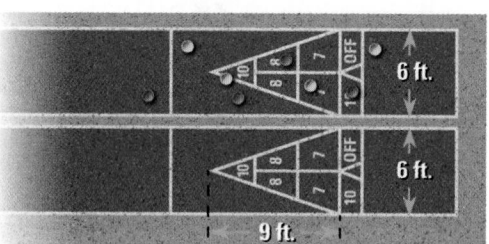

Use the conversion factor to find the missing measurement.

7. 16 ounces in 1 pound

☐ ounces in 6 pounds

8. 4 cups in 1 quart

32 cups in ☒ quarts

S ÷ L

9. 1 knot is 1.15 mi/hr

☐ knots = 3.68 mi/hr

3.2

Find the perimeter of each figure.

10.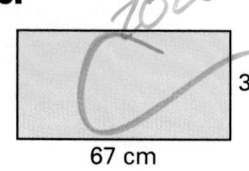

202 cm

34 cm

67 cm

11.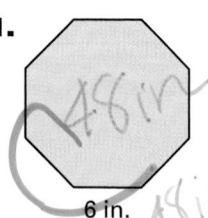

48 in

6 in.

48 in

12.

25 yd

25 yd

100 yd

13.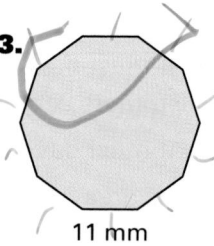

11 mm

110 mm

Test Prep

You can eliminate an answer if it has the wrong units of measurement.

14. Find the area of a rectangle that is 20 cm by 40 cm.

Ⓐ 60 cm   Ⓑ 60 cm²   Ⓒ 800 cm   Ⓓ 800 cm²

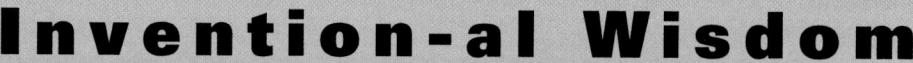

Invention-al Wisdom

Which of the following inventions has actually been awarded a patent by the U.S. Patent Office?

1. A combination rocking chair/butter churn

2. A pair of suspenders that can be used as a rope to escape from a burning building

3. A balloon powered by vultures

4. An alarm clock that wakes a person by dripping water on his or her head

If you guessed any of these, you were right. Every invention listed above has been awarded a patent by the U.S. Patent Office.

For thousands of years, people have been designing and creating inventions to make their work easier. Some inventions, like the telephone, the automobile, and the computer, have changed the way we live. Other inventions, such as the automatic egg-brander, never became widely popular. Today, the design of virtually every complex invention requires an understanding of mathematics.

1. Do all inventions make work easier?

2. Other than the telephone, the automobile, and the computer, what inventions have changed the way we live?

3. Why is it important to understand mathematics when designing an invention?

Discovering Pi

▶ **Lesson Link**
You've worked with the distance around shapes that have straight sides. Now you'll look at the distance around circles. ◄

You'll Learn ...

■ to find the circumference of a circle

... How It's Used

Bicycle riders need to calculate the circumference of their bicycle wheels when adjusting their speedometers.

Vocabulary

radius

diameter

circumference

pi

| **Explore** | **Discovering Pi** |

Circular Thinking

Materials: Tape measures, Calculators, Several circular objects

Object	Distance Around Outside	Distance Across Middle	Distance Around Outside ÷ Distance Across Middle

1. Copy the table. Your table should have at least five rows.

2. Using the tape measure, measure in centimeters the distance around the outside of five objects. Also measure the distance across the middle of each object. Make sure your distances across the middle go through the center.

3. Using a calculator, divide the distances around the outside by the distances across the middle. Round the results to 2 decimal places.

4. Describe any patterns you see in the values in the last column.

| **Learn** | **Discovering Pi** |

▶ **Language Link**

The prefix *di-* means "two." The diameter cuts a circle into two equal sections.

The **radius** of a circle is any line from the center to any point on the circle.

The **diameter** of a circle is any line from one point on the circle to another point on the circle that passes through the center.

The **circumference** of a circle is the distance around the circle.

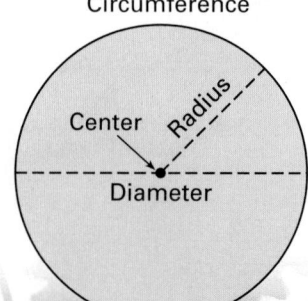

Circumference

Center Radius

Diameter

For any circle, the circumference divided by the diameter always equals 3.14159265…. This value is called **pi** and is represented by the Greek letter π. Because the digits in π go on forever, the number 3.14 is used as an approximation.

If you know the circumference of a circle, you can use π to find the diameter. If you know the diameter, you can use π to find the circumference.

Diameter × π = Circumference

Diameter ⟶ Circumference

Circumference ÷ π = Diameter

5 × π = circumference   15.7 ÷ π = diameter

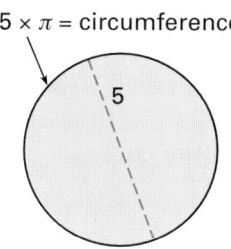
5

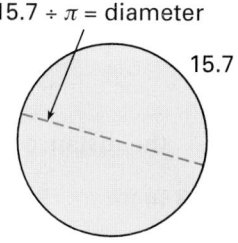
15.7

▶ **Science Link**

When building a computer, hardware engineers need to verify that the computer is doing calculations correctly. One method of checking a computer's accuracy is to have it calculate the value of π to one thousand digits.

Example 1

The diameter of one lens in the chicken eye-protector is 0.5 cm. What is the circumference?

Diameter × π = circumference

  0.5 × 3.14 = 1.57

The circumference is 1.57 cm.

Try It

a. Find the circumference of a compact disc with a diameter of 12 cm.

b. Find the diameter of a merry-go-round with a circumference of 75 ft.

c. Find the circumference.

d. Find the diameter.

6 ft

— 79 cm

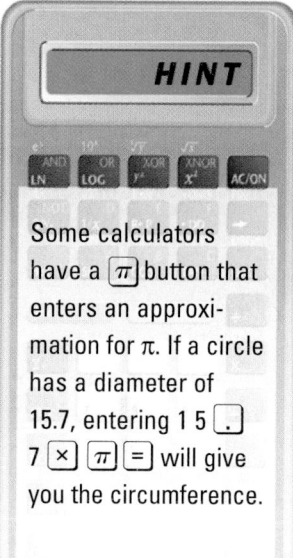

HINT

Some calculators have a ⟨π⟩ button that enters an approximation for π. If a circle has a diameter of 15.7, entering 1 5 ⟨.⟩ 7 ⟨×⟩ ⟨π⟩ ⟨=⟩ will give you the circumference.

Check | Your Understanding

1. Why do we use 3.14 as an estimate for π?

2. Will you get a more accurate estimate for π by measuring the circumference and diameter of a big circle like a tire, or a small circle like a penny? Why?

PRACTICE 4-7

Practice and Apply

Getting Started State whether each sentence is true or false.

1. The radius of a circle is always smaller than the diameter.

2. The circumference of a circle is equal to π.

3. The diameter of a circle is the distance around the circle.

Find each circumference. Use 3.14 for π.

4.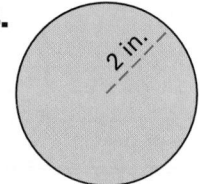
2 in.

5.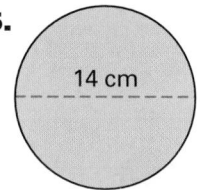
14 cm

6.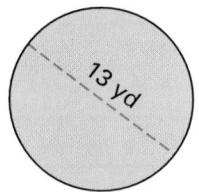
13 yd

7.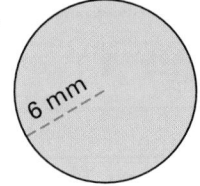
6 mm

Find the missing measurements for each circle, where r = radius, d = diameter, and C = circumference.

8. $r = 3$ mm, $d = 6$ mm, $C = \square$

9. $r = 4.5$, $d = \square$, $C = 28.26$

10. $r = 0.62$ in., $d = \square$, $C = \square$

11. $r = \square$, $d = \square$, $C = 47.1$ yd

12. $r = \square$, $d = 17.2$ yd, $C = \square$

13. $r = \square$, $d = 11$ m, $C = \square$

14. $r = \square$, $d = \square$, $C = 0.942$ km

15. $r = \square$, $d = 18.6$, $C = 58.404$

16. Karteek is making a pencil holder. The bottom of the holder is a circle with a diameter of 7 cm. How long must the felt strip be to go around the bottom?

17. The drawing shows a chewing gum locket. What is the circumference of the locket?

18. Number Sense In an experiment, Abel measured a circle but separated the data from the labels. The data is 6.8, 21.352, 3.14, and 3.4. The labels are Radius, Diameter, Circumference, and Pi. Match the data items with the correct labels.

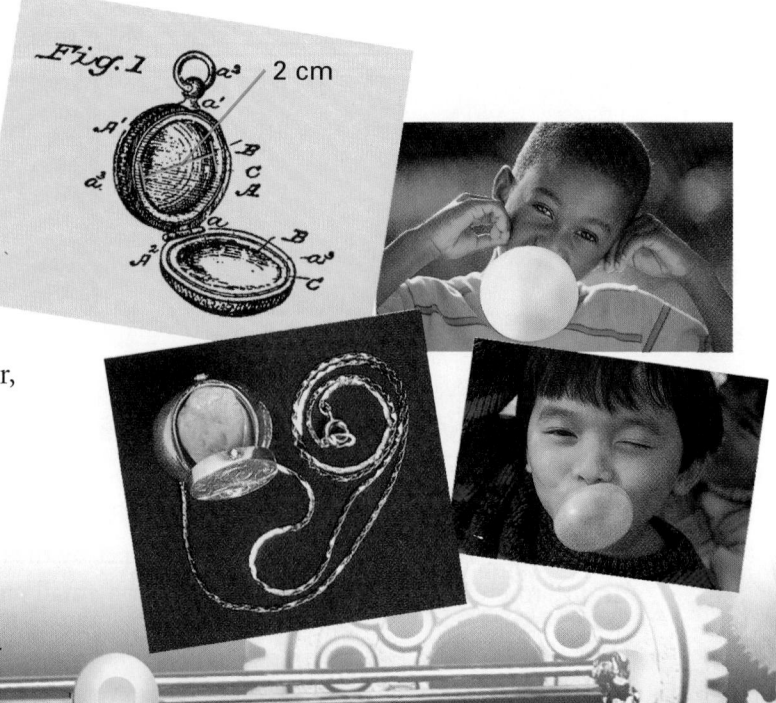

19. Hula hoops were popular during the 1960s and are still used today. A hula hoop is made by bending 2.6 meters of plastic tubing to form a circle. Find the diameter of the hula hoop, rounded to hundredths of a meter.

20. **Test Prep** A circle's circumference is 53 in. What is its radius rounded to the nearest tenth of an inch?

  Ⓐ 8.4 in.   Ⓑ 16.8 in.   Ⓒ 26.5 in.   Ⓓ None of these

Problem Solving and Reasoning

21. **Communicate** When you multiply the diameter of a circle by π to get the circumference, why is the answer never exact?

22. **Critical Thinking** Pat's bicycle wheel has a radius of 13 inches. If she rides the bicycle 1 mile (63,360 inches), how many times has the wheel rotated? Explain.

23. **Critical Thinking** A grass fire is burning a circular region with a radius of 65 feet. How many firefighters are needed to surround the fire if they stand 10 feet apart from each other and 2 feet from the fire? Explain.

24. **Critical Thinking** An ice skater is following a path of two circles shaped like a figure eight. One loop has a diameter of 8 meters, and the other loop has a diameter of 10 meters. How far does the skater travel in one complete figure eight? Explain.

Mixed Review

Write in expanded form. *[Lesson 2-4]*

25. 11658^1 **26.** 28^4 **27.** 3^5 **28.** 56^2 **29.** 9^6 **30.** 7^3

31. 12^5 **32.** 36^8 **33.** 6^3 **34.** 41^7 **35.** 13^{11} **36.** 8^5

Estimate each sum or difference. *[Lesson 2-6]*

37. $567 + 324$ **38.** $49 + 52 + 53 + 50$ **39.** $23 - 12$ **40.** $227 + 225 + 224$

41. $452 - 262$ **42.** $9324 + 675$ **43.** $\$16 - \$9$ **44.** $6218 - 3281$

Project Progress

Sketch the final golf hole. Make sure it uses a circle, or part of a circle, in its shape.

Calculate the perimeter of the final golf hole. If 1 cm = 2 feet, is the sketch a reasonable size?

Problem Solving

Understand
Plan
Solve
Look Back

Area of Circles

You'll Learn ...

■ to find the area of circles

... How It's Used

Umpires use the area of a circle to verify that the pitcher's mound in a baseball diamond is the right size.

▶ **Lesson Link** You know how to find the distance around the outside of a circle. Now you'll learn how to find the area inside a circle. ◀

Explore | Area of Circles

A Square Peg in a Round Hole

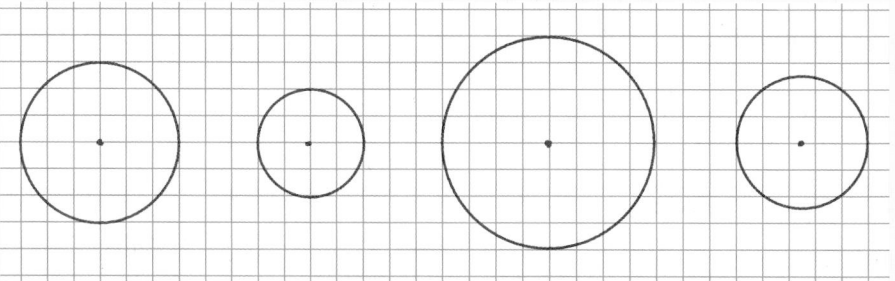

1. Estimate the area of each circle.

2. For each circle, draw a square whose sides are as long as the radius of the circle. Label it "radius square," and find the area.

3. For each circle, estimate the number of radius squares that would fit inside the circle.

4. Describe any patterns you observe in your results for Step 3.

Learn | Area of Circles

The circumference and the diameter of a circle are related by the number π. The radius and the area of a circle are also related by the number π. If you know the radius of a circle, you can use π to find the area.

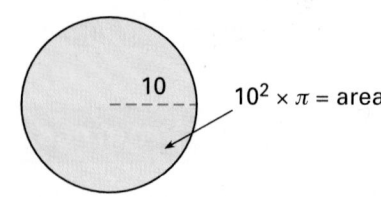

$10^2 \times \pi$ = area

This can also be described by the formula: Area $= \pi \times r^2$, where r is the radius.

Examples

Find the area.

1

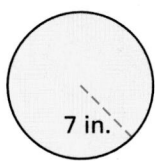

7 in.

Area = $\pi \times r^2$
  = 3.14×7^2
  = 3.14×49
  = 153.86 in^2

2

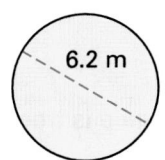

6.2 m

The diameter is 6.2 m. The radius is half the diameter, or 3.1 m.

Area = $\pi \times r^2$
  = 3.14×3.1^2
  = 3.14×9.61
  = 30.1754 m^2

3 The "Combined Grocer's Package, Grater, Slicer, and Mouse and Fly Trap" has a lid with a 4-inch diameter. What is the area of the lid?

The radius is half of the diameter, or 2 in.

Area = $\pi \times r^2$
  = 3.14×2^2
  = 3.14×4
  = 12.56 in^2

(No Model)

COMBINED GROCER'S PACKAGE, GRATER, SLICER, AND MOUSE AND FLY TRAP.

No. 586,025.   Patented July 6, 1897.

Fig. 1.   Fig. 2.   Fig. 3.   Fig. 4.   Fig. 7.   Fig. 8.   Fig. 6.   Fig. 5.

Try It

Find the area.

a.

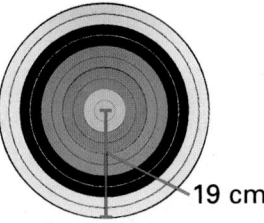

19 cm

b.

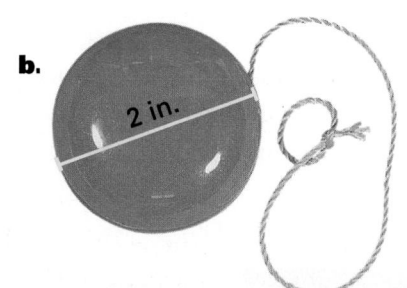

2 in.

Check Your Understanding

1. Why is the area of a circle calculated in square units?

2. If you know the radius of a circle, how do you find the circumference? The area?

PRACTICE 4-8

Practice and Apply

Getting Started State whether each sentence is true or false.

1. If you know the circumference of a circle, you can find the area.

2. The area of a circle is twice the radius.

3. The units of measure for the area of a circle are always cm^2.

Find the area of each circle. Use 3.14 for π.

4.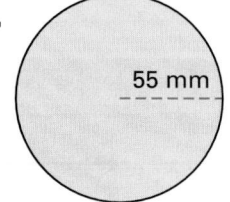
55 mm

5.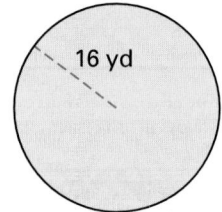
16 yd

6.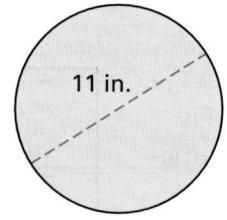
11 in.

7.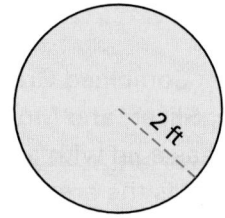
2 ft

Find the area of each circle, where r = radius and d = diameter.

8. $r = 4$ cm

9. $d = 12.8$ feet

10. $d = 62$ cm

11. $r = 17$ feet

12. $r = 10$ inches

13. $r = 50$ mm

14. $d = 16$ yards

15. $r = 0.6$ miles

Given the circumference of a circle, find the radius and the area rounded to the nearest tenth.

16. $C = 12$ feet

17. $C = 8.2$ km

18. $C = 63$ cm

19. $C = 3.14$ mm

20. $C = 7$ inches

21. $C = 1.33$ miles

22. $C = 21$ yards

23. $C = 18$ meters

24. History Stonehenge is a group of stones set in circles in southwestern England. Built almost 5000 years ago, the stones may have been used to determine when astronomical events would occur. The largest ring of stones is 30 m in diameter. What is its area?

25. In 1879 a fire-escape device for safely jumping out of windows was invented. It used a parachute and padded shoes. If the opened and flattened parachute is a circle with a diameter of 1.3 yards, what is the area?

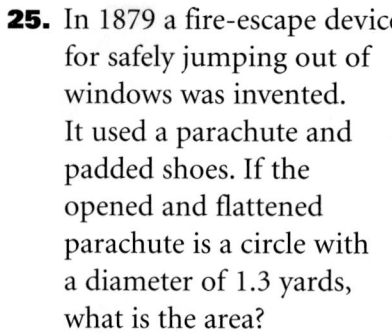

26. Science A sand dollar is an animal that lives slightly buried in the sand of shallow coastal waters. Its thin, circular body is about 2 to 4 inches wide. What are the smallest and largest areas of sand dollars?

27. [Test Prep] On a water ride at the amusement park, a rotating valve sprays water for 15 feet in all directions. How large is the area that gets wet? Round to the nearest tenth.

Ⓐ 31.4 ft² Ⓑ 94.2 ft²

Ⓒ 706.5 ft² Ⓓ 2220.7 ft²

Use the Carpet Comparison scatterplot for Exercises 28–30. All of the carpets are circles.

28. How much does the carpet with a diameter of 3 feet cost?

29. Which carpet costs the most per square foot?

30. Which carpet has the largest circumference?

Carpet Comparison

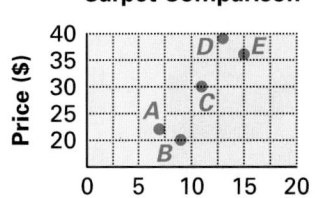

Problem Solving and Reasoning

31. Critical Thinking Charlene has a circular rug in a square room. The area of the rug is about 113 ft². The rug reaches from wall to wall. Estimate the area of the room. Explain your estimate.

32. [Journal] Is the area of a circle with a diameter of 2 inches greater than or less than the area of a 2-inch square? Explain without using numbers.

33. Communicate Circle A has a radius of 12 feet; Circle B, 7 feet; Circle C, 36 inches; Circle D, 132 inches.

a. Order the circles by area from least to greatest. Explain.

b. Does the list change if the circles are ordered by circumference? Explain.

Mixed Review

For each scatterplot, determine if there is a trend. *[Lesson 1-3]*

Airplane Flights

34.

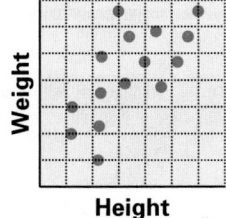

Weight / Height

35.

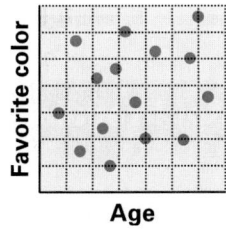

Favorite color / Age

36.

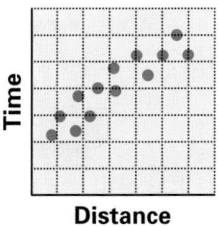

Time / Distance

Estimate each product or quotient. *[Lesson 2-7]*

37. 26 × 3   **38.** $92 ÷ 31   **39.** 78 × 3   **40.** 565 ÷ 53

41. 82 × 16   **42.** 678 ÷ 35   **43.** 2056 × 439   **44.** 729 ÷ 96

4-8 • Area of Circles **253**

Area of Irregular Figures

You'll Learn ...

■ to find the area
of irregular figures

... How It's Used

Surveyors calculate the
area of irregular figures
when surveying property.

▶ **Lesson Link**   You know how to find the area of squares, rectangles, parallelograms, triangles and circles. Now you will see how to use this knowledge to find the area of an irregular figure. ◀

Explore   Area of Irregular Figures

View Points

The three designs below are for portable ramps. Each ramp is made of three pieces of wood, each of the same thickness. The rectangular piece is the surface, and the two triangular pieces are the supports. The supports are connected to the surface by hinges so that the ramp can easily be folded and carried away.

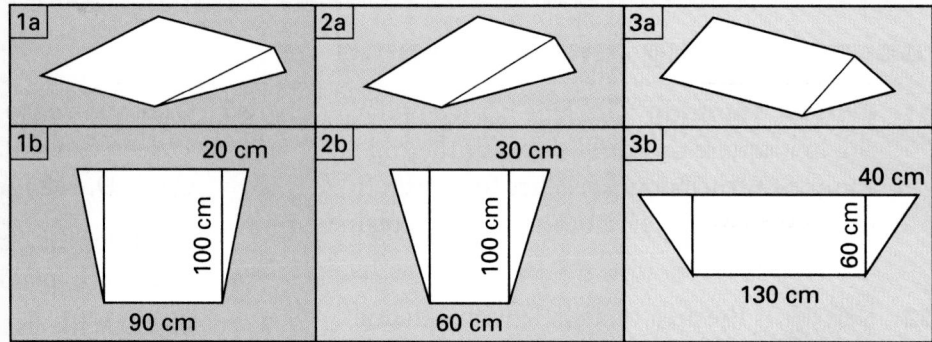

1a   2a   3a

1b   20 cm   2b   30 cm   3b   40 cm
100 cm   100 cm   60 cm
90 cm   60 cm   130 cm

1. Which ramp has the largest surface (rectangular piece)? Explain how you got your answer.

2. Which ramp has the largest support (triangular piece)? Explain how you got your answer.

3. Which ramp uses the most wood? Explain how you got your answer.

Learn   Area of Irregular Figures

Figures are not always perfect rectangles, triangles, or circles. To find the area of an irregular figure, you may need to break it down into smaller familiar figures. Then you can find the area of each smaller figure.

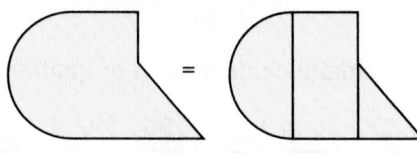

Example 1

Find the area.

The figure can be divided into a triangle and a square.

The square has a base of 8 and a height of 8. The area is base × height, or 8 × 8, which is 64 units².

The triangle has a height of 8. The base is 13 − 8, or 5. The area is base × height ÷ 2, or 8 × 5 ÷ 2, which is 20 units².

The total area is 64 + 20, or 84 units².

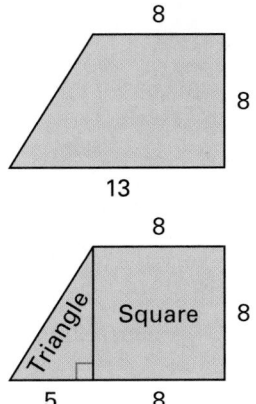

Sometimes, part of an irregular figure is a semicircle, or half of a circle. To find the area of half a circle, find the area of a whole circle with the same radius, and then divide the area in half.

▶ **Language Link**

The prefix *semi-* means "half." A semiannual event happens once every half year.

Example 2

What is the area of the candy part of the "candy pin"?

The top part of the badge is a semicircle with a radius of 0.8 cm.

$$\text{Area of circle} = \pi \times \text{radius}^2$$
$$= 3.14 \times 0.8^2$$
$$= 2.0096 \text{ cm}^2$$

Since the figure is only a semicircle, you must divide the area in half.

Area of semicircle = 2.0096 ÷ 2, or 1.0048 cm²

The bottom part is a triangle with a base of 1.6 cm and a height of 2 cm.

$$\text{Area of triangle} = \text{base} \times \text{height} \div 2$$
$$= 1.6 \times 2 \div 2$$
$$= 1.6 \text{ cm}^2$$

The total area = 1.0048 + 1.6, or 2.6048 cm².

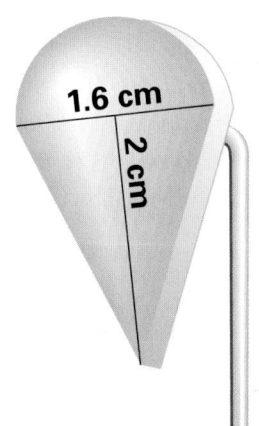

Study TIP

It often helps to write a formula down, and then write the appropriate numbers directly underneath the formula.

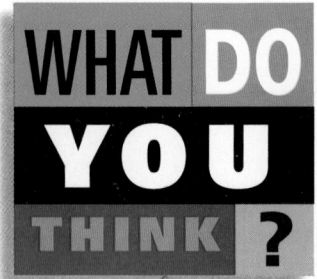

WHAT DO YOU THINK?

Ricardo and Peggy are planning how to plant their garden. The sketch shows the shape of the garden. All of the measurements are in feet. What is the area of the garden?

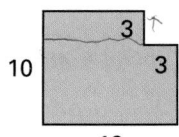

Ricardo thinks ...

I'll divide the garden into two rectangles. I'll find the missing measurements, and the area of each rectangle. Then I'll add the areas together.

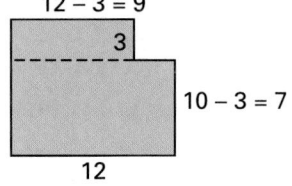

The area of the top rectangle equals $3 \times 9 = 27$.

The area of the bottom equals $12 \times 7 = 84$.

The total area is $27 + 84$, which is 111 ft^2.

Peggy thinks ...

The garden looks like a rectangle with a missing piece. I'll find the area of the rectangle, and then subtract the area of the piece missing from the top corner.

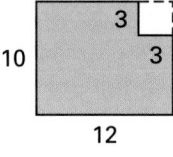
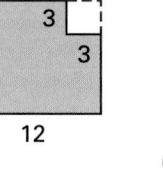

The area of the whole rectangle is $10 \times 12 = 120$.

The area of the missing piece is $3 \times 3 = 9$.

The total area $= 120 - 9$, or 111 ft^2.

What do you think?

1. Could Ricardo have split the garden into two rectangles in a different way? Would he get a different answer?

2. Which method requires more subtraction? Explain.

Check · Your Understanding

1. How can you find the area of a semicircle?

2. Can every figure be broken down into smaller figures that are easy to find the area of? Explain.

4-9 Exercises and Applications

Practice and Apply

Getting Started List the familiar figures each object could be broken into.

1.

2.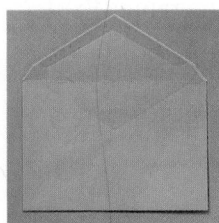

3.

Find the area of each irregular figure.

4.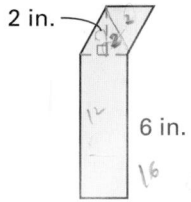
2 in.
6 in.
2 in.

5.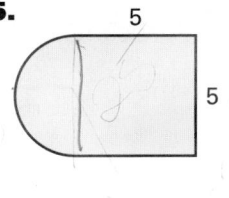
5
5

6.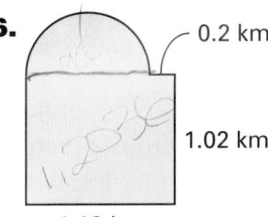
0.2 km
1.02 km
1.18 km

7.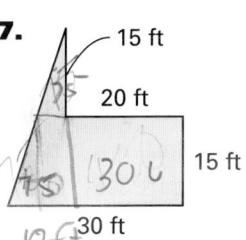
15 ft
20 ft
15 ft
30 ft

Find the area of each object.

8.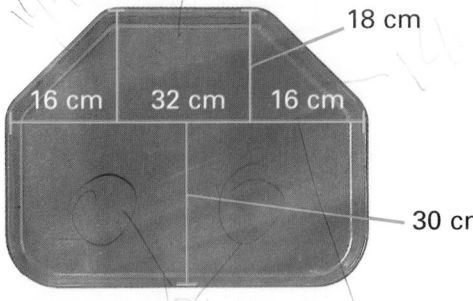
18 cm
16 cm   32 cm   16 cm
30 cm

9.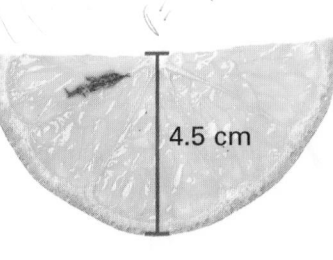
4.5 cm

10. **Test Prep** Each square in a hopscotch pattern with 10 squares is 0.3 yard by 0.3 yard. What is the total area of the pattern to the nearest hundredth?

   Ⓐ 0.90 yd²   Ⓑ 1.23 yd²   Ⓒ 1.56 yd²   Ⓓ 1.79 yd²

11. Geography Find the approximate area of South Australia. All distances are in miles.

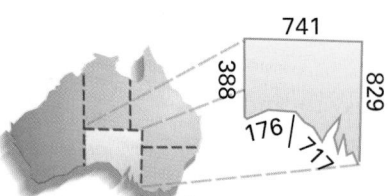

12. Find the area of the combined clothes brush, bottle, and drinking cup.

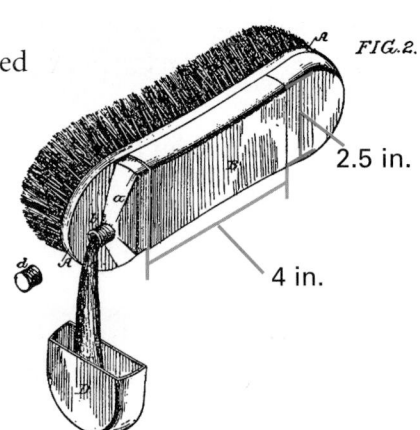

FIG. 2.

2.5 in.

4 in.

Problem Solving and Reasoning

13. Critical Thinking Caitlin is making a tablecloth for a circular table. The circumference of the table is 13.8 feet. She has a square piece of cloth that is 4.5 feet on each side. If she cuts out the largest possible circle from the cloth, will it be big enough to cover the table? Explain.

14. Choose a Strategy Sheetal is painting a cardboard cutout for her school's annual haunted house. The cardboard is a triangle 7 feet tall and 7 feet wide. It has a square opening as shown. How many square feet does Sheetal need to paint? Explain your reasoning.

2 ft

2.5 ft   2.5 ft

RIP

Problem Solving
STRATEGIES
• Look for a Pattern
• Make an Organized List
• Make a Table
• Guess and Check
• Work Backward
• Use Logical Reasoning
• Draw a Diagram
• Solve a Simpler Problem

15. Critical Thinking Joe and his dad are redoing the tile in the kitchen and living room. According to the picture, how many square feet do they have to retile? Explain.

16. **Journal** A spinner is divided into six equal sections. The radius of the spinner is 10 cm. What is the area of each section? Explain.

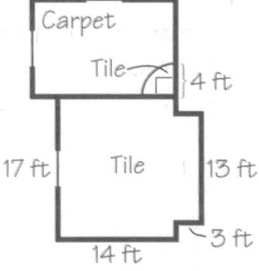

Carpet

Tile   4 ft

17 ft   Tile   13 ft

3 ft

14 ft

Mixed Review

Simplify. [Lesson 2-8]

17. $14 + 10 - 3$

18. $62 \div (1 + 1)$

19. $2^8 \div 2 + 6$

20. $5 \times 6 - 25$

21. $18 + 18 \div 3$

22. $2 \times 10 - 4 \div 2$

23. $2 \times (10 - 4) \div 2$

24. $8 + 3^3 \times 4$

Solve. [Lesson 3-7]

25. $16.1 - f = 9.1$

26. $r + 25.3 = 50.73$

27. $56.04 + k = 64.06$

28. $m - 7.25 = 19.75$

29. $e - 86.5 = 76$

30. $86.8 + q = 100.9$

31. $47.34 - g = 42.04$

32. $z + 0.13 = 6.68$

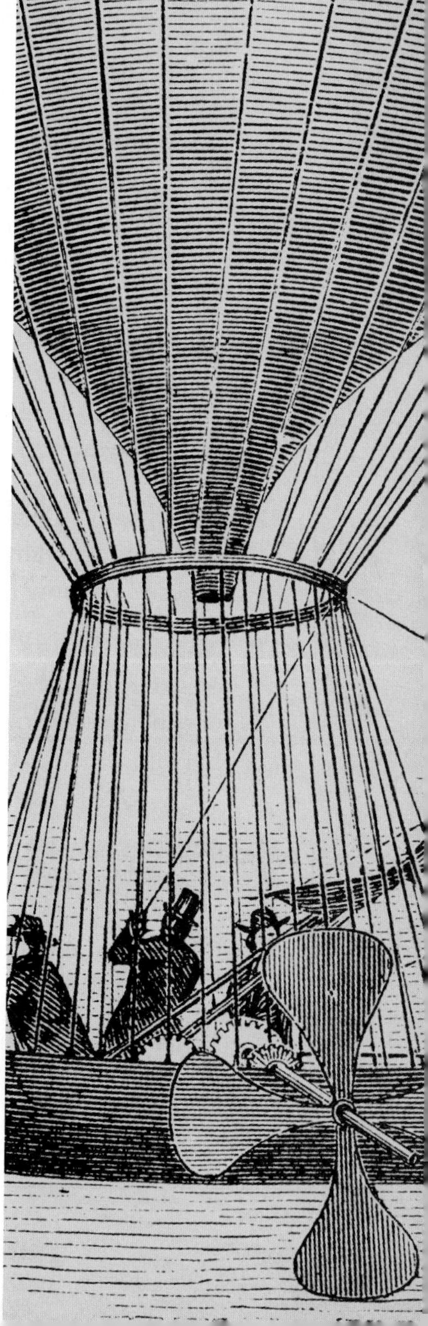

In this section you learned how to find the area of several different types of figures. Now, you will make decisions about the best way to design an invention.

Invention-al Wisdom

Materials: Rulers

1. You need to design an invention. The invention can be ordinary or weird, but it must meet the following conditions:

   a. It must serve some function.

   b. It must be made up of flat surfaces.

   c. The design must use at least one rectangle, one triangle, and either one circle or one semicircle.

2. Use a ruler to make a diagram of your invention. Label its parts clearly, and label the length of all the materials. Be sure to include appropriate units of measurement, such as centimeters or feet.

3. Calculate the amount of material needed to construct your invention.

4. Write a brief description of what the invention does.

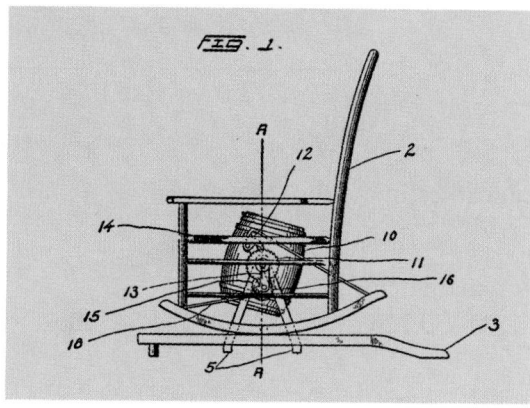
FIG. 1.

Use the conversion factor to find each missing measurement.

1. 2000 pounds in 1 ton

☐ pounds in 6 tons

2. 8 quarts in 2 gallons

37 quarts in ☐ gallons

3. 3 feet in 1 yard

27.6 feet in ☐ yards

Find the area and the distance around each figure.

4.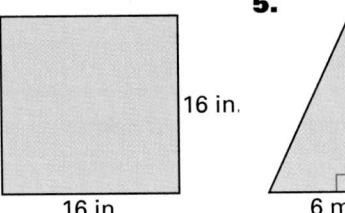

16 in.

16 in.

5.

7.2 mm

8 mm

6 mm

63.2

6.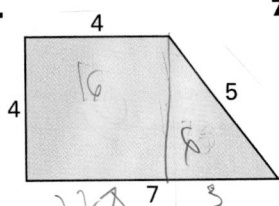

4

5

4

16

227 7   3

8

7.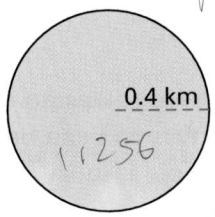

0.4 km

11.256

8.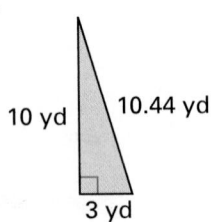

10 yd

10.44 yd

3 yd

9.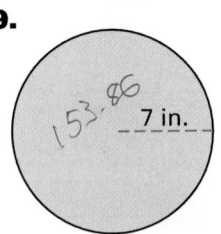

7 in.

153.86

10.

9 ft

12 ft

11. *7.065*

8

24 3

8 *24* *64* *8*

6

3 11

.119 065

12. Scott wants to place trees around the perimeter of his model train setup. If the trees are placed 2 feet apart, how many trees does he need?

13. Number Sense Which is larger, the perimeter of a square with sides 4 inches long or the perimeter of a triangle with sides 4 inches long? Explain.

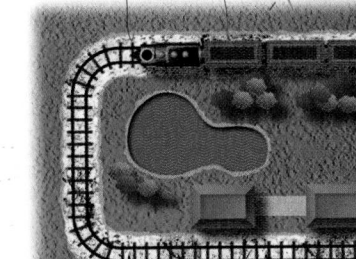

4 ft

8 ft

When finding the circumference of a circle, you can estimate the answer by using 3 for π.

14. What is the circumference of a circle with a diameter of 9 cm?

Ⓐ 2.87 cm   Ⓑ 28.26 cm   Ⓒ 150.72 cm   Ⓓ 254.34 cm

Square Roots

When you multiply a number by itself, the result is the **square** of the number. For example, the square of 3 is 3^2 or 9. This can be modeled with a square where the length of each side is the number you start with. The number squared is the area.

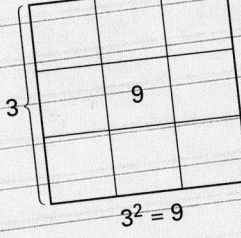

$3^2 = 9$

The opposite of squaring a number is finding the **square root**. The square root answers the question "What number times itself equals the number I started with?" For example, the square root of 16 is 4. This can be modeled by a square where the area is the number you start with. The square root is the length of one side.

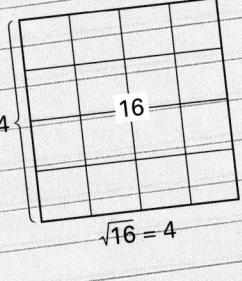

$\sqrt{16} = 4$

The symbol for a square root is $\sqrt{}$. It is called a **radical sign**.

Try It

Sketch the square root of each number by drawing a square with the given area. What is the length of one side?

1. 4   **2.** 36   **3.** 81

4. 25   **5.** 49   **6.** 100

Use number sense to find the square roots.

7. $\sqrt{400}$ **8.** $\sqrt{144}$ **9.** $\sqrt{64}$

10. $\sqrt{169}$ **11.** $\sqrt{324}$ **12.** $\sqrt{121}$

Graphic Organizer

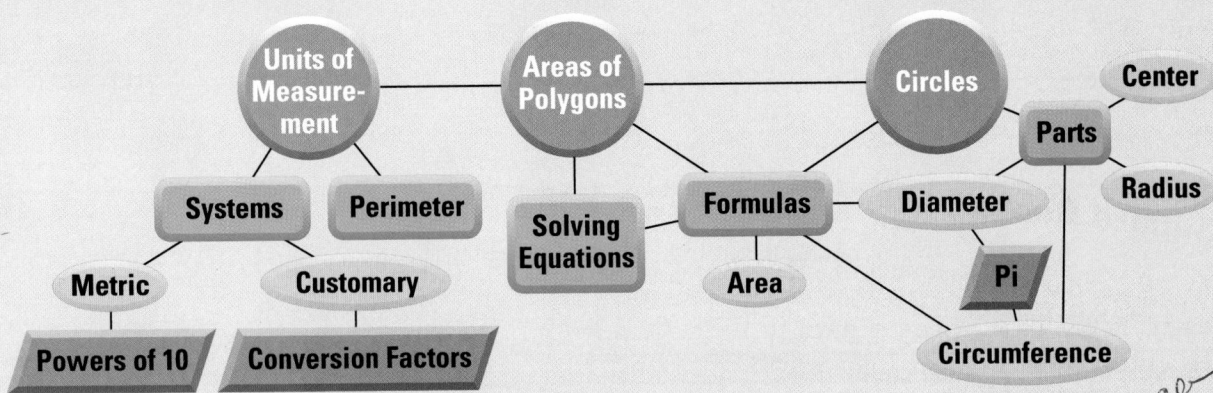

Section 4A Units of Measurement

Summary

- The **perimeter** is the distance around a figure.

- The basic units of measure of the **metric system** are the **meter**, used for length; the **gram**, used for mass; and the **liter**, used for volume.

- The customary system also has units of measure for length, weight, and capacity, such as **inch, foot, ounce, pound, quart,** and **gallon.**

- Use powers of 10 to convert from one related unit of metric measure to another. Use **conversion factors** to change from one related customary unit of measure to another.

Review

Find the perimeter of each figure.

1. 8, 2.9, 8, 6.7, 8

2. 1.37, 0.7, 0.7, 1.37

3. 1.14 m, 0.46 m, 0.807 m

Use powers of 10 or conversion factors to find each measure.

4. 5.3 km = _____ m

5. 219 ft = _____ yd

6. 4 ft = _____ in.

7. 3.5 gal = _____ qt

8. 11.726 kg = _____ g

9. 432 mm = _____ m

10. A rectangular dining room table is 44 in. by 66 in. What is the perimeter of the table? State your answer in feet.

Section 4B Area of Polygons

Summary

- **Area** is the measure of how much surface is covered.

- You can also use formulas to find the area of some polygons.

  Rectangles and squares: $A = b \times h$, where b = base and h = height.

  Parallelogram: $A = b \times h$, where b = base and h = height.

  Triangle: $A = b \times h \div 2$, where b = base and h = height.

Review

Find the area of each figure.

11. *19200 ft²*

    80 ft
    240 ft

12. 60 cm
    20 cm
    1200 cm²
    56.25 mm²
    7.5
    7.5

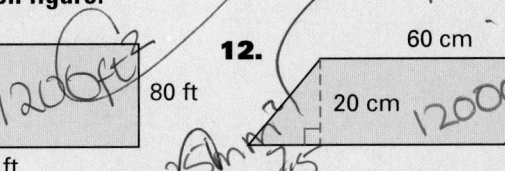

13. 5 ft
    30 ft
    75 ft²
    21 ft²

14. A square with a side 7.5 mm long

15. A door 3.5 ft wide and 6 ft high.

16. Find the height of a triangle with a base of 13.2 ft and an area of 198 ft².
    15 ft
    13.2 ft

Section 4C Circles

Summary

- The **radius** of a circle is the distance from its center to any point on the circle. The **diameter** is the distance across a circle through its center. The **circumference** is the distance around a circle.

  r –
  d –

- For any circle, the circumference divided by the diameter equals about 3.14. This number is named **pi,** and its symbol is π. *π = 3.14*

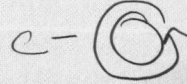
  c –

- Use $C = \pi \times d$ to find a circumference, where C is the circumference and d is the diameter. Use $d = C \div \pi$ to find the diameter.

- Use the formula $A = \pi \times r^2$ to find the area of any circle, where r = the radius.

- To find the area of an irregular polygon, divide it into figures you recognize, find the area of each and add them together to get the total area.

Review

17. **a.** Find the circumference of a circle if its diameter is 3 yards.
    b. Find its area.

18. Find the area of the irregular figure:

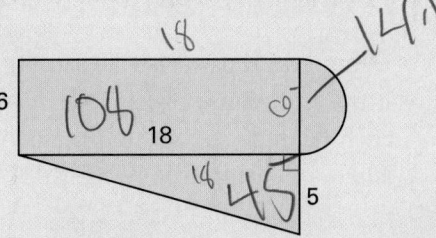
    18
    18
    6
    45
    5
    14.13

Chapter 4 Assessment

Supply the missing word in each sentence.

1. The distance from the center of a circle to any point on the circle is called the _____.

2. The value of the symbol π is the circumference of any circle divided by its _____.

3. Powers of 10 are used to convert from one related measure to another in the _____ system.

4. _____ measures the number of square units used to cover a surface.

For each figure, (a) find its perimeter and (b) find its area.

5.

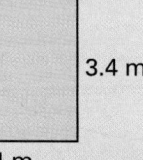

3.4 m

3.4 m

6.

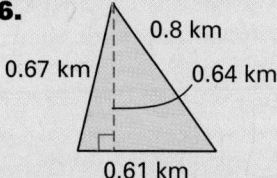

0.8 km

0.67 km   0.64 km

0.61 km

7.

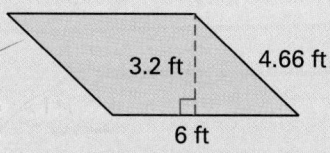

3.2 ft   4.66 ft

6 ft

Use powers of 10 or conversion factors to find each measure.

8. 12 yd = _____ ft   **9.** 75 mm = _____ cm   **10.** 1 km = _____ m   **11.** 360,000 in. = _____ ft

12. Find the diameter of a circle whose circumference is 28.26 mi.

13. Find the area of a circle to the nearest tenth if its radius is 2.5 kilometers.

14. a. What is the diameter of the semicircle?   **b.** What is its radius?

    c. How long is the perimeter of the semicircle?

    d. What is its area?

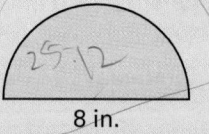

8 in.

Find the area of each irregular figure.

15.

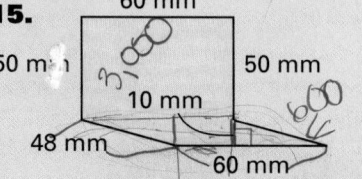

60 mm

50 mm   50 mm

10 mm

48 mm

60 mm

16.

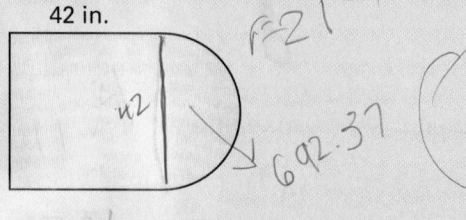

42 in.

42 in.

Performance Task

Using graph paper, draw as many triangles as possible whose area is 12 square units and whose base and height dimensions are whole numbers. As you find each triangle, label the dimensions of its base and height. When you are finished, make an organized list of the bases and heights of your triangles.

Multiple Choice

Choose the best answer.

not responsible for circled items

1. Which of the following would make you think a bar graph might be misleading? *[Lesson 1-2]*

Ⓐ All bar heights start from zero.

Ⓑ The data values are not equally spaced.

Ⓒ A broken graph symbol showing a break in the values.

Ⓓ Not here

2. What number in a frequency chart represents this set of tally marks? *[Lesson 1-4]*

||||| ||||| ||

Ⓐ 12　　Ⓑ 10　　Ⓒ 2　　Ⓓ Not here

3. What is the place value of the digit 7 in 31,076,123? *[Lesson 2-1]*

Ⓐ millions　　　Ⓑ thousands

Ⓒ ten-thousands　Ⓓ Not here

4. Use the order of operations to evaluate the expression $(18 + 9^2) \div 3$. *[Lesson 2-8]*

Ⓐ 9　　　　　Ⓑ 33

Ⓒ 45　　　　　Ⓓ 243

5. There are m marbles arranged in 7 equal groups. Write an expression to show the number of marbles in each group. *[Lesson 2-11]*

Ⓐ $m + 7$　　　　Ⓑ $m - 7$

Ⓒ $7m$　　　　　Ⓓ $\dfrac{m}{7}$

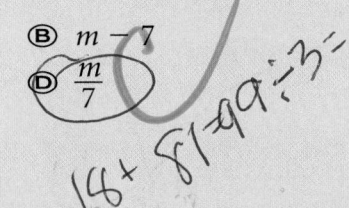

6. Round 32.874 to the nearest tenth. *[Lesson 3-2]*

Ⓐ 40　　　　　　Ⓑ 32.9

Ⓒ 32.87　　　　　Ⓓ Not here

7. If you rank these decimals from smallest to largest, which will come second: 302.607, 3026.07, 302.067, 3020.67? *[Lesson 3-3]*

Ⓐ 3026.07　　　Ⓑ 3020.67

Ⓒ 302.607　　　Ⓓ 302.067

8. Solve for x, if $x + 41.5 = 43.2$. *[Lesson 3-7]*　*give a try*

Ⓐ 1.7　　　　　Ⓑ 2.7

Ⓒ 2.8　　　　　Ⓓ Not here

9. Simplify 3.76×0.08. *[Lesson 3-9]*　*try it for fun*

Ⓐ 0.2968　　　Ⓑ 0.3008

Ⓒ 2.968　　　　Ⓓ 3.008

10. How many millimeters are in 432.6 cm? *[Lesson 4-3]*

Ⓐ 4.326　　　　Ⓑ 43.26

Ⓒ 432.6　　　　Ⓓ 4326

11. Find the area of the triangle. *[Lesson 4-6]*

Ⓐ 24 m²

Ⓑ 14 m²

Ⓒ 12 m²

Ⓓ 10 m²

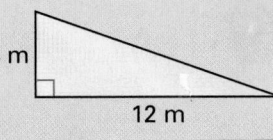

4 m

12 m

12. What is the area of a circle with a radius of 3 yd? *[Lesson 4-8]*

Ⓐ 28.26 yd²　　Ⓑ 18.84 yd²

Ⓒ 9.42 yd²　　　Ⓓ Not here

$3 \times 3 \times 3.14 = ?$

Patterns and Number Theory

Arts & Literature Link
www.mathsurf.com/6/ch5/arts

Social Studies Link
www.mathsurf.com/6/ch5/social

People of the World

About $\frac{1}{3}$ of the people in the world eat with a fork and a knife. About $\frac{1}{3}$ eat with chopsticks. About $\frac{1}{3}$ eat with their hands.

Social Studies

Angel Falls, in Venezuela, is 3212 ft high. It has the longest single drop of any waterfall in the world, 2648 ft. This is over $\frac{3}{4}$ of the entire waterfall.

Arts & Literature

A Japanese haiku poem contains 3 lines. The first line has 5 syllables, the next has 7, and the last has 5.

Composite Numbers,
So Common, Like Grains of Sand.
Prime Numbers are Gems

Entertainment Link
www.mathsurf.com/6/ch5/ent

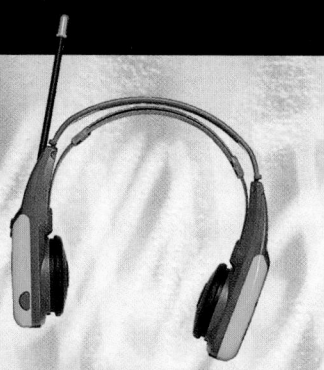

Entertainment

On an average day, $\frac{16}{100}$ of the people listening to the radio are listening to news or talk stations. $\frac{9}{100}$ of the people are listening to Top 40 stations.

Science

The Fibonacci number pattern, 1, 1, 2, 3, 5, 8, ..., describes many things in nature, including how tree branches grow and what the surface of a pineapple looks like.

KEY MATH IDEAS

The rules of divisibility describe patterns that can help you determine if a number can be divided evenly by another given number.

Every whole number greater than 1 is either a prime number or a composite number. A prime number has exactly two factors, the number itself and 1.

Fractions can be used to describe some part of a whole.

Fractions can describe amounts that are greater than one.

Decimal numbers can be converted to fraction numbers, and fraction numbers can be converted to decimal numbers.

CHAPTER PROJECT

Problem Solving

Understand
Plan
Solve
Look Back

In this project, you will create a visual presentation of your favorite number. Begin by thinking about all the different ways a single number can be written.

Problem Solving

Understand
Plan
Solve
Look Back

Identifying Missing Information

Problems on tests and quizzes usually give you all the information you need to solve a problem. Problems in real life don't always provide you with all the information. When developing a plan for solving the problem, an important skill is identifying what information is needed but hasn't been provided.

For each problem, identify what additional information is needed to solve the problem. Some of the problems may not be missing any needed information.

① The kids in the Davis-Brown family want to build a treehouse. Jamelya volunteered to get the lumber. She needs 40 ft² for the slanted roof and 30 ft² for each of the four walls. How many square feet of lumber does she need all together?

② Terrance plans to make a rope ladder for the treehouse. Each rung is 2 inches thick. The rungs will be 10 inches apart. How much rope does he need to make the ladder?

③ Ronisha wants to paint part of the treehouse green and another part white. A gallon of green paint costs $4.19. A gallon of white paint costs $5.57. How much money will Ronisha need to buy the paint?

④ Each of the four kids helped paint the treehouse. Warren painted for 4 hours. Ronisha painted for $3\frac{1}{2}$ hours. Jamelya painted for 5 hours. How much time did it take to paint the treehouse?

02.28.98 01.00.23

A Switch in Time ...

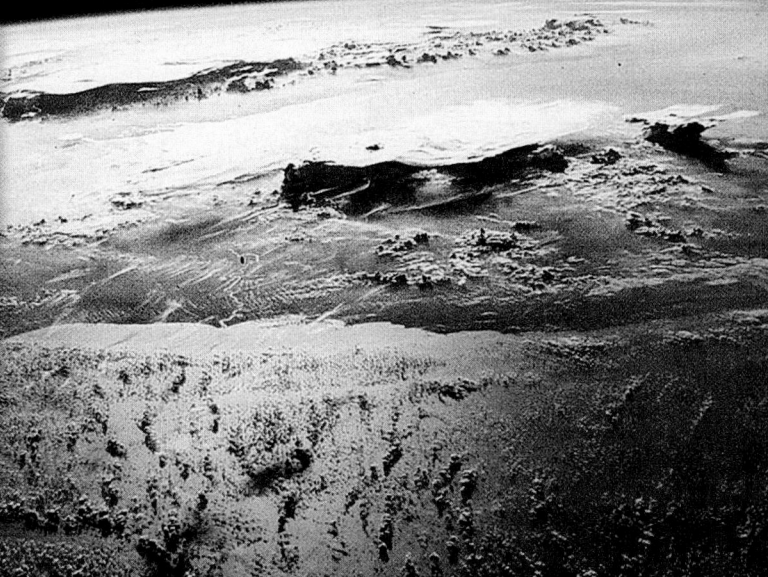

Thirty days hath September,
April, June, and November.
All the rest have 31,

Excepting February alone,
Which hath by 28, in fine,
Till leap year gives it 29.

*A*s the poem suggests, time is not a regular thing. One month doesn't always equal another. (July has more days than June.) One year doesn't always equal another. (Leap years have an extra day.) One century doesn't always equal another. (Earth is slowing down by about $\frac{1}{2}$ second each century.)

We have often changed how we keep track of time in an effort to create simpler clocks and calendars. In the 1200s, an hour was $\frac{1}{12}$ of the time from sunrise to sunset, regardless of how long that was. In the 1700s, there were no time zones. Each town kept its own time. In the early 1900s, according to Greenwich Mean Time, the day began and ended at noon. Every change has been an effort to make timekeeping more accurate and more convenient. And every change has involved mathematics.

1 Before the invention of mechanical clocks, how did humans keep track of time?

2 Why doesn't a year always equal exactly 365 days?

3 What sort of mathematics do you need to know to create an accurate clock or calendar?

5-1

Divisibility

You'll Learn ...

■ the rules of divisibility

... How It's Used

Shipping company employees use the rules of divisibility to determine if a given number of packages can be evenly packed into a given crate.

Vocabulary

divisible

▶ History Link

In 1795, the French adopted a decimal time system, with 10-day weeks, 10-hour days, 100-minute hours, and 100-second minutes. It was abandoned in 1805 because the public didn't like a 10-day week.

▶ **Lesson Link**   You've learned that the quotient of two whole numbers may or may not have a remainder. In this lesson, you'll learn ways to determine if a quotient will have a remainder without actually dividing. ◀

Explore | Divisibility

Let's Take a Vacation!   **Materials:** Calculator

Vacations often last an exact number of weeks. ("I'm taking a 4-week vacation.") But how long is a week? In most countries, it is 7 days. But ancient Rome had an 8-day week, France once had a 10-day week, and Russia had 5- and 6-day weeks.

Vacation (days)	Week Length (days)								
	2	3	4	5	6	7	8	9	10
32									
42									
60									
75									
117									
180									

1. Using a calculator, divide each vacation length by each of the week lengths. If your answer is a whole number, the week length divides evenly into the vacation length. Write "yes" in the matching square. If your answer is not a whole number, the week length does not divide evenly into the vacation length. Write "no" in the matching square.

2. Suppose you have to fill out one column without a calculator. Which would be easier, the 2 column or the 7 column. Why?

3. Did you discover any shortcuts that allowed you to write "yes" or "no" without actually dividing? If so, describe them.

4. If a week were one day long, what would the answers in that column be? Why?

A whole number is **divisible** by another whole number if you can divide the first number by the second without leaving a remainder.

$$3\overline{)21} \xrightarrow{\;7\;}$$ → 21 is divisible by 3.

$$4\overline{)21} \xrightarrow{\;5\text{ R }1\;}$$ → 21 is *not* divisible by 4.

For any number, you can list all of the numbers that are divisible by that number. Sometimes you will see patterns that can help you determine if a number is divisible by another number without actually needing to divide.

Some patterns depend upon the ones digit in the number.

DID YOU KNOW?

There are also rules of divisibility for 4, 7, and 8. But the rules are more complicated, so it's usually faster to just divide the number and see if there is a remainder.

DIVISIBILITY RULES

A whole number is divisible by   Examples

• 2 if the ones digit is even.   2, 4, 6, 8, 10, 12, 14, 16, 18, 20, …

• 5 if the ones digit is 5 or 0.   5, 10, 15, 20, 25, 30, 35, 40, 45, …

• 10 if the ones digit is 0.   10, 20, 30, 40, 50, 60, 70, 80, …

Remember

An *even* number ends in 0, 2, 4, 6, or 8. An *odd* number ends in 1, 3, 5, 7, or 9.

[Previous Course]

Example 1

Mr. Ashman is planning a lesson. He wants his students to work first in groups of 2, then in groups of 5, and finally in groups of 10. There should never be any students left over. He has 30 students in his first class, and 25 in his second class. Will the lesson work in both classes?

Is 30 divisible by 2, 5, and 10?

2?   Yes   The ones digit is even.

5?   Yes   The ones digit is 0.

10?   Yes   The ones digit is 0.

Is 25 divisible by 2, 5 and 10?

2?   No   The ones digit is not even.

5?   Yes   The ones digit is 5.

10?   No   The ones digit is not 0.

The lesson will work for the first class, but not the second.

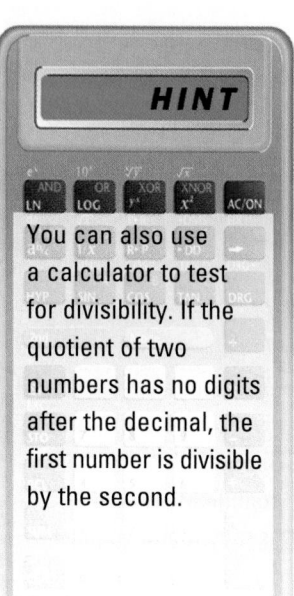

You can also use a calculator to test for divisibility. If the quotient of two numbers has no digits after the decimal, the first number is divisible by the second.

Some patterns depend upon the sum of the digits.

A whole number is divisible by	Examples
• 3 if the sum of its digits is divisible by 3.	3, 6, 9, 12, 15, 18, 21, 24, …
• 9 the sum of its digits is divisible by 9.	9, 18, 27, 36, 45, 54, 63, …

Example 2

Test 945 for divisibility by 2, 3, 5, 9 and 10.

2?   No, the ones digit is not even.

3?   Yes, $9 + 4 + 5 = 18$, which is divisible by 3.

5?   Yes, the ones digit is 5.

9?   Yes, $9 + 4 + 5 = 18$, which is divisible by 9.

10?   No, the ones digit is not 0.

Some patterns depend upon other patterns.

A whole number is divisible by	Examples
• 6 if it is divisible by both 2 and 3.	6, 12, 18, 24, 30, 36, 42, …

► **History Link**

The oldest known document on number theory was written in Babylon some time between 1900 B.C. and 1600 B.C. It was written using sexagecimal notation, which is based on the number 60.

Example 3

The ancient Babylonians recognized the value of the number 60 in timekeeping. We have 60-second minutes and 60-minute hours because 60 is easily divided into smaller parts. Test 60 for divisibility by 2, 3, 5, 6, 9, and 10.

0 is even, so it's divisible by ⬚2.

$6 + 0 = 6$, and 6 is divisible by 3, so 60 is divisible by ⬚3.
60 ends in 0, so it's divisible by ⬚5 and by ⬚10.

60 is divisible by both 2 and 3, so it is divisible by ⬚6.
$6 + 0 = 6$, and 6 is not divisible by 9, so 60 is not divisible by 9.

Try It

Tell whether the number is divisible by 2, 3, 5, 6, 9, or 10.

a. 141   **b.** 455   **c.** 684   **d.** 555   **e.** 2700

1. What are the advantages of knowing divisibility rules?

2. Which divisibility rules do you think are easiest to use? Explain.

5-1 Exercises and Applications

Practice and Apply

1. **Getting Started** Tell whether each number is divisible by 2, 5, or 10.

   a. 66   **b.** 228   **c.** 45   **d.** 120   **e.** 985   **f.** 30

Tell whether each number is divisible by 2, 3, 5, 6, 9, or 10.

2. 63	**3.** 55	**4.** 117	**5.** 81	**6.** 621	**7.** 1360
8. 35	**9.** 42	**10.** 104	**11.** 4320	**12.** 10	**13.** 90
14. 27	**15.** 68	**16.** 180	**17.** 135	**18.** 282	**19.** 56
20. 5555	**21.** 48	**22.** 362	**23.** 1110	**24.** 9	**25.** 24
26. 66	**27.** 75	**28.** 85	**29.** 695	**30.** 1587	**31.** 96

Tell whether the first number is divisible by the second.

32. 33, 3	**33.** 132, 11	**34.** 41, 5	**35.** 105, 8	**36.** 63, 4
37. 92, 9	**38.** 65, 10	**39.** 99, 11	**40.** 78, 6	**41.** 60, 4
42. 93, 2	**43.** 115, 5	**44.** 171, 9	**45.** 109, 7	**46.** 52, 6
47. 160, 8	**48.** 54, 7	**49.** 30, 4	**50.** 52, 11	**51.** 58, 8
52. 84, 7	**53.** 76, 2	**54.** 30, 10	**55.** 120, 12	**56.** 37, 3

57. **Number Sense** A leap year occurs in every year that is divisible by 4, unless the year ends in 2 zeros. Then, to be a leap year, it must be divisible by 400. Which of the following are leap years?

   a. 1900   **b.** 1999   **c.** 1066   **d.** 1776   **e.** 2000

58. **Test Prep** By how many whole numbers is 24 divisible?

   Ⓐ 3   Ⓑ 6   Ⓒ 7   Ⓓ 8

59. There are approximately 52 weeks in a year. Is this number divisible by 12? Why would it be important for you to know this?

60. History Abraham Lincoln's Gettysburg Address begins "Four score and seven years ago …" A score is 20 years, so "four score" is 80 years. A score is divisible by what numbers?

61. Determine if the number of years in each of following is divisible by 2, 3, 5, 6, 9, or 10.

   a. A decade (10 years)

   b. A century (100 years)

   c. A millennium (1000 years)

Problem Solving and Reasoning

62. Critical Thinking Marvel Models produces 53,716 model cars each month. They want to design shipping cartons that hold more than 3 but fewer than 10 models each. They want to pack each month's cars in the cartons, with no cars left over. What are their choices? Explain.

Use the rules of divisibility to find numbers that can evenly divide 53,716.

63. Communicate If a number is divisible by both 2 and 3, it is divisible by 6. If a number is divisible by 2 and 5, what other number is it divisible by? Explain.

64. Critical Thinking The solar calendar of the Aztec people had 365 days, which was 18 months of 20 days and 5 "unlucky" extra days. How could the Aztecs have rearranged their calendar so that each month had the same number of days and no "unlucky" days? Explain.

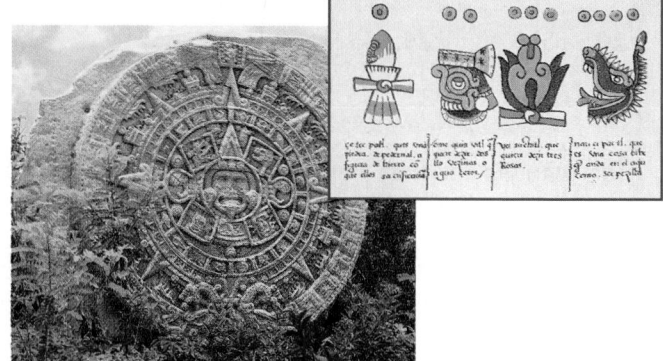

Mixed Review

Write each number in word form. *[Lesson 2-1]*

65. 54,007   **66.** 500,200   **67.** 101,110   **68.** 2345

69. 32,302   **70.** 640,000   **71.** 500,007   **72.** 6219

Multiply. *[Lesson 3-9]*

73. 32×0.5 **74.** 15×0.9 **75.** 8.1×0.6 **76.** 5.5×1.4

77. 17×0.4 **78.** 21×0.3 **79.** 68×0.2 **80.** 51×1.2

Prime Factorization

▶ **Lesson Link** ◀ You've learned to use divisibility rules to decide if one number is divisible by another. Now you'll use those rules to express whole numbers in terms of their simplest factors. ◀

Explore | Factorization

The Great Rectangle Search

Materials: Graph paper

Any number of squares can be arranged into a rectangle. Some can be arranged into only one rectangle, and some can be arranged into several different rectangles.

1. On a sheet of graph paper, copy and complete the table down to 20 squares. Two rectangles are the same if one can be turned to look like the other.

NUMBER OF SQUARES	NUMBER OF RECTANGLES	SKETCHES
1	1	▨
2	1	▨▨
3	1	▨▨▨
4	2	▬▬ ▨

2. Make a list of the numbers for which you could draw only one rectangle. Make a second list of the numbers for which you could draw more than one.

3. How many factors does each number in your first list have? How many does each number in your second list have? What can you conclude about the numbers that can be made into only one rectangle?

4. Is there a number of squares that cannot be arranged into a rectangle? Explain.

You'll Learn ...

■ the difference between prime and composite numbers

■ to find the prime factorization of a number

... How It's Used

Programmers use prime numbers when developing security programs that make it difficult to read information from other people's computers.

Vocabulary

prime number

composite number

prime factorization

Learn | Prime Factorization

Every whole number greater than 1 is either a **prime number** or a **composite number**. A prime number has exactly two factors, 1 and itself. A composite number has more than two factors.

	4	7	10	25	29
Factors	1, 2, 4	1, 7	1, 2, 5, 10	1, 5, 25	1, 29
Type	composite	prime	composite	composite	prime

The first ten prime numbers are: 2, 3, 5, 7, 11, 13, 17, 19, 23, and 29.

Every human has a unique fingerprint. Similarly, every composite number has a unique "factorprint." It is called the **prime factorization**. It's the set of primes whose product equals the number.

You can use a "factor tree" to find a prime factorization. Find two numbers whose product equals the original number, and write them below. If a number is prime, circle it. If a number is composite, continue to break it apart until you only have prime numbers left. Rewrite the prime factors at the bottom from least to greatest.

$$
\begin{array}{c}
30 \\
/ \ \backslash \\
③ \quad 10 \\
\quad\quad / \ \backslash \\
\quad\quad ② ⑤ \\
30 = 2 \times 3 \times 5
\end{array}
$$

Example 1

Find the prime factorization of 630.

$$
\begin{array}{c}
630 \\
/ \quad \backslash \\
10 \quad\quad 63 \\
/ \backslash \quad\; / \backslash \\
⑤②③\; 21 \\
\quad\quad\quad / \backslash \\
\quad\quad\quad ③\;⑦
\end{array}
$$

Use divisibility rules to find factors and draw "branches."

630 ends in 0, so it's divisible by 10. $630 \div 10 = 63$.

Circle prime factors when you find them.

Stop when "leaves" at ends of branches are all circled.

The prime factorization is $2 \times 3 \times 3 \times 5 \times 7$, or $2 \times 3^2 \times 5 \times 7$.

Try It

Find the prime factorization of each number.

a. 12   **b.** 20   **c.** 36   **d.** 45   **e.** 210

Skye and Erica need to plant a rectangular garden. Its length times its width equals 90 ft². They want to determine all the ways they could lay out the garden with whole-number dimensions.

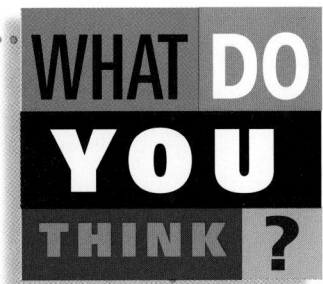
Skye thinks ...

I'll use the divisibility rules and number sense to list the pairs of factors that multiply to make 90.

Every whole number is divisible by 1.	1×90
90 ends in 0, so it's divisible by 2.	2×45
$9 + 0 = 9$, so 90 is divisible by 3.	3×30
90 ends in 0, so it's divisible by 5.	5×18
90 is divisible by 2 and 3, so also 6.	6×15
90 ends in 0, so it's divisible by 10.	9×10

Since $90 \div 2$ is an odd number, 90 is not divisible by 4 or 8. Since 7×13 is 91, 90 is not divisible by 7.

There are six ways we can lay out the garden.

Erica thinks ...

I'll use the prime factors and an organized list to help me find all the factors.

```
      90
     /  \
    9    10
   / \   / \
  ③ ③  ⑤ ②
```

1 prime factor
2, 3, 5

2 prime factors
6 (2×3), 9 (3×3),
10 (2×5), 15 (3×5)

3 prime factors
18 ($2 \times 3 \times 3$), 30 ($2 \times 3 \times 5$),
45 ($3 \times 3 \times 5$)

Including 1 and 90, there are 12 factors. So, there are 6 pairs of factors that will make 90. There are 6 ways we can lay out the garden.

What do you think?

1. Which method works better for large numbers? Why?

2. How can Skye be certain 90 isn't divisible by 4 or 8?

1. When you draw a factor tree, how can you tell which two factors to use to start the tree?

2. Why is 2 the only even prime number?

5-2 Exercises and Applications

Practice and Apply

1. **Getting Started** Use mental math to find the prime factorization.

   a. 15   **b.** 33   **c.** 14   **d.** 21   **e.** 6   **f.** 35

Given the number and its factors, tell whether it is prime or composite.

2. 45: 1, 3, 5, 9, 15, 45   3. 67: 1, 67   4. 37: 1, 37

5. 26: 1, 2, 13, 26   6. 53: 1, 53   7. 65: 1, 5, 13, 65

Find the prime factorization.

8. 58	**9.** 25	**10.** 26	**11.** 95	**12.** 405	**13.** 125
14. 56	**15.** 6	**16.** 288	**17.** 88	**18.** 87	**19.** 72
20. 50	**21.** 684	**22.** 27	**23.** 60	**24.** 32	**25.** 105
26. 96	**27.** 48	**28.** 13	**29.** 85	**30.** 297	**31.** 162
32. 5670	**33.** 165	**34.** 693	**35.** 468	**36.** 10	**37.** 42

38. Mr. Armond has 36 students in his math class. He wants to put them into groups of the same size. He also wants the number in each group to be a prime factor of 36. What are his choices?

39. **Chance** Tran dropped a marker on the board. Was it more likely to fall on a prime number or on a composite number? Explain.

40. **Test Prep** Which number appears more than once in the prime factorization of 100?

    Ⓐ Only 2   Ⓑ Only 5   Ⓒ 2 and 5   Ⓓ There are no repeated factors.

41. Olivia has three friends who live in her apartment building. One day, she noticed that she and her friends all had apartment numbers that were three-digit prime numbers less than 110. If everyone lived in a different apartment, what were the four apartment numbers?

42. The prime factorization of a number is $2 \times 3 \times 5 \times 5 \times 7 \times 13 \times 29$. What is the number?

43. History Eratosthenes designed a method, called the Sieve of Eratosthenes, to find prime numbers. Between the numbers 40 and 80, he found 10 prime numbers. What are they?

Problem Solving and Reasoning

44. Communicate An April calendar shows 30 days, labeled 1 through 30. How many days have a prime number date? How many have a composite number date? If your friend was born on a day in April, would it more likely be a prime date or a composite date? Explain.

45. Communicate Would you prefer your teacher to assign the odd-numbered problems or the prime-numbered problems for homework? Explain.

46. Communicate What is the smallest composite number that has all of the first 5 prime numbers as factors? Explain.

47. **Journal** A prime number is any whole number with exactly two factors, itself and 1. Explain why 1 isn't a prime number.

APRIL

S	M	T	W	T	F	S
			1	2	3	4
5	6	7	8	9	10	11
12	13	14	15	16	17	18
19	20	21	22	23	24	25
26	27	28	29	30		

Johnson, William H.. Untitled (Soapbox Racing), 1939-40. National Museum of American Art, Smithsonian Institute, Washington, D.C..

Mixed Review

Round each number to the given place value. *[Lesson 2-2]*

48. 456,892; thousands

49. 5,678,022; hundred-thousands

50. 923,894; hundreds

51. 5,890,324,331; millions

Divide. *[Lesson 3-10]*

52. $10 \div 6$ **53.** $12 \div 10$ **54.** $4 \div 8$ **55.** $14 \div 56$

56. $1 \div 5$ **57.** $1 \div 4$ **58.** $1 \div 10$ **59.** $1 \div 2$

Project Progress

Figure out your favorite number's prime factors. Find numbers by which your favorite number is divisible and some common multiples of your number. Pair your number with other numbers to find the least common multiple of each pair. Record all the data in a chart.

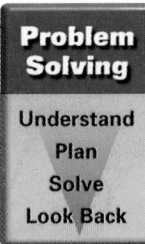

Problem Solving

Understand
Plan
Solve
Look Back

Least Common Multiples

You'll Learn ...

■ to find the least common multiple for two numbers

... How It's Used

Astronomers use least common multiples to determine when celestial objects will pass Earth at the same time.

Vocabulary

multiple

common multiple

least common multiple (LCM)

▶ Lesson Link You've learned about the numbers that divide a given number. Now you'll learn about the numbers that a given number divides. ◀

| **Explore** | **Common Multiples** |

Going In Evenly

Materials: Spreadsheet software

1. On a blank spreadsheet, enter the following information. The numbers in column A should go through 30.

	A	B	C
1		First Divisor	Second Divisor
2		2	3
3			
4	Dividend	First Quotient	Second Quotient
5	1	=A5/$B$2	=A5/$C$2
6	2		
7	3		
8	4		

2. Copy the formulas in B5 and C5 down each column to the bottom of the list in column A.

3. Columns B and C contain the number of times 2 and 3 go into the numbers from 1 to 30. How many numbers does 2 go into evenly? How many does 3 go into evenly? How many numbers do both 2 and 3 go into evenly? What's the first number they both go into evenly?

4. Change the number in B2 to 4. How many numbers do both 3 and 4 go into evenly? What's the first number they both go into evenly?

5. Change the numbers in B2 and C2 to numbers of your choice. Find a pair of numbers that both go evenly into only one of the numbers from 1 to 30.

Learn | Least Common Multiple

A **multiple** of a number is the product of the number and a whole number.

Multiples of 6: 6, 12, 18, **24**, 30, 36, 42, **48**, 54, 60, 66, **72**, …

Multiples of 8: 8, 16, **24**, 32, 40, **48**, 56, 64, **72**, 80, …

Numbers that appear on both lists are **common multiples** . The **least common multiple (LCM)** of two numbers is the *smallest* common multiple of the numbers.

One way to find the LCM of two numbers is to list multiples of both numbers. Then choose the smallest multiple that appears on both lists.

Study TIP

Factors and multiples have related meanings. The multiples of 6 are 6, 12, 18, and so on. The factors of 6 are 1, 2, 3, and 6.

Examples

1 Find the least common multiple of 10 and 12.

Multiples of 10: 10, 20, 30, 40, 50, **60,** 70, 80, 90, 100, …

Multiples of 12: 12, 24, 36, 48, **60,** …

The least common multiple of 10 and 12 is 60.

2 A U.S. President is elected every 4 years. A U.S. senator is elected every 6 years. If a senator is elected the same year as the President, how many years will it be until the senator could run for reelection during a presidential campaign?

"When I said,'term limits,' I was speaking in dog years."

© 1996 J.P. Rini from the Cartoon Bank™, Inc.

▶ **History Link**

According to the U.S. Constitution, a person can be elected to serve only two 4-year terms as President. There is no limit to the number of times a person can be elected to serve as a senator.

Multiples of 4: 4, 8, **12,** 16, 20, 24, 28, 32, …

Multiples of 6: 6, **12,** 18, 24, 30, 36, …

The senator will run for reelection during a presidential campaign in another 12 years.

Try It

Find the LCM of each pair of numbers.

a. 5, 7   **b.** 3, 10   **c.** 4, 10   **d.** 9, 15

Example 3

▶ **History Link**

Clepsydras were used in courts of law. Corrupt lawyers sometimes bribed the timekeepers to put muddy water in the clepsydra. This water would flow more slowly, and the lawyer would have more time to speak.

The clepsydra (KLEP-suh-druh), or water clock, and the hourglass were among the first clocks. In a clepsydra, water pours from one container into another at a regular rate to mark the passage of time. In an hourglass, sand flows from the top container to the bottom one.

One ancient clepsydra had to be refilled every 12 minutes. One kind of hourglass had to be turned over every 30 minutes. If you start both clocks at the same time, when will you need to restart them at the same time?

Find the least common multiple of 12 and 30.

Multiples of 30: 30, **60,** 90, 120, 150, 180, 210, 240, 270, 300, …

Multiples of 12: 12, 24, 36, 48, **60,** …

The least common multiple of 12 and 30 is 60. You will restart both clocks at the same time every 60 minutes.

Try It

Find the LCM of each pair of numbers.

a. 6, 9   **b.** 8, 2   **c.** 20, 25   **d.** 10, 12

e. 5, 11   **f.** 6, 15   **g.** 6, 54   **h.** 1297, 1

Check | Your Understanding

1. For any pair of numbers, is the least common multiple always greater than either number? Explain.

2. Terrence believes that the least common multiple of two prime numbers is always the product of those numbers. Do you think Terrence is correct? Explain.

3. What's the difference between a factor and a multiple? How many factors does 8 have? How many multiples?

Practice and Apply

1. **Getting Started** List the first five multiples of each number.

   a. 3   **b.** 10   **c.** 11   **d.** 8   **e.** 4   **f.** 5

List the first three common multiples of each pair of numbers.

2. 4, 6   3. 1, 5   4. 6, 2   5. 12, 5   6. 3, 9   7. 6, 7

8. 8, 11   9. 8, 4   10. 10, 15   11. 16, 4   12. 5, 3   13. 4, 7

Find the LCM of each pair.

14. 7, 11   15. 3, 33   16. 8, 16

17. 5, 13   18. 2, 15   19. 10, 5

20. 15, 7   21. 4, 3   22. 6, 9

23. 14, 21   24. 4, 6   25. 6, 7

26. 6, 8   27. 10, 20   28. 3, 11

29. 7, 2   30. 88, 4   31. 15, 3

32. Victoria wears slacks every 2 days. She wears her jogging shoes every 3 days. If she wears slacks with jogging shoes on June 1, what are the next three dates on which she will wear both slacks and jogging shoes?

33. The Blue Line bus arrives at Chesapeake Parkway every 20 minutes. The Express Shuttle arrives at the same stop every 3 minutes. How often do both buses arrive at the same time?

34. The key on the Race Times pictograph is missing. If the key is a whole number, give three possible times that Marty could have run.

Race Times						
David	⏱	⏱	⏱	⏱		
Marty	⏱	⏱	⏱			
Joel	⏱	⏱	⏱	⏱	⏱	

⏱ = ? min.

35. **Test Prep** Chuck has baseball practice every 5 days and trumpet practice every 6 days. How often does he have baseball practice and trumpet practice on the same day?

   Ⓐ Every 5 days
   Ⓑ Every 6 days
   Ⓒ Every 15 days
   Ⓓ Every 30 days

Problem Solving and Reasoning

Choose a Strategy For Exercises 36–39, use the following delivery schedule.

Mr. Storrit manages a warehouse. Each employee makes deliveries based on a pattern of days. Every employee made a delivery on January 1.

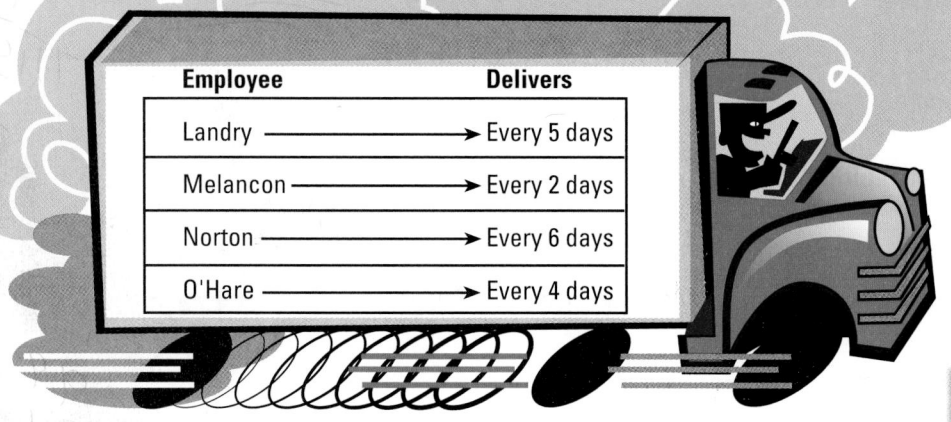

Employee	Delivers
Landry ⟶	Every 5 days
Melancon ⟶	Every 2 days
Norton ⟶	Every 6 days
O'Hare ⟶	Every 4 days

36. How often will both Norton and Melancon make deliveries?

37. How often will both Norton and O'Hare make deliveries?

38. How often will all the employees make deliveries on the same day?

39. All four employees make a delivery on January 1 of a year that's not a leap year. What's the next date when all four employees will make deliveries on the same day?

40. **Journal** Explain why there is no greatest common multiple for any pair of numbers.

41. **Critical Thinking** In a middle school, the principal plans to hide prizes in the new lockers for the students. The principal plans to put a binder in every 10th locker, a school tee shirt in every 15th locker, and a new backpack in every 50th locker. If she starts counting at locker number 1, what is the number of the first locker in which the principal will put all three prizes?

150th locker

42. **Communicate** What is the LCM of 0.3 and 0.7? Explain.

10 : 2⁵, 30, 40, 50, 60
15 : 30, 45, 60
50 : 50, 100

> ## Problem Solving
> ### STRATEGIES
> - Look for a Pattern
> - Make an Organized List
> - Make a Table
> - Guess and Check
> - Work Backward
> - Use Logical Reasoning
> - Draw a Diagram
> - Solve a Simpler Problem

Mixed Review

Compare, using > or < . *[Lesson 2-3]*

43. 23,301 ☐ 23,103

44. 7,377 ☐ 73,777

45. 501,501 ☐ 501,105

Divide. *[Lesson 3-11]*

46. 42 ÷ 0.7

47. 100 ÷ 0.05

48. 6.32 ÷ 0.01

Our calendar is based on the number 365, the approximate number of days it takes Earth to orbit the sun. What might the calendar be like if you lived on a planet with a different orbital period? In this investigation, you'll use factors and multiples to find out.

A Switch in Time …

The planet Venus orbits the sun once for every 225 days on Earth. So a Venus-year equals 225 Earth days.

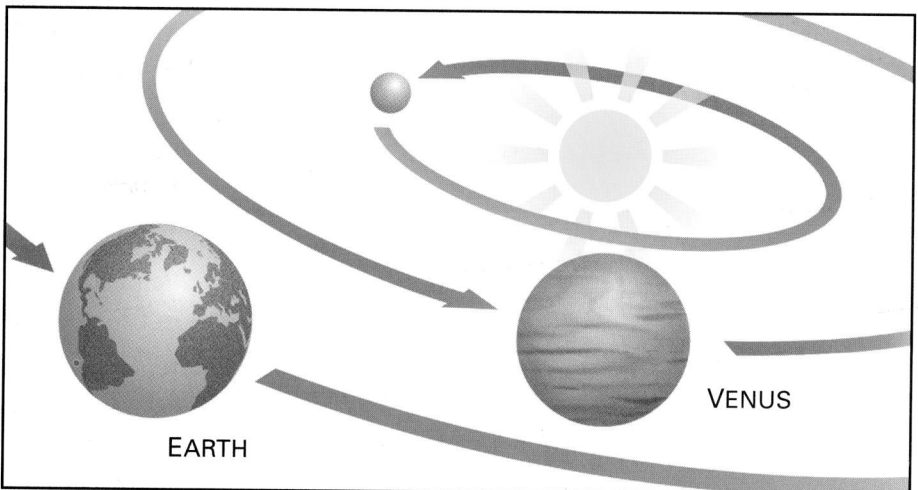

EARTH

VENUS

1. Divide Venus's 225-day year into months, all with the same number of days. Divide each month into weeks, all with the same number of days. Give names to the months and to the days of the week. Explain how you decided on the length of a month and a week.

2. Draw a calendar for a sample month on Venus.

3. Venus begins a new year every 225 days. Earth begins a new year every 365 days. Suppose both planets begin a new year on the same day. How many days will pass before that happens again? How many years is that on Earth? On Venus?

4. Earth children on their 12th birthdays are 4383 days old. This is equal to 12 Earth years, 144 Earth months, or about 626 Earth weeks. According to your Venus calendar, 4383 days equals how many years on Venus? How many months? How many weeks?

Section 5A Review

Tell whether the first number is divisible by the second.

1. 6, 4 **2.** 31, 7 **3.** 48, 2 **4.** 63, 9 **5.** 22, 6 **6.** 80, 10

7. 175, 5 **8.** 882, 9 **9.** 78, 6 **10.** 16, 8 **11.** 72, 3 **12.** 54, 11

Find the prime factorization.

13. 76 **14.** 24 **15.** 22 **16.** 59 **17.** 12 **18.** 44

19. 114 **20.** 243 **21.** 73 **22.** 85 **23.** 81 **24.** 32

List the first seven multiples of each number.

25. 2 **26.** 6 **27.** 7 **28.** 9 **29.** 0 **30.** 12

Find the LCM of each pair.

31. 3, 6 **32.** 5, 15 **33.** 6, 9 **34.** 8, 12 **35.** 10, 20 **36.** 9, 2

37. Social Studies Members of the House of Representatives are elected in years divisible by 2. Which years between 1996 and 2006 will have congressional elections?

38. Number Sense A short way of writing May 10, 1962, is 5/10/62. When Mrs. Ahearn writes the date of her birth in this way, the numbers are the first three odd multiples of 7. When is her birthday?

39. The prime factorization of a number is $3 \times 3 \times 5 \times 13$. What is the number?

40. What is the smallest number that is divisible by 2, 3, 4, 5, 6, 9, and 10? Explain how you found your answer.

41. If you choose a two-digit number at random, is it more likely that the number will be divisible by 5 or by 7? Explain.

Test Prep

You can use the rules of divisibility to help determine if a number is prime or composite.

42. Which number is a prime number?

Ⓐ 63 Ⓑ 78 Ⓒ 109 Ⓓ 115

REVIEW 5A

Meanwhile, Back at the WRENCH

Using a tool can make your work easy...but choosing a tool can make your work hard! That's because there are so many tools to choose from. A recent book listed nearly a thousand tools used by workers. Take wrenches, which are used to tighten or loosen bolts or other fasteners. Some wrenches adjust to different sizes, like monkey wrenches, spud wrenches, and chain wrenches.

Other wrenches have fixed sizes, like box wrenches, open-end wrenches, and crow's foot wrenches. There are wrenches that are designed for special purposes, like spark plug wrenches, basin wrenches, and bicycle wrenches.

To make matters even more complicated, every type of wrench comes in a variety of sizes. In this section, you'll learn how we use both fractions and decimals to measure such sizes. And you'll learn about special tools we use to measure the sizes of items as different as bones, fabric, flour, and rain.

1 Name a tool you have used to measure the size of an item. What units were used? Were they fractional or decimal measurements?

2 What problems might occur if your wrenches were sized in inches and the bolts you wanted to tighten were sized in millimeters?

3 Why do we have so many different kinds of tools? Why are different systems of measurement used to size them?

287

Understanding Fractions

▶ **Lesson Link** In the last chapter, you learned to use decimals, which name amounts using place values less than one. Now you'll learn to use fractions, which express numbers as equal parts of the whole. ◀

You'll Learn ...

■ to represent values between whole numbers as fractions

... How It's Used

Plumbers use fractions when measuring pipes and fittings.

Vocabulary

fraction

denominator

numerator

equivalent fractions

A **fraction** describes part of a whole when the whole is cut into equal parts. On this ruler, the inches are divided into 4 equal parts. Each part is 1 of the 4 parts, or $\frac{1}{4}$.

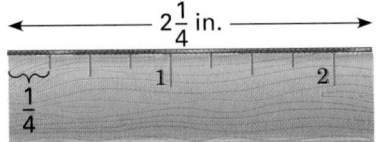

Explore   Fractions

Halve It Your Way

Materials: 4 sheets of paper of different colors, Scissors

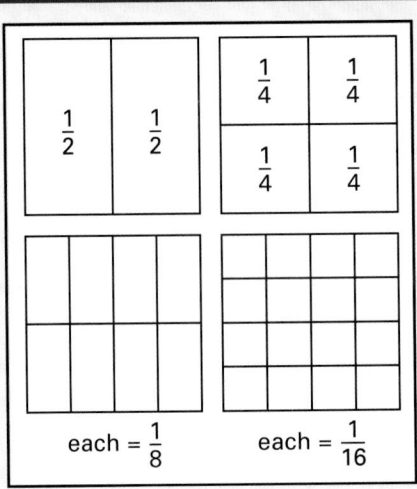

each = $\frac{1}{8}$ each = $\frac{1}{16}$

1. Cut the first sheet of paper into halves and label each piece $\frac{1}{2}$. Cut the second sheet into fourths and label each piece $\frac{1}{4}$. Cut the third sheet into eighths and label each piece $\frac{1}{8}$. Cut the fourth sheet into sixteenths and label each piece $\frac{1}{16}$.

2. Notice that two of your $\frac{1}{4}$ pieces fit perfectly on a $\frac{1}{2}$ piece. This shows that 2 fourths, or $\frac{2}{4}$, equal $\frac{1}{2}$. Use your pieces to find five other pairs of equal fractions. Make a sketch like the one shown for each pair of equal fractions. Do not use $\frac{2}{4} = \frac{1}{2}$ as one of your pairs.

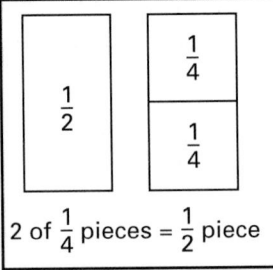

2 of $\frac{1}{4}$ pieces = $\frac{1}{2}$ piece

3. A rain gauge at City Hall showed that $\frac{1}{2}$ in. of rain fell during the night. A rain gauge at the airport showed that $\frac{4}{8}$ in. of rain had fallen. Which gauge recorded more rain? Explain.

4. Two cars have the same-size gas tank. One car has $\frac{3}{4}$ of a tank of gas. The other car has $\frac{11}{16}$ of a tank of gas. Which car has more gas? Explain.

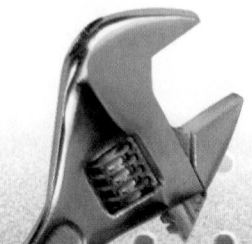

A fraction describes a portion of something that has been divided into equal parts. The bottom number, called the **denominator**, gives the number of parts in the whole. The top number, the **numerator**, tells how many of the parts are being named.

You can read the fraction $\frac{5}{8}$ two ways: "five eighths" or "five out of eight."

When the numerator and denominator are the same number, the fraction is equal to 1.

$\frac{6}{6}$ = ⬜ = one whole = 1

Example 1

A slotted screwdriver has an end that looks like a —. A Phillips screwdriver has an end that looks like a +. What fraction of all the screwdrivers shown are slotted screwdrivers? What fraction are Phillips screwdrivers?

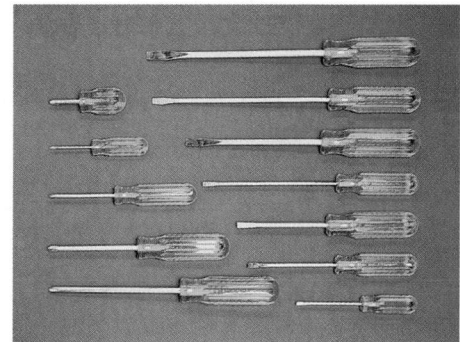

There are 12 screwdrivers. Seven of those are slotted. The fraction that are slotted is $\frac{7}{12}$. There are five Phillips screwdrivers, so $\frac{5}{12}$ of the screwdrivers are Phillips screwdrivers.

▶ **Industry Link**

Many screwdrivers have been invented for special purposes. Five-sided screwdrivers are used for caps and valves on fire hydrants. Hexagonal-head screwdrivers were used to put armor together in the 15th century.

Recall that the same number can be expressed in different ways using decimals. For example, 5.2 = 5.20 = 5.200 = 5.2000.

Fractions can also have different names. Two fractions that name the same amount are **equivalent fractions**. In the first rectangle, 2 of 3 equal parts are shaded. In the second rectangle, 4 of 6 equal parts are shaded. The same amount is shaded in both rectangles, so $\frac{2}{3} = \frac{4}{6}$.

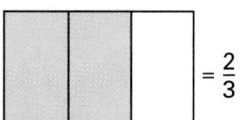 $= \frac{2}{3}$

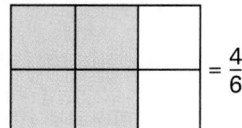 $= \frac{4}{6}$

Remember

When you annex zeros to the end of a decimal, you do not change its value. **[Page 148]**

Example 2

$\frac{3}{5}$ of the rectangle has been shaded.
Name a fraction equivalent to $\frac{3}{5}$.

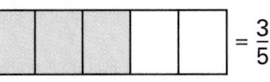 $= \frac{3}{5}$

You can draw a line across the rectangle,
cutting it into 10 pieces. Then 6 pieces are
shaded. $\frac{3}{5} = \frac{6}{10}$

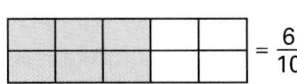 $= \frac{6}{10}$

In some situations, you may need to find one fraction equivalent
to a given fraction. In other situations, it may be helpful to find
two equivalent fractions.

Example 3

Chinese chopsticks are 10 inches long
with flat ends. Japanese chopsticks are
7 to 8 inches long with pointed ends.
What fraction of the individual chopsticks
are Chinese? Give two equivalent fractions for your answer.

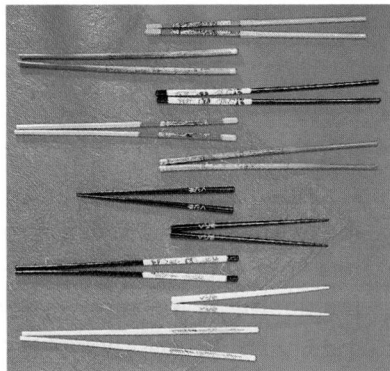

There are 20 chopsticks. 14 of them are
Chinese. $\frac{14}{20}$ of the chopsticks are Chinese.
There are 10 pairs of chopsticks. 7 of them
are Chinese. $\frac{7}{10}$ of the chopstick pairs are
Chinese. $\frac{14}{20} = \frac{7}{10}$.

Try It

a. What fraction of the
jalapeño peppers are red?
What fraction are not?

b. What fraction does the shaded part of
the rectangle represent? Name an equivalent
fraction.

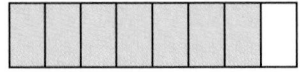

Check | Your Understanding

1. How are the top number of a fraction and the bottom number different?

2. How many fractions can you use to describe a portion of a whole? Explain.

3. Give a real-world example to show that $\frac{1}{4} = \frac{2}{8}$.

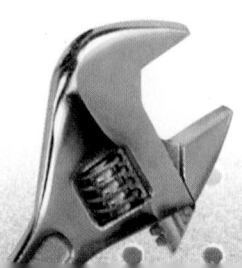

Practice and Apply

1. **Getting Started** What fraction does the shaded part represent?

a. 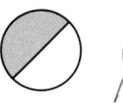 1/2   **b.** 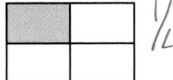 ¼   **c.** 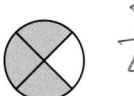 5/8   **d.** ⊗ 3/4

For each fraction, draw a model and name an equivalent fraction.

2. $\dfrac{3}{4}$ **3.** $\dfrac{7}{9}$ **4.** $\dfrac{1}{2}$ **5.** $\dfrac{12}{17}$ **6.** $\dfrac{5}{8}$ **7.** $\dfrac{2}{3}$

8. $\dfrac{12}{12}$ **9.** $\dfrac{8}{16}$ **10.** $\dfrac{11}{11}$ **11.** $\dfrac{4}{10}$ **12.** $\dfrac{6}{7}$ **13.** $\dfrac{3}{8}$

14. $\dfrac{1}{9}$ **15.** $\dfrac{6}{8}$ **16.** $\dfrac{2}{7}$ **17.** $\dfrac{2}{4}$ **18.** $\dfrac{8}{11}$ **19.** $\dfrac{9}{10}$

The window shown has equal-size sections made of both stained glass and clear glass.

20. What fraction of the window is made of stained glass?

21. What fraction of the window is made of clear glass?

22. Suppose three sections of the window need to be replaced. Name two fractions that describe this amount.

23. **Test Prep** Which fraction expresses one out of seven equal pieces?

Ⓐ $\dfrac{7}{1}$ Ⓑ $\dfrac{1}{7}$ Ⓒ $\dfrac{7}{7}$

Geometry Use the shapes pictured to answer Exercises 24–26.

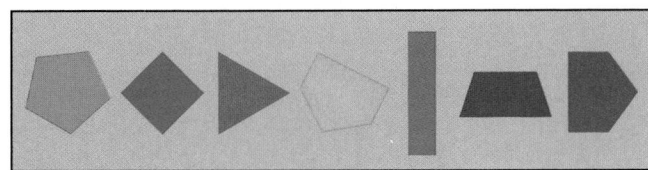

24. What fraction of the shapes shown have five sides?

25. What fraction of the shapes do not have exactly three sides?

26. Which fraction is larger, the fraction of the shapes with four sides or the fraction of the shapes with five sides?

27. Industry Celia needs 20 nails and 8 screws to build a bookshelf. What fraction of the hardware she needs are screws?

28. Name two fractions that describe the number of square picture frames. Identify the numerators and denominators.

Problem Solving and Reasoning

Use the drill-bit size chart for Exercises 29–30.

29. Critical Thinking The bit sizes increase according to a mathematical pattern. What will the size of the #10 drill bit be?

30. Critical Thinking What number bit would you need to drill a $\frac{3}{4}$-inch hole?

Number	Bit Size
#4	$\frac{1}{4}$ in.
#5	$\frac{5}{16}$ in.
#6	$\frac{6}{16}$ in.
#7	$\frac{7}{16}$ in.
#8	$\frac{2}{4}$ in.

31. Communicate Which of these figures are divided into fourths? Explain.

a.

b.

c.

d.

32.  Explain what happens to the value of a fraction when the numerator gets bigger and the denominator stays the same. What happens when the denominator gets bigger and the numerator doesn't change?

Mixed Review

Round to the underlined place value. *[Lesson 3-2]*

33. 101.9<u>3</u> **34.** 6.79<u>2</u> **35.** 48.<u>2</u>5 **36.** <u>0</u>.672 **37.** <u>8</u>.7 **38.** 12.<u>7</u>02

Solve. *[Lesson 3-12]*

39. $92.4n = 9240$ **40.** $p \div 0.05 = 5$

41. $1.45h = 2.9$ **42.** $w \div 3 = 333.3$

Fractions in Lowest Terms

▶ **Lesson Link** You've seen that different fractions can have equal values. Now you'll learn the simplest way to name a fraction. ◀

Explore | Equivalent Fractions

Fractions in Action

1. Complete the table. Every row should have equivalent fractions created by multiplying the shaded and total pieces by the same number.

Model	Fraction	$\frac{\times 2}{\times 2}$	$\frac{\times 3}{\times 3}$	$\frac{\times 4}{\times 4}$
	$\frac{1}{2}$	$= \frac{2}{4}$	$= \frac{?}{6}$	$= \frac{?}{?}$

2. Complete the table. Every row should have equivalent fractions created by dividing the shaded and total pieces by the same number. If a fraction can't be done, write "Can't do."

Model	Fraction	$\frac{\div 2}{\div 2}$	$\frac{\div 3}{\div 3}$	$\frac{\div 4}{\div 4}$
	$\frac{6}{12}$	$= \frac{3}{6}$	$= \frac{2}{4}$	Can't do

3. Can every fraction be turned into an equivalent fraction with larger numbers? With smaller numbers? Explain.

You'll Learn ...

■ to write a fraction in lowest terms

... How It's Used

Organic gardeners must write fractions in lowest terms in order to be certain they are caring for their crops correctly.

Vocabulary

lowest terms

greatest common factor (GCF)

Learn | Fractions in Lowest Terms

You can find equivalent fractions by multiplying or dividing the numerator and denominator of a given fraction by the same non-zero number.

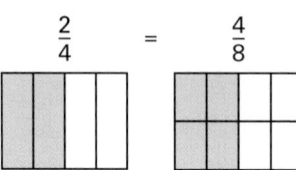

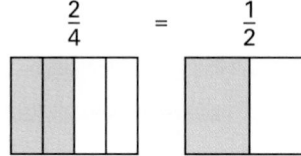

$$\frac{2}{4} = \frac{4}{8} \qquad\qquad \frac{2}{4} = \frac{1}{2}$$

Example 1

Problem Solving TIP

When looking for equivalent fractions, try multiplying and dividing by easy numbers like 2, 3, and 10.

Find two fractions equivalent to $\frac{9}{12}$.

$$\frac{9 \times 2}{12 \times 2} = \frac{18}{24}$$ Multiply numerator and denominator by 2.

$$\frac{9}{12} =$$

$$\frac{18}{24} =$$

$$\frac{9 \div 3}{12 \div 3} = \frac{3}{4}$$ Divide numerator and denominator by 3.

$$\frac{9}{12} =$$

$$\frac{3}{4} =$$

Two fractions equivalent to $\frac{9}{12}$ are $\frac{18}{24}$ and $\frac{3}{4}$.

Remember

A fraction in lowest terms is also known as a fraction in simplest terms.

[Previous course]

When you multiply to find equivalent fractions, you can use any non-zero number as a multiplier. When you divide, you must find a number that divides both the numerator and the denominator. If there is no whole number other than 1 that divides both, the fraction is in **lowest terms**.

Example 2

A size-15 knitting needle measures about $\frac{24}{60}$ of an inch. What is this fraction in lowest terms?

$$\frac{24 \div 4}{60 \div 4} = \frac{6}{15}$$ Divide numerator and denominator by 4.

$$\frac{6 \div 3}{15 \div 3} = \frac{2}{5}$$ Divide numerator and denominator by 3.

There are no numbers that divide into both 2 and 5. $\frac{24}{60}$ in lowest terms is $\frac{2}{5}$.

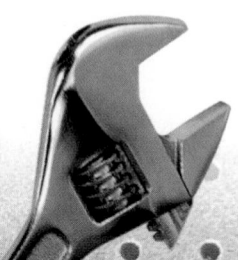

294 *Chapter 5 • Patterns and Number Theory*

You can reduce a fraction to lowest terms in one step if you divide by the greatest whole number that divides the numerator and the denominator. That number is called the **greatest common factor (GCF)** .

Remember

Unlike the greatest common factor, the least common multiple is the smallest number that two numbers divide. **[Page 281]**

Examples

3 Find the GCF of 36 and 90.

Factors of 36: 1, 2, 3, 4, 6, 9, 12, 18, 36

Factors of 90: 1, 2, 3, 5, 6, 9, 10, 15, 18, 30, 45, 90

The common factors of 36 and 90 are 1, 2, 3, 6, 9, and 18. The *greatest* common factor is 18.

4 Find the GCF of 24 and 30, and use it to reduce $\frac{24}{30}$.

Factors of 24: 1, 2, 3, 4, 6, 8, 12, 24

Factors of 30: 1, 2, 3, 5, 6, 10, 15, 30

The common factors of 24 and 30 are 1, 2, 3, and 6. The *greatest* common factor is 6.

$$\frac{24 \div 6}{30 \div 6} = \frac{4}{5}$$

$\frac{24}{30}$ in lowest terms is $\frac{4}{5}$.

MENTAL MATH

Using the rules of divisibility can help you to find the factors of a number.

Try It

Find two fractions equivalent to the given fraction.

a. $\frac{6}{10}$ **b.** $\frac{12}{15}$ **c.** $\frac{7}{21}$

Find the GCF of the given pair of numbers.

d. 15, 20   **e.** 10, 12   **f.** 18, 45

Write in lowest terms.

g. $\frac{8}{10}$ **h.** $\frac{21}{28}$ **i.** $\frac{36}{54}$

Check | Your Understanding

1. How can you use the GCF when reducing a fraction to lowest terms?

2. You can write fractions in lowest terms. Can you also write them in "highest terms"? Explain.

Practice and Apply

1. **Getting Started** State if each fraction is in lowest terms.

   a. $\frac{3}{7}$ **b.** $\frac{4}{8}$ **c.** $\frac{1}{10}$ **d.** $\frac{1}{16}$ **e.** $\frac{3}{9}$ **f.** $\frac{2}{15}$

Find two fractions equivalent to each fraction.

2. $\frac{3}{5}$ 3. $\frac{6}{18}$ 4. $\frac{5}{20}$ 5. $\frac{1}{6}$ 6. $\frac{2}{7}$ 7. $\frac{9}{21}$

8. $\frac{12}{24}$ 9. $\frac{10}{25}$ 10. $\frac{21}{35}$ 11. $\frac{11}{33}$ 12. $\frac{7}{11}$ 13. $\frac{4}{9}$

Write in lowest terms.

14. $\frac{7}{14}$ 15. $\frac{5}{25}$ 16. $\frac{20}{30}$ 17. $\frac{6}{18}$ 18. $\frac{12}{36}$ 19. $\frac{8}{10}$

20. $\frac{6}{8}$ 21. $\frac{9}{15}$ 22. $\frac{3}{21}$ 23. $\frac{4}{24}$ 24. $\frac{21}{35}$ 25. $\frac{6}{9}$

26. $\frac{10}{12}$ 27. $\frac{11}{44}$ 28. $\frac{2}{8}$ 29. $\frac{5}{30}$ 30. $\frac{8}{36}$ 31. $\frac{3}{18}$

Find the GCF of each pair.

32. 4, 8   33. 15, 25   34. 12, 15   35. 6, 8   36. 3, 7   37. 2, 5

38. 18, 27   39. 16, 24   40. 11, 23   41. 10, 100   42. 35, 24   43. 36, 16

44. 22, 66   45. 27, 72   46. 64, 32   47. 48, 28   48. 11, 17   49. 3, 105

50. **Test Prep** The head of a sledgehammer is shaped like a barrel. Which fraction in lowest terms describes the number of hammers that are sledgehammers?

    Ⓐ $\frac{1}{2}$ Ⓑ $\frac{1}{3}$ Ⓒ $\frac{4}{8}$ Ⓓ $\frac{4}{12}$

51. **Test Prep** Which fraction in lowest terms describes the number of hammers that don't have blue handles?

    Ⓐ $\frac{1}{6}$ Ⓑ $\frac{2}{12}$

    Ⓒ $\frac{5}{6}$ Ⓓ $\frac{10}{12}$

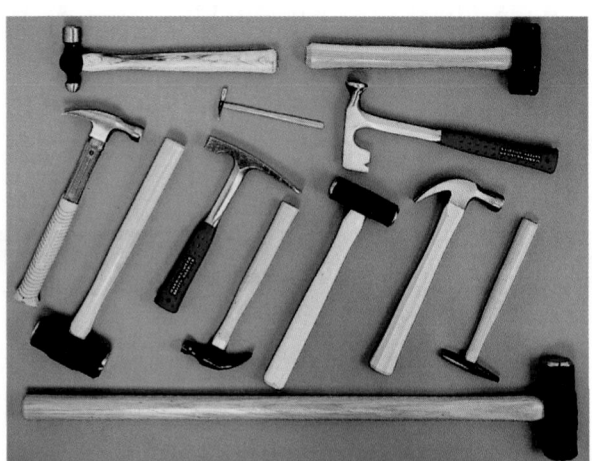

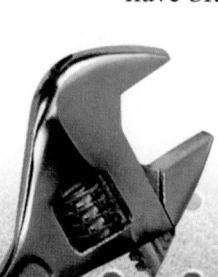

PRACTICE 5-5

52. History Medieval carpenters used tools with narrow cutting edges, called gouges, to shape their work. The width of one paring gouge was about $\frac{4}{16}$ in. Write the width in lowest terms.

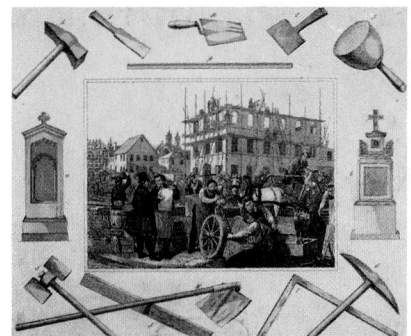

Problem Solving and Reasoning

53. Choose a Strategy Marilyn sold $\frac{3}{6}$ of the raffle tickets at a carnival. Darren sold $\frac{2}{8}$ of them. Jamelya sold the rest. Who sold more tickets, Marilyn by herself, or Darren and Jamelya together? Explain.

54. 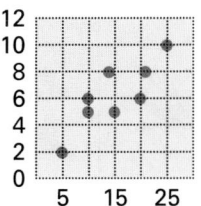 Explain the difference between LCM and GCF. Can the LCM and GCF of two numbers ever be equal? Explain.

55. Critical Thinking Explain why $\frac{2}{17}$, $\frac{11}{13}$, $\frac{2}{3}$, and $\frac{5}{7}$ cannot be written in lower terms. What do the numbers making up the fractions have in common?

56. Communicate What is the GCF of 1 and x? Explain.

Problem Solving

STRATEGIES

- Look for a Pattern
- Make an Organized List
- Make a Table
- Guess and Check
- Work Backward
- Use Logical Reasoning
- Draw a Diagram
- Solve a Simpler Problem

Mixed Review

57. For each point in the graph, approximate the data represented by the point. *[Lesson 1-3]*

Use the Maximum Weight graph for Exercises 58–61. *[Lesson 1-1]*

58. What is the maximum weight for a flyweight boxer?

59. What is the difference in the maximum weights for the cruiserweight and the welterweight?

60. Tony weighs 76 kg. What weight class is he in?

61. Which two weight classes have the largest difference? What is the difference between those two classes?

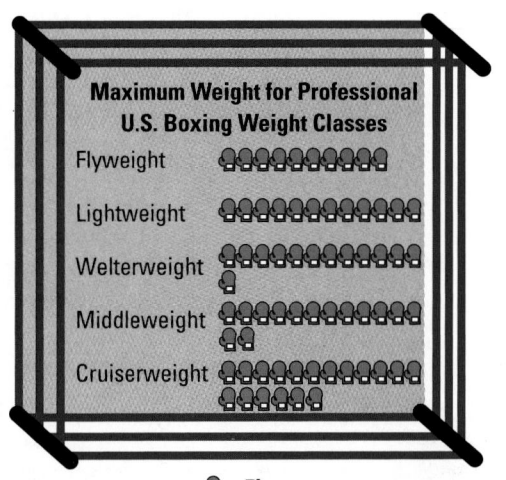

Maximum Weight for Professional U.S. Boxing Weight Classes

Flyweight
Lightweight
Welterweight
Middleweight
Cruiserweight

= 5kg

Improper Fractions and Mixed Numbers

You'll Learn ...

■ to convert between improper fractions and mixed numbers

... How It's Used

Deli clerks use improper fractions and mixed numbers when weighing meats and cheeses.

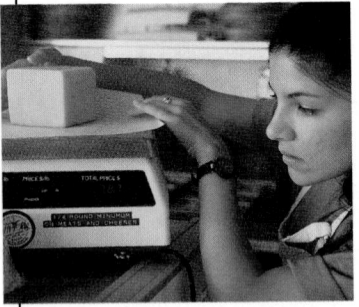

Vocabulary

improper fraction

mixed number

▶ **Lesson Link** So far in this section, you've worked mainly with fractions less than a whole. Now you'll look at fractions greater than a whole. ◀

An **improper fraction** has a numerator that is greater than or equal to its denominator. A **mixed number** combines a whole number and a fraction.

Proper	$\frac{2}{3}$
Improper	$\frac{20}{9}$
Mixed	$3\frac{4}{5}$

Explore   Improper Fractions and Mixed Numbers

Hexagons Plus

Materials: Pattern blocks or Power Polygons

1. Use pattern blocks to complete the table.

The "whole"	The "parts"	Fraction naming one "part"	Improper fraction: all "parts"	Mixed number: all "parts"
(hexagon)	(8 triangles)	$\frac{1}{6}$	$\frac{7}{6}$	$1\frac{1}{6}$
(trapezoid)	(8 triangles)			
(hexagon)	(4 rhombi)			
(rhombus)	(5 triangles)			
(trapezoid)	(3 rhombi)			

2. Can any improper fraction be written as a mixed number? Can any mixed number be rewritten as an improper fraction? Explain.

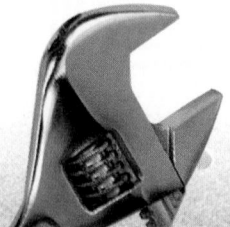

A proper fraction has a value less than 1. Recall that a proper fraction can have many names.

Improper fractions and mixed numbers have values greater than 1. Improper fractions and mixed numbers can also have many names. Sometimes, one is easier to use than the other.

Proper Fractions

$$\frac{1}{2} = \frac{2}{4} = \frac{3}{6} = \frac{4}{8}$$

Improper Fractions

$$\frac{4}{3} = \frac{8}{6} = \frac{12}{9} = \frac{16}{12}$$

Mixed Numbers

$$7\frac{1}{2} = 7\frac{2}{4} = 7\frac{3}{6} = 7\frac{4}{8}$$

Remember

The order of operations states:

(1) do operations in parentheses;
(2) do operations with exponents;
(3) multiply and divide from left to right; and
(4) add and subtract from left to right.
[Page 99]

Divide the numerator by the denominator. The whole number part is the whole number in the mixed number. The remainder is the numerator in the fraction part.

$$\frac{13}{4} = 13 \div 4 = 3\text{ R }1 = 3\frac{1}{4}$$

Improper Fraction → Mixed Number

To get the improper fraction numerator, multiply the fraction denominator by the whole number, then add the mixed-number numerator.

$$2\frac{1}{3} = \frac{(3 \times 2) + 1}{3} = \frac{7}{3}$$

Examples

1 Rewrite $\frac{11}{4}$ cups as a mixed number.

$$\frac{11}{4} = 11 \div 4 = 4\overline{)11}^{\,2\text{ R }3}$$ Divide numerator by denominator.

$$\frac{11}{4} = 2\frac{3}{4}$$

2 Write $4\frac{3}{5}$ as an improper fraction.

$$4\frac{3}{5} = \frac{(5 \times 4) + 3}{5} = \frac{23}{5}$$ Multiply denominator and whole number and add numerator.

Try It

Write as a mixed number.   **a.** $\frac{14}{3}$ **b.** $\frac{26}{9}$ **c.** $\frac{35}{4}$

Write as an improper fraction.   **d.** $1\frac{5}{6}$ **e.** $4\frac{1}{8}$ **f.** $2\frac{3}{5}$

1. Can a mixed number be equal to 1? Explain.

2. Can an improper fraction equal a whole number? Explain.

5-6 Exercises and Applications

Practice and Apply

1. **Getting Started** | Identify each fraction as proper or improper.

a. $\frac{9}{10}$ b. $\frac{12}{3}$ c. $\frac{3}{2}$ d. $\frac{4}{6}$ e. $\frac{17}{8}$ f. $\frac{8}{2}$

Write each mixed number as an improper fraction.

2. $1\frac{8}{8}$ 3. $1\frac{9}{5}$ 4. $1\frac{6}{3}$ 5. $3\frac{1}{3}$ 6. $4\frac{9}{8}$ 7. $2\frac{6}{4}$

8. $1\frac{2}{5}$ 9. $2\frac{4}{5}$ 10. $1\frac{1}{4}$ 11. $3\frac{1}{10}$ 12. $5\frac{4}{5}$ 13. $2\frac{9}{12}$

Write each improper fraction as a mixed number.

14. $\frac{10}{3}$ 15. $\frac{14}{5}$ 16. $\frac{15}{8}$ 17. $\frac{11}{2}$ 18. $\frac{14}{3}$ 19. $\frac{23}{8}$

20. $\frac{50}{7}$ 21. $\frac{99}{10}$ 22. $\frac{201}{2}$ 23. $\frac{805}{8}$ 24. $\frac{40}{9}$ 25. $\frac{29}{11}$

Science Write the mixed number as an improper fraction or the improper fraction as a mixed number.

26. Washing the dishes with the water running wastes $25\frac{2}{3}$ gallons of water.

27. A running faucet uses $3\frac{7}{8}$ gallons of water every minute.

28. Flushing a toilet uses $\frac{28}{5}$ gallons of water.

29. **Measurement** Caesar has a tool box that is $15\frac{3}{4}$ in. long. His hammer is $\frac{45}{4}$ in. long. Will the hammer fit in the tool box?

30. **Test Prep** Choose the mixed number equivalent to $\frac{10}{6}$.

Ⓐ $\frac{5}{3}$ Ⓑ $\frac{6}{10}$ Ⓒ $1\frac{4}{6}$ Ⓓ $2\frac{2}{6}$

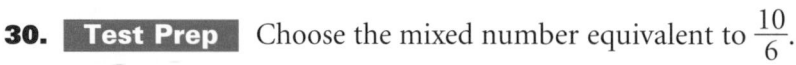

PRACTICE 5-6

Problem Solving and Reasoning

31. Critical Thinking Darrell needs to measure a board about 6 feet long. He can't find his ruler, but he knows his hand is $\frac{1}{2}$ a foot long. How many hand lengths will he have to mark to get the length he needs?

32. Critical Thinking The picture models a number greater than one. Write the value it represents as a mixed number and as an improper fraction. Explain.

33. [Journal] Explain why an improper fraction can be written as a mixed number but a fraction less than 1 cannot.

34. Communicate Which is more, $\frac{9}{4}$ slices of cantaloupe or $1\frac{1}{2}$ slices? Explain your decision.

Mixed Review

Find the mean, median, and mode with and without the outlier. Which does the outlier affect the most? *[Lesson 1-9]*

35. 20, 31, 32, 34, 35, 35, 35, 36, 37

36. 7, 4, 3, 6, 20, 7, 7, 4, 5, 2, 2, 1, 2

37. Make a line plot of the data in Exercise 35. *[Lesson 1-4]*

38. Make a line plot of the data in Exercise 36. *[Lesson 1-4]*

Convert. *[Lesson 4-3]*

39. 2 mi = ☐ ft
40. 60 in. = ☐ ft
41. 27 ft = ☐ yd
42. 3 lb = ☐ oz

43. 5 mi = ☐ ft
44. 108 in. = ☐ ft
45. 90 ft = ☐ yd
46. 7 lb = ☐ oz

Project Progress

In your chart, write several versions of your favorite number as a fraction and as a decimal. Compare one of the fraction versions of your number to other fractions and record the comparisons in your chart.

Problem Solving

Understand
Plan
Solve
Look Back

Converting Fractions and Decimals

▶ Lesson Link You've learned to write numbers using decimal notation and fraction notation. Now you'll learn to convert between the two notations. ◀

You'll Learn ...

■ to convert between fractions and decimals

... How It's Used

International travelers have to understand the connection between fractions and decimals when traveling to foreign countries.

Vocabulary

terminating decimal

repeating decimal

Explore **Fractions and Decimals**

Making the Grid

Materials: Tenths grids, 10 × 10 grids

Modeling Fractions on a Tenths Grid

- Divide the strips into a number of groups equal to the denominator. Each group should have the same number of strips.

- Color in as many groups as the numerator.

- Describe the number modeled in the grid.

1 2 3 4 5

$\frac{3}{5} = 0.6$

1. Model these fractions as decimals.

   a. $\frac{1}{2}$ **b.** $\frac{2}{5}$ **c.** $\frac{7}{10}$ **d.** $\frac{4}{5}$

Modeling Fractions on a 10 × 10 Grid

- Divide the squares into a number of groups equal to the denominator. Each group should have the same number of squares.

- Color in as many groups as the numerator.

- Describe the number modeled in the grid.

$\frac{3}{4} = 0.75$

2. Model these fractions as decimals.

   a. $\frac{4}{10}$ **b.** $\frac{1}{4}$ **c.** $\frac{3}{20}$ **d.** $\frac{13}{50}$

3. Could you model $\frac{1}{4}$ on a 10-strip grid? Explain.

4. Could you model $\frac{1}{3}$ on a 10-strip grid? Could you model it on a 100-strip grid? Explain.

5. Which of the following would have more shaded squares, a grid showing $\frac{3}{10}$ or a grid showing 0.3? Explain.

Fractions and decimals are two different ways of describing numbers in between whole numbers. It's important to be able to compare these numbers, even if some are written as decimals and some as fractions.

Rewrite the digits of the decimal as the numerator. Write the denominator equal to the place value of the decimal number.

$0.9 = $ nine tenths $= \frac{9}{10}$

$0.013 = $ thirteen thousandths $= \frac{13}{1000}$

Decimal   Fraction

Divide the numerator by the denominator. You may need to go several places past the decimal point.

$$\frac{3}{4} = 4\overline{)3.00} \begin{array}{c} 0.75 \\ \underline{28} \\ 20 \\ \underline{20} \end{array}$$

Examples

1 Write 0.775 as a fraction in lowest terms.

$0.775 = \frac{775}{1000}$ Write the fraction.

$= \frac{775 \div 25}{1000 \div 25}$ The greatest common factor of 775 and 1000 is 25.

$= \frac{31}{40}$ Divide.

2 Jane needs to drill a hole at least 0.7 inch wide. Her hand drill has a #10 auger bit, which is $\frac{5}{8}$ of an inch wide. Is the auger bit big enough?

$$\frac{5}{8} = 8\overline{)5.000} \begin{array}{c} 0.625 \\ \underline{48} \\ 20 \\ \underline{16} \\ 40 \\ \underline{40} \end{array}$$ Divide the numerator by the denominator.

The drill bit is 0.625 inches wide.
$0.625 < 0.7$. No, it is not big enough.

When you convert a fraction to a decimal, there are two kinds of answers you can get, a *terminating decimal* or a *repeating decimal.*

A **terminating decimal** ends:

A **repeating decimal** repeats a pattern of digits continuously:

$$\frac{5}{8} = 8\overline{)5.000}^{\;0.625} = 0.625$$

$$\begin{array}{r} 48 \\ \hline 20 \\ 16 \\ \hline 40 \\ 40 \\ \hline \end{array}$$

$$\frac{4}{11} = 11\overline{)4.000000}^{\;0.363636\ldots}$$

$$\begin{array}{r} 33 \\ \hline 70 \\ 66 \\ \hline 40 \\ 33 \\ \hline \end{array}$$

$\frac{5}{8} = 0.625.$ The decimal ends.

$\frac{4}{11} = 0.3636\ldots$ The decimal repeats.

To represent a repeating decimal, draw a bar over the repeating digits.
$\frac{4}{11} = 0.\overline{36}.$

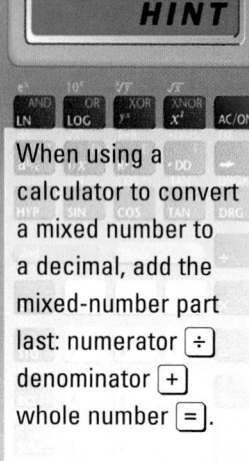

HINT

When using a calculator to convert a mixed number to a decimal, add the mixed-number part last: numerator ÷ denominator + whole number =.

Example 3

Paleontologists use calipers to measure the width of solid objects. A paleontologist measures two bones as $\frac{1}{9}$ in. and $\frac{3}{32}$ in. Write these measures as decimals. Which decimal value is larger? Which bone is larger?

Use a calculator to divide.

1 ÷ 9 = 0.111111…, so $\frac{1}{9}$ is the repeating decimal $0.\overline{1}$.

3 ÷ 32 = 0.09375, so $\frac{3}{32}$ is the terminating decimal 0.09375.

$0.\overline{1}$ is larger than 0.09375. The first bone is larger.

Try It

Write as a fraction in lowest terms.

a. 0.8   **b.** 0.24   **c.** 0.375

Write as a decimal. State whether the decimal terminates or repeats.

d. $\frac{1}{5}$ **e.** $\frac{13}{20}$ **f.** $\frac{12}{33}$

1. Can all fractions be changed into decimals? Explain.

2. How can you tell if a fraction is less than, equal to, or greater than 1?

5-7 Exercises and Applications

Practice and Apply

1. **Getting Started** Write each decimal in fraction form.

    a. 0.3   **b.** 0.7   **c.** 0.11   **d.** 0.37   **e.** 0.121   **f.** 0.333

Rewrite using bar notation.

2. 0.33333333…   **3.** 0.14141414…   **4.** 0.827272727…   **5.** 1.345345…

Write each fraction as a decimal. State whether the decimal terminates or repeats.

6. $\frac{2}{5}$ **7.** $\frac{2}{11}$ **8.** $\frac{7}{10}$ **9.** $\frac{9}{20}$ **10.** $\frac{2}{22}$ **11.** $\frac{7}{25}$

12. $\frac{17}{20}$ **13.** $\frac{4}{6}$ **14.** $\frac{11}{6}$ **15.** $\frac{5}{2}$ **16.** $\frac{62}{62}$ **17.** $\frac{5}{4}$

18. $\frac{7}{9}$ **19.** $\frac{72}{100}$ **20.** $\frac{5}{8}$ **21.** $\frac{3}{4}$ **22.** $\frac{5}{6}$ **23.** $\frac{4}{8}$

Write each decimal as a fraction in lowest terms.

24. 0.25   **25.** 0.4   **26.** 0.75   **27.** 0.44   **28.** 0.3   **29.** 0.67

30. 0.168   **31.** 0.35   **32.** 0.64   **33.** 0.52   **34.** 0.332   **35.** 0.192

36. 0.6   **37.** 0.7   **38.** 0.36   **39.** 0.128   **40.** 0.28   **41.** 0.88

42. **Measurement** Chi is using a set of measuring cups that contains these measures: $\frac{1}{4}$ cup, $\frac{1}{3}$ cup, $\frac{1}{2}$ cup, and 1 cup. Write the decimal name for each measure.

43. **Measurement** Melissa is using a set of wrenches that come in these sizes: 0.125 inch, 0.25 inch, 0.375 inch, 0.5 inch, 0.625 inch, 0.75 inch, and 0.875 inch. Write each wrench size as a fraction in lowest terms.

44. Career Jeff is entering data from the Measurement graph into a computer spreadsheet. It will be easier to enter the kilograms in decimal form. What values should Jeff enter for the following dates?

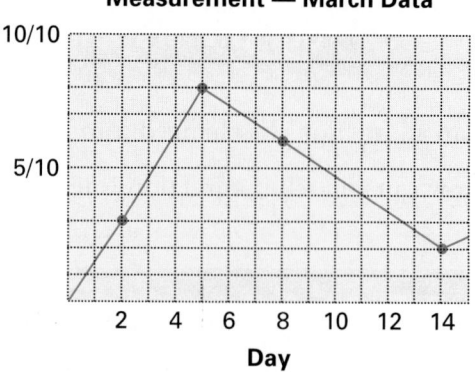

Measurement — March Data

a. March 2   b. March 5

c. March 8   d. March 14

45. | Test Prep | Choose the equivalent decimal for $\frac{5}{6}$.

Ⓐ 0.3333   Ⓑ $0.\overline{3}$

Ⓒ 0.8   Ⓓ $0.8\overline{3}$

Problem Solving and Reasoning

46. Communicate Is $\frac{2}{3}$ closer to 0.67 or 0.667? Explain.

47. Critical Thinking Using long division, write $\frac{2}{99}$ and $\frac{37}{99}$ as decimals. Which process takes more steps? Explain why.

48. Communicate Mimi is converting $\frac{1}{3}$ to a decimal, using division, but the division problem never ends. Explain why this happens. How should Mimi write the decimal?

49. Journal Explain the difference between a terminating decimal and a repeating decimal.

Mixed Review

Simplify mentally. *[Lesson 2-5]*

50. 60×10 **51.** $175 + 425$ **52.** $86 + 24$ **53.** $3 \times 68 \times 10$

54. $8000 \div 200$ **55.** 300×50 **56.** $17 + 70 + 30$ **57.** 34×3

58. Make a bar graph of the data. *[Lesson 1-5]*

Mass of U.S. Coins (grams)				
Penny	Nickel	Dime	Quarter	Half Dollar
2.60	5.14	2.26	5.47	10.99

Draw a model for each of the fractions. *[Lesson 5–4]*

59. $\frac{1}{3}$ **60.** $\frac{2}{5}$ **61.** $\frac{3}{7}$ **62.** $\frac{9}{10}$ **63.** $\frac{3}{12}$ **64.** $\frac{1}{4}$

TECHNOLOGY

Using a Spreadsheet • Finding Decimal Equivalents for Common Fractions

Problem: What patterns can you see in decimal equivalents for fifths?

You can use your spreadsheet to quickly calculate the decimal equivalents for fractions.

1 Enter the information into the spreadsheet as shown:

2 In cell B4, enter the formula =B1/B2

	A	B	C	D	E	F	G
1	Numerator	1	2	3	4	5	
2	Denominator	5	5	5	5	5	
3							
4	Decimal						
5							

	A	B	C	D	E	F	G
1	Numerator	1	2	3	4	5	
2	Denominator	5	5	5	5	5	
3							
4	Decimal	0.2	0.4	0.6	0.8	1.0	
5							

3 Copy the formula across the row to column F. You may need to format row 4 to see all the numbers after the decimal place.

Solution: Each decimal goes up by 0.2.

TRY IT

a. Find a decimal pattern for ninths.

b. Find a decimal pattern for sevenths.

ON YOUR OWN

▶ Why do you think the division formula uses a "/" and not a "÷" for division?

▶ Is the decimal value in C4 always twice as big as the decimal value in B4? Explain.

▶ When converting a fraction pattern with an even denominator into decimals, the number 0.5 always appears as one of the decimal equivalents. Why?

Comparing and Ordering

You'll Learn ...

■ to compare and order fractions

... How It's Used

Disc jockeys order fractions when determining which songs have been played the most.

Vocabulary

common denominator

▶ **Lesson Link** You've learned to compare and order decimals. In this lesson, you'll learn how to do the same with fractions. ◀

Explore | Comparing and Ordering

The 3 Rs—Plus 7 More

Materials: Fraction Bars®

The "R-value" of a building material measures how well the material keeps heat in or out. The table gives the approximate R-values of ten common building materials in alphabetical order.

1. A building contractor has asked you to arrange the materials in order of their R-values. Use your number sense to guess the order of the ten fractions from least to greatest.

2. Use fraction bars to order the fractions. Compare the results with your guesses.

3. Use the fraction bars to help you sketch a bar graph of the ten R-values. On your graph, order the bars from least to greatest.

Material	R-Value
Asphalt roof shingle	$\frac{5}{12}$
Common brick	$\frac{1}{4}$
Half-inch gypsum board	$\frac{7}{12}$
Hardwood finish flooring	$\frac{2}{3}$
Lightweight gypsum plaster	$\frac{1}{3}$
Stucco	$\frac{1}{6}$
Three-eighths-inch plywood	$\frac{1}{2}$
Wood bevel siding	$\frac{3}{4}$
Wood roof shingles	$\frac{11}{12}$
Wood siding shingles	$\frac{5}{6}$

Learn | Comparing and Ordering

Tools and building materials are commonly measured in inches and fractions of inches. In order to know which screw, nail, saw blade, or chisel is the largest or smallest, you must be able to compare fractions.

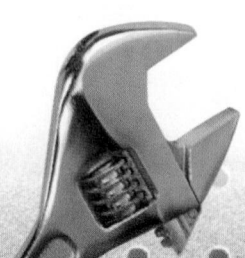

One way to do this is to convert the fractions so that they have the same denominator. Then compare the numerators. When two fractions have the same denominator, it is called a **common denominator** .

The smallest common denominator is also known as the least common denominator, or LCD.

Examples

1 Compare $\frac{5}{6}$ and $\frac{7}{8}$.

Rewrite each fraction by multiplying the numerator and the denominator by the denominator of the *other* fraction.

$\frac{5}{6} = \frac{5 \times 8}{6 \times 8} = \frac{40}{48}$ Multiply numerator and denominator by the denominator of $\frac{7}{8}$.

$\frac{7}{8} = \frac{7 \times 6}{8 \times 6} = \frac{42}{48}$ Multiply numerator and denominator by the denominator of $\frac{5}{6}$.

Since $\frac{42}{48} > \frac{40}{48}, \frac{7}{8} > \frac{5}{6}$.

2 Mayra has drill bits measuring $\frac{5}{32}$ in., $\frac{3}{16}$ in., and $\frac{1}{8}$ in. She wants to use the largest bit. Which one should she use?

8 and 16 are factors of 32, so you can rewrite $\frac{1}{8}$ and $\frac{3}{16}$ with a denominator of 32.

$\frac{1}{8} = \frac{1 \times 4}{8 \times 4} = \frac{4}{32}$

$\frac{3}{16} = \frac{3 \times 2}{16 \times 2} = \frac{6}{32}$

The drill bits measure in order: $\frac{4}{32}$ in., $\frac{5}{32}$ in., and $\frac{6}{32}$ in. She should use the $\frac{3}{16}$ in. bit.

MENTAL MATH

You can get a denominator of 32 by multiplying 8 by 4.

You can also compare fractions by rewriting them as decimals. Then compare the decimals.

Example 3

Clay needs $\frac{5}{8}$ yd of vinyl fabric to make a cover for his tennis racket. He found a piece marked as $\frac{2}{3}$ yd. Should he buy it?

5 ÷ 8 = 0.625

2 ÷ 3 = 0.6666...   Use a calculator to write the fractions as decimals.

$0.\overline{6} > 0.625$, so $\frac{2}{3} > \frac{5}{8}$. Clay should buy the fabric.

Try It

Decide which fraction is greater. **a.** $\frac{3}{8}, \frac{7}{16}$ **b.** $\frac{3}{4}, \frac{5}{6}$ **c.** $\frac{8}{11}, \frac{5}{7}$

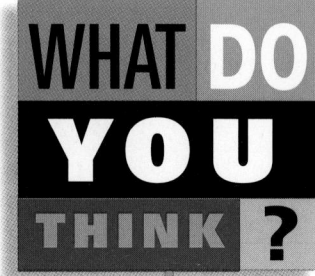

WHAT DO YOU THINK?

For a report on recycling, Peggy and Zack read that 8 out of every 21 aluminum cans were recycled in 1990. In 1993, 5 out every 14 aluminum cans were recycled. They wanted to know whether the fraction of cans recycled increased or decreased from 1990 to 1993.

Peggy thinks ...

I'll rewrite the fractions as decimals using my calculator.

$8 \div 21 = 0.3809524$

$5 \div 14 = 0.3571429$

$0.3809524 > 0.3571429$, so the fraction decreased from 1990 to 1993.

Zack thinks ...

I'll rewrite $\frac{8}{21}$ and $\frac{5}{14}$ with a common denominator.

$$\frac{8 \times 14}{21 \times 14} = \frac{112}{294} \qquad \frac{5 \times 21}{14 \times 21} = \frac{105}{294}$$

$\frac{112}{294} > \frac{105}{294}$, so the fraction decreased from 1990 to 1993.

What do you think?

1. Name a pair of fractions for which Peggy's method would be faster than Zack's method. Name a pair of fractions for which Zack's method would be faster than Peggy's.

2. What other real-world situations might involve comparing fractions?

Check | **Your Understanding**

1. Since $5 > 4$, is $\frac{5}{8} > \frac{4}{3}$? Explain.

2. Two fractions have the same numerator. How can you use the denominators to compare the fractions?

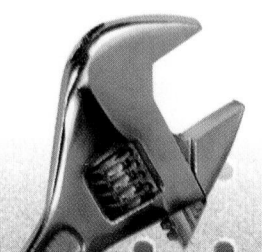

Practice and Apply

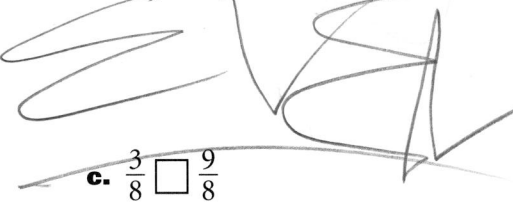

1. **Getting Started** Compare using <, >, or =.

   a. $\frac{1}{5} \square \frac{2}{5}$ **b.** $\frac{3}{7} \square \frac{2}{7}$ **c.** $\frac{3}{8} \square \frac{9}{8}$

   d. $\frac{16}{20} \square \frac{7}{20}$ **e.** $\frac{7}{12} \square \frac{11}{12}$ **f.** $\frac{5}{2} \square \frac{8}{2}$

Give the least common denominator that could be used to compare each pair of fractions. Then compare using <, >, or =.

2. $\frac{2}{3} \square \frac{8}{12}$ 3. $\frac{5}{6} \square \frac{5}{8}$ 4. $\frac{1}{4} \square \frac{5}{12}$

5. $\frac{3}{6} \square \frac{6}{9}$ 6. $\frac{4}{10} \square \frac{6}{15}$ 7. $\frac{3}{4} \square \frac{6}{8}$

8. $\frac{5}{8} \square \frac{10}{24}$ 9. $\frac{1}{11} \square \frac{3}{12}$ 10. $\frac{3}{7} \square \frac{6}{3}$

11. $\frac{7}{11} \square \frac{2}{3}$ 12. $\frac{9}{15} \square \frac{3}{5}$ 13. $\frac{5}{10} \square \frac{7}{14}$

Order from smallest to largest.

14. $\frac{2}{3}, \frac{2}{6}, \frac{4}{9}$ 15. $\frac{7}{9}, \frac{5}{6}, \frac{4}{8}$ 16. $\frac{18}{4}, \frac{16}{5}, \frac{19}{20}$ 17. $\frac{3}{11}, \frac{11}{3}, \frac{11}{11}$

18. $\frac{9}{12}, \frac{3}{6}, \frac{15}{18}$ 19. $\frac{4}{5}, \frac{4}{6}, \frac{4}{7}$ 20. $\frac{32}{10}, \frac{25}{100}, \frac{16}{1}$ 21. $\frac{3}{5}, \frac{2}{7}, \frac{3}{8}$

22. $\frac{1}{2}, \frac{1}{4}, \frac{1}{3}$ 23. $\frac{3}{22}, \frac{10}{11}, \frac{2}{33}$ 24. $\frac{4}{10}, \frac{3}{5}, \frac{6}{7}$ 25. $\frac{7}{36}, \frac{13}{4}, \frac{1}{6}$

26. **Measurement** Flannery has $3\frac{5}{8}$ yards of ribbon. Does she have enough to complete a project that calls for $3\frac{1}{2}$ yards?

27. Order the wood screw lengths, in inches, from longest to shortest:

    $\frac{1}{4}, \frac{3}{8}, \frac{10}{32}, \frac{10}{16}, \frac{7}{8}, \frac{2}{16}$

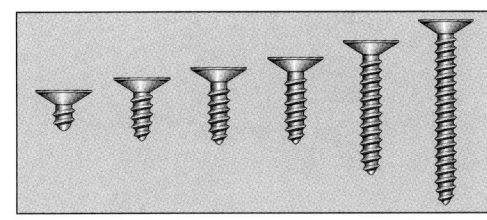

28. Industry $\frac{3}{5}$ of the tourists who visit Florida come during the summer. $\frac{3}{10}$ travel to Florida during the winter. During which season does Florida get more tourists?

29. On a recent test, Renaldo got $\frac{5}{6}$ of the problems correct and Julius got $\frac{7}{9}$ of them correct. All the problems were worth the same amount. Who got the higher grade?

Problem Solving and Reasoning

30. Critical Thinking Order from smallest to largest.

a. $0.34, \frac{2}{3}, 0.145$

b. $\frac{1}{2}, 0.23, \frac{2}{3}, 0.4$

c. $\frac{3}{4}, 0.77, \frac{1}{7}$

31. **Journal** Can you always tell by looking at a calculator display if a decimal terminates or repeats? Explain your answer.

32. Communicate Explain which is bigger, 0.3 or $0.\overline{3}$.

33. Choose a Strategy Zoe is planning a conference. Here is the schedule for the day:
the first meeting, snack,
the second meeting, lunch,
the third meeting, an afternoon break,
and the last meeting.
The four meetings will be $\frac{1}{2}, \frac{4}{2}, \frac{45}{30}$, and $\frac{9}{12}$ of an hour long. The longest meeting should be after the snack and the second longest right after lunch. The shortest meeting should be after the break. How long is the first meeting? The second? The third? The fourth?

> **Problem Solving**
>
> ## STRATEGIES
>
> - Look for a Pattern
> - Make an Organized List
> - Make a Table
> - Guess and Check
> - Work Backward
> - Use Logical Reasoning
> - Draw a Diagram
> - Solve a Simpler Problem

Mixed Review

Evaluate each expression for $x = 5, 9,$ and $11.$ *[Lesson 2-10]*

34. $\dfrac{495}{x}$

35. $x - 5$

36. $8x$

37. $\dfrac{990}{x}$

38. $5x$

39. $7x$

40. $x + 10$

41. $13 - x$

42. $x + 101$

Make a stem-and-leaf diagram of the data. *[Lesson 1-6]*

43. $1, 4, 4, 5, 7, 11, 11, 12, 12, 13, 14$

44. $101, 102, 105, 105, 108, 111, 112$

45. $31, 31, 32, 30, 27, 28, 26, 33, 28, 31$

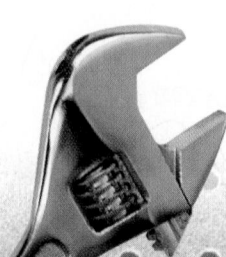

In this section, you've seen that tools come in many sizes. In the United States, we use the customary system of measurement, so tools made here are sized with fractions. In countries that use the metric system, tools are sized with decimals. Now that you've studied both fractions and decimals, you're ready for a problem that faces anyone who uses tools: How do I deal with both fraction and decimal sizes?

Meanwhile, Back at the Wrench

Materials: Calculator

Otto Mechanic uses 32 wrenches to work on car engines. Sixteen of the wrenches were made in Europe and are sized in millimeters. Sixteen were made in the United States and are sized in fractions of an inch. One evening after finishing a difficult job, Otto tossed all of his wrenches onto a table and went home. Here, in no particular order, are the sizes of the wrenches. The metric sizes, given in millimeters, have also been converted to decimal inches.

Metric								
Size (mm)	9	16	20	3	25	7	4	12
Size (in.)	0.354	0.630	0.787	0.118	0.984	0.276	0.157	0.472
Size (mm)	17	13	8	22	6	18	14	10
Size (in.)	0.669	0.512	0.315	0.866	0.236	0.709	0.551	0.394

Customary								
Size (in.)	$\frac{5}{16}$	$\frac{7}{32}$	$\frac{5}{8}$	$\frac{1}{2}$	$\frac{3}{4}$	$\frac{9}{32}$	$\frac{9}{16}$	$\frac{1}{8}$
	$\frac{13}{16}$	$\frac{3}{8}$	$\frac{21}{32}$	$\frac{7}{8}$	$\frac{3}{16}$	$\frac{3}{32}$	$\frac{1}{4}$	$\frac{7}{16}$

Order Otto's 32 wrenches from the smallest size to the largest.

Tell whether the first number is divisible by the second. Find the prime factorization of the first number.

1. 27, 9   **2.** 180, 10   **3.** 32, 5   **4.** 99, 6   **5.** 48, 4   **6.** 35, 3

Determine what fraction each shaded part represents. Identify the numerator and denominator of each fraction.

7. 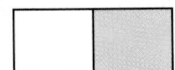   **8.** 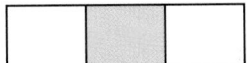   **9.**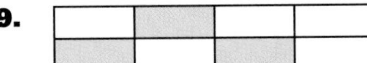

Write each fraction in lowest terms and as a decimal.

10. $\frac{4}{6}$ **11.** $\frac{18}{24}$ **12.** $\frac{2}{8}$

13. $\frac{5}{15}$ **14.** $\frac{8}{12}$ **15.** $\frac{12}{24}$

Write each mixed number as an improper fraction and each improper fraction as a mixed number.

16. $4\frac{1}{7}$ **17.** $\frac{32}{10}$ **18.** $\frac{99}{11}$

19. $7\frac{4}{5}$ **20.** $12\frac{7}{8}$ **21.** $\frac{42}{5}$

22. Fine Arts Noriko and Ava are dancing together in the talent show. Noriko does a shuffle step every 5 steps and Ava does a shuffle every 7 steps. On what number step will they do the shuffle at the same time?

23. Beverly, Tom, and Maye are building a clubhouse. Beverly cut $\frac{2}{5}$ of the wood. Tom cut $\frac{3}{10}$ of the wood and Maye cut the rest. Who cut the most wood? The least?

Test Prep

To compare fractions, estimate to find out if they are near 0, $\frac{1}{2}$, or 1.

24. Which statement is true?

Ⓐ $\frac{2}{9} > \frac{7}{8}$ Ⓑ $\frac{3}{6} > \frac{1}{5}$ Ⓒ $\frac{3}{4} > \frac{4}{3}$ Ⓓ $\frac{6}{7} > \frac{7}{8}$

REVIEW 5B

Venn Diagrams

A **Venn diagram** is one or more loops that show how a group of numbers, words, or pictures are related. Every loop has a rule. The things in the loop follow that rule. The things outside the loop don't.

In this Venn diagram, all the words in the loop start with the letter "b." All the words outside the loop don't.

A Venn diagram can have more than one loop. Things that match one rule but not the other go in one loop but not the other. Things that match both rules go in both loops.

The numbers in the purple loop are divisible by 2. The numbers in the blue loop are divisible by 3. The numbers in both loops are divisible by 2 and 3.

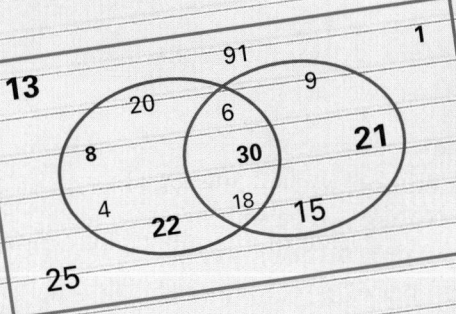

Try It

1. Draw a Venn diagram with one loop where all the shapes inside the loop are triangles. There should be at least three shapes in the loop and three shapes outside the loop.

2. Draw a Venn diagram with two loops where one loop represents numbers bigger than 20 and the other loop represents odd numbers. Put at least twelve numbers in the diagram. Three of them should be in both loops.

3. Draw a Venn diagram with two loops. One loop should have the numbers divisible by 5. The other should have the numbers divisible by 10. Put at least 9 numbers in the diagram.

Chapter 5 Summary and Review

Graphic Organizer

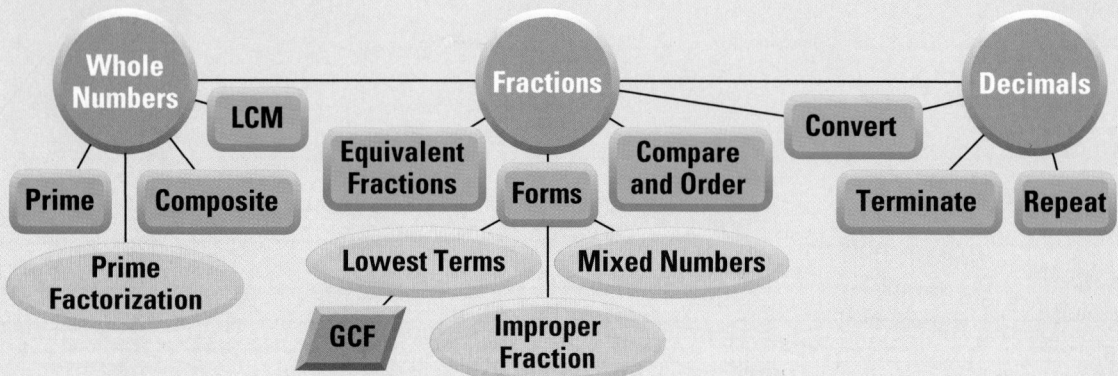

Section 5A   Number Theory

Summary

- A whole number is **divisible** by another whole number if the first number can be divided by the second number without leaving a remainder.

- A **prime number** has exactly two factors, itself and 1. A **composite number** has more than two factors.

- The **prime factorization** of a number is the set of prime numbers whose product equals the number.

- To find the prime factorization of a number, you can use the divisibility rules and a factor tree.

- The **least common multiple** of two numbers is their smallest common multiple.

Review

Test each number for divisibility by 2, 3, 5, 6, 9, and 10.

1. 234   **2.** 68   **3.** 6000   **4.** 255

Label each number as prime or composite.

5. $2 \times 2 \times 3 \times 3$ **6.** 1×143 **7.** $2 \times 3 \times 3 \times 7$ **8.** 3×29

Find the least common multiple for each number pair.

9. 36, 54   **10.** 14, 18

Summary

- The **denominator** of a fraction tells the number of parts in the whole. The **numerator** tells how many parts are being named.

- An **improper fraction** has a numerator greater than or equal to its denominator. A **mixed number** combines a whole number and a fraction.

- Fraction values can be written as decimals whose digits either terminate or repeat.

- **Equivalent fractions** name the same amount.

- A fraction is in **lowest terms** when its numerator and denominator have no common factors other than 1.

- The **greatest common factor** is the largest whole number that divides evenly into two numbers.

- If two fractions have the same denominator, it is called a **common denominator**.

Review

What fraction does the shaded part of each model represent?

11. 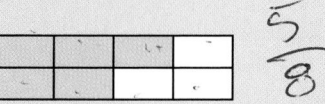 $\frac{5}{8}$

12. ⬭⚪⬭⬭⬭⚪

13. Identify the numerator and the denominator in the fraction $\frac{11}{3}$.

Write each fraction in lowest terms.

14. $\frac{16}{24}$ **15.** $\frac{125}{1000}$ **16.** $\frac{12}{72}$ **17.** $\frac{648}{810}$

Rewrite each fraction as a mixed number or an improper fraction.

18. $\frac{17}{4}$ **19.** $8\frac{3}{5}$ **20.** $\frac{47}{7}$ **21.** $2\frac{8}{9}$

22. Four rubber bands have lengths of $2\frac{3}{4}$, $\frac{7}{8}$, $1\frac{1}{4}$, and $\frac{7}{2}$ inches. List their lengths in order from shortest to longest.

Rewrite each fraction as a decimal.

23. $\frac{4}{6}$ **24.** $\frac{11}{2}$ **25.** $\frac{3}{8}$ **26.** $\frac{7}{5}$

Rewrite each decimal as a fraction in lowest terms or a mixed number.

27. 0.05   **28.** 3.8   **29.** 0.625   **30.** 2.023

Tell whether each number is divisible by 2, 3, 5, 6, 9, and 10.

1. 3447

2. 485

3. 2400

Identify each number as prime or composite.

4. $2 \times 2 \times 2 \times 2 \times 2 \times 2$

5. 1×47

6. 3×109

7. Find the prime factorization of 234.

8. Find two fractions equivalent to $\frac{3}{12}$.

9. A pet store has 30 cages. The owner wants to arrange the cages in equal groups. How many ways can she do this?

10. a. Identify the numerator and denominator of the fraction $\frac{5}{8}$.

b. Write $\frac{5}{8}$ as a decimal number.

11. Find the least common multiple of 9 and 12.

12. The prime factorization of a number is $2 \times 2 \times 3 \times 7$. What is the number?

13. A yardstick was used to measure a fish. What fraction of a yard represents the length of the fish?

14. If John walks to the park every third day, and Sue walks to the park every fourth day, how often will they walk to the park on the same day?

Write each fraction in lowest terms.

15. $\frac{16}{56}$

16. $\frac{120}{360}$

Find the GCF of each pair of numbers.

17. 30, 50

18. 42, 70

Write each fraction as a decimal and each decimal as a fraction or mixed number.

19. $\frac{3}{8}$

20. $\frac{13}{4}$

21. 0.65

22. 5.035

Performance Task

Use U.S. coins whose values are more than a penny and less than a dollar. Think of all the different groups of the same kind of coins you could form and have a dollar or less. Organize your data for each coin in a table that shows the number of coins in each group, the fraction of a dollar each group represents, and its value written in dollars and cents: $0.75. What number patterns can you find?

Performance Assessment

Choose one problem.

Stop and Go Patterns

Create a three-column table. Write these fractions in the first column: $\frac{1}{2}, \frac{1}{3}, \frac{1}{4}, \frac{1}{5}, \frac{1}{6}, \frac{1}{7}, \frac{1}{8}, \frac{1}{9}, \frac{1}{10}, \frac{1}{11}, \frac{1}{12}, \frac{1}{15}, \frac{1}{16}, \frac{1}{18}, \frac{1}{20}$. Use a calculator to fill in the second column with the decimal value equivalent to each fraction. In the third column, mark each decimal with an **R** if it repeats and with a **T** if it doesn't.

Fraction	Decimal	T or R?
$\frac{1}{2}$	0.5	T
⋮		
$\frac{1}{20}$		

Make a list of all the denominators of the fractions for which the equivalent decimals terminated. Find their prime factorizations. Describe a pattern that can help you predict which fractions convert to terminating decimals and which ones don't.

Prime Time

For each pair of numbers:
30 and 35   18 and 45

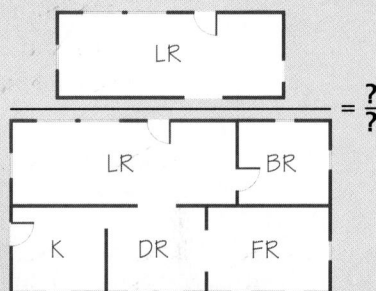

Find the prime factorization of the pair of numbers. Then find the LCM of the pair of numbers and the prime factorization of the LCM.

How can the prime factorization of each pair of numbers help you find their LCM?

AREA BREAK DOWN

Measure and record the floor areas of at least five rooms in your home. Find the total of the areas you measured. What fractional part is each floor area of the total areas you measured? What kind of graph would be used to show this data? Explain.

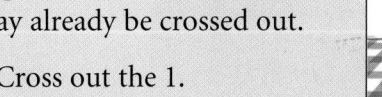
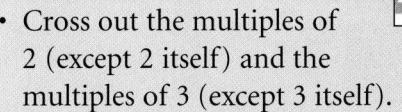
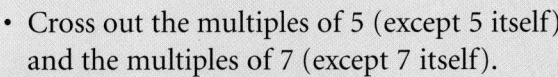

Number Strain

Use a 10 × 10 grid numbered from left to right from 1 through 100. Follow the steps to cross out numbers on the grid. As you go through the steps, some of the numbers may already be crossed out.

• Cross out the 1.

• Cross out the multiples of 2 (except 2 itself) and the multiples of 3 (except 3 itself).

• Cross out the multiples of 5 (except 5 itself) and the multiples of 7 (except 7 itself).

What are the numbers that have not been crossed out called?

Explain why there were no steps listed for crossing out the multiples of 4, 6, 8, or 9.

6 Adding and Subtracting Fractions

Entertainment Link
www.mathsurf.com/6/ch6/ent

People of the World

The country with the most telephones per person is Sweden. If the telephones were evenly distributed, $\frac{17}{25}$ of Sweden's total population would have a telephone.

Entertainment

$\frac{1}{3}$ of the money spent on newly published comic books goes to Marvel Comics, the publishers of *The X-Men* and *Spider-Man*. $\frac{1}{5}$ goes to DC Comics, the publishers of *Batman* and *Superman*.

Arts & Literature

In 15th century Italy, church buildings were designed so that heights of the walls were either $\frac{1}{2}$, $\frac{2}{3}$, or $\frac{3}{4}$ the distance across the church.

Science Link
www.mathsurf.com/6/ch6/sci

Science

A male California sea lion grows to be between $6\frac{1}{2}$ and $8\frac{1}{6}$ feet tall and will have a weight between 440 and 660 pounds.

Social Studies

If the World Trade Center Towers in New York City were stacked one on top of the other, the combined height would be more than $\frac{1}{2}$ mile high.

KEY MATH IDEAS

Fractions can be added when they have like denominators.

Fractions with unlike denominators can also be added. But, you must first convert the fractions to equivalent fractions with the same denominator.

Rounding can help you estimate sums and differences of mixed numbers.

Some mixed number sums have an improper fraction in the answer. These mixed numbers can be regrouped so that they are no longer improper fractions.

Sometimes when subtracting, you need to borrow from the whole number part of a mixed number. This is similar to borrowing in whole number subtraction.

CHAPTER PROJECT

Problem Solving

Understand
Plan
Solve
Look Back

In this project, you will create a cookbook for animals. Begin by thinking about the kinds of animals you're interested in, and the sort of things that might be fed to that animal if it were in a zoo, farm, or aquarium.

Problem Solving Focus

Problem Solving

Understand
Plan
Solve
Look Back

Interpreting Math Phrases

In some problems, numerical information is given directly. At other times, numerical information is given as a comparison, such as "Neil had *three more than* Doreen". When making a plan to solve a problem, you must be able to correctly interpret these comparison phrases.

For each problem, write down the answer and the arithmetic for how you got the answer. For example, if you added 5 to 7 to get 12, write "5 + 7 = 12".

1 David had seven butterflies in his insect collection. Jennifer had eight more butterflies than David. How many butterflies did Jennifer have?

2 Patty had twelve crickets. Lila had four crickets less than Patty. How many crickets did Lila have?

3 Camille had twenty grasshoppers. Barbara had half as many grasshoppers as Camille. How many grasshoppers did Barbara have?

4 Richard had three dragonflies. Phoebe had three times as many dragonflies as Richard. How many did Phoebe have?

5 Ada had ten more ladybugs than Mark. Mark had fourteen ladybugs. How many did Ada have?

6 Jack had twice as many beetles as Lois. Jack had six beetles. How many did Lois have?

7 Kristen had half as many bees as Terri. Kristen had seven bees. How many did Terri have?

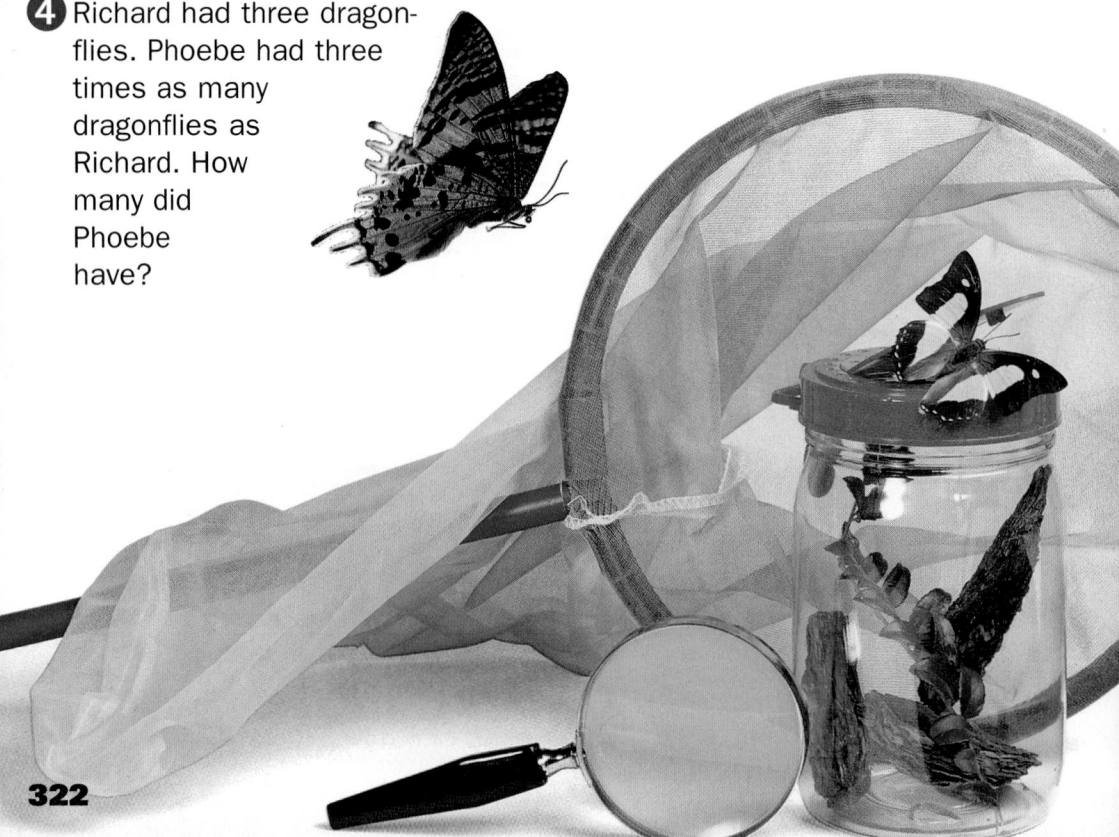

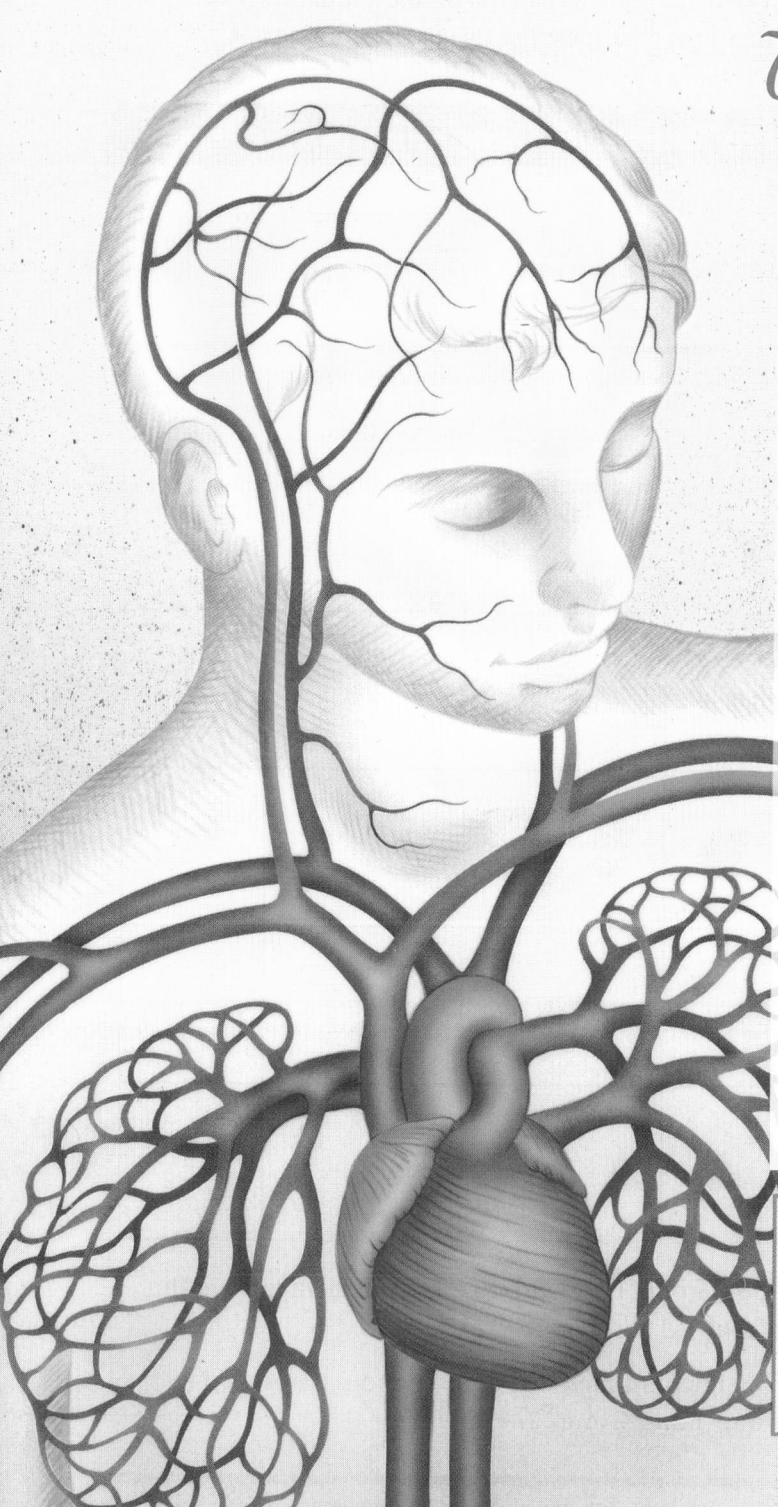

What's Your Type?

*I*magine sitting down at the dinner table while your mother is serving dinner.

"Can I have a potato please?"

"What's your type?"

"I'm O-negative."

"Sorry. I didn't cook any O-negative potatoes. All of these potatoes are AB-positive."

"Can you cook an O-negative potato for me?"

"I don't think we have any. Only 7 out of every 100 potatoes are O-negative."

"Can't I just eat one of the AB-positive potatoes?"

"Don't be ridiculous, dear. The wrong kind of potato could kill you."

Fortunately, there's no such thing as a food type. But there is such a thing as a blood type. If you ever need to have a blood transfusion, you may not be able to use just any blood. You need blood that matches your type and Rh factor. People with AB+ blood can use O– blood, but people with O– blood can't use AB+ blood.

People who work in the health care industry must have a good understanding of what blood is and how it works. Fractions are useful in describing the different parts of blood and the different ways it can be used.

1 Why is it important for health care professionals to have a good understanding of blood?

2 How could fractions be used to describe blood?

323

Adding and Subtracting Fractions with Like Denominators

▶ **Lesson Link** You have learned how to work with individual fractions. Now you will add and subtract fractions that have the same denominator. ◀

You'll Learn ...

■ to add and subtract fractions with like denominators

... How It's Used

Painters use fractions when mixing paints to get a particular color.

Vocabulary

like denominators

| Explore | Fractions with Like Denominators |

Block Heads!

Materials: Pattern blocks or Power Polygons

1. Copy the table below and use pattern blocks to complete the table.

The "Whole"	Group 1	Group 2	Fraction Names For Group 1 Plus Group 2	Sum
			$\frac{1}{2} + \frac{4}{2}$	$\frac{5}{2}$

2. The fraction names for Group 1 and Group 2 should always have the same denominator. Why?

3. For each problem, did the sum have the same denominator as the denominators in Group 1 and Group 2? Explain.

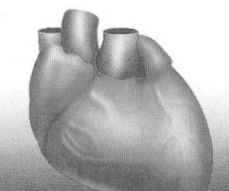

Two fractions with the same denominator have **like denominators** .

$\frac{1}{4}$ and $\frac{3}{4}$ = 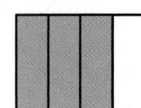 and

Remember

Like denominators are also known as common denominators.
[Page 309]

When you add and subtract fractions with like denominators, the denominator acts as a label. It tells you what size pieces you're using. The numerators tell the number of pieces you add or subtract .

Examples

1 Add $\frac{2}{7} + \frac{4}{7}$.

 + 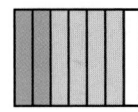 =

$\frac{2}{7} + \frac{4}{7} = \frac{2+4}{7}$ Add numerators only. Denominators do not change.

$= \frac{6}{7}$

2 When an adult man donates blood, he donates about $\frac{1}{2}$ of a quart. The body of an average man contains about 5, or $\frac{10}{2}$, quarts of blood. How much blood is in his body after donation?

$\frac{10}{2} - \frac{1}{2} = \frac{10-1}{2}$ Subtract numerators only. Denominators do not change.

$= \frac{9}{2}$

There are $\frac{9}{2}$ of a quart, or $4\frac{1}{2}$ quarts, left in his body.

Try It

Simplify.   **a.** $\frac{3}{10} + \frac{4}{10}$ **b.** $\frac{5}{7} - \frac{3}{7}$ **c.** $\frac{8}{2} + \frac{9}{2}$ **d.** $\frac{4}{9} - \frac{4}{9}$

▶ **Science Link**

In 1940, Charles Drew revolutionized the way doctors cared for patients by devising a blood bank plan for adequate storage of blood.

Check   Your Understanding

1. When you add or subtract fractions with like denominators, why doesn't the denominator change?

2. What values can *n* have to make the equation $\frac{3}{n} + \frac{5}{n} = \frac{8}{n}$ true?

Practice and Apply

1. **Getting Started** Tell if the fractions have like denominators or not.

a. $\frac{6}{7}, \frac{4}{7}$ **b.** $\frac{9}{10}, \frac{13}{10}$ **c.** $\frac{1}{2}, \frac{1}{3}$ **d.** $\frac{22}{11}, \frac{11}{22}$ **e.** $\frac{8}{8}, \frac{8}{8}$

Simplify. Write each answer in lowest terms.

2. $\frac{3}{5} + \frac{1}{5}$ **3.** $\frac{9}{10} - \frac{8}{10}$ **4.** $\frac{7}{8} + \frac{5}{8}$ **5.** $\frac{4}{3} + \frac{2}{3}$ **6.** $\frac{23}{8} - \frac{13}{8}$

7. $\frac{4}{3} - \frac{3}{3}$ **8.** $\frac{98}{10} + \frac{2}{10}$ **9.** $\frac{3}{4} - \frac{1}{4}$ **10.** $\frac{4}{11} + \frac{3}{11}$ **11.** $\frac{12}{18} - \frac{9}{18}$

12. $\frac{15}{19} + \frac{5}{19}$ **13.** $\frac{7}{9} - \frac{3}{9}$ **14.** $\frac{6}{8} - \frac{4}{8}$ **15.** $\frac{5}{13} + \frac{1}{13}$ **16.** $\frac{34}{12} - \frac{30}{12}$

State whether the answer is greater than, less than, or equal to 1.

17. $\frac{7}{9} + \frac{2}{9}$ **18.** $\frac{1}{2} + \frac{3}{2}$ **19.** $\frac{2}{7} + \frac{6}{7}$ **20.** $\frac{3}{4} - \frac{2}{4}$ **21.** $\frac{5}{6} - \frac{3}{6}$

22. $\frac{9}{5} - \frac{4}{5}$ **23.** $\frac{7}{12} + \frac{7}{12}$ **24.** $\frac{1}{10} - \frac{1}{10}$ **25.** $\frac{16}{13} + \frac{4}{13}$ **26.** $\frac{5}{4} - \frac{1}{4}$

Tillie's volleyball team had a picnic. Team members brought food or games. The bar graph represents the players who brought an item of food. Use the graph for Exercises 27–30.

27. What fraction of the students who brought food brought fruit or drinks?

28. What fraction of the students who brought food brought fruit, drinks, or salad?

29. If 17 students went to the picnic, what fraction brought games?

30. If 17 students went to the picnic, what fraction of them brought fruit or bread?

31. **Science** Plasma is the liquid part of blood. Blood is about $\frac{11}{20}$ plasma. What fraction represents the other components of blood?

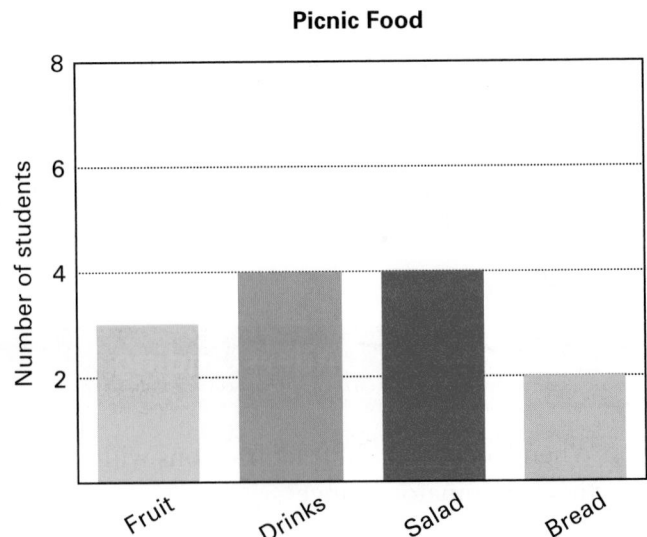

Picnic Food

32. **Test Prep** Choose the correct answer for $\frac{3}{10} + \frac{3}{10}$.

Ⓐ $\frac{3}{20}$ Ⓑ $\frac{3}{10}$ Ⓒ $\frac{6}{20}$ Ⓓ $\frac{3}{5}$

33. **Geography** About $\frac{3}{50}$ of the earth's surface is covered with land that can be farmed. $\frac{12}{50}$ is desert, tundra, ice, or mountains. $\frac{35}{50}$ is liquid. What fraction of the earth's surface is not covered with water?

Problem Solving and Reasoning

34. **Communicate** Galen added $\frac{3}{5}$ and $\frac{1}{5}$. His answer was $\frac{4}{10}$. Explain why Galen's answer does not make sense. What is the correct answer?

35. **Journal** Explain why you add the numerators in a fraction addition problem, but not the denominators.

36. **Choose a Strategy** Sandra makes bracelets, necklaces, and chokers using leather string. A bracelet requires $\frac{7}{12}$ ft of string, and a necklace requires $\frac{22}{12}$ ft. She has $\frac{81}{12}$ ft, which is exactly enough to make 3 bracelets, 2 necklaces, and 1 choker. How much string does each choker require? Explain.

37. **Communicate** For the equation $\frac{3}{11} + \frac{x}{y} = \frac{10}{11}$, name two values for both x and y that will make the equation true. Explain your reasoning.

> **Problem Solving**
> # STRATEGIES
> - Look for a Pattern
> - Make an Organized List
> - Make a Table
> - Guess and Check
> - Work Backward
> - Use Logical Reasoning
> - Draw a Diagram
> - Solve a Simpler Problem

Mixed Review

Find the perimeter for each figure. *[Lesson 4-1]*

38.
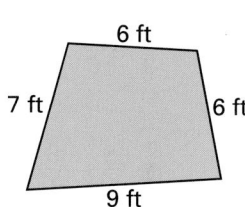
6 ft, 7 ft, 6 ft, 9 ft

39.
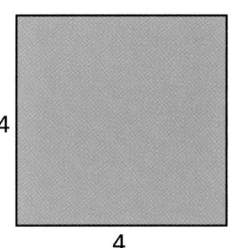
4, 4

40.
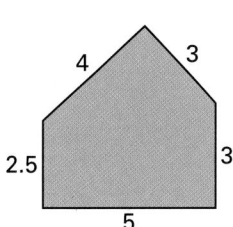
4, 3, 2.5, 3, 5

41.
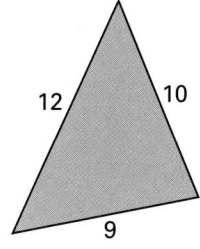
12, 10, 9

Find the next three numbers in the pattern. *[Lesson 2-9]*

42. 47, 51, 55, 59, 63, …

43. 12, 13, 15, 18, 22, 27, …

6-2 Adding and Subtracting Fractions with Unlike Denominators

► **Lesson Link** You have added and subtracted fractions with the same denominator. Now you will work with fractions that have different denominators. ◄

You'll Learn ...

■ to add and subtract fractions with unlike denominators

... How It's Used

Composers often work with fractional amounts that have different denominators.

Vocabulary

unlike denominators

least common denominator (LCD)

Explore   Fractions with Unlike Denominators

Fraction Action

Materials: Fraction Bars®

Adding Fractions with Unlike Denominators

$$\frac{1}{2} + \frac{1}{3} = \frac{5}{6}$$

- Draw and label a model of the first fraction.

- Draw and label a model of the second fraction next to the first fraction.

- Underneath the first two pictures, draw and label a picture of a fraction that has the same length as the first two models combined.

1. Model these problems.

a. $\frac{1}{3} + \frac{1}{4}$ **b.** $\frac{1}{4} + \frac{3}{6}$ **c.** $\frac{1}{2} + \frac{1}{6}$ **d.** $\frac{1}{3} + \frac{2}{6}$

Subtracting Fractions with Unlike Denominators

- Draw and label a model of the first fraction.

- Under the first model, draw and label a model of the second fraction.

- Next to the second model, draw and label a fraction that equals the difference between the first and second models.

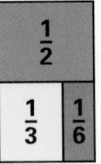

$$\frac{1}{2} - \frac{1}{3} = \frac{1}{6}$$

2. Model these problems.

a. $\frac{1}{2} - \frac{1}{6}$ **b.** $\frac{1}{3} - \frac{1}{4}$ **c.** $\frac{2}{3} - \frac{1}{4}$ **d.** $\frac{5}{6} - \frac{3}{4}$

3. In what way is adding fractions with different denominators different from adding fractions with the same denominator?

Learn | Fractions with Unlike Denominators

Fractions with like denominators are easy to add and subtract because they represent pieces of the same size. Fractions with different denominators, or **unlike denominators**, are not as easy to work with because they represent pieces of different sizes.

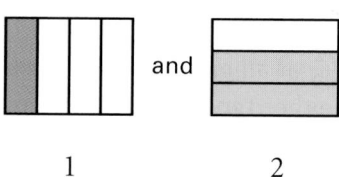 and

$$\frac{1}{4} \qquad \frac{2}{3}$$

In order to add or subtract fractions with unlike denominators, you need to change them to equivalent fractions with the same denominator. As you saw before, one way to do this is to multiply the numerator and the denominator of each fraction by the denominator of the other fraction.

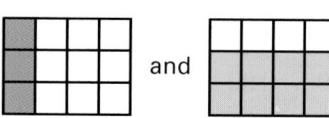 and

$$\frac{1 \times 3}{4 \times 3} = \frac{3}{12} \qquad \frac{2 \times 4}{3 \times 4} = \frac{8}{12}$$

Example 1

Dwayne is playing Count Dracula in the school production of *Dracula*. He still has to memorize $\frac{3}{4}$ of his lines. If he memorizes $\frac{1}{3}$ of them today, what fraction of his lines will he have left to memorize?

$\frac{3}{4} - \frac{1}{3}$ Write an expression for the problem.

$\frac{3}{4} = \frac{3 \times 3}{4 \times 3} = \frac{9}{12}$ Multiply numerator and denominator by 3.

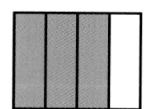 =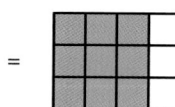

$\frac{1}{3} = \frac{1 \times 4}{3 \times 4} = \frac{4}{12}$ Multiply numerator and denominator by 4.

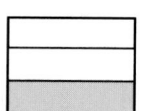 =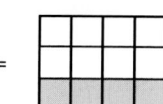

$\frac{3}{4} - \frac{1}{3} = \frac{9}{12} - \frac{4}{12}$ Rewrite the expression using equivalent fractions.

$= \frac{9 - 4}{12} = \frac{5}{12}$ Subtract.

He will have $\frac{5}{12}$ of his lines left to memorize.

▶ **Literature Link**

In 1897, Bram Stoker wrote *Dracula,* the story of a vampire who drank human blood to survive. This was not the first published story about vampires, but it's one of the most famous.

Try It

Simplify.   **a.** $\frac{1}{2} + \frac{1}{3}$ **b.** $\frac{5}{6} - \frac{1}{3}$ **c.** $\frac{1}{4} + \frac{3}{5}$ **d.** $\frac{3}{5} - \frac{1}{2}$

Sometimes it is easier to find the least common multiple of the two denominators and convert both fractions to that denominator. In fractions, this number is known as the **least common denominator** .

Examples

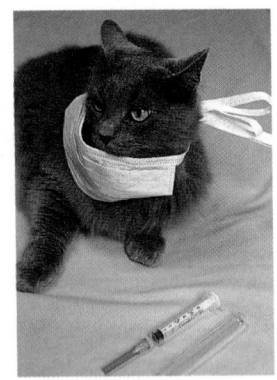

► Science Link

There are three cat blood types: A, B, and AB. There are eight human blood types: A+, A−, B+, B−, AB+, AB−, O+, and O−.

2 $\frac{73}{100}$ of all cats have type A blood. $\frac{13}{50}$ have type B blood. What fraction has either type A blood or type B blood?

The least common denominator of 50 and 100 is 100. Only the second fraction needs to be changed to an equivalent fraction.

$$\frac{13}{50} = \frac{13 \times 2}{50 \times 2} = \frac{26}{100}$$ Multiply numerator and denominator by 2.

$$\frac{73}{100} + \frac{26}{100} = \frac{73 + 26}{100}$$ Add.

$$= \frac{99}{100}$$

$\frac{99}{100}$ of all cats have either type A or type B blood.

3 What is $\frac{3}{10} - \frac{1}{4}$?

The least common multiple of 10 and 4 is 20.

$$\frac{3}{10} = \frac{3 \times 2}{10 \times 2} = \frac{6}{20}$$ Multiply top and bottom by 2.

$$\frac{1}{4} = \frac{1 \times 5}{4 \times 5} = \frac{5}{20}$$ Multiply top and bottom by 5.

$$\frac{6}{20} - \frac{5}{20} = \frac{6 - 5}{20} = \frac{1}{20}$$ Subtract.

Try It

Simplify.   **a.** $\frac{3}{4} - \frac{1}{2}$ **b.** $\frac{1}{3} + \frac{2}{6}$ **c.** $\frac{5}{6} - \frac{2}{15}$ **d.** $\frac{5}{9} + \frac{1}{6}$

Check   Your Understanding

1. Why is it necessary for fractions to have like denominators before you add or subtract them?

2. When is it easier to add fractions using the least common denominator instead of any common denominator?

Practice and Apply

1. **Getting Started** Name a common denominator for each pair.

    a. $\frac{1}{2}, \frac{1}{3}$ **b.** $\frac{2}{3}, \frac{3}{6}$ **c.** $\frac{3}{4}, \frac{5}{8}$ **d.** $\frac{6}{7}, \frac{9}{11}$ **e.** $\frac{4}{6}, \frac{4}{8}$

Simplify. Write each answer in lowest terms.

2. $\frac{3}{5} + \frac{1}{4}$ 3. $\frac{5}{12} - \frac{1}{6}$ 4. $\frac{1}{2} + \frac{1}{3}$ 5. $\frac{3}{4} - \frac{7}{12}$ 6. $\frac{9}{10} - \frac{1}{2}$

7. $\frac{3}{4} + \frac{1}{2}$ 8. $\frac{7}{8} - \frac{5}{6}$ 9. $\frac{1}{4} + \frac{5}{7}$ 10. $\frac{4}{11} + \frac{4}{44}$ 11. $\frac{7}{6} - \frac{3}{5}$

12. $\frac{5}{8} + \frac{3}{4}$ 13. $\frac{3}{10} + \frac{3}{4}$ 14. $\frac{3}{9} + \frac{3}{2}$ 15. $\frac{19}{25} - \frac{3}{5}$ 16. $\frac{9}{13} - \frac{9}{26}$

Find the missing numerators.

17. $\frac{2}{5} + \frac{7}{10} = \frac{?}{10} + \frac{?}{10}$ 18. $\frac{3}{4} + \frac{5}{6} = \frac{?}{12} + \frac{?}{12}$ 19. $\frac{5}{8} - \frac{1}{6} = \frac{?}{24} - \frac{?}{24}$

20. $\frac{3}{8} + \frac{1}{2} = \frac{?}{8} + \frac{?}{8}$ 21. $\frac{4}{9} - \frac{1}{3} = \frac{?}{9} - \frac{?}{9}$ 22. $\frac{3}{4} - \frac{1}{3} = \frac{?}{36} - \frac{?}{36}$

23. **Science** Most of the cells in your blood are either red blood cells, white blood cells, or platelets. When you cut yourself, blood platelets help the blood to clot so that you don't bleed to death. Platelets can survive for $\frac{10}{14}$ of a week. White blood cells can survive for more than $\frac{126}{21}$ weeks. How much longer is the life span of a white blood cell?

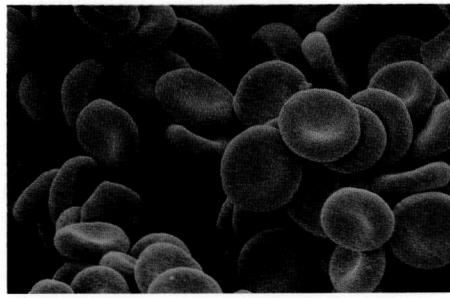

Red blood cells

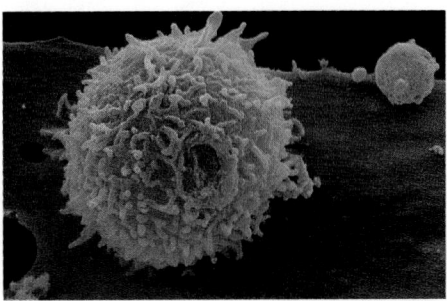

White blood cell

24. **Test Prep** Sam has a science test on Thursday. On Monday, he studied $\frac{2}{9}$ of the material. On Tuesday he studied $\frac{1}{3}$. How much material has he already reviewed?

    Ⓐ $\frac{3}{12}$ Ⓑ $\frac{5}{9}$ Ⓒ $\frac{7}{9}$ Ⓓ $\frac{3}{3}$

PRACTICE 6-2

25. Science When you are at rest, the fraction of total blood that flows to the skeletal muscles is about $\frac{1}{6}$. The fraction of total blood that flows to the skeletal muscles is $\frac{5}{7}$ when you are exercising. What is the difference between the two amounts of blood?

Problem Solving and Reasoning

26. Critical Thinking A recipe for fruit punch calls for $\frac{3}{8}$ of a quart of lemon drink, $\frac{3}{2}$ of a quart of orange juice, $\frac{1}{10}$ of a quart of cranberry juice, and $\frac{3}{4}$ of a quart of soda water. How large a container is needed for the punch? Explain.

27. Choose a Strategy Denzel had walked $\frac{1}{3}$ of the way to school when he realized he had dropped a book. He turned around, and had covered $\frac{1}{4}$ of the distance between home and school before finding it. What fraction of the total distance between home and school did Denzel now have to walk? Explain.

Problem Solving

STRATEGIES

- Look for a Pattern
- Make an Organized List
- Make a Table
- Guess and Check
- Work Backward
- Use Logical Reasoning
- Draw a Diagram
- Solve a Simpler Problem

28. Critical Thinking Four people are sharing a pizza. Ana would like to eat $\frac{1}{8}$, Jon wants $\frac{1}{4}$, Yi wants $\frac{1}{3}$, and Lisa would like $\frac{1}{6}$. What is the least number of slices of the same size that must be cut for each person to get what he or she wants? How much pizza is left over? Explain.

29. Critical Thinking Find the next 3 numbers in the pattern: $\frac{1}{12}, \frac{1}{6}, \frac{1}{4}, \frac{1}{3}, \frac{5}{12}, \ldots$ Explain how you found them.

Mixed Review

Find the area of each shape. [Lesson 4-4]

30.

5

14

31.

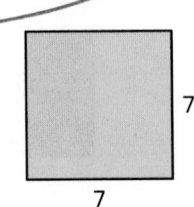

7

7

32.

0.5

12

Write an expression to describe each situation. [Lesson 2-10]

33. Henri had h hens. Each laid 4 eggs. How many eggs did Henri have?

34. Julia read b books last week and 2 books this week. How many books did Julia read?

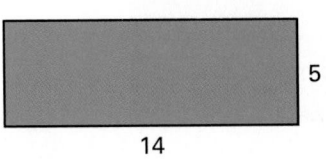

TECHNOLOGY

Using a Fraction Calculator • Finding Fraction Sums and Differences

Problem: What is the sum of $\frac{7}{17} + \frac{16}{29}$?

Sometimes, fractions involve large numbers that are not easy to work with. A fraction calculator can help you add or subtract the fractions.

1 Type in the numerator of the first fraction, and then press the $\boxed{/}$ button.

2 Type in the denominator of the first fraction, and then press the $\boxed{+}$ button.

3 Type in the numerator of the second fraction, and then press the $\boxed{/}$ button.

4 Type in the denominator of the second fraction, and then press the $\boxed{=}$ button.

Solution: The answer is $\frac{475}{493}$.

TRY IT

a. What is $\frac{5}{23} + \frac{14}{37}$?

b. What is $\frac{18}{21} - \frac{4}{41}$?

ON YOUR OWN

▶ What does the calculator display show if the sum of two fractions is bigger than 1?

▶ The sum of the fractions $\frac{45}{51} + \frac{67}{91}$ has a denominator bigger than 1000. What does the calculator do when the answer has a four-digit denominator?

▶ How can you find the sum of two fractions with a non-fraction calculator?

Solving Fraction Equations: Addition and Subtraction

You'll Learn …

■ to solve equations by adding and subtracting fractions

… How It's Used

Scientists on Antarctica use fraction equations to convert temperatures between Celsius and Fahrenheit.

▶ **Lesson Link** You have solved simple equations with whole numbers. You have also learned to add and subtract fractions. Now you will combine these ideas as you learn to solve equations by adding and subtracting fractions. ◀

Explore	**Fraction Equations: Addition and Subtraction**

Where's the Blood?

When the body is at rest, blood is distributed throughout the circulatory system as shown.

Organ	Fraction of Blood	Organ	Fraction of Blood
Capillaries	$\frac{1}{20}$	Systemic arteries	$\frac{1}{10}$
Heart	$\frac{1}{10}$	Systemic veins	$\frac{13}{20}$
Lungs	$\frac{1}{10}$		

A cardiologist prepared the table below by adding together the blood from two different parts of the circulatory system. Unfortunately, the data in the second column was accidentally deleted.

Organ 1	Organ 2	Sum	Organ 1	Organ 2	Sum
Heart	???	$\frac{2}{10}$	Heart	???	$\frac{15}{20}$
Lungs	???	$\frac{3}{20}$	Veins	???	$\frac{14}{20}$
Arteries	???	$\frac{15}{20}$	Lungs	???	$\frac{2}{10}$

1. For each line in the second table, find the amount of blood in Organ 2. Write down which of the organs from the first table Organ 2 could be. If there is more than one possible answer, list all of them.

2. Would it be easier if all of the fractions had the same denominator or if all of the fractions had different denominators? Explain.

3. Which organ from the first table has the most blood? The least? How can you tell?

Recall that you can solve addition and subtraction equations with whole numbers and decimals by using mental math. The same method can work for solving equations with fractions.

Examples

1 Solve $x - \frac{2}{8} = \frac{5}{8}$.

$x - \frac{2}{8} = \frac{5}{8}$ Read as "What number minus $\frac{2}{8}$ equals $\frac{5}{8}$?"

$\frac{7}{8} - \frac{2}{8} = \frac{5}{8}$ Use mental math.

$\frac{5}{8} = \frac{5}{8}$ ✓   Check to see that the equation is true.

x is equal to $\frac{7}{8}$.

Problem Solving TIP

Since all of the denominators are the same, you can rewrite this as a simpler problem: $x - 2 = 5$.

2 Kevin had to write a report about the human eye. He wrote $\frac{3}{11}$ of the report on Monday. By Tuesday night, he had written a total of $\frac{7}{11}$ of the report. How much of the report did he write on Tuesday?

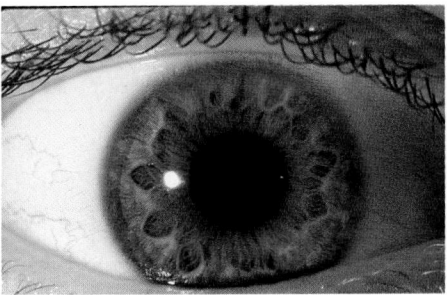

► Science Link

The light from a camera flash can light up the blood vessels in your retina. This is why some people in photographs have red eyes.

$\frac{3}{11} + x = \frac{7}{11}$ Read as "$\frac{3}{11}$ plus what number equals $\frac{7}{11}$?"

$\frac{3}{11} + \frac{4}{11} = \frac{7}{11}$ Use mental math.

$\frac{7}{11} = \frac{7}{11}$ ✓   Check to see that the equation is true.

He wrote $\frac{4}{11}$ of the report on Tuesday.

Try It

Solve.

a. $\frac{2}{9} + x = \frac{8}{9}$ **b.** $\frac{15}{3} - x = \frac{7}{3}$ **c.** $\frac{1}{4} + x = \frac{5}{4}$

Some equations involve fractions with unlike denominators. To solve these equations, you need to change the fractions to equivalent fractions with like denominators.

Examples

▶ Science Link

Red blood cells are important because they carry oxygen from the lungs to the other organs in your body.

3 $\frac{43}{100}$ of your blood is made up of only red blood cells. $\frac{9}{20}$ of your blood is made up of red and white blood cells. What fraction of your blood is made up of only white blood cells?

$$\frac{9}{20} = \frac{9 \times 5}{20 \times 5} = \frac{45}{100}$$ Change to an equivalent fraction.

$$x + \frac{43}{100} = \frac{45}{100}$$ Read as "What number plus $\frac{43}{100}$ equals $\frac{45}{100}$?"

$$\frac{2}{100} + \frac{43}{100} = \frac{45}{100}$$ Use mental math.

$\frac{2}{100}$ of your blood is made up of only white blood cells.

4 Solve $x - \frac{5}{6} = \frac{1}{15}$.

The least common denominator of 6 and 15 is 30.

$$\frac{5}{6} = \frac{5 \times 5}{6 \times 5} = \frac{25}{30}$$

Change to equivalent fractions.

$$\frac{1}{15} = \frac{1 \times 2}{15 \times 2} = \frac{2}{30}$$

$$x - \frac{25}{30} = \frac{2}{30}$$ Read as "What number minus $\frac{25}{30}$ equals $\frac{2}{30}$?"

$$\frac{27}{30} - \frac{25}{30} = \frac{2}{30}$$ Use mental math.

$$x = \frac{27}{30}$$

MENTAL MATH

Sometimes the least common multiple of two numbers is the product of the two numbers. But if the numbers share a prime factor, the least common multiple will be smaller than the product.

Check | Your Understanding

1. Why is it necessary to rewrite fraction equations that involve addition or subtraction so that both fractions have the same denominator?

2. How are the x in $\frac{2}{3} - x$ and the x in $\frac{2}{3} - x = \frac{1}{3}$ different?

3. When solving equations, how can you check to see that the answer you got is the correct answer?

6-3 Exercises and Applications

Practice and Apply

1. **Getting Started** Solve.

a. $\dfrac{2}{5} + p = \dfrac{7}{5}$

b. $\dfrac{3}{7} - k = \dfrac{1}{7}$

c. $w + \dfrac{4}{9} = \dfrac{9}{9}$

d. $r - \dfrac{9}{10} = \dfrac{3}{10}$

Solve. Write each answer in lowest terms.

2. $\dfrac{1}{3} + j = \dfrac{5}{6}$

3. $r + \dfrac{2}{5} = \dfrac{7}{10}$

4. $t - \dfrac{4}{5} = \dfrac{1}{10}$

5. $v - \dfrac{1}{2} = \dfrac{3}{8}$

6. $d + \dfrac{7}{9} = \dfrac{8}{9}$

7. $\dfrac{80}{5} - x = 12$

8. $q - \dfrac{1}{8} = \dfrac{3}{4}$

9. $4 - b = \dfrac{3}{7}$

10. $\dfrac{17}{100} + a = \dfrac{67}{100}$

11. $\dfrac{11}{12} - h = \dfrac{3}{4}$

12. $g + \dfrac{1}{8} = \dfrac{1}{6}$

13. $f - \dfrac{4}{9} = \dfrac{6}{3}$

14. $e + \dfrac{5}{28} = \dfrac{5}{14}$

15. $\dfrac{15}{22} - z = \dfrac{1}{2}$

16. $x - \dfrac{23}{4} = \dfrac{24}{3}$

17. $3 + y = \dfrac{10}{3}$

Write a true equation using the fractions given.

18. $\dfrac{1}{3}, \dfrac{2}{3}, 1$

19. $\dfrac{3}{4}, \dfrac{1}{2}, \dfrac{1}{4}$

20. $\dfrac{5}{6}, \dfrac{1}{3}, \dfrac{1}{2}$

21. $\dfrac{7}{12}, \dfrac{1}{6}, \dfrac{5}{12}$

22. $\dfrac{51}{36}, \dfrac{5}{6}, \dfrac{7}{12}$

23. $\dfrac{14}{18}, \dfrac{1}{3}, \dfrac{90}{81}$

24. $\dfrac{3}{11}, \dfrac{8}{11}, \dfrac{5}{11}$

25. $\dfrac{2}{12}, \dfrac{13}{15}, \dfrac{7}{10}$

Write and solve an equation for each situation.

26. At the Blood Research Clinic, Peter and Jen tested $\frac{11}{12}$ of the clinic's blood samples. If Peter tested $\frac{3}{5}$ of the samples, how many did Jen test?

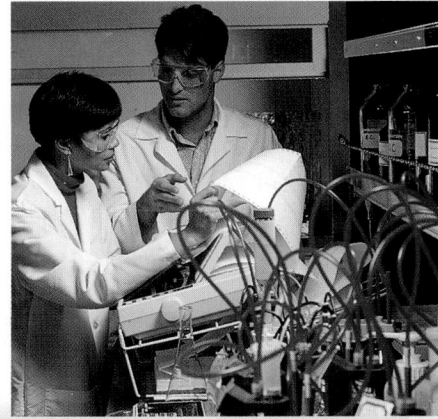

27. Antwon baked a batch of cookies. He and his family ate $\frac{1}{5}$ of the cookies on Monday, and some more cookies on Tuesday. After Tuesday, $\frac{2}{3}$ of the cookies had been eaten. What fraction of the cookies were eaten on Tuesday?

28. **Operation Sense** Pam had $\frac{7}{9}$ of a yard of string. After she cut some, she had $\frac{1}{3}$ of a yard left. How much string did Pam cut?

29. Marilyn collected $\frac{3}{4}$ of a pound of sea shells. She used some to decorate a picture frame, and she had $\frac{1}{6}$ of a pound left. How many pounds of shells did she use to decorate the frame?

PRACTICE 6-3

30. **Science** A blood bank estimates that $\frac{3}{10}$ of the blood on hand is type O blood. It anticipates a need for $\frac{9}{20}$ of the blood to be type O. How much more type O blood is needed?

31. **Test Prep** At the Sierra Road Inn, $\frac{7}{11}$ of the parking lot was full. Choose an equation that shows how much of the lot was empty.

Ⓐ $\frac{7}{11} + x = 1$ Ⓑ $\frac{7}{11} - x = 1$ Ⓒ $x - \frac{7}{11} = 1$

Problem Solving and Reasoning

32. **Journal** Write an equation using unlike denominators that you can solve using mental math. Explain how you would use mental math to solve it.

33. **Critical Thinking** The perimeter of the lid to Janice's rectangular jewelry box is $\frac{10}{4}$ of a yard. If the longer sides are $\frac{3}{4}$ of a yard, how long are the shorter sides? Explain.

34. **Communicate** Write a problem that could be solved with the equation $\frac{7}{10} + y = \frac{26}{20}$. Explain how you created the problem and solve it.

35. **Communicate** Explain the difference in the use of x in $\frac{1}{3} + x = \frac{4}{5}$ and in $\frac{1}{3} + \frac{x}{5} = \frac{4}{5}$.

Mixed Review

Find the area of each parallelogram. *[Lesson 4-5]*

36.

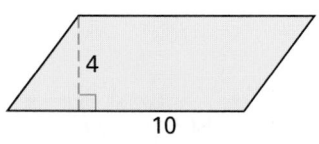

4

10

37.

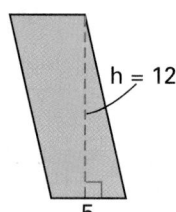

h = 12

5

38.

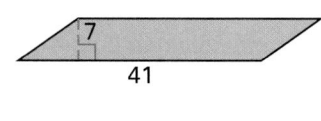

7

41

State if the equation is true for the given value of the variable. *[Lesson 2-12]*

39. $x + 17 = 50; x = 43$ **40.** $5j = 60; j = 14$ **41.** $21 - k = 14; k = 7$

Project Progress

Make a table for each of your recipes. In the first column, list the number of servings and amounts of ingredients in the original recipe. In the second column, list half the amounts listed in the first column. In the third column, list double the amounts in the first column.

Problem Solving

Understand
Plan
Solve
Look Back

Section 6A Connect

In this section, you've learned how to add and subtract different types of fractions. Now you'll use that knowledge to prepare information about different types of blood.

What's Your Type?

Every person has only one blood type. A person who needs a blood transfusion cannot receive blood from just anyone. The blood must be a certain type, or complications could arise, and the person could even die. The data from the American Red Cross shows what fraction of the population has each of the eight blood types.

A+	A−	B+	B−	AB+	AB−	0+	0−
$\frac{17}{50}$	$\frac{3}{50}$	$\frac{2}{25}$	$\frac{3}{200}$	$\frac{1}{25}$	$\frac{1}{200}$	$\frac{39}{100}$	$\frac{7}{100}$

The following table lists the types of blood that a person of each blood type can receive.

Patient Type	Can RECEIVE types...	Patient Type	Can RECEIVE types...
A+	A+, A−, 0+, 0−	AB+	A+, A−, B+, B−, AB+, AB−, 0+, 0−
A−	A−, 0−	AB−	A−, B−, AB−, 0−
B+	B+, B−, 0+, 0−	0+	0+, 0−
B−	B−, 0−	0−	0−

1. Determine the fraction of the population from which each patient type can receive blood.

2. If a person can receive a large number of blood types, can that person receive blood from a larger fraction of the population? Explain.

3. People with 0− blood are known as "universal donors." Why do you think they are called this?

4. A "universal recipient" is a person who can receive blood from anyone, regardless of their blood type. What fraction of the population are universal recipients? Explain.

Simplify. Write each answer in lowest terms.

1. $\dfrac{3}{11} + \dfrac{5}{11}$

2. $\dfrac{3}{5} - \dfrac{1}{5}$

3. $\dfrac{1}{8} + \dfrac{3}{8}$

4. $\dfrac{9}{10} - \dfrac{6}{10}$

5. $\dfrac{3}{4} + \dfrac{3}{5}$

6. $\dfrac{5}{8} + \dfrac{2}{5}$

7. $\dfrac{1}{4} + \dfrac{1}{6}$

8. $\dfrac{4}{5} - \dfrac{1}{4}$

9. $\dfrac{5}{9} - \dfrac{1}{3}$

10. $\dfrac{1}{3} - \dfrac{1}{4}$

11. $\dfrac{7}{10} + \dfrac{1}{4}$

12. $\dfrac{5}{6} - \dfrac{3}{8}$

13. Industry Newspaper ads are available in sizes that are a fraction of a page: $\frac{1}{8}, \frac{1}{4}, \frac{1}{2},$ and $\frac{3}{4}$. Find a combination of ads that will take up a whole page. Explain your reasoning.

14. Health A cup of milk contains $\frac{11}{100}$ of the daily USDA cholesterol allowance. A serving of cooked chicken contains $\frac{19}{75}$ of this allowance. If you eat a serving of cooked chicken and drink a cup of milk, what fraction of your USDA cholesterol allowance have you had?

15. When counting the amount of blood at the hospital blood bank, Christine determined that about $\frac{2}{5}$ of the blood was type O and about $\frac{1}{4}$ of the blood was type A. What fraction of the blood is neither type O nor type A?

Solve. Write each answer in lowest terms.

16. $\dfrac{5}{9} - x = \dfrac{11}{36}$

17. $j + \dfrac{1}{3} = \dfrac{7}{12}$

18. $\dfrac{7}{10} + w = \dfrac{9}{10}$

19. $t - \dfrac{1}{2} = \dfrac{1}{4}$

20. $y + \dfrac{1}{10} = \dfrac{4}{5}$

21. $\dfrac{3}{4} - z = \dfrac{1}{12}$

22. $r - \dfrac{1}{3} = \dfrac{4}{15}$

23. $\dfrac{5}{6} + p = \dfrac{29}{24}$

Test Prep

After simplifying an expression, write the fraction in lowest terms.

24. Choose the correct solution to $\dfrac{5}{12} - \dfrac{1}{6}$.

Ⓐ $\dfrac{1}{4}$ Ⓑ $\dfrac{1}{3}$ Ⓒ $\dfrac{2}{3}$ Ⓓ $\dfrac{5}{6}$

REVIEW 6A

Deep Waters Still Run

Police Report
Date: July 17
Filed by: Officer Arlene Smith

When the Parker family returned from vacation, their house was not as they had left it. The piano had been moved to the kitchen. The books in the living room were severely damaged. The car left in the garage would no longer start.

All the doors and windows were locked. There was no sign of forced entry. The only clue was found by the Parkers' daughter. It was a ball of ants.

Have you figured out who committed the crime? If you think it was Mother Nature, you're right. The Parkers weren't crime victims. They were flood victims.

Floods are one of the most powerful forces of nature. They bring great benefits, and they can cause great damage. Mixed numbers are one of the most powerful ideas in mathematics. They can be used to help predict floods, and help people prepare for floods.

1 What kind of damage can a flood cause?

2 How can a flood be a good thing?

3 How could mixed numbers be used to predict and prepare for floods?

341

Estimation: Sums and Differences of Mixed Numbers

You'll Learn ...

■ to estimate sums and differences of mixed numbers

... How It's Used

Day care providers use estimates of mixed numbers when ordering supplies.

▶ **Lesson Link**   In earlier lessons, you used rounding to make estimates with whole numbers and fractions. Now you'll use rounding to estimate sums and differences of mixed numbers. ◀

Explore   Mixed Number Estimation

Breaking the Banks

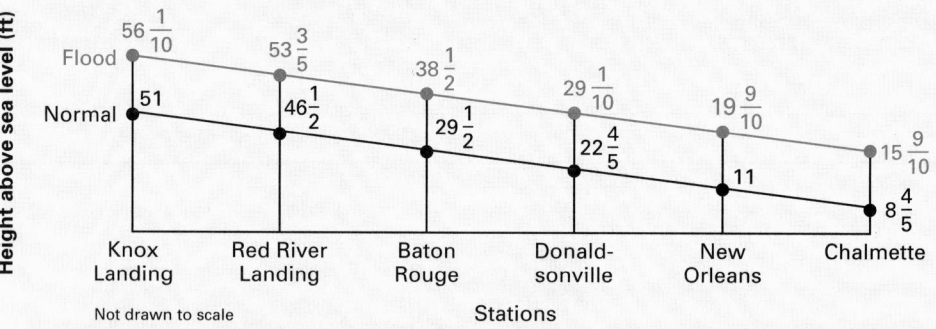

1974 Mississippi River Flood Levels

The black line in the diagram lists the normal level of the river at 6 recording stations on the Mississippi River in Louisiana. The red line gives the river's highest level during the 1974 flood.

1. Rank the stations by the amount of flooding at the station. The first station should be where the flood level was closest to the normal level. The last station should be where the flood level was farthest from the normal level.

2. Each number represents the normal level of the river in between two of the stations. Which station is each point closest to?

a. $50\frac{1}{2}$ **b.** $12\frac{2}{3}$ **c.** $22\frac{3}{5}$ **d.** $30\frac{1}{11}$ **e.** $10\frac{6}{7}$ **f.** $48\frac{1}{4}$

▶ **Geography Link**

The source of the Mississippi River is Lake Itasca, Minnesota. The mouth is in Louisiana, south of New Orleans.

Learn   Estimation: Mixed Numbers

Recall that a *mixed number* contains a whole number and a fraction. You can estimate sums and differences of mixed numbers by rounding each number to the nearest whole number.

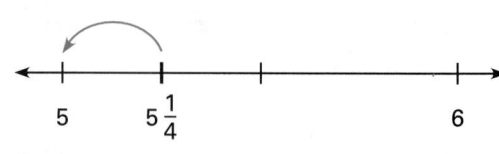

To round a mixed number, look at the fractional part of the mixed number.

Drop the fraction and leave the whole number unchanged if the fractional part is less than $\frac{1}{2}$.

Round up to the next whole number if the fractional part is $\frac{1}{2}$ or greater.

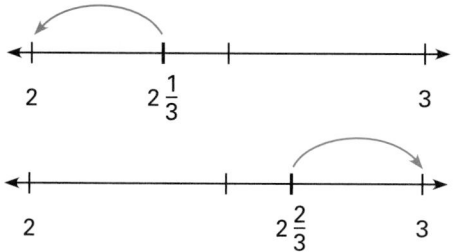

Examples

Round the mean annual rainfall amounts to the nearest inch.

1 Lagos, Nigeria: $72\frac{3}{8}$ in.

The numerator of the fraction, 3, is less than half the denominator, 8. Therefore, $\frac{3}{8} < \frac{1}{2}$.

$72\frac{3}{8}$ rounds down to 72.

2 Athens, Greece: $17\frac{13}{16}$ in.

The numerator of the fraction, 13, is more than half the denominator, 16. Therefore, $\frac{13}{16} > \frac{1}{2}$.

$17\frac{13}{16}$ rounds up to 18.

▶ **Geography Link**

Lagos, Nigeria, is the second most populated city in Africa. Cairo, Egypt, is the first.

3 Estimate the sum:

$4\frac{1}{3} + 6\frac{3}{4}$

Round: $4\frac{1}{3} \rightarrow 4$

$\qquad 6\frac{3}{4} \rightarrow 7$

Estimate: $4 + 7 = 11$

4 Estimate the difference:

$9\frac{1}{2} - 6\frac{9}{10}$

Round: $9\frac{1}{2} \rightarrow 10$

$\qquad 6\frac{9}{10} \rightarrow 7$

Estimate: $10 - 7 = 3$

Try It

Round to the nearest whole number. **a.** $6\frac{2}{7}$ **b.** $1\frac{1}{2}$ **c.** $3\frac{5}{8}$

d. Estimate the sum: $3\frac{1}{2} + 11\frac{7}{8}$ **e.** Estimate the difference: $8\frac{2}{3} - 1\frac{4}{9}$

Check Your Understanding

1. How is rounding mixed numbers like rounding fractions?

2. Describe methods you can use to tell if a fraction is greater than, equal to, or less than $\frac{1}{2}$.

3. Describe a situation where it might be a good idea to round a mixed number up to the next whole number, even if the number would normally be rounded down.

6-4 Exercises and Applications

Practice and Apply

Getting Started State whether each fraction is closer to 0 or to 1.

1. $\frac{3}{7}$
2. $\frac{9}{15}$
3. $\frac{5}{8}$
4. $\frac{7}{10}$
5. $\frac{11}{16}$
6. $\frac{2}{9}$

Round to the nearest whole number.

7. $4\frac{3}{8}$
8. $3\frac{1}{9}$
9. $4\frac{7}{10}$
10. $12\frac{1}{5}$
11. $25\frac{3}{5}$

12. $1\frac{6}{12}$
13. $33\frac{4}{8}$
14. $11\frac{7}{9}$
15. $8\frac{4}{9}$
16. $65\frac{5}{10}$

17. $6\frac{2}{3}$
18. $5\frac{1}{5}$
19. $2\frac{2}{7}$
20. $7\frac{12}{96}$
21. $18\frac{34}{101}$

Estimate.

22. $10\frac{11}{20} - 3\frac{6}{25}$
23. $1\frac{2}{9} + 8\frac{1}{4}$
24. $7\frac{5}{6} - 5\frac{12}{13}$
25. $4\frac{3}{7} + 3\frac{1}{5}$

26. $4\frac{1}{3} + 7\frac{3}{4} + 2\frac{8}{9}$
27. $11\frac{5}{8} - 4\frac{1}{6}$
28. $3\frac{1}{9} + 4\frac{1}{8} + 7\frac{1}{5}$
29. $7\frac{5}{8} - 2\frac{4}{5}$

30. $9\frac{1}{9} - 3\frac{1}{3}$
31. $12\frac{1}{2} + 7\frac{3}{7} + 5\frac{5}{8}$
32. $8\frac{7}{10} - 1\frac{1}{2}$
33. $3\frac{2}{5} + 12\frac{1}{6}$

34. $10\frac{3}{5} + 5\frac{2}{3}$
35. $22\frac{5}{12} - 2\frac{3}{5}$
36. $13\frac{1}{10} + 8\frac{1}{8}$
37. $\frac{1}{10} + 7\frac{2}{13}$

38. Dimitri lives near the Colorado River. He should evacuate his home when the river reaches 28 feet. The river is now at $21\frac{7}{10}$ feet and is predicted to rise another $6\frac{1}{2}$ feet this evening. Will Dimitri need to evacuate?

39. At noon, the Colorado River measured a depth of 26 feet. By midnight, the river had fallen by $5\frac{3}{8}$ feet. About how deep was the river at midnight?

40. Shannon and Kelly want $14\frac{1}{2}$ feet of rope for a game of tug of war. Shannon has an $8\frac{1}{4}$ foot length of rope. Kelly has a $5\frac{2}{3}$ foot length of rope. If they tie the two ropes together, will it be long enough?

PRACTICE 6-4

344 *Chapter 6 • Adding and Subtracting Fractions*

41. Number Sense Estimate the median of $5\frac{3}{4}$, $5\frac{1}{3}$, $3\frac{1}{4}$, $1\frac{7}{8}$, $6\frac{1}{10}$, $1\frac{1}{5}$, $7\frac{1}{9}$, $3\frac{8}{9}$.

42. | Test Prep | Estimate Eduardo's time in a triathlon if it takes him $\frac{3}{4}$ of an hour to complete the swim, $1\frac{1}{3}$ hours to complete the bike ride, and $1\frac{1}{12}$ hours for the run.

   Ⓐ 1 hour   Ⓑ 2 hours   Ⓒ 3 hours   Ⓓ 4 hours

43. Use the chart to estimate the total weekly rainfall.

Day	Sunday	Monday	Tuesday	Wednesday	Thursday	Friday	Saturday
Rainfall (in.)	0	$1\frac{1}{2}$	$1\frac{9}{10}$	0	$2\frac{3}{10}$	$\frac{3}{11}$	$1\frac{3}{7}$

Problem Solving and Reasoning

44. Critical Thinking Estimate the value of x. Explain what you did.

   a. $7\frac{1}{4} + x = 10\frac{1}{5}$ **b.** $9\frac{5}{8} - x = 3\frac{1}{2}$ **c.** $x + 7\frac{1}{10} = 15\frac{4}{5}$

45. Communicate Compare rounding mixed numbers by rounding to the nearest whole number with rounding mixed numbers by always rounding up. Which is easier? Which is more accurate? Explain.

46. Critical Thinking At the county fair, Brian entered his frog Horton in the frog jumping contest. Horton's first jump was $10\frac{7}{8}$ feet. His second was $11\frac{1}{5}$ feet, and his third was $9\frac{4}{5}$ feet. Estimate the average length of Horton's jumps. Explain.

Mixed Review

Find the area. *[Lesson 4-6]*

47.

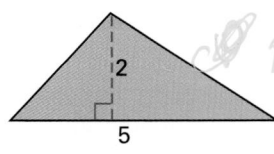

2
5

48.

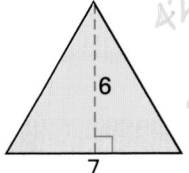

6
7

49.

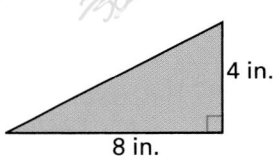

4 in.
8 in.

Solve. *[Lesson 2-13]*

50. $m + 22 = 43$ **51.** $n - 11 = 10$ **52.** $15 + v = 27$ **53.** $44 - x = 12$

54. $12b = 36$ **55.** $\frac{x}{2} = 4$ **56.** $3c = 15$ **57.** $\frac{e}{11} = 2$

58. $5z = 35$ **59.** $j + 7 = 13$ **60.** $14 - f = 10$ **61.** $\frac{40}{x} = 8$

Adding Mixed Numbers

You'll Learn ...

■ to add mixed numbers

... How It's Used

Farmers add mixed numbers when working with rainfall data.

▶ **Lesson Link** In the last lesson, you estimated sums of mixed numbers. Now you'll learn how to find mixed number sums exactly. ◀

Explore | **Adding Mixed Numbers**

Another Fine Mix!

Materials: Fraction Bars®

Adding Mixed Numbers

- Draw and label the whole number for the first mixed number.
- Next to that, draw and label the fraction for the first number.
- Next to that, draw and label the whole number for the second mixed number.
- Next to that, draw and label the fraction for the second number.
- Using a whole number and a fraction less than 1, describe the model.

$$1\frac{3}{4} + 1\frac{1}{2} = 3\frac{1}{4}$$

| 1 | $\frac{1}{4}$ | $\frac{1}{4}$ | $\frac{1}{4}$ | 1 | $\frac{1}{2}$ |
| 1 | 1 | | 1 | | $\frac{1}{4}$ |

1. Model each problem.

a. $1\frac{1}{4} + 2\frac{1}{2}$ **b.** $1\frac{2}{3} + 1\frac{3}{6}$ **c.** $1\frac{3}{8} + 2\frac{1}{8}$ **d.** $1\frac{3}{6} + 2\frac{1}{2}$

2. Does the whole number in the answer always equal the sum of the two whole numbers in the problem? Explain.

3. Is the sum of two mixed numbers always a mixed number? Explain.

Learn | **Adding Mixed Numbers**

To add mixed numbers:

$$5\frac{2}{3} + 1\frac{1}{4}$$

1. Add the whole numbers.

$$5 \ + 1 \qquad\qquad = 6$$

2. Add the fractions.

$$\frac{2}{3} + \ \frac{1}{4} = \frac{8+3}{12} = \ \frac{11}{12}$$

3. Put the two parts together.

$$= 6\frac{11}{12}$$

If the sum of the fractions is an improper fraction, you may need to rewrite it as a mixed number, and add the whole number parts together.

Examples

1 Add: $1\frac{1}{3} + 2\frac{1}{2}$

$$1\frac{1}{3} = 1\frac{2}{6}$$
$$+2\frac{1}{2} = +2\frac{3}{6}$$
$$\overline{\hspace{2cm}}$$
$$3\frac{5}{6}$$

Estimate: $1 + 3 = 4$

Rewrite the fractions using the LCD of 6.

Add whole numbers and add fractions.
Compare with the estimate.

You can also find the sum using a model.

1	$\frac{1}{3}$	1	1	$\frac{1}{2}$

1	1	1	$\frac{1}{6}$ $\frac{1}{6}$ $\frac{1}{6}$ $\frac{1}{6}$ $\frac{1}{6}$

2 During the 1993 flood, the Mississippi River rose to $27\frac{9}{10}$ feet. Then it rose another $3\frac{3}{5}$ feet. Find the river's final height.

$$27\frac{9}{10} = 27\frac{9}{10}$$
$$+3\frac{3}{5} = +3\frac{6}{10}$$
$$\overline{\hspace{2cm}}$$
$$30\frac{15}{10}$$

Estimate: $28 + 4 = 32$

Rewrite the fractions using the LCD of 10.

Add whole numbers and add fractions.

$$= 30 + 1\frac{5}{10}$$ Rewrite the improper fraction as a mixed number.

$$= 31\frac{5}{10}, \text{ or } 31\frac{1}{2}$$ Add and write in lowest terms.

The final height was $31\frac{1}{2}$ feet.

Try It

Add. **a.** $6 + 2\frac{3}{4}$ **b.** $1\frac{1}{2} + 3\frac{1}{4}$ **c.** $3\frac{7}{8} + 2\frac{5}{8}$ **d.** $4\frac{7}{12} + 2\frac{5}{6}$

▶ **Language Link**

The word "Mississippi" comes from the Native American Algonquin language. It means "Father of Waters."

(detail) Currier & Ives, n/ath. & James. "On The St. Lawrence Indian Encampment." Library of Congress, Washington, DC.

Check Your Understanding

1. Could you add mixed numbers by first changing them to decimals? Explain your answer.

2. When adding the fractional parts of mixed numbers, why do you sometimes need to rewrite the fraction sum?

Practice and Apply

Even

Getting Started Add.

1. $6 + 5\frac{2}{3}$

2. $8 + 7\frac{3}{8}$

3. $4\frac{1}{2} + 2$

4. $3\frac{6}{7} + 9$

Add. Write each answer as a whole or mixed number in lowest terms.

5. $5\frac{1}{3} + 4\frac{2}{6}$

6. $6\frac{1}{2} + 2\frac{5}{6}$

7. $35 + 27\frac{3}{4}$

8. $47\frac{1}{2} + 49\frac{3}{7}$

9. $8\frac{2}{4} + 2\frac{1}{2}$

10. $12\frac{3}{5} + 3\frac{4}{5}$

11. $1\frac{7}{8} + 3\frac{5}{6}$

12. $9\frac{3}{7} + 1\frac{2}{7}$

13. $1\frac{3}{5} + 5\frac{1}{5}$

14. $3\frac{4}{5} + 15$

15. $8\frac{2}{9} + 7\frac{2}{3}$

16. $22\frac{3}{4} + 19\frac{2}{5}$

17. $7\frac{4}{9} + 5\frac{2}{3}$

18. $45\frac{3}{4} + 21\frac{7}{8}$

19. $1\frac{3}{10} + 12\frac{4}{5}$

20. $2\frac{4}{5} + 3\frac{1}{2}$

21. $9\frac{3}{7} + 12\frac{1}{3}$

22. $12\frac{2}{3} + 7\frac{5}{8}$

23. $3\frac{3}{8} + 4\frac{5}{8}$

24. $8\frac{2}{3} + 8\frac{3}{4}$

25. $9\frac{7}{9} + 32$

26. $7\frac{1}{3} + 2\frac{2}{3}$

27. $42\frac{1}{6} + 9\frac{11}{12}$

28. $93\frac{1}{12} + 7$

29. Career The U.S. Geological Survey measured the depth of a Rio Grande River channel during flooding. The difference between the highest and lowest depths was $9\frac{3}{4}$ feet. If the lowest reading was $28\frac{1}{2}$ feet, what was the highest reading?

30. **Test Prep** Samantha ran her part of a 400-meter relay in $1\frac{1}{2}$ minutes. Juana ran in $1\frac{1}{3}$ minutes, Anna in $1\frac{3}{8}$, and Adrienne in $1\frac{1}{4}$. How long did it take their team to run the race?

Ⓐ $4\frac{11}{24}$ min.

Ⓑ $5\frac{11}{24}$ min.

Ⓒ $13\frac{1}{24}$ min.

Ⓓ 4 min.

PRACTICE 6-5

Use the table for Exercises 31–33.

Damages from 1984 Lower Mississippi River Flood (millions of dollars)				
Urban Development	Rural Development	Agricultural Crops	Government and Utilities	Miscellaneous
$5\frac{1}{4}$	$5\frac{1}{2}$	$1\frac{2}{3}$	$2\frac{4}{5}$	$\frac{2}{3}$

31. How much damage was done to Urban and Rural Development?

32. How much damage was done to Government and Utilities, and to Miscellaneous?

33. What was the total damage?

Problem Solving and Reasoning

34. Communicate Describe a situation where you use addition and would want to write $7\frac{5}{3}$ as $8\frac{2}{3}$. Explain your reasoning.

36. **Journal** Describe some similarities and differences between adding with whole numbers and adding with mixed numbers.

35. Choose a Strategy The combined area of Shapes A and B is $4\frac{2}{3}$ m². The area of Shape B is $1\frac{1}{3}$ m² more than the area of Shape A. Find the areas of both shapes.

Problem Solving
STRATEGIES

- Look for a Pattern
- Make an Organized List
- Make a Table
- Guess and Check
- Work Backward
- Use Logical Reasoning
- Draw a Diagram
- Solve a Simpler Problem

Mixed Review

Find the circumference of each object. *[Lesson 4-7]*

37.

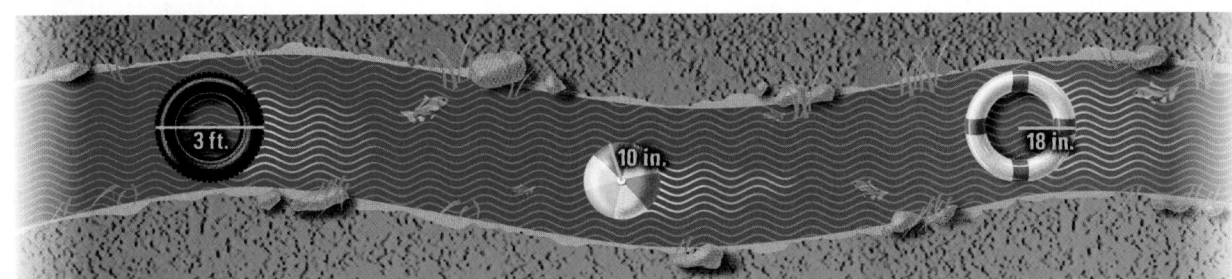

3 ft.   10 in.   18 in.

Write in standard form. *[Lesson 3-6]*

38. 3.1×10^3 **39.** 4.27×10^5 **40.** 5.45×10^7 **41.** 1.124×10^6

42. 7.11×10^4 **43.** 9.0×10^9 **44.** 2.22×10^3 **45.** 6.663×10^{11}

Subtracting Mixed Numbers

You'll Learn ...

■ to subtract mixed numbers

... How It's Used

Carpenters subtract mixed numbers when determining the amount of lumber needed to finish a project.

▶ **Lesson Link** You've seen that rewriting fractions may be necessary when you add mixed numbers. You may also need to rewrite to subtract mixed numbers. ◀

Explore | Subtracting Mixed Numbers

What Difference Does It Make?

Materials: Fraction Bars®

$$2\frac{1}{4} - 1\frac{1}{2} = \frac{3}{4}$$

Subtracting Mixed Numbers

1		1		$\frac{1}{4}$
1		$\frac{1}{2}$	$\frac{1}{4}$ $\frac{1}{4}$	$\frac{1}{4}$

- Draw and label the whole number for the first mixed number.

- Next to that, draw and label the fraction for the first number.

- Below the first whole number, draw and label the whole number for the second mixed number.

- Next to that, draw and label the fraction for the second number.

- Next to the second mixed-number model, draw and label a model that equals the difference between the first and second model.

1. Model these problems.

a. $2\frac{3}{4} - 1\frac{1}{4}$ **b.** $3\frac{2}{3} - 1\frac{1}{6}$ **c.** $2 - \frac{3}{4}$ **d.** $4\frac{1}{4} - 1\frac{1}{2}$ **e.** $4\frac{3}{8} - 3\frac{3}{4}$

2. Can you subtract two mixed numbers if the fraction in the second mixed number is larger than the fraction in the first mixed number? Explain.

3. If one mixed number is subtracted from another mixed number, is the difference always a mixed number? Explain.

Learn | Subtracting Mixed Numbers

When subtracting whole numbers, you sometimes have a digit in the second number that's larger than the digit in the same place value in the first number. In order to subtract, you need to regroup the first number.

$$
\begin{array}{r}
6\,1 \\
7\,2 \\
-\ 1\,8 \\
\hline
5\,4
\end{array}
$$

You can use a similar process when subtracting mixed numbers.

	$9\frac{1}{5} - 4\frac{4}{5} = ?$	$7 - 2\frac{1}{3} = ?$
1. Rewrite the whole number.	$8 + 1 + \frac{1}{5}$	$6 + 1$
2. Rewrite the 1 as a fraction with the same numerator and denominator.	$8 + \frac{5}{5} + \frac{1}{5}$	$6 + \frac{3}{3}$
3. If rewriting a mixed number, add the fraction parts together.	$8\frac{6}{5} - 4\frac{4}{5} = 4\frac{2}{5}$	$6\frac{3}{3} - 2\frac{1}{3} = 4\frac{2}{3}$

Examples

1 Subtract $7\frac{2}{9} - 3\frac{2}{3}$.

$7\frac{2}{9} = 6 + 1 + \frac{2}{9} = 6 + \frac{9}{9} + \frac{2}{9} = 6\frac{11}{9}$ Rewrite the whole number.

$-3\frac{2}{3} =$ $-3\frac{6}{9}$ Rewrite with a common denominator.

$\phantom{-3\frac{2}{3} =} = 3\frac{5}{9}$ Subtract.

2 Prior to the construction of the Aswan Dam, Egypt's Nile River flooded its banks each summer, fertilizing nearby fields. If the river rose 3 feet above flood level, then fell $1\frac{5}{12}$ feet, find the final height of the river.

$3 \;\rightarrow\; 2\frac{12}{12}$ Rewrite the whole number.

$-1\frac{5}{12} \rightarrow 1\frac{5}{12}$

$\phantom{-1\frac{5}{12} \rightarrow} 1\frac{7}{12}$ Subtract fractions.
          Subtract whole numbers.

You can also find the difference using a model.

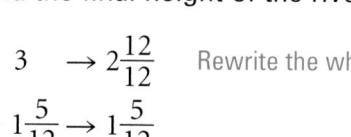

The river's height was $1\frac{7}{12}$ feet above flood level.

Try It

Subtract.   **a.** $6\frac{1}{5} - 2\frac{4}{5}$ **b.** $8\frac{1}{2} - 3\frac{2}{3}$ **c.** $12 - 9\frac{5}{9}$

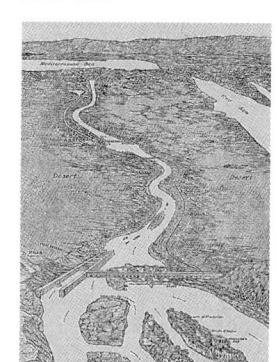

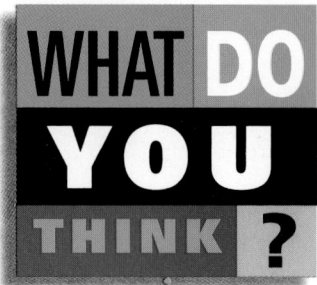

Dams are used to control floods by storing water during heavy rains. During a rainy spell, the height of the water behind a dam rose from $14\frac{5}{6}$ ft to $19\frac{2}{3}$ ft.

Zack and Tyreka wanted to know how much the water had risen.

Zack thought …

I'll subtract fraction from fraction and whole number from whole number.

$$19\frac{2}{3} = 19\frac{4}{6} \qquad \text{Rewrite using the LCD.}$$

$$= 18\frac{10}{6} \qquad \text{Regroup.}$$

$$19\frac{2}{3} = 18\frac{10}{6}$$

$$-14\frac{5}{6} = 14\frac{5}{6}$$

$$4\frac{5}{6}$$

The water rose $4\frac{5}{6}$ feet.

Tyreka thought…

I'll subtract by rewriting the mixed numbers as improper fractions.

$$19\frac{2}{3} = \frac{59}{3} = \frac{118}{6} \qquad \text{Rewrite using the LCD.}$$

$$-14\frac{5}{6} = \qquad \frac{89}{6}$$

$$\frac{29}{6}$$

$$\frac{29}{6} = 4\frac{5}{6} \qquad \text{Rewrite as mixed number.}$$

The water rose $4\frac{5}{6}$ feet.

What do you think?

1. Why did both Zack and Tyreka use the least common denominator?

2. If the mixed numbers didn't involve borrowing, would one method be faster than the other? Explain.

Check | Your Understanding

1. How could you use a calculator to subtract mixed numbers?

2. How is subtracting mixed numbers like subtracting whole numbers?

3. In a subtraction problem, when might you need to convert a whole number into a mixed number?

Practice and Apply

Getting Started Subtract.

1. $6\frac{3}{4} - 4$

2. $7\frac{7}{8} - 2$

3. $12\frac{1}{2} - 10$

4. $3\frac{4}{5} - 2$

Subtract. Write each answer as a whole or mixed number in lowest terms.

5. $7\frac{1}{2} - 6\frac{1}{4}$

6. $7\frac{2}{9} - 6\frac{1}{3}$

7. $2\frac{1}{4} - 1\frac{3}{4}$

8. $9\frac{1}{6} - 4\frac{2}{3}$

9. $1\frac{1}{3} - \frac{2}{3}$

10. $4\frac{5}{6} - 2\frac{1}{6}$

11. $2\frac{1}{6} - 1\frac{1}{8}$

12. $5\frac{1}{5} - 3\frac{2}{3}$

13. $9\frac{7}{8} - 1\frac{6}{8}$

14. $4\frac{1}{3} - 3\frac{1}{4}$

15. $7\frac{3}{5} - 4\frac{2}{5}$

16. $10\frac{7}{10} - 4\frac{4}{5}$

17. $6\frac{3}{4} - 2\frac{1}{5}$

18. $3\frac{2}{3} - \frac{2}{3}$

19. $1\frac{1}{4} - \frac{1}{2}$

20. $2\frac{1}{6} - 1\frac{1}{2}$

21. $6\frac{4}{5} - 3\frac{1}{5}$

22. $7\frac{1}{2} - 1\frac{3}{4}$

23. $8\frac{5}{7} - 2\frac{1}{4}$

24. $4\frac{1}{8} - 1\frac{5}{9}$

25. Helen and Joe expected the stream near their house to rise to 9 feet when the snow melted. It only rose to $7\frac{4}{5}$ feet. By how much was their prediction off?

26. Algebra A large financial institution trading on the New York Stock Exchange listed its highest selling price in the last year at $80\frac{3}{8}$ points. The difference between its highest and lowest prices was $26\frac{1}{2}$ points. Write and solve an equation to find the lowest selling price.

27. **Test Prep** Subtract $15\frac{3}{8} - 11\frac{1}{5}$.

   Ⓐ $1\frac{67}{40}$ Ⓑ $3\frac{7}{10}$

   Ⓒ $4\frac{7}{40}$ Ⓓ $4\frac{2}{3}$

28. Wahn has a box of macaroni and cheese that contains 6 servings. He plans to eat $3\frac{1}{3}$ servings. How many servings will be left?

Health The circle graph shows the number of hours Kente spends playing sports. Use the graph for Exercises 29 and 30.

Weekly Sports (hrs)

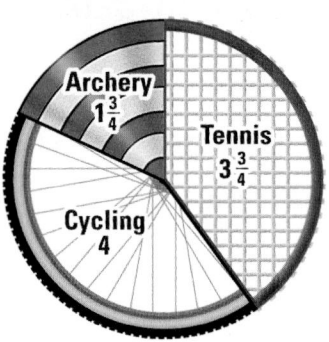

29. How many more hours did Kente spend cycling than practicing archery?

30. Kente predicted that he would play tennis for 7 hours during the week. By how much was his prediction off?

Problem Solving and Reasoning

31. Critical Thinking $5\frac{x}{11} - 2\frac{y}{11} =$ a whole number. List three possible values for x and y. Explain.

32. Critical Thinking If you change one of the digits in $3\frac{1}{4} + 2\frac{5}{8}$ to a 9, and you want to get the smallest possible answer, which digit should you change?

33. Journal Describe some similarities and differences between subtracting with whole numbers and subtracting with mixed numbers.

Mixed Review

Find the areas of the shapes. [Lesson 4-9]

34.

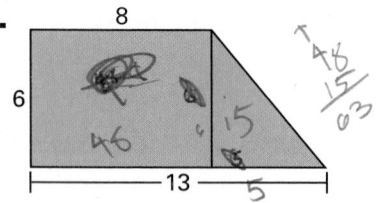

35.

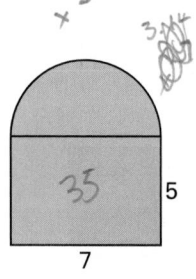

36.

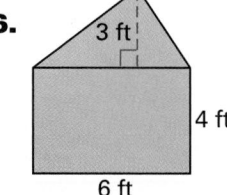

Write each number in scientific notation. [Lesson 3-4]

37. 340,000   **38.** 47,500   **39.** 5,000,000   **40.** 4000   **41.** 6,200,000

Project Progress

Complete the columns in your recipe tables. Organize the tables into a cookbook. Illustrate your book with pictures of the foods or the animals that the recipes are designed for.

Problem Solving

Understand

Plan

Solve

Look Back

PROBLEM SOLVING 6-6

In this section, you've learned how to add and subtract mixed numbers. In the following investigation, you'll use mixed numbers as you look at two of the main causes of floods.

Deep Waters Still Run

Each winter, snow falls in the Sunset Mountains. Each spring, the snow melts and flows into the Wolverine River. The Wolverine River will flood in July if *both* of the following conditions are met:

a. The total amount of precipitation (rain or snow) during December, January, February, and March is greater than 30 inches.

b. The total amount of time during April, May, and June when air temperatures exceed 90°F is greater than $11\frac{1}{2}$ days.

The table gives data for November 1994 to June 1995.

	Nov	Dec	Jan	Feb	Mar	Apr	May	Jun
Precipitation (in.)	$3\frac{3}{4}$	$6\frac{1}{12}$	$8\frac{3}{4}$	$9\frac{5}{6}$	$6\frac{2}{3}$	$1\frac{1}{2}$	$1\frac{5}{12}$	$\frac{5}{8}$
Days over 90°	0	0	0	0	$1\frac{3}{5}$	$2\frac{4}{5}$	$3\frac{3}{10}$	$4\frac{1}{2}$

1. Estimate the amount of precipitation from December through March.

2. Estimate the number of days over 90°F from April through June.

3. Do your estimates indicate that the river will flood in July? Explain.

4. Find the exact amount of precipitation from December through March.

5. Find the exact number of days over 90°F from April through June.

6. Do your exact figures indicate that the river will flood in July? Explain.

7. Why does temperature affect the possibility that the river will flood? What other factors might affect the possibility?

355

Simplify. Write each answer in lowest terms.

1. $4\frac{1}{5} - 2\frac{3}{5}$

2. $15 + 7\frac{4}{7}$

3. $\frac{7}{9} - \frac{2}{5}$

4. $12\frac{7}{8} - 8\frac{3}{8}$

5. $6\frac{1}{3} - 2\frac{7}{9}$

6. $\frac{9}{11} + \frac{6}{11}$

7. $33\frac{1}{3} + 78\frac{1}{8}$

8. $\frac{4}{5} - \frac{1}{8}$

9. $2\frac{1}{3} + 3\frac{5}{3}$

10. $6\frac{5}{6} - 4\frac{2}{3}$

11. $20 - 15\frac{1}{3}$

12. $11\frac{7}{8} - 8\frac{5}{8}$

13. $2\frac{4}{18} - 2\frac{3}{18}$

14. $3\frac{4}{5} + 10\frac{1}{2}$

15. $6\frac{3}{4} - 3\frac{1}{2}$

16. $1\frac{5}{8} + 2\frac{7}{24}$

17. During the 1973 Mississippi River flood, the Fifth Army Corps of Engineers used a number of vehicles to help with the disaster. $\frac{5}{7}$ were Jeeps. $\frac{5}{21}$ were tank trucks. What fraction were neither Jeeps nor tank trucks?

18. Rob and Thomas Lin and Helen and Sarah Seleca spent an afternoon painting a house. Rob used $3\frac{1}{3}$ gallons of paint. Sarah used $4\frac{1}{4}$. Thomas used $5\frac{3}{5}$. Helen used $4\frac{4}{5}$. Did the Lins or the Selecas use more paint? How much more?

19. Estimation Steve plans to do chores for $1\frac{1}{3}$ hours, homework for $2\frac{1}{4}$ hours, and play basketball for $2\frac{3}{4}$ hours. Estimate the amount of time this will take.

20. Robyn ran $2\frac{2}{3}$ miles in the morning and $3\frac{1}{4}$ miles after school. How many miles did she run all together?

Test Prep

In order to eliminate answers, first determine if the answer is a mixed number or a whole number.

21. Choose the correct answer. $5\frac{2}{6} + 2\frac{2}{3}$

Ⓐ $\frac{8}{3}$ Ⓑ $2\frac{2}{3}$ Ⓒ 7   Ⓓ 8

22. Choose the correct answer. $5\frac{3}{4} + 3\frac{3}{4}$

Ⓐ 2   Ⓑ $8\frac{1}{2}$ Ⓒ 9   Ⓓ $9\frac{1}{2}$

Elapsed Time

When you subtract with whole numbers, you sometimes have to borrow from the tens place because you don't have a large enough digit in the ones place. The same thing can take place when you subtract time. You may need to borrow from the hour part if the minute part isn't big enough.

...ille	Allentown	Danford	Weslaco
	2:11	3:06	3:42
	3:46	4:41	5:17
	5:05	6:00	6:36
	6:05	7:00	7:36
	7:10	8:05	8:41

HEDULE

The bus leaves Allentown at 3:46 and arrives at Weslaco at 5:17. How long does the bus ride last?

```
  5:17
− 3:46
  ?:?1
```

You can subtract 6 minutes from 7 minutes. But you can't subtract 40 minutes from 10 minutes. So, you will need to borrow from the 5 hours.

```
  4 7
  5:17
− 3:46
  1:31
```

When you borrow, remember 1 hour doesn't equal 100 minutes. It equals 60 minutes. So, only add 6 to the ten-minute place.

The ride takes 1 hour and 31 minutes.
To find the arrival time, add the length of the trip to the start time.

Try It

Find the elapsed time for each trip.

1. Leaves 6:05 AM, arrives 7:15 AM.
2. Leaves 9:15 PM, arrives 11:26 PM.
3. Leaves 8:36 AM, arrives at noon.

Find each arrival time.

4. Leaves 4:00 PM, trip takes 3 hours 15 minutes
5. Leaves 1:15 AM, trip takes 6 hours 36 minutes.

Chapter 6 Summary and Review

Graphic Organizer

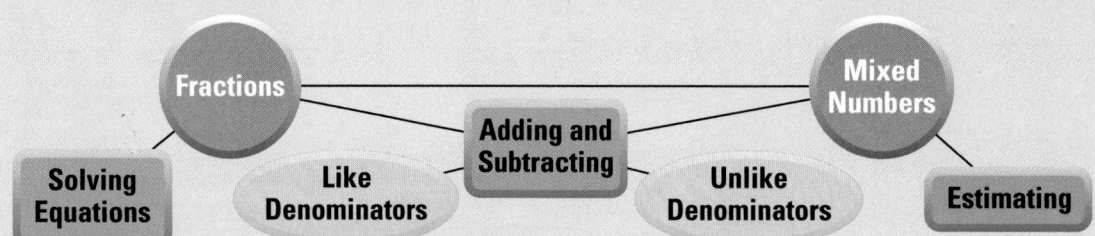

Section 6A Adding and Subtracting Fractions

Summary

- You can add or subtract fractions with **like denominators** by adding or subtracting their numerators. You keep the same denominator because you are adding or subtracting pieces of the same size.

- If the fractions have **unlike denominators,** you must change the fractions to equivalent fractions with like denominators. It is sometimes faster to change to equivalent fractions using the **least common denominator.**

- You can add or subtract fractions to solve fraction equations.

Review

1. Write the problem this model represents.

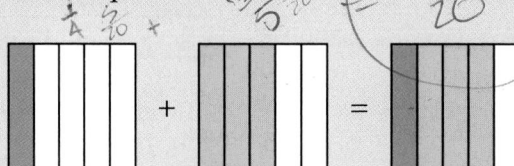

Name the least common denominator of each pair.

2. $\frac{1}{3}, \frac{1}{12}$ **3.** $\frac{1}{4}, \frac{1}{7}$ **4.** $\frac{1}{6}, \frac{1}{10}$ **5.** $\frac{1}{9}, \frac{1}{21}$

Add or subtract. Write each answer in lowest terms.

6. $\frac{5}{7} - \frac{3}{7}$ **7.** $\frac{3}{15} + \frac{8}{15}$ **8.** $\frac{5}{12} + \frac{7}{12}$ **9.** $\frac{3}{5} - \frac{2}{5}$

10. $\frac{7}{8} + \frac{3}{8}$ **11.** $\frac{11}{14} - \frac{5}{7}$ **12.** $\frac{2}{3} + \frac{1}{2}$ **13.** $\frac{1}{3} - \frac{1}{5}$

14. $\frac{2}{11} + \frac{1}{2}$ **15.** $\frac{5}{6} + \frac{1}{7}$ **16.** $\frac{7}{8} - \frac{2}{3}$ **17.** $\frac{7}{8} - \frac{7}{9}$

Solve each equation.

18. $\frac{3}{13} + x = \frac{12}{13}$ **19.** $y - \frac{1}{4} = \frac{1}{2}$ **20.** $z + \frac{1}{5} = \frac{9}{10}$

Section 6B Adding and Subtracting Mixed Numbers

Summary

- You can estimate sums and differences of mixed numbers by rounding each mixed number to the nearest whole number. To find the nearest whole number, you must decide if the fractional part of the mixed number is more or less than one-half.

- You add mixed numbers by adding the fractions and whole numbers separately. If there is an improper fraction in the sum, you will need to rewrite it as a mixed number.

- You subtract mixed numbers by subtracting the fractions and whole numbers separately. You may need to rewrite the whole number in order to subtract.

plant A

Review

Round each mixed number to the nearest whole number.

21. $3\frac{3}{8}$ *3*

22. $4\frac{4}{7}$ *5*

23. $1\frac{1}{2}$ *2*

24. $78\frac{11}{16}$ *79*

25. $\frac{5}{9}$ *1*

26. $13\frac{8}{11}$ *14*

Estimate each sum or difference.

27. $7\frac{1}{2} + 11\frac{5}{8}$ *20*

28. $5\frac{1}{3} - 2\frac{5}{7}$ *2*

29. $3\frac{7}{16} - 1\frac{4}{9}$ *2*

30. $4\frac{2}{3} - 1\frac{4}{9}$ *A*

31. A flag maker wants to attach a $15\frac{3}{4}$-inch tassel on the side of a flag. He has an $18\frac{1}{2}$-inch tassel. How much must he trim off the tassel in order to use it on the flag?

Simplify each expression.

32. $3\frac{3}{5} + 2\frac{1}{5}$

33. $5\frac{1}{6} + 8\frac{1}{2}$

34. $7\frac{7}{8} - 3\frac{1}{8}$

35. $6\frac{12}{17} - 6\frac{5}{17}$

36. $11\frac{5}{11} - 2\frac{5}{8}$

37. $2\frac{3}{7} + 11$

38. $3\frac{2}{3} - 1\frac{1}{2}$

39. $24 - 7\frac{2}{9}$

40. $6 + 3\frac{2}{3}$

41. $7\frac{1}{4} - 4\frac{5}{12}$

42. $31\frac{4}{7} - 2\frac{5}{7}$

43. $11\frac{5}{11} + 2\frac{6}{11}$

Find the perimeter of each figure.

44.

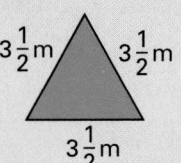

$3\frac{1}{2}$m $3\frac{1}{2}$m

$3\frac{1}{2}$m

45.

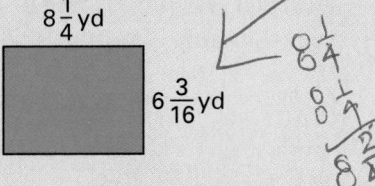

$8\frac{1}{4}$ yd

$6\frac{3}{16}$ yd

Find the least common multiple of each number pair.

1. 5, 6

2. 12, 15

3. 5, 20

4. 30, 35

Add or subtract. Write each answer in lowest terms.

5. $\dfrac{8}{9} - \dfrac{2}{9}$

6. $\dfrac{4}{17} + \dfrac{7}{17}$

7. $\dfrac{6}{11} + \dfrac{8}{11}$

8. $\dfrac{3}{8} - \dfrac{1}{8}$

9. $\dfrac{5}{6} + \dfrac{5}{6}$

10. $\dfrac{10}{12} - \dfrac{3}{6}$

11. $\dfrac{1}{3} + \dfrac{1}{2}$

12. $\dfrac{1}{2} - \dfrac{1}{7}$

13. $\dfrac{4}{15} + \dfrac{1}{2}$

14. $\dfrac{3}{4} + \dfrac{9}{10}$

15. $\dfrac{3}{5} - \dfrac{3}{8}$

16. $\dfrac{3}{4} - \dfrac{2}{9}$

Solve each equation.

17. $\dfrac{7}{15} + w = \dfrac{9}{15}$

18. $k - \dfrac{1}{5} = \dfrac{3}{10}$

19. $x + \dfrac{1}{4} = \dfrac{5}{7}$

20. Maria and John volunteered to fill sandbags to strengthen a dike during the flood. John filled $8\frac{1}{2}$ bags. They filled a total of 25. Write an equation to find how many bags Maria filled, and then solve it.

Estimate each sum or difference.

21. $3\dfrac{1}{3} + 6\dfrac{7}{11}$

22. $11\dfrac{1}{2} - 7\dfrac{3}{5}$

23. $8\dfrac{10}{21} - 2\dfrac{1}{19}$

24. $5\dfrac{4}{5} - 5\dfrac{4}{10}$

25. Find the sum of $9\frac{3}{5}$ and $4\frac{4}{5}$.

26. Find the difference between $11\frac{8}{11}$ and $7\frac{5}{11}$.

Simplify each expression.

27. $2\dfrac{1}{5} + 5\dfrac{3}{5}$

28. $8\dfrac{1}{8} + 7\dfrac{1}{10}$

29. $6\dfrac{6}{8} - 3\dfrac{5}{8}$

30. $11\dfrac{10}{13} - 6\dfrac{4}{13}$

31. $2\dfrac{9}{10} - 2\dfrac{2}{5}$

32. $11\dfrac{4}{9} + 3$

33. $12\dfrac{2}{3} - 1\dfrac{1}{2}$

34. $17 - 9\dfrac{5}{7}$

35. $3 + 9\dfrac{1}{4}$

36. $13\dfrac{1}{3} - 10\dfrac{7}{8}$

37. $50\dfrac{1}{8} - 16\dfrac{7}{9}$

38. $10\dfrac{5}{10} + 13\dfrac{5}{10}$

Performance Task

Notice that $5\frac{3}{7}$, $4\frac{10}{7}$, and $3\frac{17}{7}$ all equal $\frac{38}{7}$. For each improper fraction, find three equivalent mixed numbers with the same denominators.

a. $\dfrac{13}{3}$

b. $\dfrac{27}{5}$

c. $\dfrac{73}{10}$

Multiple Choice

Choose the best answer.

1. What age and height does point *B* represent? *[Lesson 1-3]*

Age and Height

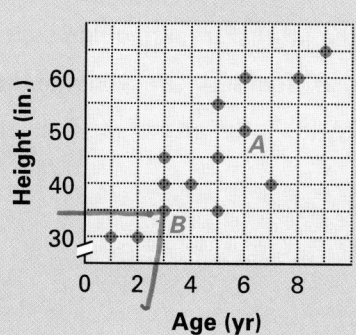

Ⓐ 3 yrs, 35 in.　　Ⓑ 3 yrs, 40 in.

Ⓒ 4 yrs, 40 in.　　Ⓓ None of these

2. Find the median of the data in the stem-and-leaf plot. *[Lesson 1-7]*

Stem	Leaf
2	2 3 6
3	4 4 8 9 9
4	1 1 1 3 7

Ⓐ 1　Ⓑ 36　Ⓒ 39　Ⓓ None of these

3. Simplify 1025 × 4. *[Lesson 2-5]*

Ⓐ 500　　　　　Ⓑ 1100

Ⓒ 4100　　　　Ⓓ None of these

4. Which of the following would you represent with a variable? *[Lesson 2-10]*

Ⓐ number of feet in a mile

Ⓑ number of dimes in a dollar

Ⓒ number of letters in your first name

Ⓓ number of jackets sold each day

5. Which expression represents 4,500,000 in scientific notation? *[Lesson 3-4]*

Ⓐ 4.5×10^5　　　Ⓑ 4.5×10^6

Ⓒ 45×10^5　　　Ⓓ 45×10^6

6. Joyce cut a 1.75-inch piece of cord off the end of a cord 8.5-inch long. What length of cord was left? *[Lesson 3-6]*

Ⓐ 6.75 in.　　　Ⓑ 7.75 in.

Ⓒ 7.85 in.　　　Ⓓ 10.25 in.

7. Simplify 67.5 ÷ 0.25. *[Lesson 3-11]*

Ⓐ 23　Ⓑ 27　Ⓒ 230　Ⓓ 270

8. What is the area of a rectangle 3 ft long and 7 ft wide? *[Lesson 4-4]*

Ⓐ 10 ft　Ⓑ 10 ft²　Ⓒ 21 ft　Ⓓ 21 ft²

9. Find the area of the figure. *[Lesson 4-9]*

Ⓐ 20 ft²

Ⓑ 24 ft

Ⓒ 24 ft²

Ⓓ None of these

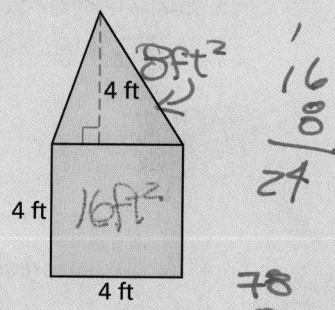

10. Find the prime factorization of 78. *[Lesson 5-2]*

Ⓐ 2 × 34　　　　Ⓑ 70 + 8

Ⓒ 2 × 3 × 13　　Ⓓ 2 × 39

11. Write $\frac{63}{252}$ in lowest terms. *[Lesson 5-5]*

Ⓐ $\frac{7}{28}$　Ⓑ $\frac{1}{4}$　Ⓒ $\frac{9}{84}$　Ⓓ None of these

12. Write $10\frac{3}{5}$ as a decimal. *[Lesson 5-7]*

Ⓐ 106　Ⓑ 50.3　Ⓒ 10.6　Ⓓ 10.06

7 Multiplying and Dividing Fractions

Entertainment Link
www.mathsurf.com/6/ch7/ent

Arts & Literature Link
www.mathsurf.com/6/ch7/arts

Arts & Literature

Upon completion, the statue of Chief Crazy Horse at Thunderhead Mountain, South Dakota, will be the largest free-standing statue in the world at 563 feet tall. The model of the statue on display is $\frac{1}{34}$ the size of the final statue.

Entertainment

At the 1996 Centennial Olympic Games in Atlanta, Naim Suleymanoglu of Turkey won the gold medal in the 141-pound division of weightlifting by lifting 413 pounds. This was over $2\frac{3}{4}$ times his own body weight.

People of the World

One out of every 6 people in the world lives in India. With a world population of 5,423,000,000 people, there are about 900,000,000 people in India.

Science

Carbon 14 is radioactive. It takes 5,730 years for $\frac{1}{2}$ of the radioactive material to decay. If a sample has decayed so that only $\frac{1}{4}$ is radioactive, the sample is 11,460 years old.

KEY MATH IDEAS

Fraction products and quotients can be estimated by rounding fractions to the closest whole numbers.

Multiplying fractions is similar to multiplying whole numbers. To find the product, multiply the numerators and then multiply the denominators.

When you multiply by a fraction less than 1, the product is smaller than the number you started with.

When you divide by a fraction less than 1, the quotient is bigger than the number you started with.

Social Studies

Louis XIV, king of France from 1643 to 1715, had the longest documented reign of any monarch. Franklin Delano Roosevelt, U.S. President from 1933 to 1945, served as U.S. President the longest. His time as a national leader was $\frac{1}{6}$ that of Louis XIV.

CHAPTER PROJECT

Problem Solving

Understand
Plan
Solve
Look Back

In this project, you will interview senior citizens to determine how much they paid for common items when they were your age, and how those prices compare to the prices of things today. Begin by thinking about what they bought back then that you buy today.

Problem Solving Focus

Identifying Missing Information

When you plan a project, you are often told how the finished product should look. But you may not be told all the information you will need in order to complete that product. A critical problem-solving skill is being able to determine what information you need to complete a project or answer a question.

Identify what additional information would be needed to solve each problem. Some of the problems may not be missing any needed information.

1 Mr. and Mrs. Halloran and their children David and Jennie are planning to drive to Arches National Park. Mrs. Halloran suggests that they drive 400 miles each day. At this rate, how long will it take them to get there?

2 The Hallorans stopped at a restaurant and everyone ordered the all-you-can-eat shrimp. Mrs. Halloran had twice as much shrimp as David. Jennie had three more pieces than Mr. Halloran. Who ate the most shrimp?

3 At the park, Jennie bought a souvenir map for $2.25, three postcards at $0.50 each, and a key ring for $1.00. How much money did she have left?

4 David had to write a 500-word report about the trip for his Language Arts class. He wrote half of the report at the park, and half of what was left on the way home. How many words did he have to write to finish the report?

SECTION **7A**

Multiplying Fractions

▶ Industry Link ▶ www.mathsurf.com/6/ch7/recipes

A TASTE FROM THE NORTH PACIFIC

The four recipes below are all authentic recipes. One of the four is different than the other three. Can you tell which recipe it is?

Chicken-Fried Muskrat

Dressed muskrat
Marinade:
  1 quart water plus
  1 tablespoon salt
  Salt, pepper, paprika, to taste
Flour
Bacon fat
Sliced onions
1 cup sour cream

Sweet and Sour Porcupine

Legs of porcupine
2 sliced onions
1 cup cider vinegar
$^3/_4$ cup brown sugar
$^1/_2$ teaspoon nutmeg
Fat

Wallpaper Paste

4 cups flour
1 cup sugar
1 gallon warm water
1 quart cold water

Eskimo Ice Cream (Akutaq)

2 cups seal oil
Bowl of loose snow
$1^1/_2$ pounds of reindeer fat
Wild berries

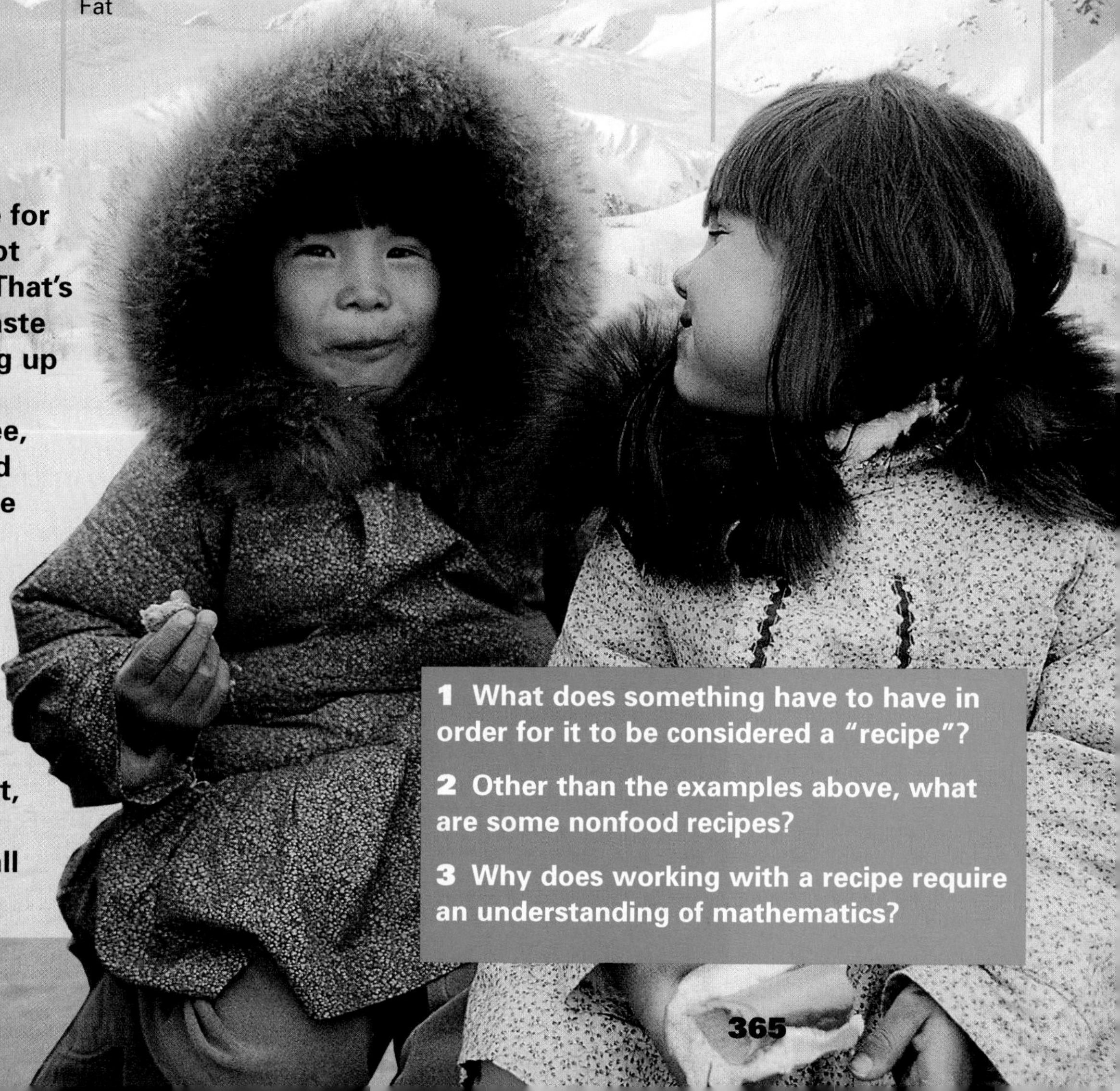

All the recipes are for food dishes, except for the third one. That's a recipe for the paste used when putting up wallpaper.

As you can see, recipes aren't used just for food. There are recipes for making candles, air fresheners, soap, paint, and cold cream. All recipes, whether they're food recipes or not, have one thing in common ... they all use mathematics.

1 What does something have to have in order for it to be considered a "recipe"?

2 Other than the examples above, what are some nonfood recipes?

3 Why does working with a recipe require an understanding of mathematics?

Estimation: Products and Quotients of Fractions

You'll Learn ...

■ to estimate products and quotients of fraction problems

... How It's Used

Farmers estimate fraction products when ordering feed for their animals.

▶ **Lesson Link** In the last chapter you learned to estimate sums and differences of fractions. Now you'll use these skills to estimate products and quotients of fractions. ◀

Explore | **Estimating Products of Fractions**

Bringing Home the Dough

Ramon plans to use this recipe to make bread dough ornaments to sell at the school fair.

Ornaments

$3\frac{1}{4}$ cups flour

1 cup salt

$1\frac{1}{2}$ cups water

Makes 25 snowflake ornaments

1. About how much flour, how much salt, and how much water will Ramon need to make each of the following numbers of snowflake ornaments?

  a. 50   **b.** 100   **c.** 70   **d.** 90   **e.** 12

2. Ramon will charge $4 for a snowflake ornament. A star ornament is $\frac{3}{4}$ the size of a snowflake. If Ramon charges $\frac{3}{4}$ the price of a snowflake, about how much should he charge? Explain.

3. A bell ornament is $2\frac{2}{3}$ times the size of a snowflake. If Ramon charges $2\frac{2}{3}$ times the price of a snowflake, about how much should he charge?

4. If Ramon only had 1 cup of flour, and he adjusted the recipe accordingly, about how many snowflake ornaments could he make? Explain.

Learn | **Estimation: Products and Quotients of Fractions**

You can use rounding to estimate products and quotients of fractions and mixed numbers.

• Round each factor to the nearest whole number.

• Multiply or divide the whole numbers.

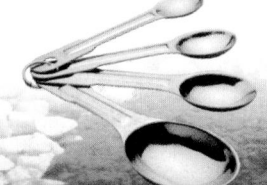

Examples

1 Estimate: $3\frac{1}{4} \times 5\frac{7}{8}$.

$\frac{1}{4} < \frac{1}{2}$, so $3\frac{1}{4}$ rounds down to 3.

$\frac{7}{8} > \frac{1}{2}$, so $5\frac{7}{8}$ rounds up to 6.

Estimate: $3 \times 6 = 18$.

2 Estimate: $8\frac{2}{3} \div 1\frac{1}{5}$.

$\frac{2}{3} > \frac{1}{2}$, so $8\frac{2}{3}$ rounds up to 9.

$\frac{1}{5} < \frac{1}{2}$, so $1\frac{1}{5}$ rounds down to 1.

Estimate: $9 \div 1 = 9$.

Remember

A fraction is less than $\frac{1}{2}$ if the numerator is less than half the denominator. **[Page 343]**

Try It

Estimate: **a.** $4\frac{3}{4} \times 3\frac{1}{6}$ **b.** $1\frac{1}{3} \times 2\frac{1}{2}$ **c.** $5\frac{2}{3} \div 1\frac{4}{5}$ **d.** $1\frac{1}{3} \div \frac{3}{4}$

When finding a product, if you round one number up, your result will be an *over*estimate.

When finding a quotient, if you round the dividend up, you will also get an overestimate. However, rounding the divisor up results in an *under*estimate. This is because the rounded number will divide the dividend into larger groups, so your estimate will have a smaller number of groups than the exact answer.

Example 3

A gardener wants to build a 36 ft fence using $3\frac{1}{2}$ ft long planks. About how many planks should the gardener buy to be sure there are enough?

Problem Solving TIP

You can also solve the problem by rewriting $3\frac{1}{2}$ as a decimal before you divide.

Estimate: $36 \div 3\frac{1}{2}$. To be sure there is enough wood, you should overestimate. Round the divisor *down*. This will give you a smaller number to divide by. As a result, the quotient will be greater: $36 \div 3 = 12$.

The gardener should buy 12 planks.

Check Your Understanding

1. When rounding fractions to the closest whole number, when do you round up?

2. Give a real-world circumstance with fractions where you should overestimate.

PRACTICE 7-1

Practice and Apply

Getting Started Round each mixed number to the nearest whole number.

1. $4\frac{2}{3}$ **2.** $3\frac{3}{7}$ **3.** $6\frac{1}{8}$ **4.** $5\frac{7}{10}$ **5.** $8\frac{1}{2}$ **6.** $8\frac{4}{8}$

Estimate.

7. $3\frac{1}{5} \times 4\frac{7}{8}$ **8.** $12\frac{1}{8} \div 6\frac{1}{3}$ **9.** $9\frac{1}{2} \times 4\frac{7}{8}$ **10.** $15\frac{1}{7} \div 2\frac{9}{10}$

11. $2\frac{2}{3} \times 3\frac{6}{7}$ **12.** $12\frac{9}{10} \div 6\frac{7}{8}$ **13.** $8\frac{3}{5} \times 7\frac{3}{4}$ **14.** $10\frac{2}{5} \div 5\frac{4}{13}$

15. $6\frac{3}{8} \times 10\frac{2}{5}$ **16.** $10\frac{4}{7} \div 5\frac{1}{2}$ **17.** $6\frac{8}{10} \times 5\frac{3}{9}$ **18.** $13\frac{4}{7} \div 3\frac{2}{7}$

19. $4\frac{1}{4} \times 7\frac{3}{13}$ **20.** $12\frac{2}{6} \div 4\frac{1}{3}$ **21.** $2\frac{1}{2} \times 4\frac{1}{9}$ **22.** $17\frac{5}{11} \div 3\frac{3}{10}$

23. $5\frac{2}{11} \times 8\frac{1}{10}$ **24.** $8\frac{5}{10} \div 3\frac{5}{6}$ **25.** $10\frac{2}{7} \times 3\frac{4}{9}$ **26.** $14\frac{6}{9} \div 6\frac{3}{8}$

27. $9\frac{5}{9} \times 2\frac{2}{9}$ **28.** $7\frac{5}{8} \div 2\frac{1}{4}$ **29.** $6\frac{1}{3} \times 1\frac{3}{11}$ **30.** $3\frac{2}{3} \div 1\frac{2}{4}$

31. **Test Prep** Which products are less than 10?

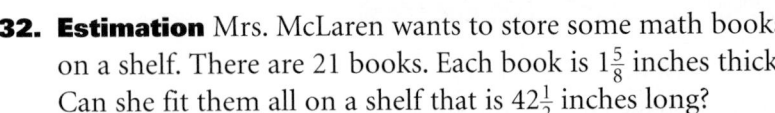

I. $1\frac{7}{8} \times 4\frac{5}{8}$ II. $6\frac{1}{2} \times 3\frac{1}{3}$ III. $2\frac{1}{3} \times 5\frac{1}{5}$

Ⓐ only I   Ⓑ only II   Ⓒ only III   Ⓓ I and III

32. **Estimation** Mrs. McLaren wants to store some math books on a shelf. There are 21 books. Each book is $1\frac{5}{8}$ inches thick. Can she fit them all on a shelf that is $42\frac{1}{2}$ inches long?

33. **History** Native Americans and the early European settlers used every part of the common swamp cattail as food. A recipe for cattail pancakes calls for $2\frac{2}{3}$ cups of cattail pollen. You have 6 cups of cattail pollen. Do you have enough to triple the recipe?

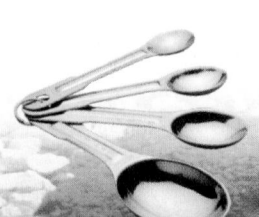

34. A plumber needs 15 pieces of pipe, each $4\frac{1}{4}$ feet long. Will 58 feet of pipe be enough?

35. **Social Studies** The population of Massachusetts in 1890 was $2\frac{1}{4}$ million. The population in 1990 was $6\frac{1}{6}$ million. About how many times larger was the population in 1990?

Boston, Massachusetts – 1890

Boston, Massachusetts – 1990

Problem Solving and Reasoning

36. **Critical Thinking** Use estimation to complete the table. Explain your reasoning.

Full Price	$3.73	$4.65	$6.99	$8.23
$\frac{1}{2}$ Price				
$\frac{3}{4}$ Price				

37. **Critical Thinking** Give five pairs of values for x and y so that $5\frac{x}{y}$ will round to 6 when rounded to the nearest whole number. What do all of your pairs of numbers have in common?

38. [Journal] In $6\frac{1}{4} \div 1\frac{1}{2}$, if you round only the first number up, you will get an overestimate. If you round only the second number up, you will get an underestimate. Explain why.

Mixed Review

Convert. *[Lesson 4-2]*

39. 8 m = ☐ cm   **40.** 126 L = ☐ mL   **41.** 976 mm = ☐ cm

42. 29 mL = ☐ L   **43.** 453 g = ☐ kg   **44.** 0.34 km = ☐ m

Tell whether the first number is divisible by the second. *[Lesson 5-1]*

45. 34, 9   **46.** 55, 5   **47.** 62, 4   **48.** 88, 11   **49.** 76, 2   **50.** 54, 3

51. 1520, 10   **52.** 63, 6   **53.** 50, 7   **54.** 32, 8   **55.** 72, 6   **56.** 5556, 5

Multiplying by a Whole Number

You'll Learn ...

■ to multiply whole numbers by fractions

... How It's Used

Zoologists multiply whole numbers and fractions when describing an animal's diet.

▶ **Lesson Link** In earlier lessons, you learned to multiply decimals by whole numbers. Now you'll multiply fractions by whole numbers. ◀

Explore | **Multiplying by a Whole Number**

A Strip in Time

Materials: Colored pencils

Multiplying a Fraction by a Whole Number

- Draw a number of strips equal to the whole number.

- Divide the strips into equal sections. The number of sections should be equal to the fraction denominator.

- In each strip, color in the number of sections equal to the numerator.

- Describe the number modeled.

$$= 3 \times \frac{4}{5}$$

1. Model these problems.

   a. $2 \times \frac{2}{5}$ **b.** $7 \times \frac{1}{2}$ **c.** $\frac{2}{3} \times 5$ **d.** $4 \times \frac{5}{9}$

   e. $\frac{4}{5} \times 3$ **f.** $\frac{2}{7} \times 1$ **g.** $6 \times \frac{2}{2}$ **h.** $\frac{1}{8} \times 8$

2. Why does your answer have the same denominator as the fraction in the problem? Why does your answer have a different numerator?

3. Is your answer bigger than the whole number you started with or smaller than the whole number you started with? Why?

Learn | **Multiplying by a Whole Number**

You can model the product 3×5 by showing 3 sets with 5 objects in each set. In the same way, you can model the product $3 \times \frac{5}{6}$ by showing 3 sets with $\frac{5}{6}$ in each set.

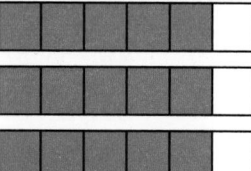

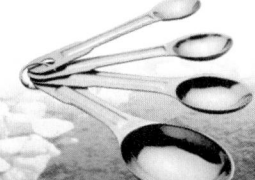

To multiply a fraction or mixed number by a whole number, write both factors as fractions. Then write the product of the numerators over the product of the denominators. Simplify if necessary.

Example 1

A recipe for hummingbird food calls for $1\frac{5}{8}$ cups of sugar. How much sugar should you use to triple the recipe?

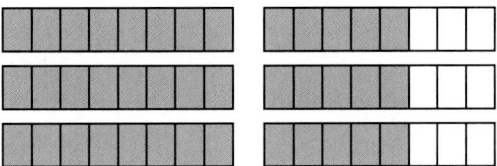

Multiply: $3 \times 1\frac{5}{8}$

$3 \times 1\frac{5}{8} = \frac{3}{1} \times \frac{13}{8}$ Write the factors as fractions.

$\qquad = \frac{3 \times 13}{1 \times 8}$ Multiply the numerators. Multiply the denominators.

$\qquad = \frac{39}{8}$ or $4\frac{7}{8}$ Simplify.

You should use $4\frac{7}{8}$ cups of sugar.

Some problems ask you to find the fractional part of a whole number. These problems can be solved using multiplication with fractions.

Example 2

About $\frac{2}{3}$ of the 360 students at Kensington Middle School belong to an after-school club or activity. How many students is this?

$360 \times \frac{2}{3} = \frac{360}{1} \times \frac{2}{3}$ Write the factors as fractions.

$\qquad = \frac{360 \times 2}{1 \times 3}$ Multiply the numerators. Multiply the denominators.

$\qquad = \frac{720}{3}$ or 240 Simplify.

240 students participate in a club or activity.

Problem Solving TIP

In math problems, the word *of* frequently suggests multiplication.

Try It

Simplify.

a. $4 \times \frac{2}{3}$ **b.** $3 \times 1\frac{3}{4}$ **c.** $\frac{1}{2}$ of 16 **d.** $\frac{5}{6}$ of 30

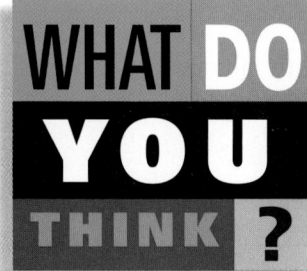

WHAT DO YOU THINK?

Lauren and Skye are making wallpaper paste. They have $2\frac{3}{4}$ cups of sugar, and they want to adjust the recipe to use all of it. They need to determine how much flour to use in the adjusted recipe.

Wallpaper Paste

4 cups flour
1 cup sugar
1 gallon warm water
1 quart cold water

Lauren thinks ...

I'll multiply the 4 cups of flour by $2\frac{3}{4}$ using the Distributive Property.

First, I'll multiply 4 times the whole number in $2\frac{3}{4}$. $\qquad 4 \times 2 = \qquad 8$

Next, I'll multiply 4 times the fraction in $2\frac{3}{4}$. $\qquad 4 \times \dfrac{3}{4} = +\underline{3}$

Now I'll add the results. $\qquad\qquad\qquad\qquad\qquad\qquad 11$

We need 11 cups of flour.

Skye thinks ...

I'll multiply by writing both factors as fractions.

$$4 \times 2\frac{3}{4} = \frac{4}{1} \times \frac{11}{4}$$
$$= \frac{4 \times 11}{1 \times 4}$$
$$= \frac{44}{4} = 11$$

We need 11 cups of flour.

What do you think?

1. Why did Lauren add $8 + 3$ instead of multiplying 8×3?

2. Which method is easier to use mentally? Explain.

Check | Your Understanding

1. Is the product of a whole number and a proper fraction always larger than either number? Explain.

2. Are the products $12 \times \dfrac{3}{5}$ and $\dfrac{3}{5} \times 12$ equal? Explain.

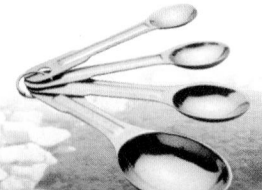

7-2 Exercises and Applications

Practice and Apply

Getting Started Write the multiplication problem each model represents.

1.

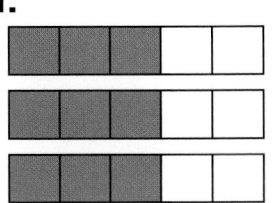

2.

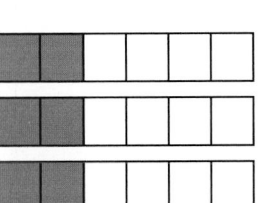

3.

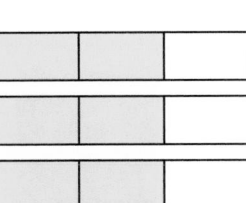

4.

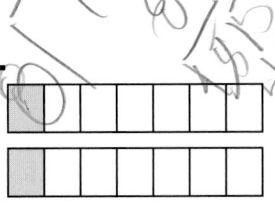

Simplify.

5. $\frac{1}{3} \times 2$

6. $\frac{1}{6} \times 8$

7. $2 \times \frac{3}{10}$

8. $3\frac{3}{8} \times 5$

9. $10 \times \frac{2}{3}$

10. $\frac{2}{7} \times 7$

11. $\frac{2}{3} \times 3$

12. $4 \times \frac{5}{7}$

13. $\frac{1}{4} \times 6$

14. $3 \times \frac{3}{11}$

15. $\frac{3}{5} \times 11$

16. $\frac{4}{8} \times 6$

17. $5 \times \frac{4}{9}$

18. $\frac{3}{7} \times 9$

19. $9 \times \frac{6}{10}$

20. $1 \times \frac{11}{12}$

21. $3 \times 1\frac{7}{12}$

22. $4\frac{5}{9} \times 12$

23. $7 \times 1\frac{5}{6}$

24. $12 \times 2\frac{10}{11}$

25. $2\frac{2}{5} \times 4$

26. $6 \times \frac{3}{7}$

27. $8 \times 3\frac{3}{8}$

28. $5\frac{2}{7} \times 10$

29. Health Complete the table for calories in orange juice.

Servings	$\frac{1}{4}$	$\frac{1}{2}$	$\frac{3}{4}$	1	$1\frac{1}{2}$	2
Ounces				8		
Calories				110		

30. **Test Prep** Andrew has read $\frac{3}{4}$ of his 304-page book. How many pages has he read?

Ⓐ 76   Ⓑ 152   Ⓒ 228   Ⓓ None of these

31. History In colonial times, houses in New England were often painted with a glazed whitewash. One gallon of whitewash includes $\frac{3}{4}$ lb rice and $\frac{1}{2}$ lb sugar. How much of these ingredients are needed for 3 gallons of whitewash?

Science Use the Life Span graph for Exercises 32 and 33.

32. The maximum recorded life span for a baboon is $2\frac{1}{4}$ times the average. What is the maximum recorded life span?

33. The maximum recorded life span of a domestic cat is $2\frac{1}{3}$ times the average life span. What is the maximum recorded life span?

Average Life Span of Animals

Problem Solving and Reasoning

34. Journal Explain how you can tell without multiplying if the product of $\frac{9}{10}$ and 15 is more than 15 or less than 15.

35. Critical Thinking Which does *not* have the same product as $6 \times 2\frac{1}{2}$? Explain.

    Ⓐ $6 \times \frac{5}{2}$ Ⓑ $\frac{6}{1} \times \frac{2}{5}$ Ⓒ $2\frac{1}{2} \times 6$ Ⓓ 6×2.5

36. Critical Thinking Castile soap is named for the kingdom of Castile in Spain where the soap was first produced. To make about 36 bars, 1 pound 9 ounces of olive oil is needed. If a pound of olive oil costs $8.00, how much does the olive oil for this recipe cost? Explain.

Mixed Review

Convert. *[Lesson 4-3]*

37. 1176 inches = ☐ feet   **38.** 38 feet = ☐ inches   **39.** 96 inches = ☐ feet

40. 102 feet = ☐ inches   **41.** 204 inches = ☐ feet   **42.** 48 feet = ☐ inches

Find the prime factorization. *[Lesson 5-2]*

    43. 63   **44.** 1060   **45.** 17   **46.** 99   **47.** 57   **48.** 34

Multiplying by a Fraction

▶ **Lesson Link**   In the last lesson, you learned to multiply fractions and mixed numbers by whole numbers. Now you'll multiply fractions and mixed numbers by fractions. ◀

Explore   Multiplying by a Fraction

Inner Sections

Materials: Colored pencils

Multiplying a Fraction by a Fraction

$$\frac{2}{5} \times \frac{3}{4} = \frac{6}{20}$$

- Draw a rectangle. Divide it vertically into equal sections. There should be as many sections as the denominator of the first number.

- Divide the rectangle horizontally into equal sections. There should be as many sections as the denominator of the second number.

- Color in a number of vertical strips equal to the numerator in the first number.

- Use a different color to shade a number of horizontal strips equal to the numerator in the second number.

- Describe the area where both colors overlap.

1. Model these problems.

a. $\frac{1}{2} \times \frac{1}{3}$ **b.** $\frac{1}{4} \times \frac{2}{5}$ **c.** $\frac{5}{6} \times \frac{2}{3}$

d. $\frac{2}{7} \times \frac{2}{7}$ **e.** $\frac{1}{5} \times \frac{3}{5}$ **f.** $\frac{1}{2} \times \frac{5}{8}$

2. Describe the pattern between the numerators in the problem and the numerator in the answer.

3. Describe the pattern between the denominators in the problem and the denominator in the answer.

4. Is your answer bigger or smaller than both of the fractions you started with? Why?

Learn | Multiplying by a Fraction

When adding fractions with unlike denominators, you must first rename the fractions so they have like denominators. You do not need to do this for multiplication. To multiply with fractions, write both factors as fractions. Then write the product of the numerators over the product of the denominators.

Example 1

A recipe for dying wool calls for $\frac{1}{4}$ pound of tea leaves for each pound of wool. Find the amount of leaves needed to dye $\frac{2}{3}$ pound of wool.

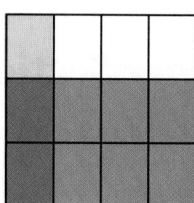

$$\frac{1}{4} \times \frac{2}{3} = \frac{1 \times 2}{4 \times 3}$$ 　Multiply the numerators.
Multiply the denominators.

$$= \frac{2}{12} \text{ or } \frac{1}{6}$$ 　Simplify.

You need $\frac{1}{6}$ pound of tea leaves.

Some problems may ask you to find the fractional part of a fraction. You can solve these problems using multiplication.

Example 2

Mr. Hamilton bought $2\frac{1}{2}$ gallons of milk. He used half of it to make ice cream. How much did he use?

$$2\frac{1}{2} \times \frac{1}{2} = \frac{5}{2} \times \frac{1}{2}$$ 　Write the mixed number as a fraction.

$$= \frac{5 \times 1}{2 \times 2}$$ 　Multiply the numerators. Multiply the denominators.

$$= \frac{5}{4} \text{ or } 1\frac{1}{4}$$ 　Simplify.

He used $1\frac{1}{4}$ gallons of milk.

Try It

Multiply.

a. $\frac{4}{5} \times \frac{3}{7}$ 　　**b.** $\frac{8}{9}$ of $1\frac{1}{2}$ 　　**c.** $1\frac{2}{3} \times 1\frac{3}{7}$ 　　**d.** $\frac{1}{9}$ of $\frac{2}{5}$

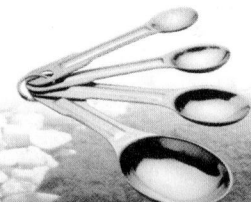

Check Your Understanding

1. Give two fractions whose product is $\frac{8}{15}$. Explain your reasoning.

2. How is multiplying two fractions different from adding two fractions?

7-3 Exercises and Applications

Practice and Apply

Getting Started Write the multiplication problem each model represents.

1. 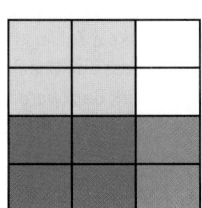 2. 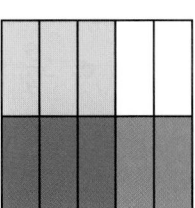 3. 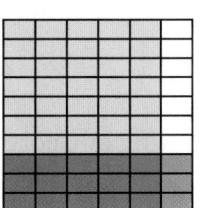 4.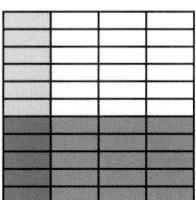

Find each product.

5. $\frac{3}{7} \times \frac{2}{3}$

6. $\frac{5}{9} \times \frac{1}{2}$

7. $\frac{3}{4} \times \frac{7}{10}$

8. $\frac{1}{5} \times \frac{1}{5}$

9. $\frac{11}{15} \times 4\frac{6}{7}$

10. $7\frac{1}{3} \times \frac{7}{9}$

11. $\frac{13}{17} \times \frac{6}{11}$

12. $\frac{1}{9} \times \frac{7}{13}$

13. $\frac{4}{5} \times 10\frac{3}{8}$

14. $6\frac{2}{5} \times \frac{9}{11}$

15. $\frac{13}{20} \times \frac{1}{3}$

16. $\frac{2}{5} \times \frac{10}{11}$

17. $\frac{9}{13} \times 2\frac{9}{13}$

18. $\frac{2}{5} \times \frac{7}{10}$

19. $\frac{4}{7} \times 2\frac{3}{8}$

20. $5\frac{5}{7} \times 5\frac{8}{9}$

21. $\frac{11}{21} \times \frac{1}{2}$

22. $9\frac{2}{9} \times 3\frac{4}{9}$

23. $\frac{1}{8} \times \frac{3}{8}$

24. $\frac{4}{5} \times \frac{3}{8}$

25. $\frac{6}{11} \times \frac{6}{11}$

26. $8\frac{2}{5} \times \frac{3}{7}$

27. $\frac{4}{7} \times 4\frac{9}{14}$

28. $\frac{5}{8} \times \frac{8}{9}$

29. **Science** An alligator is $12\frac{1}{2}$ feet long. Its tail is half as long as its total length. How long is the alligator's tail?

30. **Test Prep** Which of these expressions has the greatest product?

    Ⓐ $\frac{4}{5} \times 4$ Ⓑ $\frac{4}{5} \times 2\frac{1}{2}$ Ⓒ $\frac{4}{5} \times \frac{4}{5}$ Ⓓ $\frac{4}{5} \times 3$

31. The recipe for a pint of paste includes $\frac{1}{4}$ cup sugar, $\frac{1}{4}$ cup flour, $1\frac{3}{4}$ cups water, and $\frac{1}{4}$ teaspoon cinnamon oil. How much sugar, flour, and water is needed to make a half pint of paste?

32. The distance between Tad's house and his school is $\frac{2}{3}$ of a mile. If he walks halfway to school, how far has he walked?

Problem Solving and Reasoning

33. **Choose a Strategy** To make $\frac{3}{4}$ cup of powdered-milk paint, you mix $\frac{1}{2}$ cup of powdered nonfat milk and $\frac{1}{2}$ cup of water. Adjust this recipe to make one whole cup of paint. Explain your method.

34. **Critical Thinking** Without using multiplication, explain whether the product is greater than or less than the second factor.

   a. $\frac{2}{3} \times \frac{5}{8}$ **b.** $\frac{9}{6} \times \frac{1}{2}$ **c.** $\frac{1}{4} \times \frac{12}{5}$ **d.** $5\frac{3}{4} \times 5\frac{3}{4}$

35. **Critical Thinking** A painting of George Washington by Gilbert Stuart is $28\frac{1}{2}$ inches long and $23\frac{5}{8}$ inches wide. The museum wants to make a print of the painting that will be half as long and half as wide. What will the dimensions of the print be? What are the areas of the print and the painting?

> **Problem Solving**
> ## STRATEGIES
> - Look for a Pattern
> - Make an Organized List
> - Make a Table
> - Guess and Check
> - Work Backward
> - Use Logical Reasoning
> - Draw a Diagram
> - Solve a Simpler Problem

Mixed Review

Convert. *[Lesson 4-3]*

36. 1 mile = ☐ feet   **37.** 10,560 feet = ☐ inches   **38.** 6 miles = ☐ feet

39. 15,840 feet = ☐ inches   **40.** 10 miles = ☐ feet   **41.** 5280 feet = ☐ inches

Find the LCM of each pair. *[Lesson 5-3]*

42. 99, 3   **43.** 6, 3   **44.** 2, 45   **45.** 8, 4   **46.** 16, 24   **47.** 5, 7

48. 14, 4   **49.** 18, 8   **50.** 6, 10   **51.** 29, 1   **52.** 27, 6   **53.** 3, 9

Project Progress

Make a list of at least 15 things you buy today that you think senior citizens purchased when they were your age. Then, interview your senior citizen and record the amounts paid for each item. Make sure that you collect data about at least 10 items.

> **Problem Solving**
>
> Understand
> Plan
> Solve
> Look Back

In this section, you've learned to multiply fractions and mixed numbers. You've also seen how this skill can be used to adjust the sizes of recipes. Now you'll use what you've learned to decide how much a restaurant owner should charge for items on the menu.

A Taste from the North Pacific

The appetizer menu for Li's Chinese Restaurant is shown here. Each "order" consists of several pieces of the same food.

Appetizers

2 Egg Rolls	$3.00
5 Fried Won Ton	$2.00
4 Barbecued Spareribs	$6.00
6 Fried Prawns	$4.50
9 Pot Stickers	$5.25

Mr. Li has decided to change the number of pieces he serves in an order. The new numbers are shown here but the prices are missing.

Appetizers

3 Egg Rolls
4 Fried Won Ton
6 Barbecued Spareribs
8 Fried Prawns
6 Pot Stickers

1. Express the new number of pieces in an order as a fraction of the old number. Write each fraction in lowest terms. (For example, the new egg roll order is $\frac{3}{2}$ as large as the old order.)

2. Estimate the new prices Mr. Li should charge.

3. Find the exact new prices by multiplying the fractions you found in Question 1 by the old prices.

4. Explain a method for finding the new prices that doesn't involve fractions.

REVIEW 7A

Estimate each product or quotient.

1. $8\frac{7}{8} \div 3\frac{1}{3}$

2. $8\frac{9}{10} \times 2\frac{7}{8}$

3. $9\frac{3}{5} \times 2\frac{7}{8}$

4. $15\frac{1}{7} \div 2\frac{9}{10}$

5. $1\frac{5}{6} \div 1\frac{1}{6}$

6. $15\frac{2}{3} \div 4\frac{3}{7}$

7. $10\frac{4}{5} \times 1\frac{3}{9}$

8. $12\frac{1}{6} \times 3\frac{5}{8}$

Measurement For Exercises 9 and 10, use the cold cream recipe.

9. For each ingredient, find the amount you would use to triple the cold cream recipe.

10. For each ingredient, find the amount you would use to make 6 times as much cold cream.

Homemade Cold Cream

1 ounce bowstring wax*
$6\frac{1}{2}$ tablespoons mineral oil
3 tablespoons water
$\frac{1}{4}$ teaspoon borax

*Used for archery.
Found in sports specialty stores.

11. Boneless chicken breasts are selling for $2.99 a pound. Can you buy $1\frac{3}{4}$ pounds for $6?

12. Kele bought $3\frac{1}{4}$ pound of trail mix. On his hike, he ate $\frac{2}{3}$ of it. How much trail mix did he eat?

13. **Communicate** An urban planner designed a bridge that was $3\frac{1}{3}$ miles long. The construction manager reported that $\frac{1}{2}$ of the bridge was complete. How many miles of bridge had been completed?

Test Prep

If a test question asks you to give an answer in lowest terms, you can eliminate any answers that are not in lowest terms.

14. What is $\frac{3}{4} \times \frac{10}{12}$ in lowest terms?

Ⓐ $\frac{5}{8}$

Ⓑ $\frac{15}{24}$

Ⓒ $\frac{30}{48}$

Ⓓ $1\frac{18}{30}$

15. What is $\frac{9}{10} \times \frac{2}{6}$ in lowest terms?

Ⓐ $\frac{18}{60}$

Ⓑ $\frac{9}{30}$

Ⓒ $\frac{6}{20}$

Ⓓ Not here

364.4 Smoots and One Ear

In 1958, several students at the Massachusetts Institute of Technology (M.I.T.) measured the length of the Massachusetts Avenue Bridge. However, they didn't measure the length in feet, yards, or meters. Their unit of measurement was a fellow student named Oliver R. Smoot, Jr.

They laid Oliver down on the sidewalk and painted a mark to show his height. They repeated the process over 300 times until they had measured the entire bridge.

In 1989, the city rebuilt the bridge, but they preserved the Smoot. A plaque on the bridge now reads:

> THIS PLAQUE PLACED IN HONOR OF
>
> ## THE SMOOT
>
> WHICH JOINED THE ANGSTROM, METER AND LIGHT YEAR AS STANDARDS OF LENGTH, WHEN IN OCTOBER 1958 THE SPAN OF THIS BRIDGE WAS MEASURED, USING THE BODY OF OLIVER REED SMOOT, M.I.T. '62 AND FOUND TO BE PRECISELY *364.4 SMOOTS AND ONE EAR*
>
> COMMEMORATED AT OUR 25TH REUNION
>
> JUNE 6, 1987
>
> M.I.T. CLASS OF 1962

There are many unusual and interesting measurements used in the world. Like the Smoot, they may not be well known. But they all involve mathematics.

1 What other kinds of units could the students have used to measure the bridge?

2 When might it be better to use a made-up unit as opposed to a well-known unit?

Dividing Whole Numbers by Fractions

You'll Learn ...

■ to divide a whole number by a fraction

... How It's Used

Structural engineers divide whole numbers by fractions when building tunnels.

Vocabulary

reciprocal

▶ **Lesson Link** In the last section, you learned to multiply whole numbers by fractions. Now you'll divide whole numbers by fractions. ◀

Explore Dividing Whole Numbers by Fractions

Circles and Strips Forever

Dividing a Whole Number by a Fraction

$4 \div \frac{2}{3} = 6$

- Draw a number of strips equal to the whole number.
- Divide the strips into equal pieces. The number of pieces in each strip should be equal to the fraction denominator.
- Circle groups of equal pieces. The number of pieces in each circled group should equal the numerator.
- Describe the number of groups circled.

1. Model these problems.

a. $6 \div \frac{2}{3}$ **b.** $7 \div \frac{1}{2}$ **c.** $5 \div \frac{5}{6}$ **d.** $4 \div \frac{3}{6}$ **e.** $2 \div \frac{2}{7}$

2. When you divide a whole number by a fraction less than 1, is the quotient larger or smaller than the original whole number? Why?

3. Will $3 \div \frac{2}{5}$ have a whole-number answer? Explain.

Learn Dividing Whole Numbers by Fractions

You can think of division as taking a given amount and breaking it down into groups of a certain size. For example, 6 ÷ 2 can be modeled as 6 loaves of bread divided into groups of 2. The quotient, 3, is the number of groups you have.

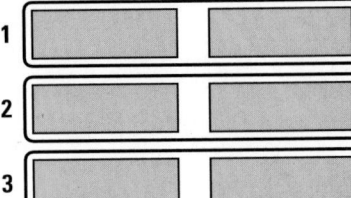

You can think of dividing by fractions in the same way. For example, $6 \div \frac{2}{3}$ is the same as 6 loaves of bread divided into groups of $\frac{2}{3}$. The number of groups you have, 9, is the quotient.

Notice that to find the answer, you first found the number of thirds by multiplying the number of loaves, 6, by the denominator, 3. Then, you divided the number of thirds by the numerator, 2.

$$6 \div \frac{2}{3} = 6 \times 3 \div 2 = 9$$

Dividing by a fraction is the same as multiplying by its **reciprocal**. Reciprocals are numbers whose numerators and denominators have been switched. When two numbers are reciprocals, their product is 1.

Remember

The numerator is the number on top of a fraction. The denominator is the number on the bottom. **[Page 289]**

Dividing

$$6 \div \frac{2}{3} = 9$$

Multiplying by reciprocal

$$6 \times \frac{3}{2} = \frac{6}{1} \times \frac{3}{2}$$

$$= \frac{18}{2}$$

$$= 9$$

Examples

1 Divide: $2 \div \frac{3}{4}$

$2 \div \frac{3}{4} = \frac{2}{1} \times \frac{4}{3}$ Multiply by the reciprocal of the fraction.

$\qquad = \frac{2 \times 4}{1 \times 3}$

$\qquad = \frac{8}{3}$ or $2\frac{2}{3}$

2 1 *nail* $= \frac{9}{4}$ in. of cloth. Find the length of 5 in. of cloth in nails.

$5 \div \frac{9}{4} = \frac{5}{1} \times \frac{4}{9}$ Multiply by the reciprocal.

$\qquad = \frac{20}{9}$ or $2\frac{2}{9}$ Simplify.

A 5-inch piece of cloth is $2\frac{2}{9}$ nails long.

DID YOU KNOW?

Three measurements used primarily for cloth include the *nail*, the *finger*, and the *span*. A *finger* is equal to $4\frac{1}{2}$ inches. A *span* is equal to 9 inches.

Try It

Divide.   **a.** $4 \div \frac{3}{5}$ **b.** $1 \div \frac{4}{7}$ **c.** $10 \div \frac{17}{4}$ **d.** $3 \div \frac{3}{5}$

Peter and Erica have a recipe that makes 9 quarts of punch. They want to know how many $\frac{3}{4}$-quart (3-cup) servings the recipe will make.

Peter thinks ...

I'll use mental math.

How many groups of $\frac{3}{4}$ quart are in 9 quarts?

Every whole quart has one $\frac{3}{4}$ in it, plus $\frac{1}{4}$ left over.

In 9 quarts, there are nine $\frac{3}{4}$ quarts, which is 9 servings.

There are nine $\frac{1}{4}$ quarts left over. They can be regrouped as three $\frac{3}{4}$ quarts, which is another 3 servings.

That equals 9 + 3 or 12 groups of $\frac{3}{4}$ quart.

We will have 12 servings.

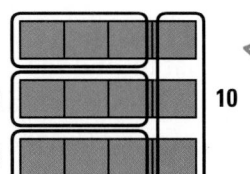
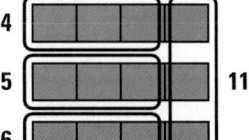
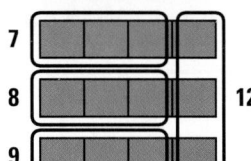

Erica thinks ...

I'll divide 9 by $\frac{3}{4}$. To do that, I'll multiply $\frac{9}{1}$ by the reciprocal of $\frac{3}{4}$.

$$9 \div \frac{3}{4} = \frac{9}{1} \times \frac{4}{3} = 12$$

We will have 12 servings.

What do you think?

1. Whose method is easier to use without paper and pencil? Explain.

2. How could you find the answer by writing 9 quarts as $\frac{36}{4}$ quarts?

Check Your Understanding

1. How could you use the "multiply by the reciprocal" rule to divide 20 by 5?

2. If you divide a whole number by a proper fraction, is the quotient larger or smaller than the whole number? Explain.

Practice and Apply

Getting Started State the reciprocal.

1. $\frac{5}{7}$ **2.** $\frac{1}{2}$ **3.** $\frac{2}{9}$ **4.** $\frac{10}{14}$ **5.** $\frac{1}{4}$ **6.** $\frac{4}{5}$

Simplify.

7. $6 \div \frac{2}{3}$ **8.** $2 \div \frac{3}{5}$ **9.** $3 \div \frac{6}{7}$ **10.** $1 \div 1\frac{1}{2}$

11. $9 \div \frac{4}{5}$ **12.** $7 \div \frac{6}{5}$ **13.** $4 \div 3\frac{5}{8}$ **14.** $5 \div \frac{1}{4}$

15. $10 \div 7\frac{2}{3}$ **16.** $8 \div 8\frac{7}{8}$ **17.** $3 \div \frac{10}{11}$ **18.** $5 \div \frac{9}{2}$

19. $16 \div \frac{2}{5}$ **20.** $7 \div 6\frac{3}{4}$ **21.** $8 \div 2\frac{1}{6}$ **22.** $2 \div 4\frac{2}{7}$

23. $1 \div 3\frac{5}{9}$ **24.** $4 \div 1\frac{1}{2}$ **25.** $9 \div \frac{6}{7}$ **26.** $6 \div \frac{8}{12}$

27. $11 \div \frac{13}{2}$ **28.** $10 \div 9\frac{8}{9}$ **29.** $3 \div 11\frac{1}{3}$ **30.** $7 \div 2\frac{3}{8}$

31. **Test Prep** Which two expressions have the same quotient as $6 \div 1\frac{3}{4}$?

I. $\frac{6}{1} \div \frac{7}{4}$ II. $\frac{6}{1} \times \frac{7}{4}$ III. $\frac{6}{1} \div \frac{4}{7}$ IV. $\frac{6}{1} \times \frac{4}{7}$

Ⓐ I and II   Ⓑ I and IV

Ⓒ III and II   Ⓓ III and IV

32. **Science** $\frac{4}{5}$ of a cubic foot of copper weighs 440 pounds. What is the weight of 1 cubic foot of copper?

33. **Social Studies** As a result of the 1990 census, Pennsylvania has 21 seats in the House of Representatives. This is $\frac{7}{10}$ as many seats as Texas has. How many seats does Texas have?

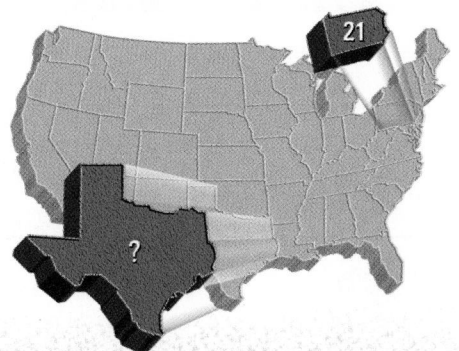

Problem Solving and Reasoning

34.  **Journal** Explain how you can tell if two numbers are reciprocals of each other.

35. Critical Thinking This recipe makes 1 batch of cookies. About how many batches can you make if you change the recipe to include the following? Explain your answers.

   a. A 2-pound bag of flour? (1 cup $= \frac{1}{4}$ pound)

   b. A pound of margarine? (1 cup $= \frac{1}{2}$ pound)

   c. A 4-pound bag of white sugar? (1 cup $= \frac{1}{2}$ pound)

36. Communicate Is $4 \div \frac{2}{5}$ the same as $\frac{2}{5} \div 4$? Explain your reasoning.

37. Critical Thinking A *ream* of paper is 500 sheets. A *quire* of paper is $\frac{1}{20}$ of a ream. Monique wanted to know how many sheets of paper were in a quire. She calculated $500 \div \frac{1}{20} = 10,000$, and decided a quire of paper was 10,000 sheets. Is her answer reasonable? Explain.

Chocolate Chip Cookies

$2\frac{1}{4}$ cups flour
1 teaspoon baking soda
1 teaspoon salt
1 cup margarine
$\frac{3}{4}$ cup white sugar

$\frac{1}{4}$ cup packed brown sugar
1 teaspoon vanilla extract
2 eggs
2 cups chocolate chips

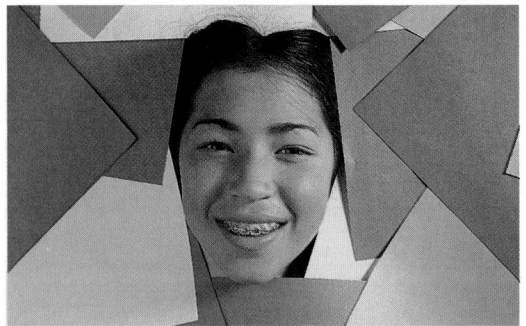

Mixed Review

Convert. *[Lesson 4-3]*

38. 144 ounces = ☐ pounds   **39.** 56 pounds = ☐ ounces   **40.** 80 ounces = ☐ pounds

41. 100 gallons = ☐ quarts   **42.** 64 quarts = ☐ gallons   **43.** 40 gallons = ☐ quarts

For each fraction, draw a model. *[Lesson 5-4]*

44. $\frac{1}{4}$ **45.** $\frac{7}{8}$ **46.** $\frac{4}{7}$ **47.** $\frac{80}{100}$ **48.** $\frac{9}{15}$ **49.** $\frac{5}{7}$

Project Progress

Choose 10 of the items from your list. Make a chart detailing how much each item cost when your senior citizen was your age, and how much it costs today. Estimate the fraction or mixed number you would need to multiply the old price by to get the current price.

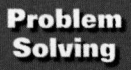

Problem Solving

Understand
Plan
Solve
Look Back

Dividing Fractions by Fractions

▶ **Lesson Link**   In the last lesson, you learned to divide whole numbers by fractions. Now you'll divide fractions by fractions. ◀

Explore   Dividing Fractions by Fractions

Wish Upon a Bar

Materials: Fraction Bars®

Dividing a Fraction by a Fraction

- Using a Fraction Bar®, draw and label the first fraction.

- Under that, use a Fraction Bar® to draw as many models of the second fraction as will fit.

- Describe the number of models below the first fraction.

$\frac{2}{3} \div \frac{1}{12} = 8$

$\frac{1}{12}$

1. Model each problem.

   a. $\frac{3}{6} \div \frac{1}{12}$ **b.** $\frac{1}{2} \div \frac{1}{4}$ **c.** $\frac{2}{3} \div \frac{1}{6}$ **d.** $\frac{2}{4} \div \frac{2}{12}$

2. When you divide a fraction by a fraction less than 1, why is the answer bigger than the fraction you started with?

3. How is dividing a fraction by a fraction similar to dividing a whole number by a fraction?

4. Can you use Fraction Bars® to divide $\frac{1}{2} \div \frac{1}{5}$? Explain.

You'll Learn ...

■ to divide a fraction by a fraction or a whole number

... How It's Used

Choreographers divide fractions by fractions when fitting a dance routine to a particular tempo of music.

Learn   Dividing Fractions by Fractions

When you divide a whole number by a fraction, you get the same result as if you had multiplied the whole number by the fraction's reciprocal. This is also true when you divide a fraction by a fraction.

Dividing   Multiplying by Reciprocal

$\frac{6}{7} \div \frac{3}{7} = 2$ $\frac{6}{7} \times \frac{7}{3} = \frac{42}{21}$ or 2

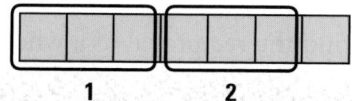

1   2

► History Link

The term *furlong* originated in the Middle Ages. The furlong was originally a "furrow long," the length of a plowed strip of land on a standard-size field.

Example 1

Horse races are measured in *furlongs* (1 furlong $= \frac{1}{8}$ mi). The Kentucky Derby is $1\frac{1}{4}$ mi long. How long is the Kentucky Derby in furlongs?

$$1\frac{1}{4} \div \frac{1}{8} = \frac{5}{4} \div \frac{1}{8} \qquad \text{Write the numbers as fractions.}$$

$$= \frac{5}{4} \times \frac{8}{1} \qquad \text{Multiply by the reciprocal.}$$

$$= 10$$

The Kentucky Derby is 10 furlongs long.

When dividing a fraction by a whole number, you can write the whole number as a fraction with 1 as its denominator. You can then multiply the fraction by the reciprocal of the whole number.

Example 2

Remember

You can rewrite a fraction in lowest terms when the numerator and the denominator share a common factor other than 1.
[Page 294]

What is $\frac{3}{5} \div 6$?

$$\frac{3}{5} \div 6 = \frac{3}{5} \div \frac{6}{1} \qquad \text{Write the whole number as a fraction with a denominator of 1.}$$

$$= \frac{3}{5} \times \frac{1}{6} \qquad \text{Multiply by the reciprocal of } \frac{6}{1}.$$

$$= \frac{3}{30} \text{ or } \frac{1}{10} \qquad \text{Simplify.}$$

Try It

Divide. **a.** $\frac{4}{5} \div \frac{5}{8}$ **b.** $\frac{3}{7} \div \frac{2}{7}$ **c.** $\frac{1}{5} \div 2$ **d.** $\frac{2}{5} \div 10$

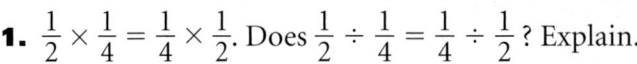

Check | Your Understanding

1. $\frac{1}{2} \times \frac{1}{4} = \frac{1}{4} \times \frac{1}{2}$. Does $\frac{1}{2} \div \frac{1}{4} = \frac{1}{4} \div \frac{1}{2}$? Explain.

2. If you find the reciprocal of a whole number, what will the numerator of that reciprocal be equal to?

Practice and Apply

Getting Started Write the division problem that each model represents.

1.

$\frac{1}{3}$	$\frac{1}{3}$	

| $\frac{1}{6}$ | $\frac{1}{6}$ | $\frac{1}{6}$ | $\frac{1}{6}$ |

2.

| $\frac{1}{5}$ | $\frac{1}{5}$ | $\frac{1}{5}$ |

$\frac{1}{10}$

3.

$\frac{1}{3}$	

| $\frac{2}{12}$ | $\frac{2}{12}$ |

4.

| $\frac{1}{4}$ | $\frac{1}{4}$ |

| $\frac{1}{6}$ | $\frac{1}{6}$ | $\frac{1}{6}$ |

Simplify.

5. $\frac{6}{15} \div \frac{3}{3}$

6. $\frac{1}{3} \div 6\frac{1}{4}$

7. $\frac{7}{8} \div \frac{1}{8}$

8. $\frac{6}{7} \div \frac{2}{7}$

9. $\frac{15}{16} \div \frac{3}{4}$

10. $\frac{1}{4} \div \frac{1}{2}$

11. $\frac{5}{7} \div 6\frac{3}{4}$

12. $\frac{1}{2} \div \frac{2}{3}$

13. $\frac{2}{3} \div 9\frac{4}{3}$

14. $1\frac{1}{2} \div \frac{1}{2}$

15. $2\frac{1}{2} \div 8$

16. $2\frac{7}{8} \div 1\frac{1}{2}$

17. $2\frac{1}{2} \div \frac{1}{4}$

18. $4\frac{1}{3} \div 3$

19. $2\frac{2}{3} \div \frac{1}{3}$

20. $\frac{1}{2} \div 3\frac{3}{4}$

21. $\frac{4}{5} \div 5$

22. $\frac{9}{14} \div \frac{3}{7}$

23. $3\frac{4}{5} \div 8\frac{1}{5}$

24. $\frac{11}{13} \div \frac{13}{11}$

25. Measurement Caroline received a letter from England telling her about the birth of a new baby. The baby weighed $\frac{1}{2}$ of a stone. One pound equals $\frac{1}{14}$ of a stone. How many pounds did the baby weigh?

26. One peck equals $\frac{1}{4}$ of a bushel. If Peter Piper had picked a half bushel of pickled peppers, how many pecks of pickled peppers would Peter Piper have picked?

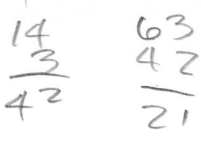

27. **Test Prep** Choose the expression with the smallest quotient.

Ⓐ $6\frac{1}{2} \div \frac{1}{2}$ Ⓑ $6\frac{1}{2} \div 3\frac{1}{2}$ Ⓒ $6\frac{1}{2} \div \frac{1}{4}$ Ⓓ $6\frac{1}{2} \div 2$

28. **Test Prep** Choose the expression with the largest quotient.

Ⓐ $5\frac{1}{2} \div \frac{1}{4}$ Ⓑ $3\frac{1}{3} \div \frac{1}{4}$ Ⓒ $7 \div \frac{1}{4}$ Ⓓ $\frac{1}{10} \div \frac{1}{4}$

29. Industry The size of letters in printed material such as newspapers or books is measured in points. One point equals $\frac{1}{72}$ of an inch.

   a. What is the point size of type that is $\frac{1}{8}$ of an inch high?

   b. What is the point size of type that is $1\frac{1}{2}$ inches high?

12 pt   The Brown Fox Jumped over the

14 pt   The Brown Fox Jumped ove

18 pt   The Brown Fox Jump

24 pt   The Brown Fox

28 pt   The Brown Fo

Problem Solving and Reasoning

30. Critical Thinking A popover recipe calls for $1\frac{1}{4}$ cups of flour and $1\frac{1}{4}$ cups of milk. If you only had a $\frac{1}{2}$-cup measure, how could you use it to complete the recipe?

31. Critical Thinking If $5 \div \frac{x}{3} = 5 \times \frac{x}{3}$, what is the value of x? Explain your reasoning.

32. Communicate Use rounding to estimate the quotient of $3\frac{5}{6}$ and $1\frac{7}{8}$. Compare your estimate to the exact quotient.

33. [Journal] Explain why $5\frac{1}{2} \div \frac{1}{2}$ has a larger quotient than $5\frac{1}{2} \div 2\frac{1}{2}$.

Mixed Review

Find the missing measurements for each circle, where r = radius, d = diameter, and C = circumference. *[Lesson 4-7]*

34. $r = \boxed{}$, $d = 1.4$ km, $C = \boxed{}$

35. $r = \boxed{}$, $d = \boxed{}$, $C = 50.24$ cm

36. $r = 4.2$ m, $d = \boxed{}$, $C = \boxed{}$

37. $r = \boxed{}$, $d = \boxed{}$, $C = 25.12$ mm

What fraction does each shaded part represent? *[Lesson 5-4]*

38.

39.

40.

41.

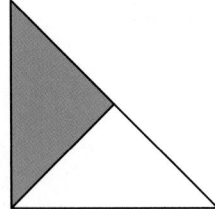
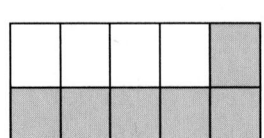

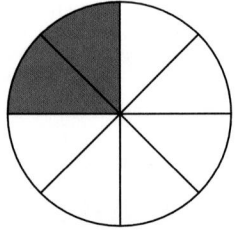

TECHNOLOGY

Using a Fraction Calculator • Finding Fraction Products and Quotients

Problem: What is the quotient of $\frac{4}{70} \div \frac{14}{51}$?

Fractions may involve large numbers that are not easy to work with. A fraction calculator can help you multiply or divide such fractions.

1 Type in the numerator of the first fraction, and then press the $\boxed{/}$ button.

3 Type in the numerator of the second fraction, and then press the $\boxed{/}$ button.

5 The calculator may indicate that the fraction is not in lowest terms. Press the $\boxed{simp}$ button and then the $\boxed{=}$ button to see the fraction in lowest terms.

4 Type in the denominator of the second fraction, and then press the $\boxed{=}$ button.

2 Type in the denominator of the first fraction, and then press the $\boxed{\div}$ button.

Solution: The answer is $\frac{204}{980}$ or, in lowest terms, $\frac{51}{245}$.

ON YOUR OWN

TRY IT

a. What is $\frac{7}{25} \times \frac{18}{31}$?

b. What is $\frac{10}{19} \div \frac{6}{37}$?

▶ When multiplying fractions, is using a fraction calculator always the fastest way to find the product? Explain.

▶ The product of the fractions $\frac{25}{91} \times \frac{25}{91}$ has a denominator bigger than 1000. What does the calculator do when the answer has a four-digit denominator?

▶ How could you use a nonfraction calculator to divide fractions?

Solving Fraction Equations: Multiplication and Division

► Lesson Link

  In earlier lessons, you solved multiplication and division equations that involved whole numbers and decimals. Now you'll use similar methods to solve multiplication and division equations involving fractions. ◄

You'll Learn ...

■ to solve multiplication and division equations containing fractions

... How It's Used

Magazine editors use fraction equations when converting a measurement from one unit to another.

| **Explore** | Solving Fraction Equations |

Truth or Dare

Each equation is followed by only one correct statement. Use your number sense to choose the correct statement, and explain how you know it's true.

1. Equation: $5w = 3$

   a. The value of w is a fraction greater than 1.

   b. The value of w is a fraction less than 1.

2. Equation: $\frac{1}{2}x = 10$

   a. The value of x is greater than 10.

   b. The value of x is less than 10.

3. Equation: $y \div \frac{2}{3} = 6$

   a. y multiplied by $\frac{2}{3}$ equals 6.

   b. y multiplied by $\frac{3}{2}$ equals 6.

4. Equation: $\frac{3}{4} \div z = \frac{3}{4}$

   a. The value of z can be written as a fraction.

   b. The value of z cannot be written as a fraction.

5. Four of the values below will make one of the above equations true. Which value will not make *any* of the above equations true?

   a. 20   **b.** $\frac{3}{5}$ **c.** 1   **d.** $\frac{4}{3}$ **e.** 4

| **Learn** | Solving Fraction Equations |

Recall that you used mental math to solve addition and subtraction equations involving fractions. You can use the same method to solve multiplication and division equations involving fractions.

When solving multiplication equations, it may help to first find the numerator of the missing value, and then the denominator.

Example 1

Solve: $\frac{2}{3}x = \frac{8}{15}$

$\frac{2}{3}x = \frac{8}{15}$ Read as "What number times $\frac{2}{3}$ equals $\frac{8}{15}$?"

$\frac{2}{3} \times \frac{4}{?} = \frac{8}{15}$ Using mental math, find the numerator.

$\frac{2}{3} \times \frac{4}{5} = \frac{8}{15}$ Using mental math, find the denominator.

$\frac{8}{15} = \frac{8}{15}$ ✓   Check to see that the equation is true.

x is equal to $\frac{4}{5}$.

Remember

To find the product of two fractions, multiply the numerators of both fractions. Then multiply the denominators of both fractions.
[Page 376]

If the equation includes whole numbers or mixed numbers, you may need to rewrite these numbers as fractions.

Example 2

Surveyors often measure distances in *chains*. A parking lot 33 yards long measured $1\frac{1}{2}$ chains. How many yards are there in a chain?

Let x = the number of yards in a chain

$1\frac{1}{2}x = 33$ Read as "What number times $1\frac{1}{2}$ equals 33?"

$\frac{3}{2}x = \frac{33}{1}$ Write the mixed number as an improper fraction.

$\frac{3}{2}x = \frac{66}{2}$ Write the whole number as a fraction with the same denominator.

$\frac{3}{2} \times \frac{22}{1} = \frac{66}{2}$ Use mental math.

1 chain equals 22 yards.

DID YOU KNOW?

A *chain* can be sub-divided into 100 equal units. Each of those units is called a *link*.

Try It

Solve for x.

a. $\frac{1}{2}x = 3$ **b.** $\frac{3}{4}x = \frac{15}{16}$ **c.** $1\frac{1}{4}x = 15$

When solving division equations, it may help to rewrite the equation as a multiplication equation by using the reciprocal of the divisor.

Example 3

Solve: $y \div \dfrac{2}{3} = \dfrac{9}{10}$

$y \times \dfrac{3}{2} = \dfrac{9}{10}$ Rewrite as a multiplication equation.

$\dfrac{3}{5} \times \dfrac{3}{2} = \dfrac{9}{10}$ Use mental math.

$\dfrac{9}{10} = \dfrac{9}{10}$ ✓   Check to see that the equation is true.

y is equal to $\dfrac{3}{5}$.

If the variable in the original equation is the divisor, you can still rewrite the equation as a multiplication equation. Don't forget that your final answer will be the reciprocal of the answer to the multiplication equation.

Example 4

Solve: $\dfrac{4}{5} \div z = \dfrac{12}{25}$

$\dfrac{4}{5} \times \mathbf{?} = \dfrac{12}{25}$ Rewrite as a multiplication equation.

$\dfrac{4}{5} \times \dfrac{3}{5} = \dfrac{12}{25}$ Use mental math to solve the multiplication equation.

$z = \dfrac{5}{3}$ Use the reciprocal for the answer to the original equation.

Try It

Solve.   **a.** $\dfrac{7}{3} \div x = 1\dfrac{1}{6}$ **b.** $\dfrac{4}{3} \div x = \dfrac{8}{21}$ **c.** $x \div 2\dfrac{2}{3} = \dfrac{9}{16}$

Check | Your Understanding

1. Why is it sometimes a good idea to rewrite a division equation as a multiplication equation?

2. If the fractions in a multiplication equation have unlike denominators, do you need to change them to fractions with like denominators? Explain.

3. What ideas are used in solving equations regardless of whether they contain whole numbers, decimals, or fractions?

Practice and Apply

Getting Started For each equation, state if the given value will make the equation true.

1. $\frac{3}{5}x = \frac{9}{10}$; $x = \frac{3}{2}$

2. $\frac{1}{3}x = \frac{1}{15}$; $x = \frac{1}{4}$

3. $z \div \frac{4}{5} = \frac{10}{16}$; $z = \frac{4}{2}$

Solve.

4. $\frac{1}{2}g = 6$

5. $3\frac{1}{6}k = \frac{4}{7}$

6. $\frac{8}{9} \div r = \frac{16}{18}$

7. $p \div \frac{5}{4} = 12$

8. $e \div \frac{6}{7} = \frac{1}{3}$

9. $\frac{4}{5}w = \frac{3}{5}$

10. $\frac{5}{6}t = 16$

11. $a \div 2\frac{2}{3} = \frac{3}{4}$

12. $q \div \frac{10}{3} = \frac{3}{4}$

13. $s \div 10\frac{7}{9} = 11\frac{3}{5}$

14. $\frac{5}{9}d = \frac{2}{7}$

15. $\frac{5}{7}f = 1\frac{4}{5}$

16. $7g = \frac{5}{8}$

17. $j \div 16 = 4\frac{1}{4}$

18. $\frac{3}{8}z = 2\frac{5}{9}$

19. $\frac{9}{2} \div c = 3\frac{3}{8}$

20. $\frac{5}{4} \div v = \frac{10}{16}$

21. $\frac{2}{3} \div b = \frac{16}{30}$

22. $6\frac{4}{5}m = \frac{2}{3}$

23. $i \div 8 = \frac{6}{7}$

24. **Test Prep** Mina made 12 cups of Jell-O. She divided it into equal servings, and each serving was $\frac{3}{4}$ of a cup. Which equation can you use to find out how many servings she has?

ⓐ $\frac{3}{4} \div s = 12$ ⓑ $12s = \frac{3}{4}$

ⓒ $12 \div s = \frac{3}{4}$

25. **History** Length was once measured in palms and spans. One inch equaled $\frac{1}{3}$ of a palm and $\frac{1}{9}$ of a span.

a. Which equation could you use to find the number of palms in 12 inches?

ⓐ $p \div \frac{1}{3} = 12$ ⓑ $\frac{1}{3}p = 12$

b. How many palms are in 12 inches?

c. Write and solve an equation to find the number of spans in 18 inches.

26. **Operation Sense** Shaun said, "I'm thinking of a fraction. If I divide it by $\frac{1}{2}$, I get $\frac{7}{12}$." What fraction was Shaun thinking of?

27. **Operation Sense** Caroline says, "I'm thinking of a fraction. If I multiply it by $\frac{2}{3}$, I get $\frac{4}{9}$. What fraction am I thinking of?"

Problem Solving and Reasoning

Critical Thinking Use the circle graph for Exercises 28–30.

28. What fraction of the total mangos went to Jack's Fruit Stand? Explain your reasoning.

30. What fraction of the total mangos went to either Glendale Grocery or the Rosewood School?

Mango Distribution

- The Santa Ana Art & Food Fest 138
- Rosewood School 267
- Jack's Fruit Stand 301
- Glendale Grocery 283

29. Which place received about $\frac{3}{10}$ of the total mangos? Explain how you can use estimation skills to determine this.

31. Choose a Strategy Explain the steps you would take to solve $\frac{2}{3}x + \frac{3}{4} = 3\frac{1}{2}$.

32. Communicate Explain why the solution of $\frac{7}{8}x = 43$ is more than 43.

Problem Solving STRATEGIES

- Look for a Pattern
- Make an Organized List
- Make a Table
- Guess and Check
- Work Backward
- Use Logical Reasoning
- Draw a Diagram
- Solve a Simpler Problem

33. Critical Thinking The Avoirdupois [a-VWA-du-PWA] system of weight measurement is the part of the customary system used to measure most things in everyday life, such as food, cars, or people. The Troy system measures the weight of precious metals and jewels. One Avoirdupois grain equals one Troy grain.

Avoirdupois Weight	Troy Weight
$27\frac{11}{32}$ grains = 1 drachma	24 grains = 1 pennyweight
16 drachmas = 1 ounce	20 pennyweights = 1 ounce
16 ounces = 1 pound	12 ounces = 1 pound

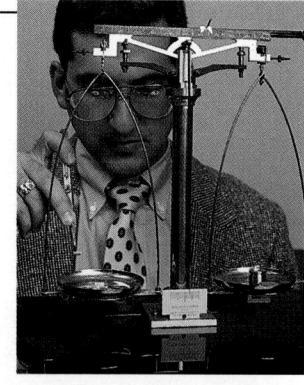

a. How many drachmas are in an Avoirdupois pound?

b. How many grains are in an Avoirdupois pound?

c. How many pennyweights are in a Troy pound?

d. How many grains are in a Troy pound?

e. The equation $x\frac{5760}{7000} = y$ can be used to convert from one type of pound to the other. Which variable represents an Avoirdupois pound? Which variable represents the Troy pound? Explain your reasoning.

Mixed Review

Name two equivalent fractions. *[Lesson 5-4]*

34. $\frac{6}{8}$ **35.** $\frac{3}{8}$ **36.** $\frac{2}{5}$ **37.** $\frac{10}{20}$ **38.** $\frac{6}{24}$ **39.** $\frac{11}{14}$

Find the GCF of each pair. *[Lesson 5-5]*

40. 4, 8 **41.** 3, 27 **42.** 18, 96 **43.** 7, 15 **44.** 33, 66

At the beginning of this section, you read that the Massachusetts Avenue Bridge was once measured using Oliver R. Smoot, Jr. as the unit of measurement. In the following exploration, you will model that activity using one of your fellow students as the unit of measurement.

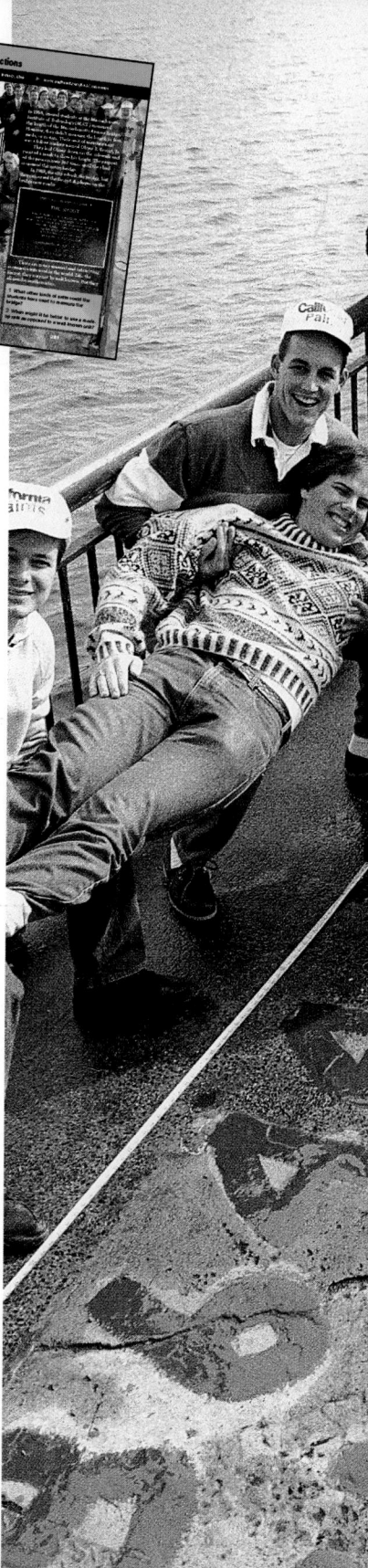

364.4 Smoots and One Ear

Materials: Masking tape

Choose a length to measure. For example, you could choose the length of the cafeteria or the length of a corridor. Choose one student in your group to be "Smoot."

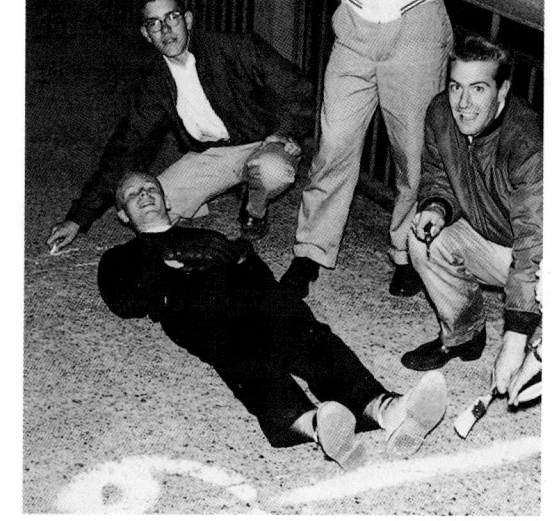

Oliver Reed Smoot, M.I.T. 1962

1. Estimate the number of Smoot heights in the length that you choose to measure.

2. Use Student X to make the measurement. Use masking tape to mark off each Smoot height measurement. When you have finished measuring, post a sign that tells the measurement. Compare your measurement with your estimate.

3. Now measure the same length using a standard unit of measurement. Use fractional units if necessary. Measure your Smoot using the same standard unit of measurement.

4. Use your measurements from Step 3 and what you have learned in this section to calculate the number of Smoot heights in the length.

5. Compare your actual Smoot measurement from Step 2 with your calculation from Step 4. Which do you think is more accurate? Why? Which measurement was easier to find?

REVIEW 7B

ACC

Simplify.

1. $4 \div \frac{1}{2}$

2. $\frac{2}{3} \div 12$

3. $2\frac{1}{2} \times 3$

4. $\frac{9}{4} \div \frac{1}{4}$

5. $\frac{6}{7} \div \frac{1}{3}$

6. $\frac{5}{4} \times \frac{6}{7}$

7. $2\frac{8}{11} \times 1\frac{3}{4}$

8. $\frac{9}{10} \times \frac{4}{5}$

9. $10 \div \frac{1}{5}$

10. $\frac{2}{5} \times \frac{2}{3}$

11. $3\frac{1}{4} \times 4$

12. $\frac{6}{10} \div \frac{1}{2}$

13. Health Ellen needs to take 2 teaspoons of medicine. She has only a $\frac{1}{2}$-teaspoon measure. How many $\frac{1}{2}$ teaspoons should she take? Explain whether Ellen should use an estimate or an exact answer.

14. Measurement The rod was once used to measure distance. There are $5\frac{1}{2}$ yards in 1 rod. How many rods are in 11 yards?

Solve.

15. $\frac{1}{2}v = 16$

16. $\frac{3}{5} \div k = 2\frac{1}{2}$

17. $x \div 6 = \frac{1}{3}$

18. $\frac{1}{3}w = 2\frac{2}{3}$

19. $2p = \frac{4}{5}$

20. $\frac{9}{5} \div e = 5$

21. $\frac{1}{2}u = \frac{4}{5}$

22. $c \div 4\frac{1}{3} = \frac{1}{3}$

23. A Shetland pony is 11 hands high. One inch $= \frac{1}{4}$ hand. Explain how you could use either multiplication or division to find this pony's height in inches.

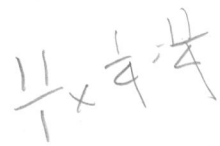

24. Write and solve an equation to find the number of centimeters in 5 inches. $\left(1 \text{ inch} \approx 2\frac{1}{2} \text{ centimeters}\right)$

25. Write and solve an equation to find the number of gallons in 12 quarts. (1 quart $= \frac{1}{4}$ gallon)

Test Prep

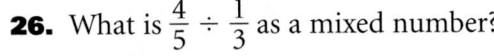

If a test question asks you to give an answer as a mixed number, you can eliminate any answers that are not mixed numbers.

26. What is $\frac{4}{5} \div \frac{1}{3}$ as a mixed number?

   Ⓐ $\frac{4}{15}$ Ⓑ $\frac{12}{5}$

   Ⓒ $1\frac{2}{5}$ Ⓓ $2\frac{2}{5}$

27. What is $\frac{2}{3} \times \frac{5}{2}$ as a mixed number?

   Ⓐ $1\frac{2}{3}$ Ⓑ $1\frac{1}{6}$

Converting Uneven Units

In the customary system of measurement, you can sometimes convert from a small unit to a large unit and get a whole-number answer. For example, you can convert 24 inches to 2 feet. Sometimes the number of units you start with doesn't equal a whole number of the larger units. For example, how many feet is 31 inches?

When this happens, find the number of times the smaller units can evenly be converted into the larger unit. Write the remainder using the smaller unit.

$$\begin{array}{r} 2\ R\ 7 \\ 12\overline{)31} \\ 24 \\ \hline 7 \end{array} = $$

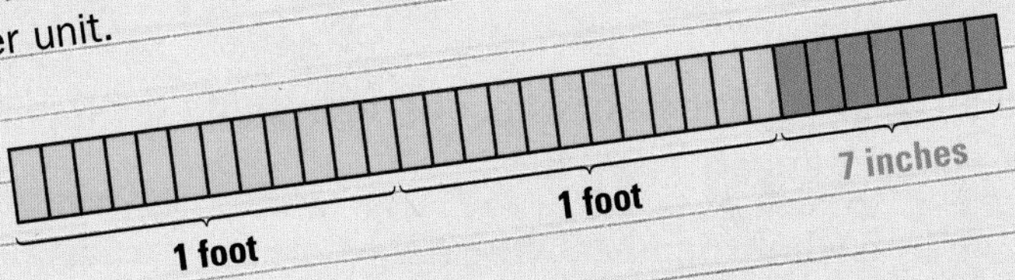

1 foot   1 foot   7 inches

For example, there are 12 inches in a foot. If you are converting 31 inches into feet, you know that 12 goes evenly into 31 twice with a remainder of 7. So 31 inches equals 2 feet 7 inches.

Try It

Convert. Each answer should be expressed using two different units.

1. 40 inches = ☐ feet

2. 79 inches = ☐ feet

3. 13 feet = ☐ yards

4. 53 feet = ☐ yards

5. 50 ounces = ☐ pounds

6. 91 ounces = ☐ pounds

7. 11 quarts = ☐ gallons

8. 31 quarts = ☐ gallons

Graphic Organizer

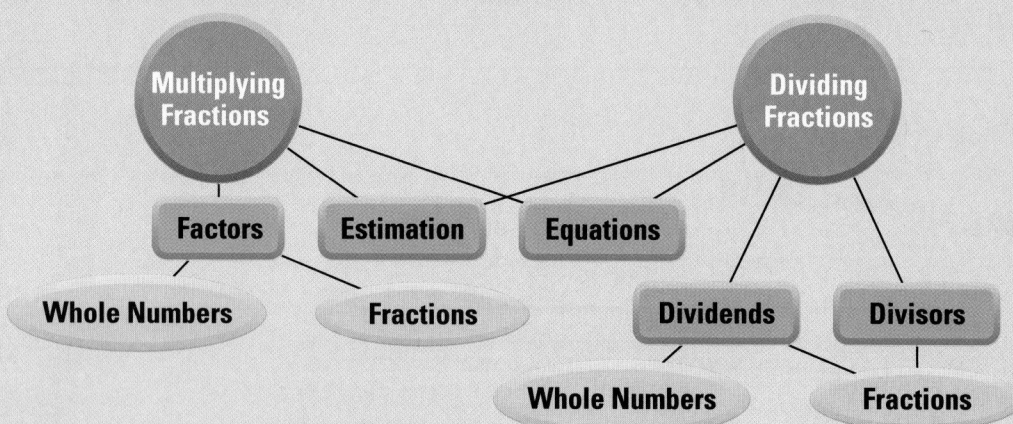

Section 7A Multiplying Fractions

Summary

- To estimate the products and quotients of fractions, first round the fractions to the nearest whole numbers.

- To multiply a fraction by a whole number, write the whole number as a fraction over 1. Then multiply the numerators, then the denominators, and simplify if necessary.

- To multiply a fraction by a fraction, first multiply the numerators, then the denominators, and simplify if necessary.

- When multiplying with mixed numbers, convert the mixed numbers into fractions before multiplying.

Review

1. Write the problem the model represents.

Estimate.

2. $7 \times 2\frac{3}{8}$

3. $9\frac{3}{4} \div 2\frac{3}{7}$

Simplify.

4. $\frac{3}{4} \times \frac{1}{8}$

5. $\frac{1}{9} \times \frac{1}{9}$

6. $\frac{2}{5} \times \frac{2}{3}$

7. $\frac{3}{7} \times \frac{4}{7}$

8. $6\frac{1}{4} \times 4$

9. $1\frac{5}{7} \times 1\frac{1}{6}$

10. $5 \times 2\frac{1}{4}$

11. $3\frac{1}{6} \times 3\frac{1}{3}$

12. A recipe calls for two and one-half cups of milk. If you are making half a recipe, how much milk would you use?

13. Is the product of a whole number and an improper fraction always larger than either number? Explain.

Section 7B   Dividing Fractions

Summary

- A number times its reciprocal equals 1. To find the **reciprocal** of a fraction, switch the numerator and the denominator.

- To divide a whole number by a fraction, multiply by the reciprocal of the fraction.

- To divide a fraction by a fraction, multiply by the reciprocal of the divisor fraction.

- To divide a fraction by a whole number, write the whole number as a fraction over 1. Then multiply by the reciprocal of this fraction.

- When solving fraction equations with multiplication and division, find the numerator of the variable first, and then the denominator. If necessary, rewrite division equations as multiplication equations.

Review

14. Write the problem the model represents.

State the reciprocal.

15. $\dfrac{5}{8}$

16. 3

Simplify.

17. $\dfrac{3}{4} \div \dfrac{1}{6}$
18. $\dfrac{5}{9} \div \dfrac{2}{3}$
19. $\dfrac{6}{7} \div \dfrac{10}{3}$
20. $\dfrac{4}{7} \div \dfrac{5}{2}$

21. $\dfrac{3}{7} \div 4$
22. $\dfrac{4}{9} \div 7$
23. $\dfrac{2}{10} \div 8$
24. $\dfrac{7}{11} \div 2$

For each equation, state if the given value will make the equation true.

25. $\dfrac{2}{3}t = \dfrac{4}{9}; t = \dfrac{2}{3}$
26. $y \div \dfrac{1}{3} = \dfrac{6}{10}; y = \dfrac{2}{10}$
27. $\dfrac{3}{4}j = \dfrac{9}{16}; j = \dfrac{4}{3}$
28. $\dfrac{1}{5} \div p = \dfrac{2}{5}; p = 2$

Solve.

29. $\dfrac{3}{5}x = \dfrac{27}{30}$
30. $\dfrac{5}{6}m = \dfrac{30}{48}$
31. $w \div \dfrac{2}{3} = \dfrac{21}{60}$
32. $q \div \dfrac{6}{5} = \dfrac{35}{18}$

33. Ursula has a string that is $2\frac{1}{2}$ feet long. If she cuts the string into equal pieces and each piece is $\frac{1}{4}$ foot long, how many pieces does she have?

Write the problem that each model represents.

1.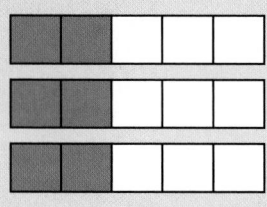

2.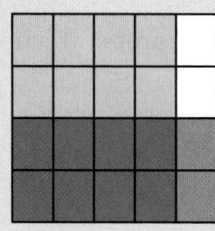

3.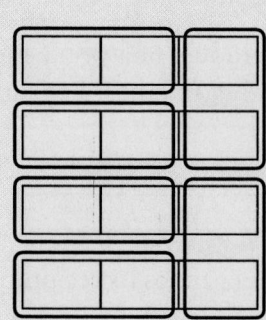

Estimate.

4. $5\frac{2}{5} \times 2\frac{6}{8}$

5. $7\frac{3}{9} \times 10\frac{1}{4}$

6. $11\frac{1}{3} \div 1\frac{5}{6}$

7. $8\frac{4}{5} \div 3\frac{8}{11}$

State the reciprocal.

8. $\frac{5}{9}$

9. $\frac{6}{11}$

10. 4

11. $4\frac{1}{3}$

Simplify.

12. $3 \times \frac{4}{9}$

13. $6 \times 3\frac{3}{7}$

14. $\frac{1}{4} \times \frac{7}{8}$

15. $8\frac{4}{5} \times \frac{4}{7}$

16. $6 \times \frac{2}{5}$

17. $7 \times \frac{3}{10}$

18. $\frac{7}{10} \times \frac{1}{5}$

19. $9\frac{1}{2} \times \frac{7}{11}$

20. $9 \div \frac{2}{5}$

21. $8 \div 1\frac{1}{9}$

22. $\frac{1}{7} \div \frac{2}{8}$

23. $4\frac{2}{3} \div 7$

24. $10 \div \frac{2}{9}$

25. $8 \div 6\frac{1}{5}$

26. $\frac{3}{8} \div \frac{5}{9}$

27. $1\frac{1}{3} \div 4$

For each equation, state if the given value will make the equation true.

28. $\frac{1}{3}g = 10$; $g = 2$

29. $\frac{4}{7}w = \frac{12}{49}$; $w = \frac{3}{7}$

30. $p \div \frac{1}{4} = 2$; $p = \frac{1}{8}$

31. $\frac{2}{9} \div r = \frac{2}{9}$; $r = \frac{2}{9}$

Solve.

32. $\frac{2}{5}g = 8$

33. $\frac{3}{11}w = \frac{15}{88}$

34. $p \div \frac{3}{2} = \frac{2}{15}$

35. $\frac{5}{7} \div r = \frac{20}{21}$

Performance Task

The multiplication table pictured shows the products when multiplying with $\frac{1}{2}$, $\frac{1}{3}$, and $\frac{1}{4}$. Draw a multiplication table that shows the products when multiplying with $\frac{1}{2}$, $\frac{1}{3}$, $\frac{2}{3}$, $\frac{1}{4}$, $\frac{2}{4}$, $\frac{3}{4}$, $\frac{1}{5}$, $\frac{2}{5}$, $\frac{3}{5}$, and $\frac{4}{5}$. If the product can be rewritten in lowest terms, show the original fraction *and* the fraction in lowest terms. Describe any patterns you see.

	$\frac{1}{2}$	$\frac{1}{3}$	$\frac{1}{4}$
$\frac{1}{2}$	$\frac{1}{4}$	$\frac{1}{6}$	$\frac{1}{8}$
$\frac{1}{3}$	$\frac{1}{6}$	$\frac{1}{9}$	$\frac{1}{12}$
$\frac{1}{4}$	$\frac{1}{8}$	$\frac{1}{12}$	$\frac{1}{16}$

Performance Assessment

Choose one problem.

The 2-3-4-5 Scramble

You can form 24 mixed numbers using three of the digits 2, 3, 4, and 5 without repeating any digits. $2\frac{3}{5}$ and $4\frac{3}{2}$ are two possibilities. $2\frac{2}{3}$ is not a possibility because it repeats the digit 2.

Find the 24 possible mixed numbers and their decimal equivalents.

Recipes of Data

Collect copies of at least 8 cake recipes. Each recipe should call for a specific amount of flour and milk or water. Compile two lists, one for the amount of flour called for, and one for the amount of milk or water called for. (For example, if a recipe calls for $4\frac{1}{2}$ cups of flour, you would write $4\frac{1}{2}$ on your flour list.) For each list of amounts: What fraction of the list are fractions? What is the mode amount? Is the mode amount a fraction?

Horsing Around

The table lists the range of height, in hands, of several breeds of draft horses.

Horse	Height (in hands)	Colors
Belgian	15.3 to 17.0	chestnut, roan
Percheron	16.0 to 17.0	gray, black
Clydesdale	16.0 to 16.2	bay, brown
Shire	17.0 to 17.1	black, bay brown, roan
German Coach	15.2 to 16.3	black
Suffolk	15.2 to 16.2	chestnut

One inch equals $\frac{1}{4}$ of a hand. Rewrite the chart to show the range of heights in inches.

High Bars

Measure the heights of seven people, including yourself. Draw a bar graph of the data. Find the mean height. Which person is closest to having the mean height? Find the median height. Are there more people shorter than the median height, or taller than the median height? Why?

The Geometry of Polygons

Cultural Link
www.mathsurf.com/6/ch8/people

Social Studies Link
www.mathsurf.com/6/ch8/social

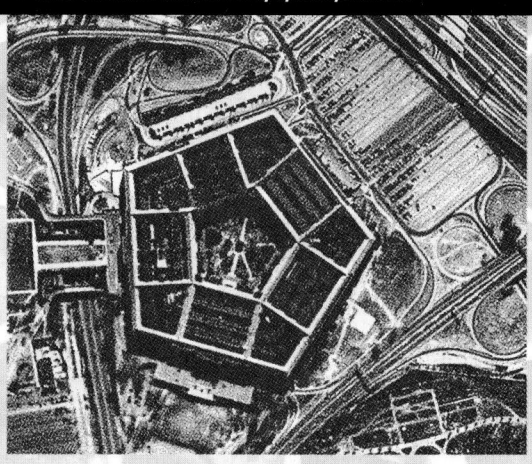

People of the World

The astrolabe was a device used by early Islamic astronomers to help them determine the time of day. In order to use it properly, an astronomer had to have a good knowledge of the stars and an understanding of how to measure angles.

Social Studies

The Pentagon is the headquarters for the United States Department of Defense. The building itself is shaped like a regular pentagon, with each side measuring 921 feet long. It contains over $17\frac{1}{2}$ miles of corridors and 7700 windows.

Arts & Literature

A tessellation is a design created by repeating a shape that fits together with no space in between. M. C. Escher (1898–1972) was an artist who is perhaps best remembered for his tessellations.

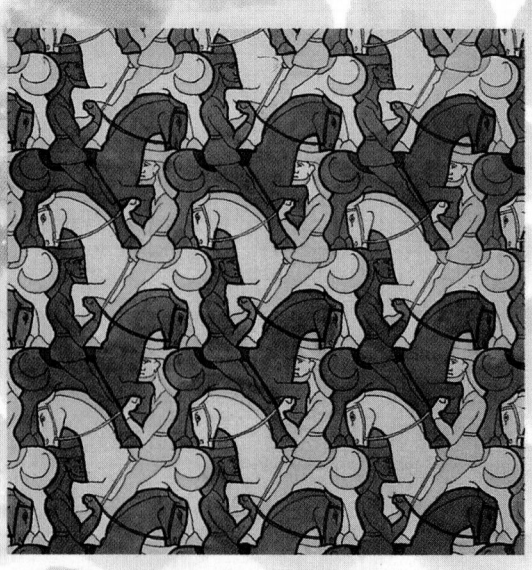

"Symmetry Drawing E67" by M. C. Escher.
© 1997 Cordon Art - Baarn, Holland.
All Rights Reserved.

Entertainment

In formal gymnastics, the floor exercise is done on a square mat with sides 12 meters long. If the gymnast does not stay within the borders of the mat, points are deducted from his or her score.

KEY MATH IDEAS

Geometric figures are made up of lines, segments, and rays.

Angles are measured in degrees. You can use a protractor to measure an angle.

Polygons can be classified according to the number of sides, size of their angles, or the lengths of their sides.

Geometric figures can be changed through reflections, rotations and translations.

Some geometric figures have symmetry. A figure may have line symmetry and/or point symmetry.

Science

Some bees communicate using the "waggle dance." This dance describes the location of a rich source of pollen. The angle formed by the bee's motion and the sun indicates the direction of the pollen.

Problem Solving

Understand
Plan
Solve
Look Back

CHAPTER PROJECT

In this project, you will create a logo for yourself, your class, your team, or any group you belong to. Start by thinking about who you want to design a logo for, and what you would want the logo to look like.

Problem Solving Focus

Interpreting Math Phrases

Many problem-solving situations use phrases like *more than*, *fewer than*, *twice as much*, or *half as much*. When developing a plan to solve the problem correctly, you need to know how to interpret these phrases.

For each problem, write down the answer and the equation for how you got the answer. For example, if you added 5 to 7 to get 12, write "5 + 7 = 12."

1 Hanna practices the flute for thirty minutes a day. Hanna practices for ten minutes more than Lynn. For how many minutes does Lynn practice?

2 Andrea has seven drums. James has two fewer drums than Andrea. How many drums does James have?

3 Dawn has thirty-four sheets of music. Rebecca has twice as many sheets of music as Dawn. How many sheets of music does Rebecca have?

4 Tito knows ten songs by heart. Tito knows twice as many songs by heart as Will. How many songs does Will know by heart?

5 Miranda has performed in five more concerts than Crystal. Crystal has performed in six concerts. In how many concerts has Miranda performed?

6 Donte has twice as many spare guitar strings as Loren. Donte has eight spare strings. How many spare strings does Loren have?

7 Marco's kazoo cost half as much as Julie's harmonica. Julie's harmonica cost twelve dollars. How much did Marco's kazoo cost?

The Tale of the Magic Paper

Long ago, a samurai came to a woman's house.
She offered him lunch. When he finished, he gave her a piece of paper.
"This is magic paper," he said. "What do you need?"
"I need a fish for my dinner."
The samurai folded the paper in strange and wonderful ways. The paper turned into a fish.
The woman cried, "How amazing! But I also need a basket."
The samurai refolded the paper, and it turned into a basket.
"How beautiful!" the woman said. "If only I had a bird to keep me company."
The samurai refolded the paper, and it turned into a bird.
"Thank you very much," the woman said. "I have given you a meal, but you have given me magic."

This story was about *origami*, the ancient Japanese art of paper folding.
Origami involves a series of folds made with precise lines and angles.
Creating origami objects involves following directions, interpreting drawings, and understanding geometry.

1 What can make a drawing difficult to describe?

2 When is it helpful to be able to describe drawings exactly?

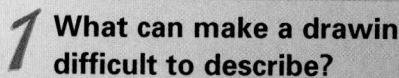

407

Classifying Lines

You'll Learn ...

■ to describe different kinds of lines

... How It's Used

Hotel receptionists use line vocabulary when giving directions to hotel guests.

Vocabulary

line

segment

endpoint

ray

intersect

perpendicular

parallel

▶ **Lesson Link** You've used number lines to order decimals, and you've used line plots to display data. Now you'll look more closely at lines to see what they are and how they are classified. ◀

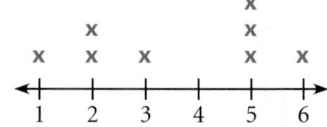

Explore | Lines

What's My Line?

In each group, one picture is different from the others. Decide which picture is different and explain how it is different.

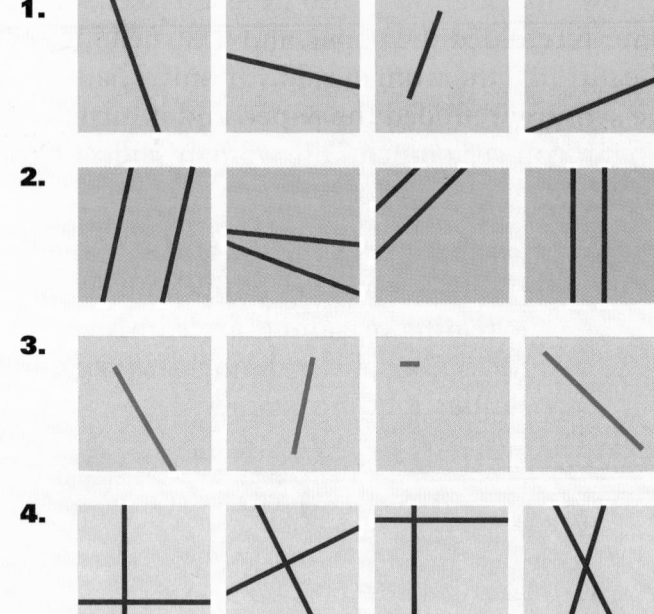

Learn | Classifying Lines

Geometry is the branch of mathematics that studies shapes and figures. In order to describe shapes exactly, mathematicians use words with precise meanings. One class of words describes the different kinds of lines used to make figures.

A **line** extends forever in both directions. To show that a figure is a line, draw an arrow at each end.

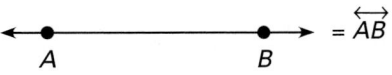

A line **segment** has two **endpoints**. The segment does not extend beyond these endpoints. To show that a figure is a segment, draw the endpoints.

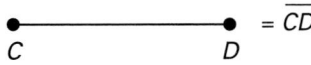

A **ray** has one endpoint, and extends forever in the other direction. To show that a figure is a ray, use an endpoint on one end and an arrow through a point on the other.

If lines cross through the same point, they **intersect**. If they intersect at right angles, they are **perpendicular**. If they do not intersect no matter how far they extend, they are **parallel**.

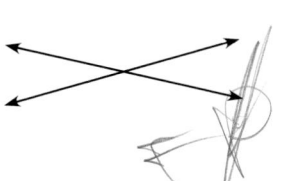

The lines intersect.   The lines are perpendicular.   The lines are parallel.

Rays and segments can also intersect, or be perpendicular or parallel.

Example 1

The origami angelfish has been labeled with several points. Describe the relationships between $\overline{AE}$ and $\overline{BE}$, $\overline{BE}$ and $\overline{CE}$, and $\overline{AD}$ and $\overline{BC}$.

$\overline{AE}$ and $\overline{BE}$ are intersecting line segments. $\overline{BE}$ and $\overline{CE}$ are perpendicular line segments. $\overline{AD}$ and $\overline{BC}$ are parallel line segments.

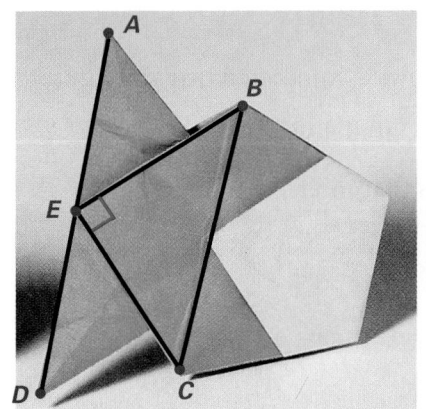

Check | Your Understanding

1. Which is longer, a segment or a line? How much longer?

2. If two segments do not intersect, does that mean they are parallel? Explain.

Practice and Apply

Getting Started State whether each figure is a line, a ray, or a segment.

1. 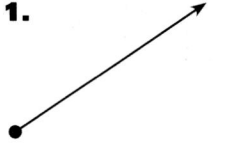   **2.**    **3.** 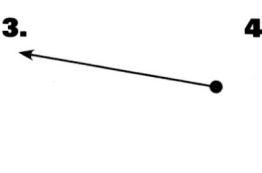   **4.**    **5.**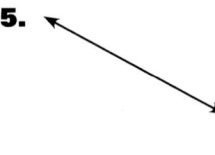

Draw an example of each.

6. $\overline{AB}$ **7.** $\overleftrightarrow{AB}$ **8.** $\overrightarrow{AB}$ **9.** $\overline{JK}$ **10.** $\overleftrightarrow{JK}$ **11.** $\overrightarrow{JK}$

Describe the relationship between the lines, rays, or segments.

12. 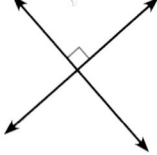   **13.** 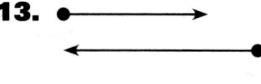   **14.**    **15.**

16. 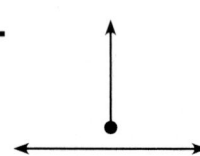   **17.** 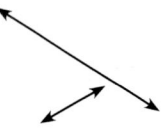   **18.** 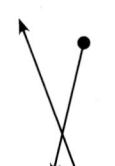   **19.**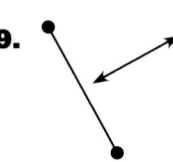

Fine Arts The photo shows a completed origami figure.

20. Name three pairs of parallel segments.

21. Name two segments that intersect but are not perpendicular.

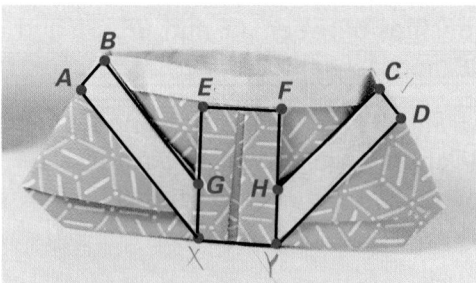

22. **Test Prep** Choose the lines that are parallel.

Ⓐ *A* and *D*

Ⓑ *C* and *E*

Ⓒ *A* and *C*

Ⓓ *E* and *D*

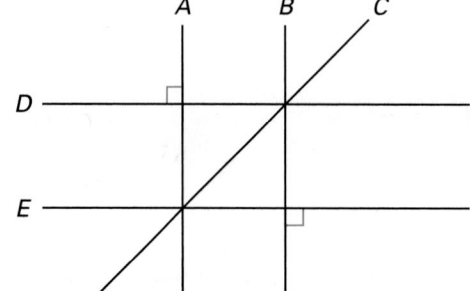

23. Miranda and Hien are walking along parallel streets in a neighborhood. If the girls are 150 feet apart when they start walking, how long will they have to walk until their paths cross?

Logic Tell whether each statement is always, sometimes, or never true.

24. The rails on a set of train tracks are parallel.

25. Two intersecting streets are perpendicular.

26. The paths of two airplanes flying above Texas will intersect.

27. A line is longer than a segment.

Problem Solving and Reasoning

28. Critical Thinking Jarred studied 50 pairs of lines. He labeled each pair with the terms *parallel, perpendicular,* and *intersecting.* The bar graph shows the number of times he used each label. The numbers in the graph do not add up to 50. Other than being a mistake, explain how this is possible.

29. Communicate List three real-world situations that involve parallel lines. Do the situations also involve perpendicular lines? Explain.

30. Communicate Is the distance between two parallel lines always the same? Explain. Use a picture or diagram in your explanation.

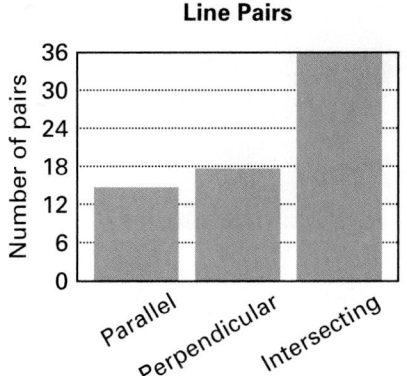

Mixed Review

Write as a mixed number. *[Lesson 5-6]*

31. $\frac{5}{3}$ **32.** $\frac{3}{2}$ **33.** $\frac{7}{3}$ **34.** $\frac{9}{4}$ **35.** $\frac{7}{2}$ **36.** $\frac{14}{6}$

37. $\frac{9}{5}$ **38.** $\frac{18}{4}$ **39.** $\frac{6}{4}$ **40.** $\frac{10}{7}$ **41.** $\frac{12}{5}$ **42.** $\frac{8}{3}$

Simplify. Write your answer as a mixed number. *[Lesson 6-1]*

43. $\frac{2}{7} + \frac{5}{7}$ **44.** $\frac{4}{5} - \frac{1}{5}$ **45.** $\frac{7}{10} + \frac{9}{10}$ **46.** $\frac{55}{100} + \frac{46}{100}$ **47.** $\frac{8}{4} - \frac{3}{4}$

48. $\frac{4}{3} - \frac{3}{3}$ **49.** $\frac{12}{15} + \frac{13}{15}$ **50.** $\frac{7}{8} - \frac{4}{8}$ **51.** $\frac{9}{12} + \frac{3}{12}$ **52.** $\frac{3}{5} - \frac{1}{5}$

Classifying Angles

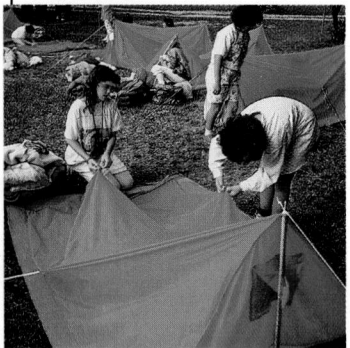

Vocabulary

angle

side

vertex

acute angle

right angle

obtuse angle

straight angle

▶ **Lesson Link**   In the last lesson, you learned that lines, rays, and segments are basic elements in geometry. Now you'll learn about a simple figure made up of these parts—the angle. ◀

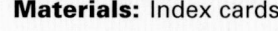

Explore   Angles

Materials: Index cards

Sailing at an Angle

The sailboat is the symbol of Origami USA, the largest U.S. organization for origami enthusiasts.

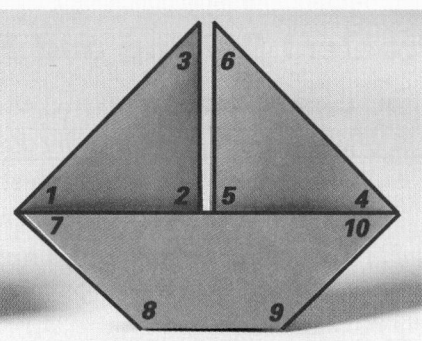

1. The edges of an index card meet to form a right angle. Use an index card to determine if each corner is less than a right angle, about equal to a right angle, or greater than a right angle.

2. Several pairs of angles in the drawing can be put together to form a single angle about equal to a right angle. Find two pairs of angles like this. Explain how you can tell that they form a right angle.

3. Without an index card, how can you decide whether an angle is about equal to, greater than, or smaller than a right angle?

Learn   Classifying Angles

An **angle** is formed by two rays with the same endpoint. The rays are the **sides** of the angle. The common endpoint is the **vertex**.

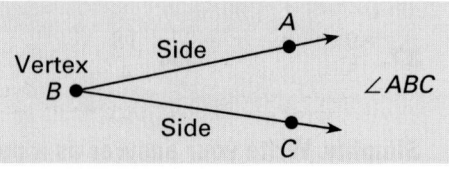

You can name an angle using a point on each side and the vertex. The angle shown can be called ∠*ABC*, read "angle *ABC*," or ∠*CBA*. The vertex must appear as the middle letter.

When it is not confusing, you can name an angle using the vertex alone. The angle shown can also be called ∠*B*.

Angles can be classified by their size.

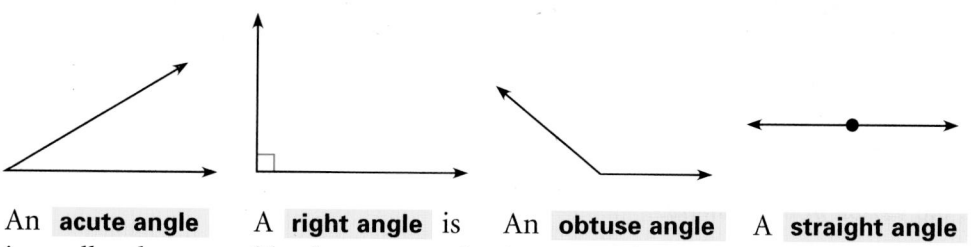

An **acute angle** is smaller than a right angle.

A **right angle** is like the corner of an index card.

An **obtuse angle** is greater than a right angle but smaller than a straight angle.

A **straight angle** is a line.

▶ **Language Link**

Some words have a nonmathematical meaning that is similar to their mathematical meaning. The word *acute* can also mean "having a sharp point." The word *obtuse* can also mean "blunt, not sharp."

Example 1

Classify each angle as acute, right, obtuse, or straight.

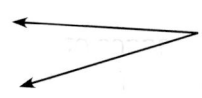

The angle is obtuse.

The angle is a right angle.

The angle is acute

Try It

Classify each angle as acute, right, obtuse, or straight.

a.
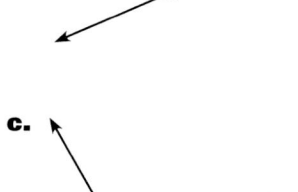

b.

c.

d.
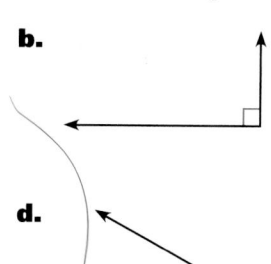

Check Your Understanding

1. Find an example of each type of angle in your classroom.

2. Why do mathematicians sometimes use three letters to name an angle instead of just using the vertex?

Practice and Apply

Getting Started State the vertex of each angle.

1.
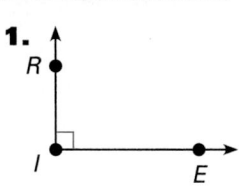

2.

3.

4.
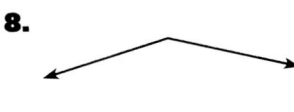

Classify each angle as acute, right, obtuse, or straight.

5.

6.

7.

8.

9.

10.
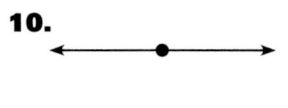

11.
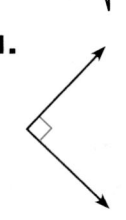

12.
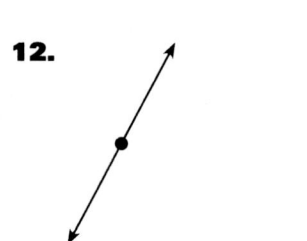

Name each angle in three ways.

13.

14.
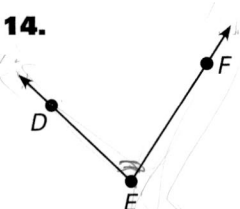

15.
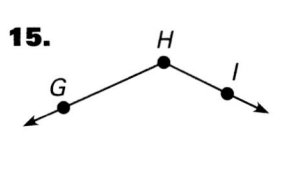

16.
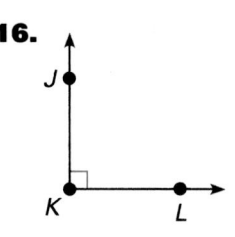

Geometry Tell whether each statement is always, sometimes, or never true.

17. Two acute angles of the same size form a right angle. *sometimes*

18. A right angle and an acute angle form an obtuse angle. *Always*

19. An angle consists of two endpoints, a vertex, and a ray. *Always*

Measurement Classify the angle made by the hands of a clock at each time.

20. 3:00   **21.** 7:15   **22.** 2:45   **23.** 6:00   **24.** 1:00   **25.** 10:00

Fine Arts Use the unfolded pattern of the inside reverse fold for Exercises 26 and 27.

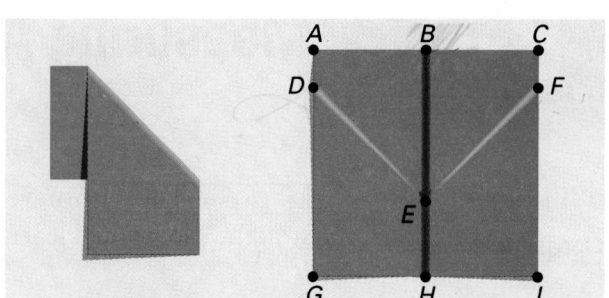

26. Name five angles and classify each as acute, right, or obtuse.

27. Name and classify two angles which make up a straight angle.

28. [Test Prep] Choose the acute angle.

Ⓐ 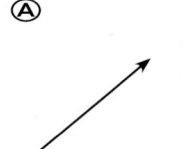   Ⓑ    Ⓒ 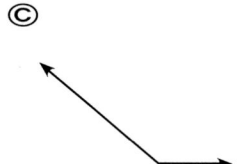   Ⓓ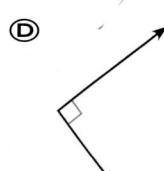

Problem Solving and Reasoning

29. Choose a Strategy What is the smallest number of sides needed to draw a polygon with exactly 5 right angles? Explain.

30. [Journal] What kind of angles are made between two perpendicular lines? Two parallel lines? Explain.

31. Communicate Two angles placed together make a straight line. If one is an obtuse angle, what is the other? Explain.

32. Critical Thinking Draw two rays that don't make an angle. Explain your drawing.

Problem Solving

STRATEGIES

- Look for a Pattern
- Make an Organized List
- Make a Table
- Guess and Check
- Work Backward
- Use Logical Reasoning
- Draw a Diagram
- Solve a Simpler Problem

Mixed Review

Write each mixed number as an improper fraction. *[Lesson 5-6]*

33. $6\frac{3}{5}$ **34.** $12\frac{2}{3}$ **35.** $3\frac{1}{2}$ **36.** $2\frac{4}{5}$ **37.** $10\frac{9}{11}$ **38.** $4\frac{1}{4}$

39. $9\frac{3}{4}$ **40.** $5\frac{2}{5}$ **41.** $2\frac{1}{6}$ **42.** $6\frac{2}{3}$ **43.** $3\frac{6}{7}$ **44.** $7\frac{3}{5}$

Simplify. *[Lesson 6-2]*

45. $\frac{7}{9} + \frac{3}{4}$ **46.** $\frac{6}{12} - \frac{2}{6}$ **47.** $\frac{2}{3} + \frac{6}{9}$ **48.** $\frac{3}{4} - \frac{5}{8}$ **49.** $\frac{1}{2} - \frac{1}{8}$

50. $\frac{12}{18} + \frac{5}{9}$ **51.** $\frac{9}{10} - \frac{2}{5}$ **52.** $\frac{2}{3} + \frac{3}{8}$ **53.** $\frac{6}{11} + \frac{6}{22}$ **54.** $\frac{4}{5} - \frac{3}{4}$

8-2 Classifying Angles   **415**

Measuring Angles

You'll Learn …

■ to measure angles

… How It's Used

Surveyors measure angles when determining the height of an object that is too large to measure with a meter stick.

Vocabulary

degree

complementary angles

supplementary angles

protractor

▶ **Lesson Link** │ You've learned to classify angles as acute, right, obtuse, or straight. Now you'll learn to measure the sizes of angles using a protractor. ◀

Explore | Measuring Angles

I'd Like a Glass of Milk and a Right Angle

Materials: Scissors

1. Trace and cut out a copy of the "slice." Then determine the number of "slices" that fit into each angle.

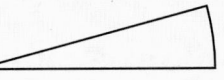

a.    b.    c.

d. 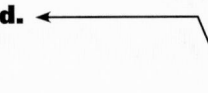   e. 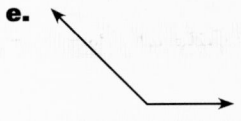   f.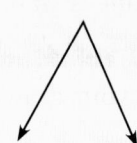

2. Rank the angles in order from fewest slices to most slices.

3. Classify each angle as acute, right, or obtuse.

4. What is the greatest number of pie slices an acute angle can have? What is the greatest number a right angle can have? What is the greatest number an obtuse angle can have?

5. If the sides of an angle are longer, then you can fit more slices into the angle. Do you agree or disagree? Explain.

6. In Step 1, if everyone in the classroom used a different-sized slice, would everyone get different answers? Explain.

Angles are measured in units called **degrees**. Use the symbol ° to indicate degrees. A complete circle measures 360°. A 1° angle is $\frac{1}{360}$ of a circle.

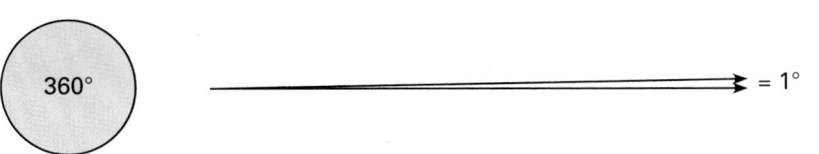

360°   = 1°

An acute angle measures more than 0° and less than 90°.

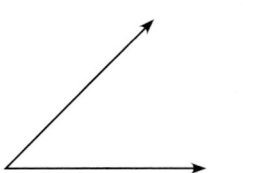

A right angle measures exactly 90°.

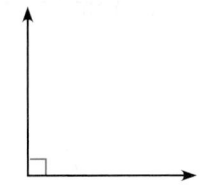

An obtuse angle measures more than 90° and less than 180°.

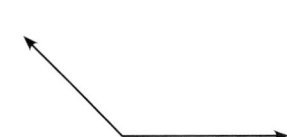

Two angles are **complementary angles** if the sum of their measures equals 90°.
Two angles are **supplementary angles** if the sum of their measures equals 180°.

A **protractor** is a tool that measures angles.

Example 1

What is the measure of ∠ABC?

Place the protractor so that the middle of its bottom edge is over the vertex, and one side of the bottom edge is over one side of the angle. Read the pair of numbers where the other side of the angle passes underneath the protractor. If the angle is an acute angle, use the smaller number in the pair. If the angle is obtuse, use the larger number.

m∠*ABC* is 70°.

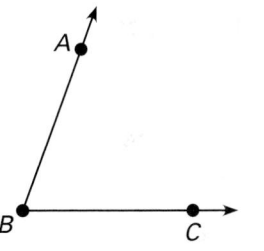

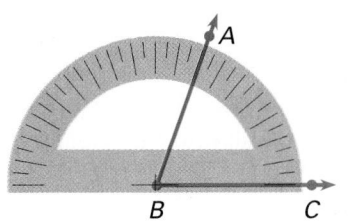

Place hole over vertex.   Place protractor line over side of angle.

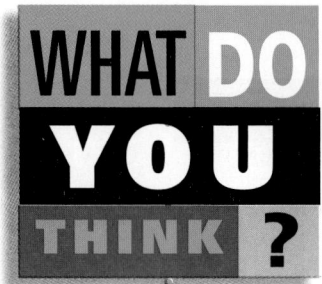

The smaller the angle between a ski jumper's body and the skis, the farther the skier will travel. Sonia and Zack help coach the ski team. They photographed the team's best jumper. Now they want to measure the angle between her body and the skis.

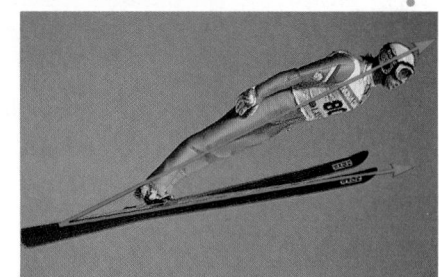

Sonia thinks ...

I'll place the bottom edge of the protractor on the ray on the ski. The other ray crosses the protractor at 15°, so the angle measures 15°.

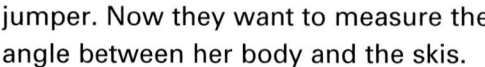

Zack thinks ...

I'll place the center of the protractor on the vertex of the angle. The two rays cross at 20° and 35°. 35° − 20° = 15°. The angle measures 15°.

What do you think?

1. The protractor is labeled with pairs of measurements. How did Sonia know that the 15° measure was the correct measure to use?

2. Explain Zack's reasoning. Could he place the protractor in other ways and still find the measure of the angle?

1. If someone tells you the measure of an angle, how can you tell if the angle is an acute angle, a right angle, or an obtuse angle?

2. What is a degree a measurement of?

8-3 Exercises and Applications

Practice and Apply

Getting Started State whether the measure of each angle is less than 90° or greater than 90°.

1.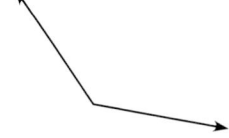

2.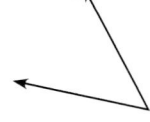

3.

4.

Estimation Estimate the measure of each angle. Then measure each with a protractor.

5.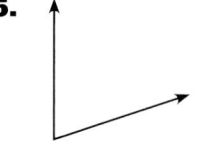

6.

7.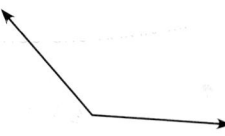

8.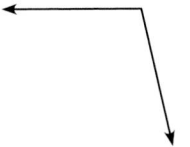

9.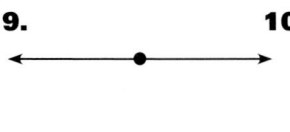

10.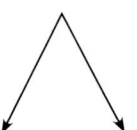

11.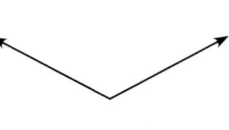

12.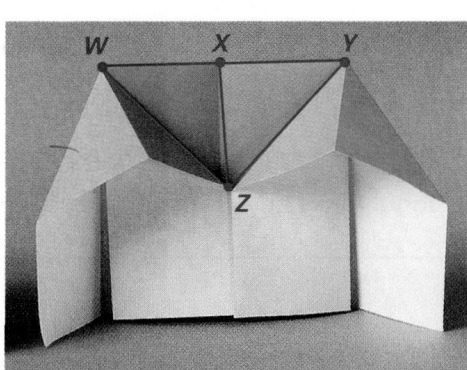

13. **Fine Arts** Name two supplementary angles and two complementary angles in the origami photo.

Draw the angle for each measure. Then classify each as acute, obtuse, or right.

14. 50°   **15.** 140°   **16.** 70°   **17.** 110°

State the angle measure that is complementary to the given angle.

18. 23°   **19.** 79°   **20.** 62°   **21.** 3°

State the angle measure that is supplementary to the given angle.

22. 127°   **23.** 52°   **24.** 60°   **25.** 90°

Read each statement and tell if it is always, sometimes, or never true.

26. Degrees are used to measure the sides of angles.

27. Two angles whose measures are 45° and 45° are complementary.

28. Two obtuse angles are supplementary.

29. **Test Prep** Estimate the measurement of the obtuse angle.

    Ⓐ 45°   Ⓑ 135°

    Ⓒ 90°   Ⓓ 270°

Problem Solving and Reasoning

30. **Journal** A clock face is divided into 360°. About how long does it take the hour hand to travel 720°? 270°? Explain.

31. **Critical Thinking** Is it easier to draw a 1° angle or a 91° angle? Explain.

32. **Communicate** How many angles can you draw that measure between 72° and 73°? Explain.

Mixed Review

Write each fraction as a decimal. *[Lesson 5-7]*

33. $\frac{1}{2}$ **34.** $\frac{2}{3}$ **35.** $\frac{1}{4}$ **36.** $\frac{3}{4}$ **37.** $\frac{1}{3}$ **38.** $\frac{5}{6}$

39. $\frac{4}{9}$ **40.** $\frac{3}{5}$ **41.** $\frac{12}{22}$ **42.** $\frac{7}{8}$ **43.** $\frac{673}{673}$ **44.** $\frac{5}{8}$

Solve. *[Lesson 6-3]*

45. $\frac{5}{6} + w = \frac{7}{8}$ **46.** $t + \frac{4}{9} = \frac{3}{4}$ **47.** $p - \frac{5}{6} = \frac{6}{11}$ **48.** $n - \frac{3}{4} = \frac{1}{2}$

49. $a + \frac{3}{8} = \frac{4}{9}$ **50.** $\frac{60}{10} - j = 5$ **51.** $b - \frac{4}{5} = \frac{1}{10}$ **52.** $4 - m = \frac{3}{5}$

Project Progress

Draw a rough sketch of your logo. Include as many shapes as possible in your logo. Make sure some of the shapes have only straight sides.

Problem Solving

Understand
Plan
Solve
Look Back

In this section, you've seen how traditional origami folds produce patterns of lines and angles. Now you'll start your own "tradition" by creating folds to illustrate what you've learned about lines and angles.

The Tale of the Magic Paper

Materials: Squares of paper, Ruler

The instructions for the octopus appear in Kunihiko Kasahara's book, *Creative Origami*. If you unfold the paper used to create the octopus, you can see many interesting line and angle patterns.

Create patterns in paper squares to model at least 12 of the terms you have learned in this lesson. Fold and then open squares to make the patterns. Darken creases with a pencil or pen. Label each figure with the term it models.

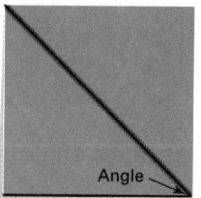

Here's a list of some of the terms you've studied in this section:

acute angle	angle	complementary angles
degree	endpoint	intersect
line	obtuse angle	parallel
perpendicular	protractor	ray
right angle	segment	side
straight angle	supplementary angles	vertex

You may use a different square to model each term. You may sometimes find it easier to create patterns that model several terms at once. Let the geometry of the square help you create useful patterns.

Handwritten in margin: GOOD JOB! A+ ★

Describe the relationship between the lines, rays, or segments.

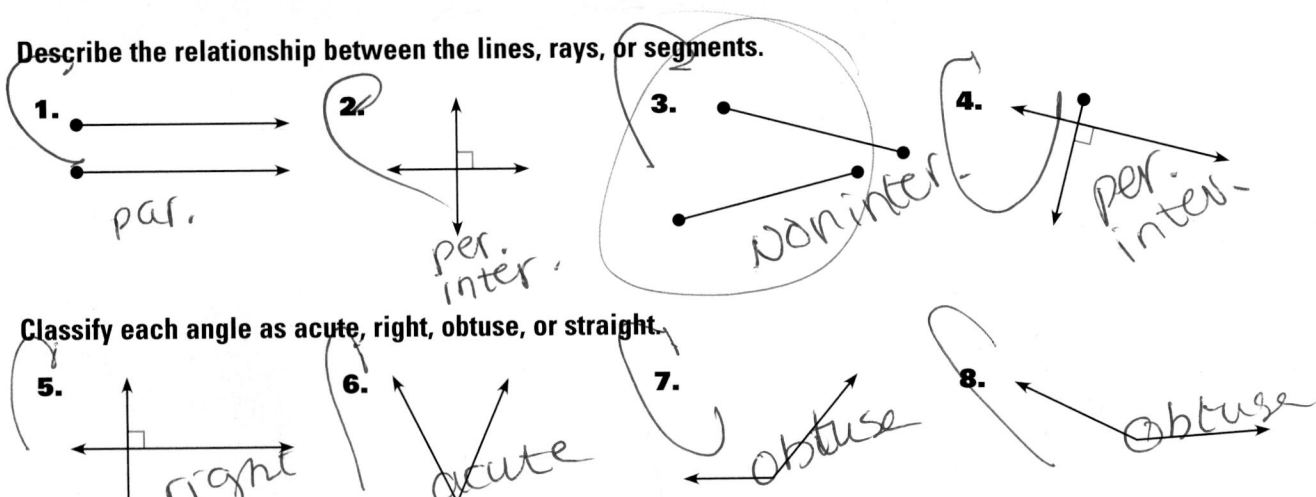

1. *par.*

2. *per. inter.*

3. *noninter-* (circled)

4. *per. inter-*

Classify each angle as acute, right, obtuse, or straight.

5. *right*

6. *acute*

7. *obtuse*

8. *obtuse*

Measure each angle and find its complement and supplement.

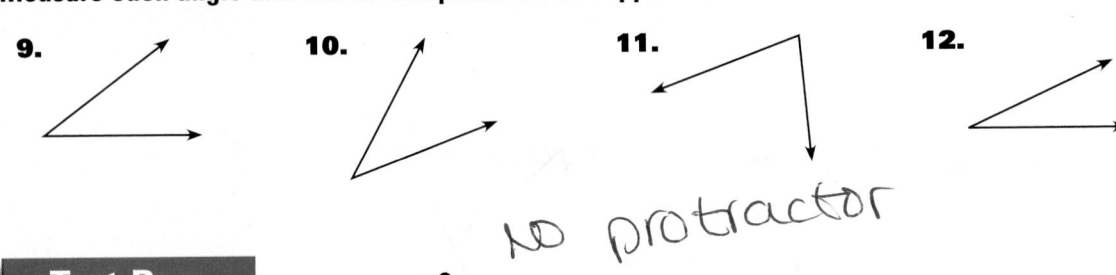

9. 10. 11. 12.

No protractor

Test Prep

When estimating the measurement of an angle, remember that a right angle is 90° and half of a right angle is 45°.

13. Rosemary is building a birdhouse. She wants the roof of the birdhouse to be at an angle more than 90° but less than 135°. Choose the angle that she could use for the roof.

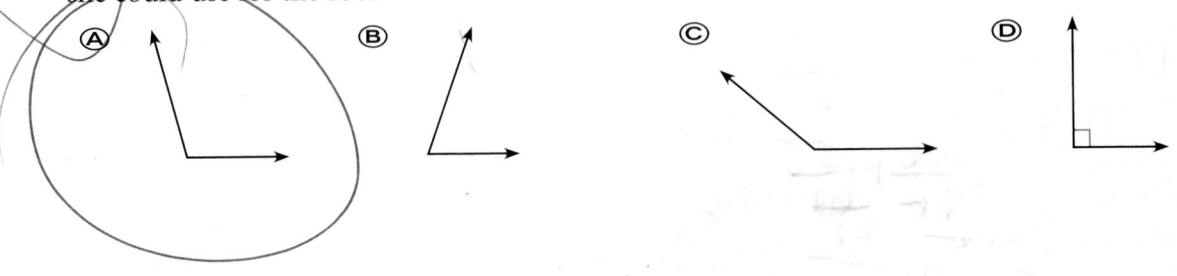

Ⓐ (circled)   Ⓑ   Ⓒ   Ⓓ

Polygons

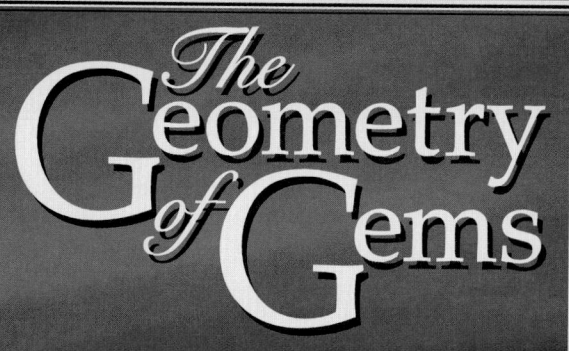

The Geometry of Gems

Not long ago, a diamond was found in the African nation of Guinea. The diamond was the size of a small onion. The owner sold it for $10 million. At that rate, 1 pound of diamonds is worth about $90 million! (One pound of onions is worth about 59¢.)

An uncut diamond is an example of a crystal. Most of the world's rocks and minerals occur as crystals. Some display fascinating geometric shapes and patterns.

A few crystals, such as diamonds, emeralds, and rubies, are prized for their rarity and beauty. Skilled gem cutters grind the crystals into attractive three-dimensional shapes.

Then they cut flat geometric shapes called facets into the surface. Their work produces jewels that are mathematical as well as artistic—and worth much more than a bag of onions!

In this section, you'll learn about the geometry of crystals and facets.

1 Why are diamonds worth more than onions?

2 What does it mean to say, "At that rate, 1 pound of diamonds is worth about $90 million"?

423

Exploring Angles in a Triangle

You'll Learn …

■ to classify triangles according to their angles

… How It's Used

Diamond cutters classify triangles when describing the cut of a particular stone.

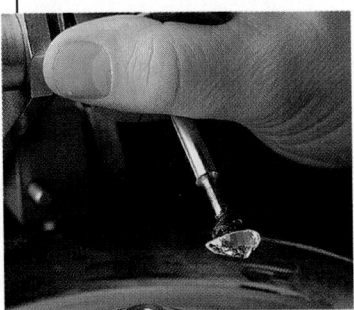

Vocabulary

triangle

acute triangle

right triangle

obtuse triangle

▶ **Lesson Link** You've learned about line segments and angles. Now you'll investigate the triangle, a figure with three line segments and three angles. ◀

Explore   Angles in a Triangle

Straight to the Sum

Materials: Ruler, Scissors, Protractor

1. Draw and cut out a large triangle. Label the angles as 1, 2, and 3.

2. Tear the triangle into three pieces as shown. Each piece should have one and only one labeled angle.

3. Put the three pieces together so that the angles are touching. Estimate the sum of the three angles of your triangle.

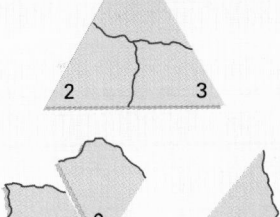

4. Using a protractor, find the measure of each angle. Calculate the sum of the angles. How does the sum compare to your estimate?

5. Repeat Steps 1–4 with two more triangles. Compare the sums of the angles for your three triangles. Describe any patterns you see in the sums.

Learn   Angles in a Triangle

A **triangle** is a closed figure made from three line segments. Like angles, triangles can be classified using the terms *acute*, *right*, and *obtuse*.

An **acute triangle** has three acute angles.

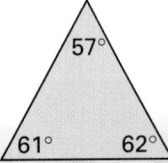

A **right triangle** has exactly one right angle.

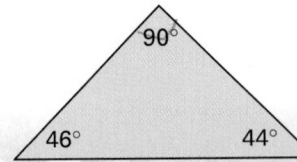

An **obtuse triangle** has exactly one obtuse angle.

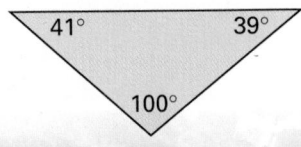

Example 1

Classify each triangle as acute, right, or obtuse.

a.

The face has one obtuse angle, so the triangle is obtuse.

b.

The face has three acute angles, so the triangle is acute.

c.

The face has a right angle, so the triangle is a right triangle.

> The sum of the angles of any triangle is always equal to 180°.

MENTAL MATH

It is easy to add 50 and 60 because they both end in the same number of zeros. $5 + 6 = 11$, so $50 + 60 = 110$.

Example 2

Find the measure of the missing angle in each triangle.

a.

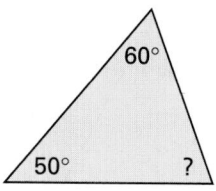

$$50° + 60° + ? = 180°$$
$$110° + ? = 180°$$
$$110° + \mathbf{70°} = 180°$$

The angle measures 70°.

b.

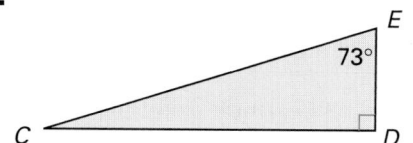

$\angle D$ is a right angle, so it measures 90°.

$$90° + 73° + ? = 180°$$
$$163° + ? = 180°$$
$$163° + \mathbf{17°} = 180°$$
$$m\angle C = 17°$$

Try It

Find the measure of the missing angle in each triangle. Then classify the triangle.

a.

5

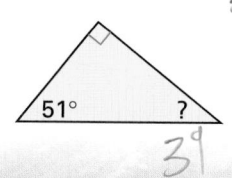

b.

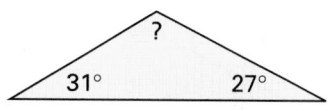

1. Can any three angles form a triangle? Explain.

2. Why can't a triangle have more than one obtuse angle?

8-4 Exercises and Applications

Practice and Apply

Getting Started Given the two angles of a triangle, find the third.

1. 100°, 40°   **2.** 60°, 60°   **3.** 80°, 20°   **4.** 50°, 50°   **5.** 30°, 50°   **6.** 80°, 90°

For Exercises 7–18, classify each triangle as acute, right, or obtuse.

7. 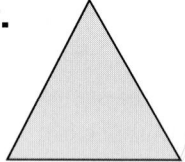   **8.** 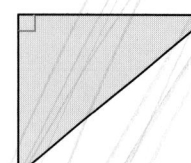   **9.** 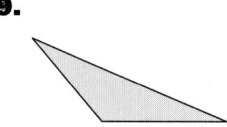   **10.**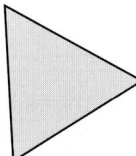

11.    **12.** 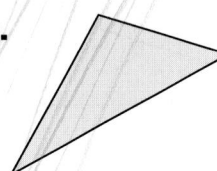   **13.**    **14.**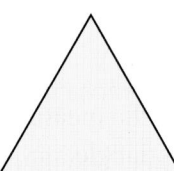

15. $m\angle T = 67°$, $m\angle H = 34°$, $m\angle W = 79°$ **16.** $m\angle S = 124°$, $m\angle D = 50°$, $m\angle P = 6°$

17. $m\angle V = 30°$, $m\angle R = 60°$, $m\angle F = 90°$ **18.** $m\angle E = 60°$, $m\angle J = 60°$, $m\angle B = 60°$

Use a protractor to determine the measure of all angles in each triangle.

19.    **20.** 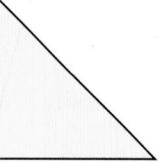   **21.** 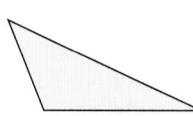   **22.**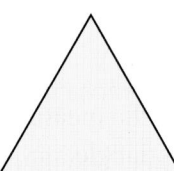

23. 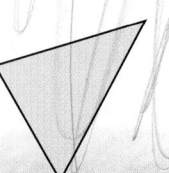   **24.** 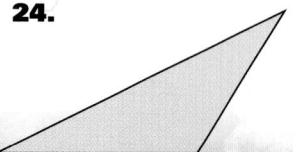   **25.** 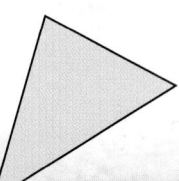   **26.**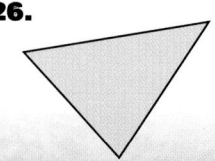

Find the measure of the missing angle in each triangle.

27. $m\angle A = 56°$, $m\angle B = 93°$, $m\angle C = \square$ **28.** $m\angle X = 115°$, $m\angle Y = 34°$, $m\angle Z = \square$

29. $m\angle L = 170°$, $m\angle M = 5°$, $m\angle N = \square$ **30.** $m\angle R = 48°$, $m\angle S = 63°$, $m\angle T = \square$

31. $m\angle I = 78°$, $m\angle J = 12°$, $m\angle K = \square$ **32.** $m\angle D = 25°$, $m\angle G = 80°$, $m\angle P = \square$

Geometry For Exercises 33–36, decide whether the angle measurements can form a triangle. If a triangle can be formed, draw and classify it.

33. 35°, 65°, 80°   **34.** 45°, 45°, 90°   **35.** 95°, 45°, 40°   **36.** 55°, 50°, 50°

37. **Science** Magnetite is one of only two common minerals that are magnetic. Magnetite was used in early versions of modern-day compasses. What are the angle measures for the magnetite crystal shown?

38. **Test Prep**   A triangle has angles *J*, *K*, and *L*. $m\angle J$ is 58°, and $\angle K$ is larger than $\angle J$. Which of the following is not a possible measure for $\angle L$?

    Ⓐ 58°   Ⓑ 32°   Ⓒ 70°   Ⓓ 51.5°

Problem Solving and Reasoning

39. **Journal** If you know the angle measurements of two triangles, can you determine which triangle has the larger area? Explain.

40. **Critical Thinking** Is the shadow of a right triangle always a right triangle? Explain.

41. **Choose a Strategy** A triangle has angles *A*, *B*, and *C*. The complement of $\angle A$ measures 58°, and the supplement of $\angle B$ measures 60°. What is the measure of $\angle C$? Explain your strategy.

Problem Solving
STRATEGIES

• Look for a Pattern
• Make an Organized List
• Make a Table
• Guess and Check
• Work Backward
• Use Logical Reasoning
• Draw a Diagram
• Solve a Simpler Problem

Mixed Review

Write each decimal as a fraction in lowest terms. *[Lesson 5-7]*

42. 0.75   **43.** 0.78   **44.** 0.596   **45.** 0.9   **46.** 0.38   **47.** 0.72

48. 0.55   **49.** 0.138   **50.** 0.7   **51.** 0.375   **52.** 0.2   **53.** 0.999

Estimate. *[Lesson 6-4]*

54. $5\frac{1}{2} - 4\frac{6}{8}$ **55.** $2\frac{6}{7} + 2\frac{1}{9}$ **56.** $4\frac{8}{9} - 2\frac{1}{3}$ **57.** $9\frac{5}{6} + 5\frac{3}{4}$

58. $6\frac{2}{7} + 9\frac{3}{7} + 4\frac{10}{11}$ **59.** $8\frac{9}{14} - 3\frac{5}{6}$ **60.** $7\frac{5}{7} + 7\frac{5}{7} + 6\frac{3}{5}$ **61.** $9\frac{4}{8} - 4\frac{3}{6}$

Exploring Sides of a Triangle

You'll Learn ...

■ to classify triangles according to their sides

... How It's Used

Sculptors classify triangles when designing a sculpture.

Vocabulary

equilateral triangle

isosceles triangle

scalene triangle

▶ **Lesson Link** You have investigated classifying triangles by their angles. Now you'll see how to classify triangles by the lengths of their sides. ◀

Explore | Sides of a Triangle

Pick Up Sticks

Materials: Cuisenaire rods

1. For each given set of rods, determine if the rods can be placed together to form a triangle. In order to count as a triangle, every rod must be touching corner to corner.

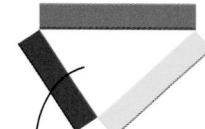 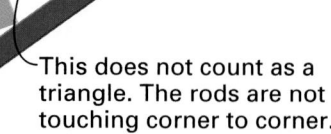

This counts as a triangle. All rods are touching corner to corner.

This does not count as a triangle. The rods are not touching corner to corner.

a. Orange, blue, dark green	**b.** Light green, yellow, dark green
c. Red, white, black	**d.** Yellow, brown, light green
e. Dark green, yellow, red	**f.** Purple, dark green, white
g. Orange, blue, white	**h.** Black, dark green, red

2. Find five new sets of three rods that can form a triangle. Find five new sets of three rods that cannot form a triangle.

3. Without actually putting them together, how can you tell whether or not three rods will form a triangle?

Learn | Sides of a Triangle

An **equilateral triangle** has three sides of the same length.

An **isoceles triangle** has two sides of the same length.

A **scalene triangle** has no sides of equal length.

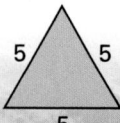
5 5
5

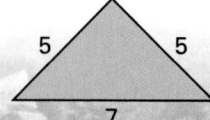
5 5
7

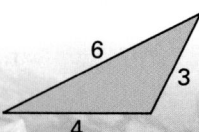
6 3
4

Example 1

The diamond is cut in the "American brilliant" style. Classify the triangles as shown that form facets *a*, *b*, and *c*.

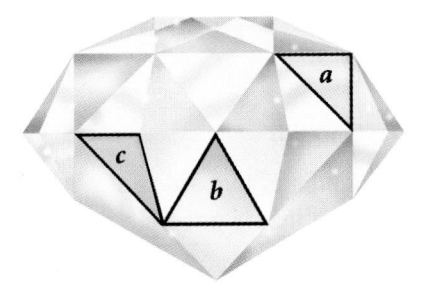

Triangle *a* has 2 equal sides, so it is isosceles. Triangle *b* has 3 equal sides, so it is equilateral. Triangle *c* has no equal sides, so it is scalene.

In order for three lengths to form a triangle, the sum of the two shortest lengths must be greater than the longest length.

In the first cabin, the combined heights of the walls was *greater than* the length of the floor.

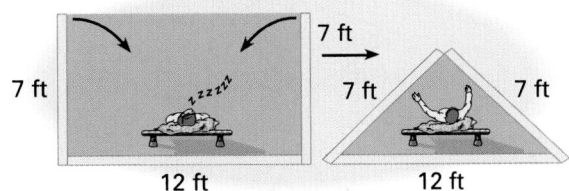

In the second cabin, the combined heights of the walls was *less than* the length of the floor.

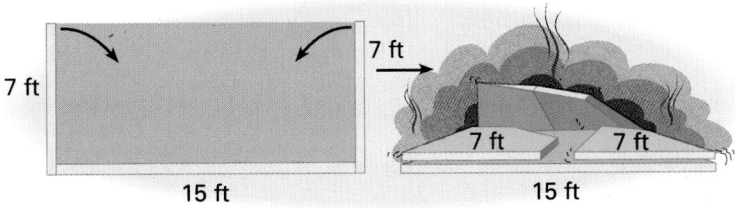

Examples

State whether the given lengths can form a triangle.

2 5 in., 9 in., 13 in.

$5 + 9 > 13$
A triangle can be formed.

3 10 cm, 14 cm, 25 cm

$10 + 14 < 25$
A triangle cannot be formed.

Try It

State whether the given lengths can form a triangle.

a. 2 ft, 5 ft, 6 ft   **b.** 11 in., 3 in., 8 in.   **c.** 3 m, 6 m, 2 m

Check Your Understanding

1. Can a right triangle also be isosceles? Explain.

2. Do all equilateral triangles have the same shape? The same size? Explain.

Practice and Apply

Getting Started Given the lengths of two sides of a triangle, state the greatest whole-number measurement that is possible for the third.

1. 1 m, 4 m   **2.** 2 in., 6 in.   **3.** 10 ft, 11 ft   **4.** 4 cm, 6 cm   **5.** 5 yd, 5 yd

For Exercises 6–17, classify each triangle as scalene, equilateral, or isosceles.

6.
1 cm   1 cm
1 cm

7.
5.5 ft
4.3 ft
2.8 ft

8.
6 yd
4.2 yd   2 yd

9.
7 m   7 m
3 m

10.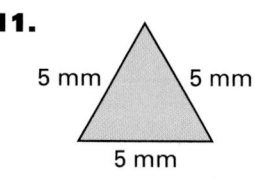
10 in.
4 in.
10 in.

11.
5 mm   5 mm
5 mm

12.
9 cm
4 cm
8 cm

13.
4.5 ft   3.2 ft
6.8 ft

14. Sides: 40 cm, 55 cm, 45 cm

15. Sides: 1.67 in., 1.53 in., 0.28 in.

16. Sides: 3 yd, 9 yd, 9 yd

17. Sides: 6 in., 6 in., 6 in.

State whether the given lengths can form a triangle. If they can, draw the triangle and classify it.

18. 5 cm, 3 cm, 2 cm   **19.** 3 in., 6 in., 8 in.   **20.** 7 m, 7 m, 10 m

21. 2.1 ft, 4.6 ft, 3.1 ft   **22.** 15 cm, 7 cm, 7 cm   **23.** 3 in., 6 in., 9 in.

24. 10 mm, 10 mm, 10 mm   **25.** 9.6 yd, 9.4 yd, 9.3 yd   **26.** 2 yd, 14 yd, 7 yd

27. History In ancient times it was thought that rock crystal was ice that had frozen so hard it would never melt. We know now that it is formed by other molecules, like silicon dioxide. Classify the triangular face of the smokey quartz rock crystal shown by the lengths of its sides.

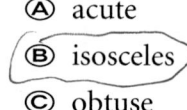

28. **Test Prep** Classify the triangle by the lengths of its sides.

Ⓐ acute

Ⓑ isosceles

Ⓒ obtuse

Ⓓ scalene

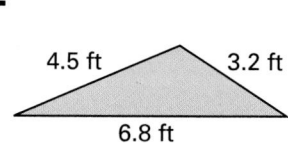
45°
5.66
4
90°   45°
4

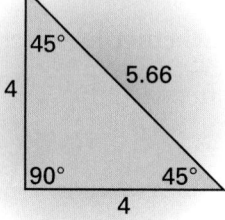

29. Geometry Jeremy has two poles for the end of his tent. They are each 4 feet long. Can he form the triangular end of his tent if he puts two pole ends together and places the other ends 9 feet apart?

Problem Solving and Reasoning

Critical Thinking Classify each triangle as acute, right, or obtuse, and also as equilateral, isosceles, or scalene.

30.
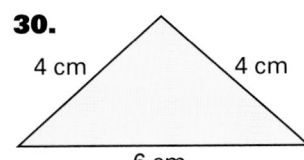
4 cm   4 cm
6 cm

31.
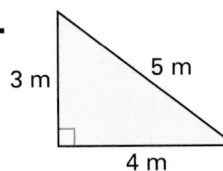
3 m   5 m
4 m

32.
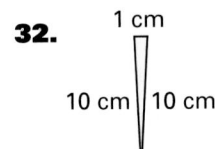
1 cm
10 cm   10 cm

33.
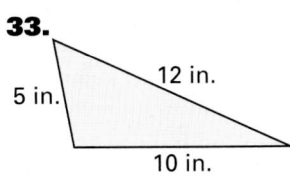
5 in.   12 in.
10 in.

Critical Thinking Explain whether it is possible to draw each triangle. If it is possible, draw the triangle.

34. An obtuse right triangle   **35.** A scalene acute triangle   **36.** An isosceles right triangle

37. Communicate If you fold an equilateral triangle in half, what kind of triangles are the smaller two triangles? Explain.

Mixed Review

Compare using, >, <, or =. *[Lesson 5-8]*

38. $\frac{3}{4} \square \frac{1}{3}$ **39.** $\frac{7}{8} \square \frac{6}{7}$ **40.** $\frac{5}{9} \square \frac{7}{10}$ **41.** $\frac{2}{4} \square \frac{9}{18}$ **42.** $\frac{20}{10} \square \frac{15}{3}$

Simplify. *[Lesson 6-5]*

43. $4\frac{3}{5} + 6\frac{2}{3}$ **44.** $3\frac{1}{4} + 4\frac{3}{7}$ **45.** $10 + 13\frac{4}{8}$ **46.** $62\frac{3}{4} + 3\frac{5}{9}$

47. $6\frac{1}{5} + 5\frac{2}{7}$ **48.** $8\frac{4}{7} + 9\frac{10}{14}$ **49.** $5\frac{6}{7} + 1\frac{4}{5}$ **50.** $7\frac{2}{7} + 4\frac{6}{9}$

Project Progress

When you have finished your rough sketch, draw a revised version. Add any polygons as needed, and describe these polygons.

Problem Solving

Understand
Plan
Solve
Look Back

Polygons

You'll Learn ...

■ to classify polygons

... How It's Used

Motorists classify shapes when reading traffic signs.

Vocabulary

polygon

quadrilateral

pentagon

hexagon

octagon

regular polygon

▶ **Lesson Link** In the last lesson, you studied triangles—figures with three sides and three angles. Now you'll look at figures with more than three sides and three angles. ◀

Explore | Geometric Figures

Shape Shifters

1. Put the twelve figures at the right into four groups of three. The figures within a group must have something in common. Every figure must belong to one and only one group.

2. For each group, write one or two sentences explaining what the figures have in common.

3. Add a fifth group of three figures. These three figures must also have a common feature, but it cannot be the same as any of the features used for the first four groups.

4. In general, what features of a figure are important when comparing it to other figures?

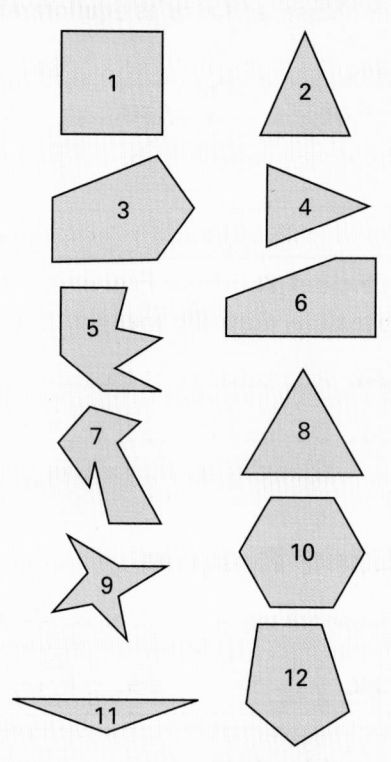

Learn | Polygons

A **polygon** is a closed figure made of line segments. The word *polygon* comes from Greek and means "many angled."

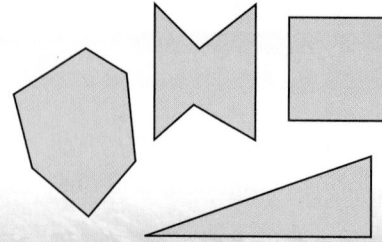

Polygons are classified by the number of sides they have. You've already studied the *triangle*, which has 3 sides. These are also polygons:

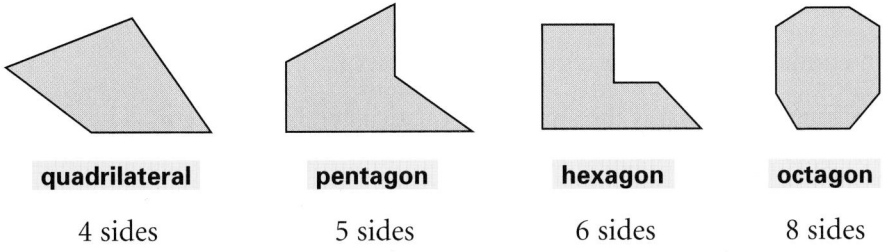

quadrilateral	**pentagon**	**hexagon**	**octagon**
4 sides	5 sides	6 sides	8 sides

In a **regular polygon**, all the sides and all the angles have the same measures.

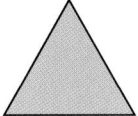  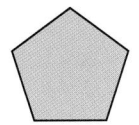 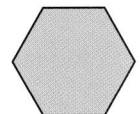 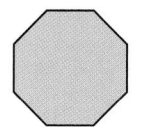

Examples

Name each polygon and tell if it appears to be regular or irregular.

1

The figure is a triangle. Its sides and angles are equal, so it is regular.

2

The figure is a quadrilateral. Neither its sides nor its angles are equal, so it is irregular.

3

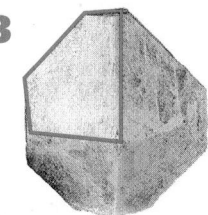

The figure is a pentagon. Neither its sides nor its angles are equal, so it is irregular.

Try It

Name each polygon and tell if it appears to be regular or irregular.

a.

b.

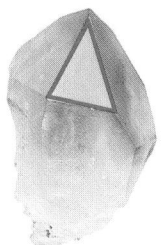

c.

1. Is an equilateral triangle a regular polygon? Explain.

2. Name something that is the shape of a quadrilateral; a pentagon; a hexagon; an octagon.

8-6 Exercises and Applications

Practice and Apply

Getting Started State why each figure is not a polygon.

1.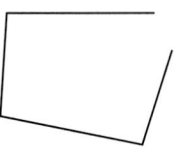

2.

3.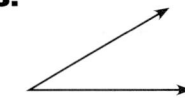

4.

Name each polygon and tell if it is regular or irregular.

5.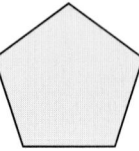

6.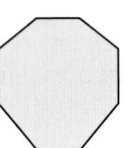

7.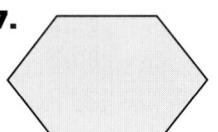

8.

9.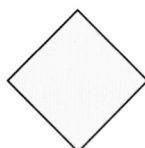

10.

11.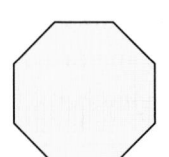

12.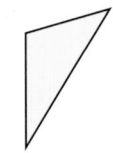

Draw an example of each figure and classify each of the angles in your drawing.

13. Irregular quadrilateral
14. Regular pentagon
15. Regular hexagon
16. Irregular octagon
17. Regular triangle
18. Irregular pentagon

Industry What kind of polygon is each traffic sign?

19.

20.

21.

22.

23. Science Rays and skates are relatives of sharks. Their fins are greatly enlarged and flap like wings when they swim. What polygon can the shape of the ray shown be most closely classified as?

Geometry State the shape of the crystal face.

24.

25.

26.

27. The floor of a ballroom in a large hotel is shaped like an octagon. How many walls does the room have?

28. **Test Prep** Classify the polygon.

   Ⓐ Regular quadrilateral   Ⓑ Irregular pentagon

   Ⓒ Regular hexagon   Ⓓ Irregular octagon

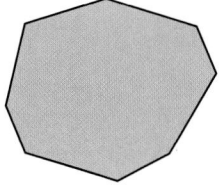

Problem Solving and Reasoning

29. Critical Thinking Find the perimeter of a regular octagon with one side measuring 5 inches. Explain how you could find the area of the figure.

30. Critical Thinking The lengths of the sides of a quadrilateral are 3.5 ft, $\frac{7}{2}$ ft, $3\frac{1}{2}$ ft, and $2\frac{3}{2}$ ft. Is the quadrilateral regular or irregular? Explain.

31. Journal Classify acute, right, obtuse, equilateral, isosceles, and scalene triangles as regular or irregular polygons. Explain your reasoning.

Mixed Review

Order from smallest to largest. *[Lesson 5-8]*

32. $\frac{3}{5}, \frac{3}{6}, \frac{3}{7}$ **33.** $\frac{8}{9}, \frac{4}{5}, \frac{7}{8}$ **34.** $\frac{13}{2}, \frac{12}{3}, \frac{14}{15}$ **35.** $\frac{6}{9}, \frac{9}{6}, \frac{6}{6}$

36. $\frac{24}{3}, \frac{24}{8}, \frac{24}{6}$ **37.** $\frac{1}{2}, \frac{1}{3}, \frac{1}{4}$ **38.** $\frac{4}{6}, \frac{6}{8}, \frac{8}{10}$ **39.** $\frac{6}{7}, \frac{7}{6}, \frac{9}{8}$

Simplify. *[Lesson 6-6]*

40. $3\frac{3}{4} - 1\frac{2}{3}$ **41.** $5\frac{4}{7} - 3\frac{4}{5}$ **42.** $6\frac{1}{3} - 3\frac{2}{6}$ **43.** $4\frac{3}{8} - 4\frac{1}{4}$ **44.** $8\frac{5}{6} - 7\frac{1}{3}$

45. $12\frac{5}{8} - 9\frac{3}{7}$ **46.** $9\frac{2}{5} - 4\frac{6}{7}$ **47.** $7\frac{1}{3} - \frac{8}{9}$ **48.** $3\frac{3}{4} - 1\frac{3}{8}$ **49.** $6\frac{4}{7} - 2\frac{1}{4}$

Quadrilaterals

You'll Learn ...

■ to classify quadrilaterals

... How It's Used

Software engineers use quadrilaterals when drawing diagrams to illustrate how a program functions.

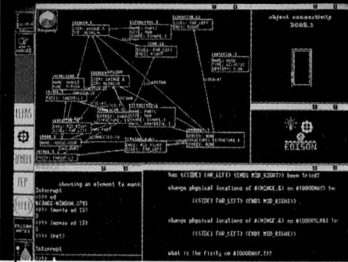

Vocabulary

trapezoid

parallelogram

rhombus

rectangle

square

▶ **Lesson Link**   In the last lesson, you learned to identify quadrilaterals. Now you'll see how quadrilaterals are classified. ◄

Explore   Quadrilaterals

In Your Own Words ...

Each group shows three examples of a particular type of quadrilateral, and one nonexample. For each type of quadrilateral, write a definition in your own words.

1.
Alpha   Alpha   Alpha   Not an alpha

2.
Beta   Beta   Beta   Not a beta

3.
Gamma   Gamma   Gamma   Not a gamma

4.
Delta   Delta   Delta   Not a delta

Learn   Quadrilaterals

Any **polygon** with four sides is a quadrilateral. There are five special types of quadrilaterals: **trapezoid** , **parallelogram** , **rhombus** , **rectangle** , and **square** . Each has a different set of features, and some figures can be classified in more than one way.

Definitions of Quadrilaterals

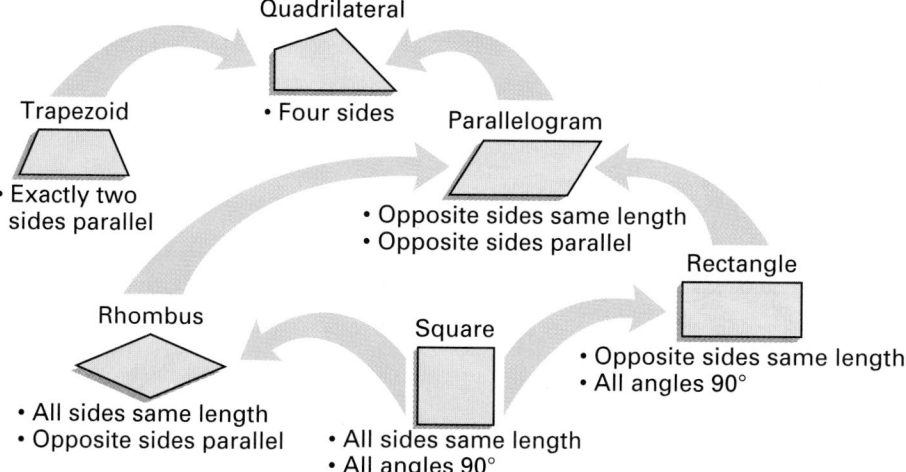

Quadrilateral
• Four sides

Trapezoid
• Exactly two sides parallel

Parallelogram
• Opposite sides same length
• Opposite sides parallel

Rectangle
• Opposite sides same length
• All angles 90°

Rhombus
• All sides same length
• Opposite sides parallel

Square
• All sides same length
• All angles 90°

▶ **Language Link**

The prefix *quad-* means "four." For example, a quadruped is an animal with four legs. A sound system that is quadraphonic uses four separate sound tracks.

Examples

1 True or false: A square is a rectangle.

A square has opposite sides of the same length, and all angles are 90°. A square is a rectangle. The statement is true.

2 Classify the figure in as many ways as possible.

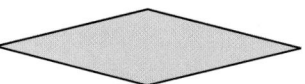

The figure is a *quadrilateral*, a *parallelogram*, and a *rhombus*.

Try It

Answer *true* or *false*.

a. A rhombus is a trapezoid.   **b.** A rectangle is a parallelogram.

c. Classify the figure in as many ways as possible.

Problem Solving TIP

The chart above can help you find all the classifications for a figure. For example, "rhombus" points to "parallelogram," which points to "quadrilateral." So, any rhombus is also a parallelogram and also a quadrilateral.

Check | Your Understanding

1. A geometry book said that a square is a "rectangular rhombus." Do you agree? Explain your reasoning.

2. How are trapezoids and parallelograms alike? How are they different?

3. Quadrilaterals can be classified based on whether or not their opposite sides are parallel. Can triangles also be classified in this way? Explain.

Practice and Apply

Getting Started For each figure, state how many pairs of opposites sides are parallel.

1.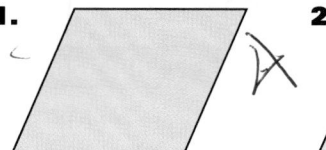

2.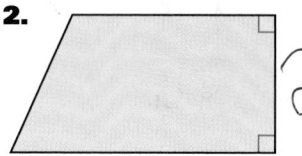

3.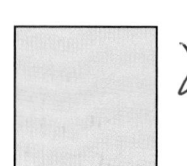

4. *none*

Answer true or false.

5. Every four-sided figure can be classified as more than one type of quadrilateral. *True*

6. A square is also a parallelogram. T

7. A trapezoid is never a rectangle.

Classify each figure in as many ways as possible.

8.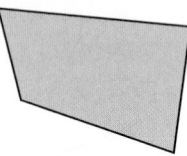

9.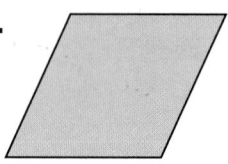

10. *trap poly*

11.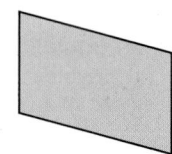

12.

13.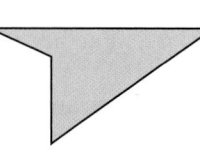

14.

15.

Draw an example of each figure. Classify each of the angles in your drawing.

16. Trapezoid 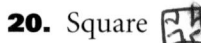 17. Parallelogram 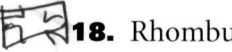 18. Rhombus

19. Rectangle 20. Square 21. Quadrilateral

22. **History** In 1851, the Crystal Palace was built in London as an exhibition hall. The roof and outer walls were built of almost 300,000 panes of glass. Are any windows parallelograms?

23. **Test Prep** What kind of quadrilaterals are the states of Nevada and Arkansas shaped like?

Ⓐ Trapezoids

Ⓑ Squares

Ⓒ Rectangles

Ⓓ Rhombuses

Measurement Given the information, can you determine the lengths of each figure's sides? If so, give the lengths.

24. A parallelogram with a perimeter of 64 inches.

25. A rhombus with a perimeter of 8 feet.

26. A trapezoid with a perimeter of 52 inches and a side of 12 inches.

Problem Solving and Reasoning

27. **Journal** Every square is also a rectangle, but every rectangle is not necessarily a square. Explain.

28. **Critical Thinking** The sides of an octagon are the same length, and all opposite sides are parallel. Can the octagon be classified as a rhombus? Explain your reasoning.

29. **Communicate** Explain why the shape of the kite shown cannot be classified as a trapezoid, a parallelogram, a rhombus, a rectangle, or a square.

Mixed Review

Compare using $>$, $<$, or $=$. *[Lesson 5-8]*

30. $\frac{1}{2}$ ☐ 0.54   **31.** $\frac{3}{4}$ ☐ 0.65   **32.** $\frac{2}{9}$ ☐ 0.4   **33.** $\frac{5}{6}$ ☐ 0.83   **34.** $\frac{2}{3}$ ☐ 0.67   **35.** $\frac{4}{5}$ ☐ 0.8

36. $\frac{5}{8}$ ☐ 0.652   **37.** $\frac{1}{7}$ ☐ 0.2   **38.** $\frac{2}{5}$ ☐ 0.4   **39.** $\frac{11}{22}$ ☐ 0.5   **40.** $\frac{6}{9}$ ☐ 0.75   **41.** $\frac{2}{6}$ ☐ 0.25

Multiply. *[Lesson 3-8]*

42. 5×6.27 **43.** 12×2.45 **44.** 3×0.151 **45.** 56.7×4

46. 34.56×100 **47.** 6.89×7 **48.** $\$34 \times 1.4$ **49.** 0.04×10

TECHNOLOGY

Using Dynamic Geometry Software • Finding Relationships in Triangles

Problem: How can you determine the relationship between the longest side of a triangle and the largest angle?

You can use geometry software to explore triangle relationships. Using the software, you can quickly create and analyze many different examples of triangles.

1 Using your geometry software, draw a triangle. Label the vertices of the triangle *A, B,* and *C.* Use the measuring tool to measure the side lengths and the angles.

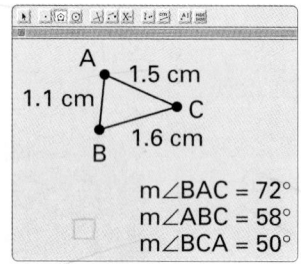

A
1.5 cm
1.1 cm
C
1.6 cm
B

m∠BAC = 72°
m∠ABC = 58°
m∠BCA = 50°

2 Record which side is the longest and which angle is the largest.

3 Drag one of the points to a new location, and record which side is now the longest, and which angle is now the largest.

4 Repeat Step 3 until you have looked at five or six triangles. Describe any patterns in your data.

Solution: The longest side is always opposite the largest angle.

TRY IT

a. Find the relationship between the shortest side and the smallest angle.

b. Find the relationship between the angles opposite the equal sides of an isosceles triangle.

ON YOUR OWN

▶ Did it help your investigation to label the vertices of the triangle as *A, B,* and *C*? Explain.

▶ When investigating triangles, is it easier to create examples on paper or with geometry software? Why?

▶ Without using geometry software, how could you verify which of two angles is the larger?

440

Section 8B Connect

In this section, you've learned to classify polygons. Now you'll use what you've learned to describe the design of a beautiful and unusual diamond.

The Geometry of Gems

Materials: Ruler

The diagram shows an unusual diamond pattern called the "cross-rose." Each polygon is a face that has been ground into the crystal by the diamond cutter.

1. Copy the pattern onto a sheet of paper. Label the points as in the figure.

2. Find examples of as many of the following figures as you can in the cross-rose design. Use letters to identify each figure.

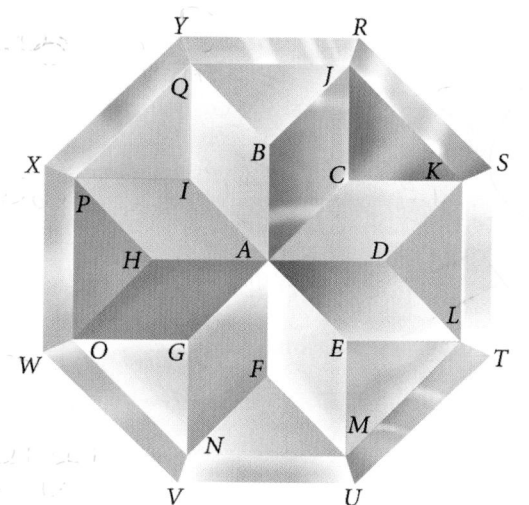

acute triangle	right triangle	obtuse triangle
equilateral triangle	isosceles triangle	scalene triangle
polygon	quadrilateral	pentagon
hexagon	octagon	regular polygon
parallelogram	rectangle	rhombus
square	trapezoid	

3. Some of the figures above cannot be found unless you add a line segment to the pattern. What figures could you find if you added a line segment? Where would you add the segment?

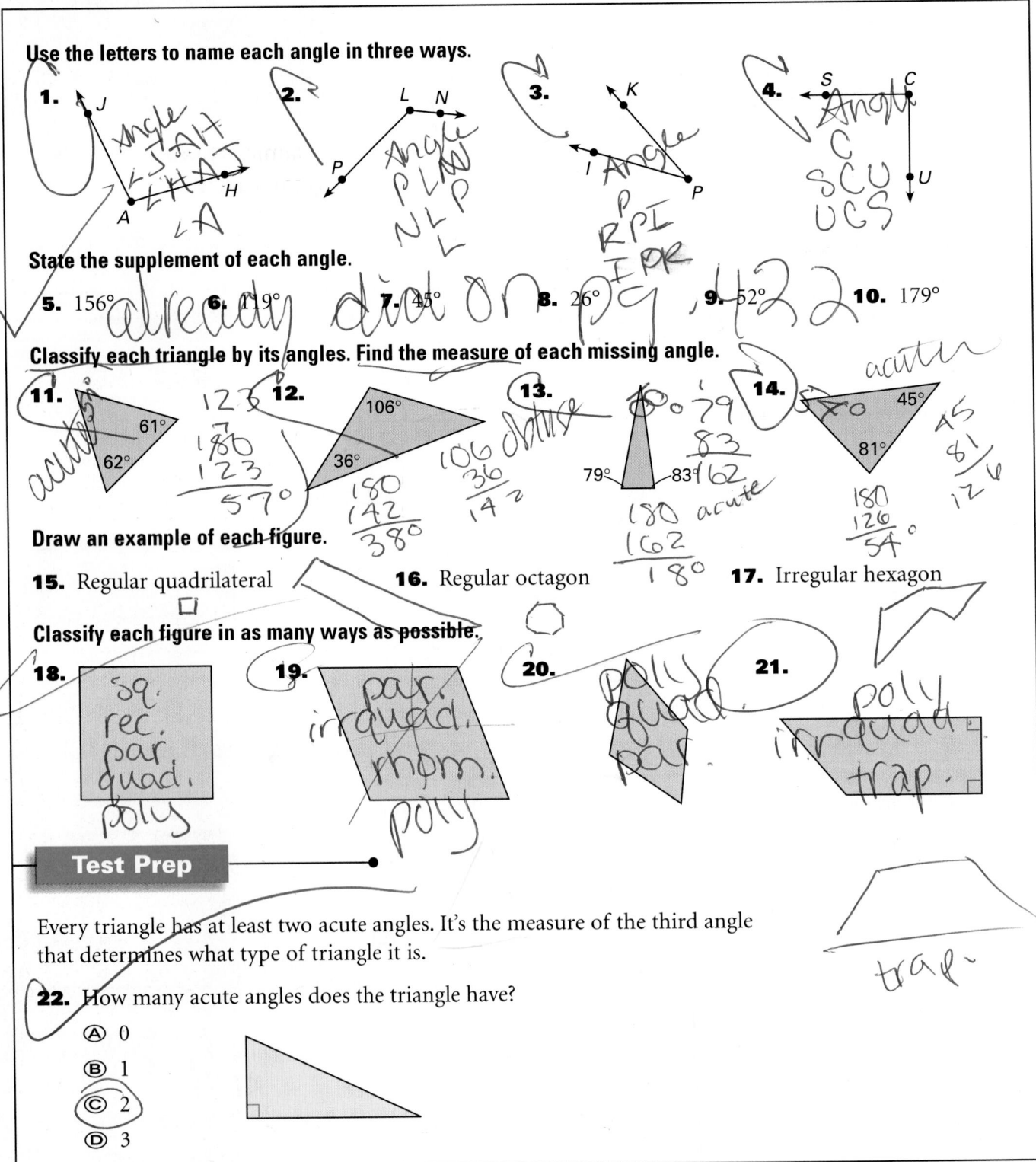

Use the letters to name each angle in three ways.

1. *(handwritten)* angle ∠JAH ∠HAJ ∠A

2. *(handwritten)* angle PLN NLP L

3. *(handwritten)* angle RPI IPR

4. *(handwritten)* Angle C SCU UCS

State the supplement of each angle. *(handwritten: already did on pg. 422)*

5. 156°   6. 119°   7. 45°   8. 26°   9. 52°   10. 179°

Classify each triangle by its angles. Find the measure of each missing angle.

11. *(handwritten)* acute, 61°, 62°, 123, 180, 123, 57°

12. *(handwritten)* 106°, 36°, 180, 142, 38°

13. *(handwritten)* 106 obtuse, 36, 142; 79°, 83°, 180 acute, 162, 180

14. *(handwritten)* acute, 79, 83, 62; 45°, 81°, 45, 81, 126, 180, 54°

Draw an example of each figure.

15. Regular quadrilateral

16. Regular octagon

17. Irregular hexagon

Classify each figure in as many ways as possible.

18. *(handwritten)* sq. rec. par. quad. poly

19. *(handwritten)* par. irr. quad. rhom. poly

20. *(handwritten)* poly quad. par.

21. *(handwritten)* poly irr. quad. trap.

Test Prep

Every triangle has at least two acute angles. It's the measure of the third angle that determines what type of triangle it is.

22. How many acute angles does the triangle have?

Ⓐ 0

Ⓑ 1

Ⓒ 2

Ⓓ 3

(handwritten in left margin: GOOD JOB!!)

(handwritten: trap.)

SECTION 8C

Transformations

▶ Fine Arts Link ▶ History Link ▶ www.mathsurf.com/6/ch8/Islam_art

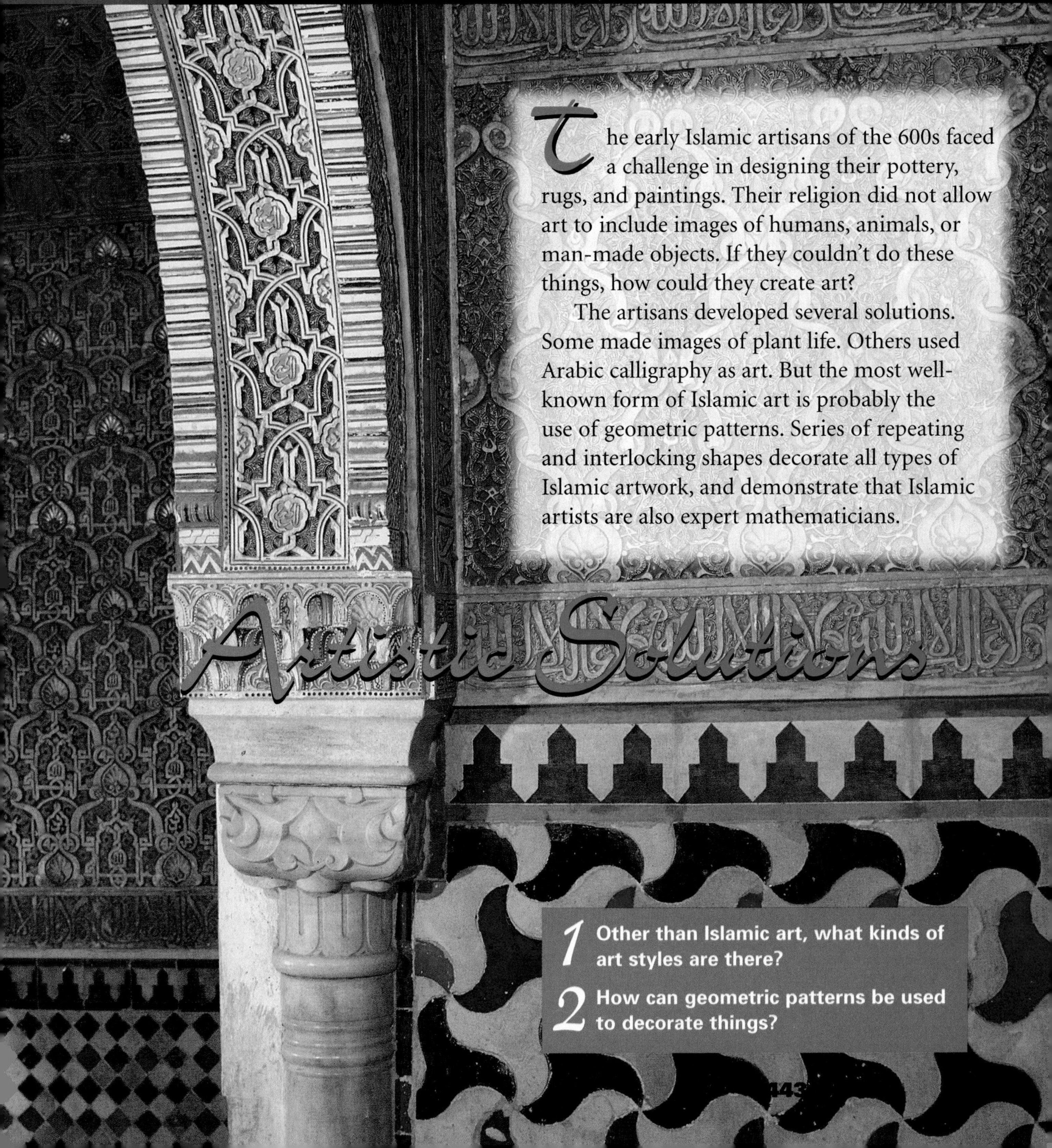

Artistic Solutions

The early Islamic artisans of the 600s faced a challenge in designing their pottery, rugs, and paintings. Their religion did not allow art to include images of humans, animals, or man-made objects. If they couldn't do these things, how could they create art?

The artisans developed several solutions. Some made images of plant life. Others used Arabic calligraphy as art. But the most well-known form of Islamic art is probably the use of geometric patterns. Series of repeating and interlocking shapes decorate all types of Islamic artwork, and demonstrate that Islamic artists are also expert mathematicians.

1 **Other than Islamic art, what kinds of art styles are there?**

2 **How can geometric patterns be used to decorate things?**

8-8

Flips and Line Symmetry

You'll Learn ...

■ to identify reflections of figures

■ to identify line symmetry

... How It's Used

Photographers use symmetry when composing portraits and landscape photographs.

Vocabulary

congruent

line symmetry

reflection

▶ **Lesson Link** In the last section, you learned to classify polygons. Now you'll investigate geometric figures involving repeated patterns. ◀

Explore Symmetry

Let's See What Unfolds ...

Materials: Unlined paper, Scissors

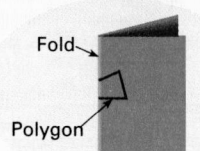

1. Fold a sheet of paper in half. Draw a polygon with one side *along the fold*. Cut out the figure. Do not cut through the fold. Sketch the shape you think it will have. Open the cutout and compare it with the one you predicted.

2. Fold a sheet from left to right, then top to bottom. With the paper as shown, draw 2 or 3 line segments from the top fold to the left fold. Repeat Step 1.

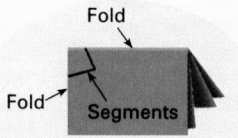

3. Fold a sheet "accordion style" with three folds. Draw a polygon with one side along the top fold. Repeat Step 1, cutting through all four layers.

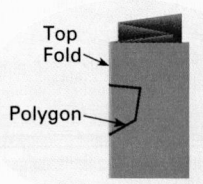

4. Compare your paper shapes. Describe anything you can find that all three shapes have in common.

Learn Flips and Line Symmetry

Two figures are **congruent** if they have the same size and shape.

A figure that can be folded into congruent halves has **line symmetry**.

A **reflection** is the mirror image of a figure that has been "flipped" over a line.

Examples

This Islamic design is an illuminated page of Nasta'liq script by Mir'Ali Haravi from the early 16th century Safavid dynasty in Iran. Tell whether each figure has line symmetry. If it does, copy the figure and draw its line(s) of symmetry.

Ink and color on paper. Gift of the Todd G. Williams Memorial Fund and the Society for Asian Art. The Asian Art Museum of San Francisco. B87-D6.

► **History Link**

Early Islamic artists believed that the universe had a natural order to it. They chose to make their designs symmetrical as a representation of this natural order.

1

Yes. The figure has two lines of symmetry.

2 No. The figure does not have line symmetry.

3 Draw the reflection of the figure over the line.

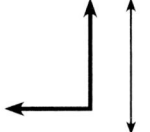   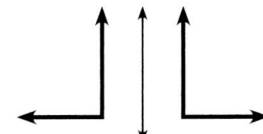

Try It

Tell whether each figure has line symmetry. If so, draw its line(s) of symmetry.

a.    b. 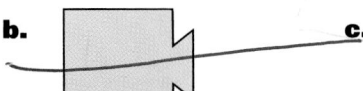   c.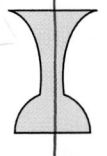

Check   Your Understanding

1. What does it mean to say that a reflection is a "mirror image"?

2. *B* is the reflection of *A*. Are *A* and *B* congruent? Explain.

Practice and Apply

Getting Started Trace each figure and draw its reflection over the line.

1.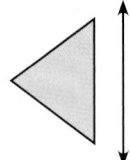

2.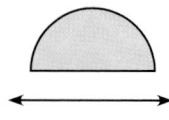

3.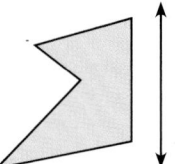

4.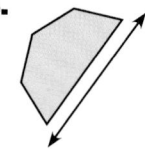

Tell if each photo has line symmetry. If it does, tell how many lines of symmetry it has.

5.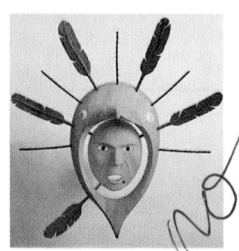

6.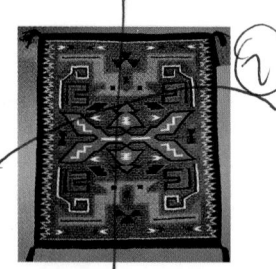

7.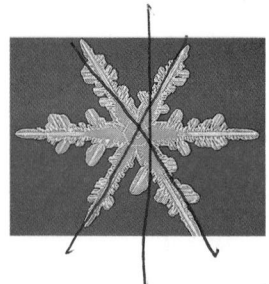

8.

Tell if each line is a line of symmetry.

9.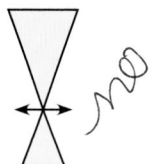

10.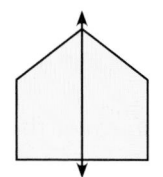

11.

12.

Tell if each pair of figures is congruent. If *not*, draw a figure that is congruent to each.

13.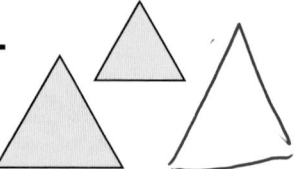

14.

15. Fine Arts This window is from the Dome of the Rock mosque in Jerusalem, Israel. Describe the lines of symmetry in the window's design.

Geometry The front wall of the Islamic palace of Mshatta was built around 743. Use the design on the wall for Exercises 16 and 17.

16. Sketch a pair of congruent figures in the design.

17. Determine the number of lines of symmetry that the design has.

18. **Test Prep** Look at the shape to the right. Choose the shape that is a reflection of this shape.

Ⓐ    Ⓑ 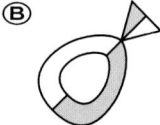   Ⓒ    Ⓓ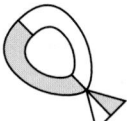

Problem Solving and Reasoning

19. Critical Thinking Draw a regular octagon, a regular hexagon, and a regular pentagon. Which polygon has the most lines of symmetry? Explain.

20. Critical Thinking A triangle has one angle of 40°. The other angles are congruent to each other. What are the measurements of the other two angles? Explain.

21. **Journal** List five objects in your classroom or home that have line symmetry. Explain why and describe the line(s) of symmetry.

Mixed Review

Order from smallest to largest. *[Lesson 5-8]*

22. $\frac{5}{6}$, 0.5, $\frac{1}{3}$ **23.** $\frac{7}{9}$, $\frac{2}{3}$, 0.75   **24.** $\frac{14}{7}$, $\frac{7}{7}$, 2.12   **25.** 1.1, $\frac{7}{6}$, 1.167

26. 2.2, 2.22, $\frac{2}{22}$ **27.** $\frac{1}{3}$, $\frac{3}{1}$, 1.3   **28.** $\frac{1}{10}$, 1.10, 10.1   **29.** 2.5, $\frac{2}{5}$, 0.25

Multiply. *[Lesson 3-9]*

30. 4.6×8.2 **31.** 9.54×3.2 **32.** 0.06×3.29 **33.** 0.92×4.76

34. 3.1×3.1 **35.** 1.9×9.1 **36.** 0.4×0.44 **37.** 6.6×0.6

Turns and Rotational Symmetry

You'll Learn ...

■ to identify rotations of figures

■ to identify rotational symmetry

... How It's Used

Quilt makers use rotational symmetry when designing the pattern for a quilt.

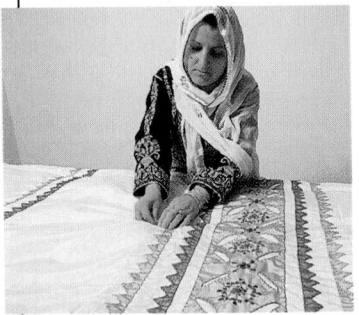

Vocabulary

rotation

clockwise

counterclockwise

rotational symmetry

▶ **Lesson Link**   In the last lesson, you saw what happens when a figure is flipped over a line. Now you'll look at what happens when a figure is turned like a wheel. ◀

Explore   Turns

Materials: Tracing paper

It's Your Turn

The 15 shapes below include 7 pairs of identical shapes. One of the shapes in each pair has been turned to face a different direction. One shape below has no match, no matter how you turn it.

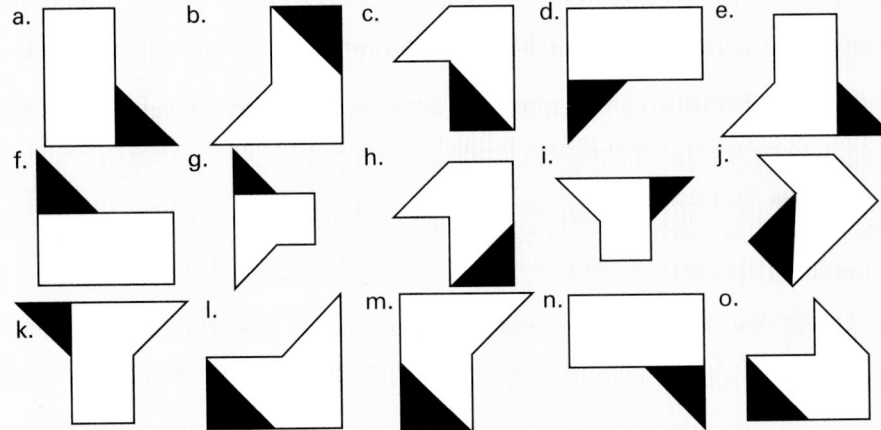

1. For each shape, find its match. Which shape has no match?

2. Draw a match for the leftover shape. Make sure it is turned to face a different direction. How can you prove the two shapes are a match?

Learn   Turns and Rotational Symmetry

A **rotation** is the image of a figure that has been turned, as if it were on a wheel. When the top of a figure turns to the right, it is turned **clockwise**. When the top turns to the left, it is turned **counterclockwise**.

 Figure   1/4 turn clockwise   1/4 turn counter-clockwise

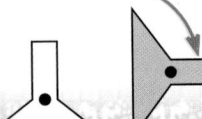 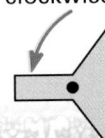

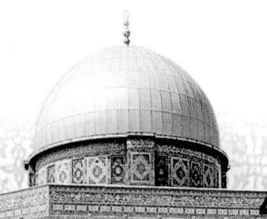

If a figure can be rotated less than a full circle, and the rotation exactly matches the original image, then the figure has **rotational symmetry** .

This figure has 180° rotational symmetry. If you turn it 180°, it will "land on itself," exactly matching the original image.

The figure at the right has 90°, 180°, and 270° rotational symmetry.

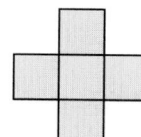

This figure does not have rotational symmetry.

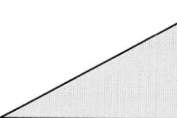

Examples

Give the least number of degrees and the direction that each figure has been rotated.

1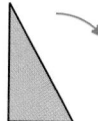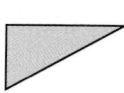

The figure has been rotated 90° clockwise.

2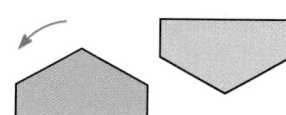

The figure has been rotated 180° counterclockwise.

3 If the figure is rotated 360°, how many times will it land on itself?

The figure will land on itself three times.

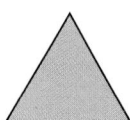

Try It

Give the number of degrees and the direction that each figure has been rotated.

a.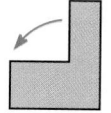

b.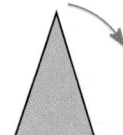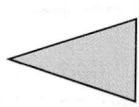

c. If the figure is rotated 360°, how many times will it land on itself?

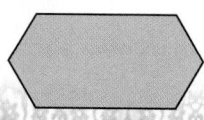

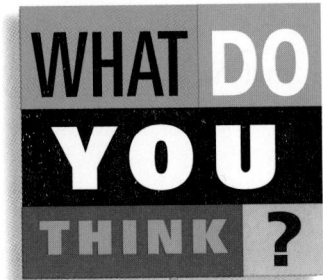

Peter and Tyreka are making a scrapbook of designs that display symmetry. They need a figure that has rotational symmetry for 180°. They want to know if they can use this mosque design.

Peter thinks ...

I'll trace the figure on tracing paper. Then I'll rotate the paper 180°.

The rotated figure matches the figure on the mosque. Therefore, the figure shows 180° rotational symmetry.

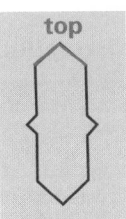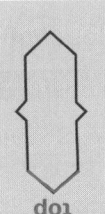

Tyreka thinks ...

I'll reflect the figure over a line vertically.

Then I'll reflect the resulting figure over a line horizontally.

The result matches the original figure. Therefore, the figure shows 180° rotational symmetry

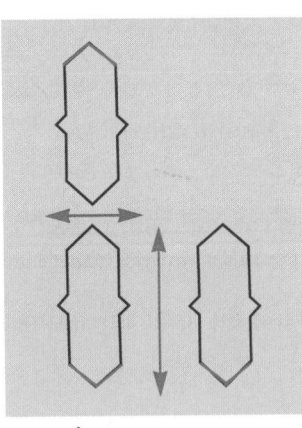

What do you think?

1. How does Tyreka's method work? Can you always use it to show that a figure has 180° rotational symmetry?

2. What advantages does Peter's method have over Tyreka's method? Tyreka's method over Peter's?

1. A figure has no rotational symmetry. How many degrees must you rotate it before it lands on itself?

2. If a figure is rotated, is it congruent to the original shape? Explain.

8-9 Exercises and Applications

Practice and Apply

Getting Started Draw a 90° counterclockwise rotation of each figure.

1.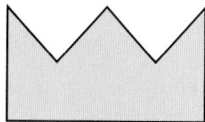

2.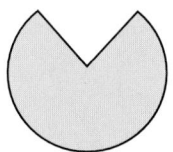

3.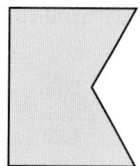

4.

What is the least rotation that will land the figure on top of itself?

5.

6.

7.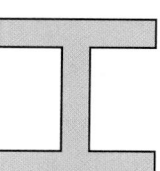

8.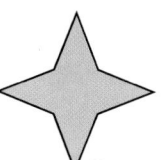

Draw a 45° clockwise rotation of the figure.

9.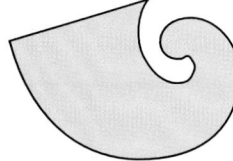

10.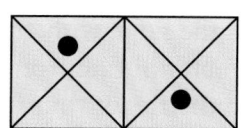

11.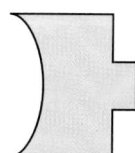

12.

13. **Fine Arts** What is the least rotation that will land the design on top of itself?

IL-KHANID STAR-SHAPED TILE, 1293. Earthenware with lustre decoration. The Avery Brundage Collection. The Asian Art Museum of San Francisco. B60 P2148.

Estimation Estimate the number of degrees that each figure has been rotated.

14.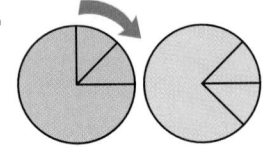

15.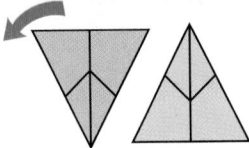

16.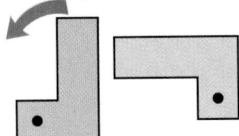

17.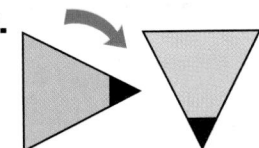

18. **Fine Arts** If one of the flowers in the pattern is rotated 360°, how many times will it land on itself?

19. **Fine Arts** What is the least number of degrees of rotation that will land a flower on top of itself?

20. **Test Prep** Choose the example of a rotation.

Ⓐ   Ⓑ   Ⓒ

Problem Solving and Reasoning

21. **Communicate** Can every figure be rotated so that it will land on top of itself? Explain.

22. **Communicate** Does the area, perimeter, or shape of a figure change when it is rotated? Explain.

23. **Critical Thinking** Fold a piece of paper in half and then in half again. Cut out a figure that has rotational symmetry. Do the same with another piece of paper. Cut out a figure that has line symmetry but not rotational symmetry. Describe the differences between the symmetries of your figures.

Mixed Review

Divide. Round the quotient to the nearest hundredth. [Lesson 3-10]

24. $36.39 \div 5$ 25. $14.2 \div 4$ 26. $1.89 \div 10$ 27. $2.86 \div 22$

28. $25.5 \div 5$ 29. $0.65 \div 11$ 30. $0.79 \div 8$ 31. $7.111 \div 3$

Divide. Round to the nearest hundredth. [Lesson 3-11]

32. $13.26 \div 0.6$ 33. $98.28 \div 5.4$ 34. $16.324 \div 1.54$ 35. $57.2 \div 21.3$

36. $37.97 \div 0.78$ 37. $100.82 \div 7.1$ 38. $0.75 \div 0.25$ 39. $39.2 \div 5.6$

Slides and Tessellations

▶ Lesson Link You know what happens to a figure when you flip it or turn it. Now you'll see what happens when you slide a figure to a new position. ◀

Explore | Slides and Tessellations

I've Got You Covered!

Materials: Tracing paper, Unlined paper

These shapes represent different tiles for sale. Which of the shapes could be used to cover the floor without having any space in between tiles?

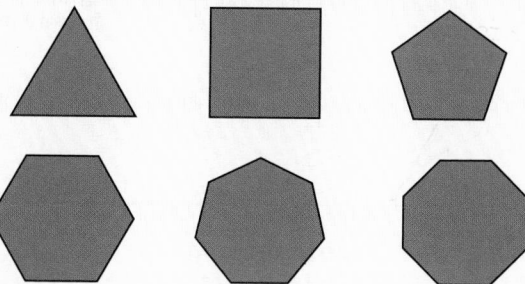

1. Copy each shape onto tracing paper several times. Copy the shapes as closely together as possible without overlaps. Then state whether each shape can or cannot be put together with copies of itself, leaving no spaces in between.

2. Draw a shape that does not appear above but that could be used to entirely cover a floor without any spaces in between.

3. Look at all of the shapes that can fit together without spaces in between. What patterns do you see that could help you determine if a shape would work without using tracing paper?

You'll Learn ...

■ to identify translations of figures and tessellations

... How It's Used

Graphic designers use translations and tessellations when designing logos and graphic artwork.

Vocabulary

translation

tessellation

Learn | Slides and Tessellations

When a figure is slid to a new position without flipping or turning, the new image is called a slide, or a **translation** .

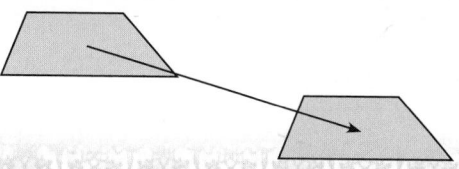

In Islamic art, the design of a mosaic wall sometimes consists of a single figure translated to every possible position on the wall. As a result, the wall is completely covered by the figure.

A pattern of congruent shapes like the one above, with no gaps or overlaps, is called a **tessellation**.

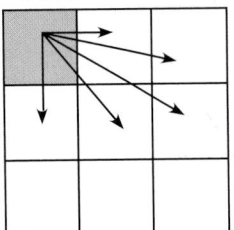

No spaces in between

A square tessellates.

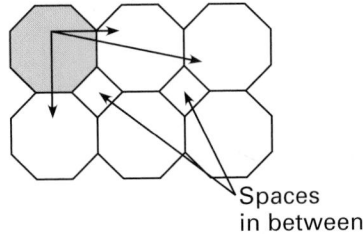

Spaces in between

A regular octagon does not tessellate.

Example

Does the figure tessellate? Make a drawing to show your answer.

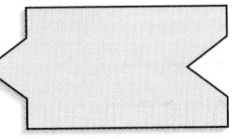

Yes, the figure tessellates.

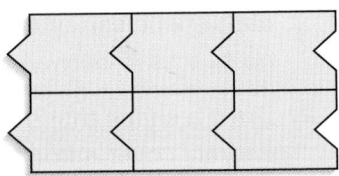

Try It

Does the figure tessellate? Make a drawing to show your answer.

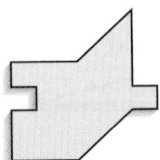

Check Your Understanding

1. Does a figure that tessellates have line symmetry? Rotational symmetry? Explain.

2. Can you tessellate any shape? Make a drawing to show your answer.

Practice and Apply

Getting Started State whether one figure is a translation of the other.

1.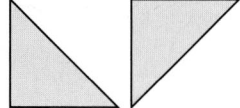

2.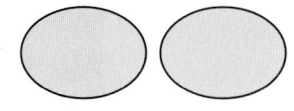

3.

4.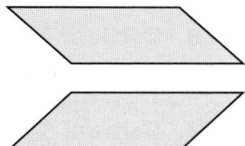

These designs can be found on the Dome of the Rock in Jerusalem, the oldest Islamic monument standing. Name the polygons that are tessellated in the designs.

5.

6.

State if the figure tessellates. Make a drawing to show your answer.

7.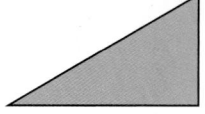

8.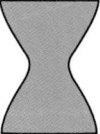

9.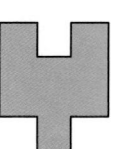

10.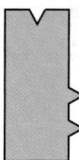

11.

12.

13.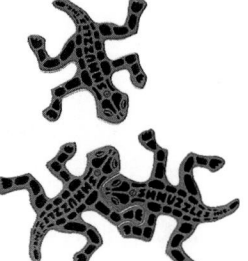

14.

15. **Science** An individual cell of honeycomb starts off as a circle, but because the cells are so close together, the circles flatten out. The result is a tessellation. What polygon is tessellated in a honeycomb?

16. **Test Prep** Which shape cannot be used to make a tessellation?

Ⓐ Rectangle   Ⓑ Circle   Ⓒ Regular hexagon   Ⓓ Not here

Problem Solving and Reasoning

17. Communicate Steve stated that all squares, rectangles, and parallelograms tessellate. Do you agree with Steve? Explain your reasoning.

18. Critical Thinking What is the base pattern of the tessellation outlined in yellow on the stone carving?

19. Critical Thinking Draw a tessellation that does not use a polygon as the figure tessellated. Explain your tessellation.

20. Choose a Strategy Is the design on the door a tessellation? If so, draw the shape that is tessellated.

Problem Solving
STRATEGIES

- Look for a Pattern
- Make an Organized List
- Make a Table
- Guess and Check
- Work Backward
- Use Logical Reasoning
- Draw a Diagram
- Solve a Simpler Problem

Mixed Review

Find the perimeter of each figure. *[Lesson 4-1]*

21.

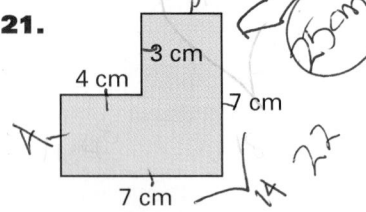

3 cm
4 cm
7 cm
7 cm

22.

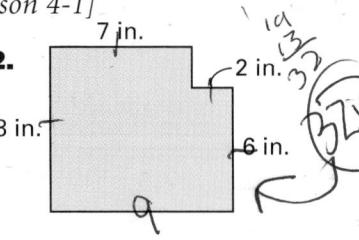

7 in.
2 in.
8 in.
6 in.

23.

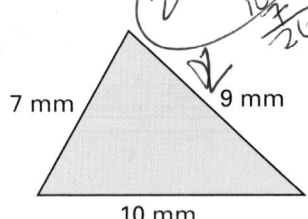

7 mm
9 mm
10 mm

Convert. *[Lesson 4-2]*

24. 6 kg = ☐ g

25. 3.1 m = ☐ mm

26. 650 mL = ☐ L

27. 5.6 cm = ☐ mm

28. 7.34 L = ☐ mL

29. 106 mm = ☐ m

Project Progress

Prepare the final rough draft of your logo. Make sure that your logo has one shape with either line or rotational symmetry. Start working on your final draft.

Problem Solving

Understand
Plan
Solve
Look Back

In this section, you've seen how polygons can be flipped, turned, and slid. You've also seen how geometric figures can be repeated to create designs known as tessellations. Now you'll use what you've learned to make a tessellation.

Artistic Solutions

Materials: Unlined paper, Colored pencils or markers, Ruler

1. Study the tiled floor in the Islamic painting. Notice that a square was used to create the tessellation.

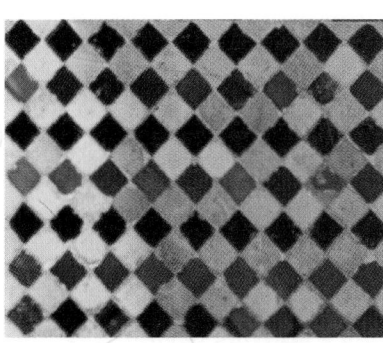

2. Study this example to see how a square can be changed to produce a new tessellation pattern.

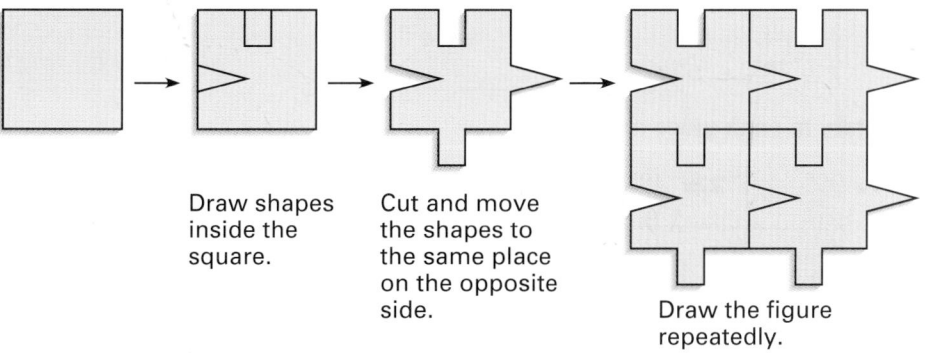

Draw shapes inside the square.

Cut and move the shapes to the same place on the opposite side.

Draw the figure repeatedly.

3. Create a design like the tiled floor above using a square tessellation of your own design.

Section 8C Review

Draw an example of each.

1. $\overline{KL}$ **2.** $\overleftrightarrow{WP}$ **3.** $\overrightarrow{SD}$ **4.** $\overline{MN}$ **5.** $\overleftrightarrow{FS}$ **6.** $\overrightarrow{LO}$

Classify each triangle by its angles. Estimate the measure of each angle.

7.  *right / obtuse*   **8.** 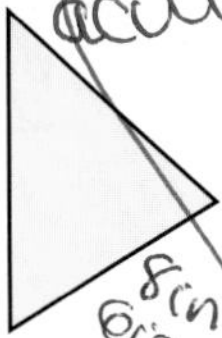 *acute*   **9.** 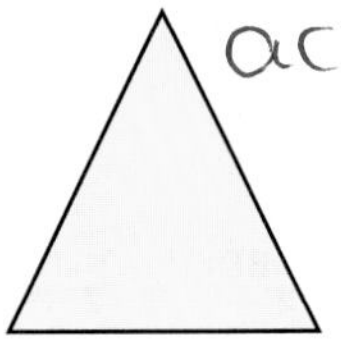 *acute*   **10.**  *90 right*

Name each polygon and tell if it has line symmetry. If it does, tell how many lines of symmetry it has.

11. 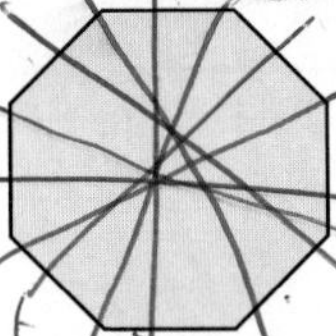 *infinity / infinite oct.*   **12.**  *NO pent.*   **13.** 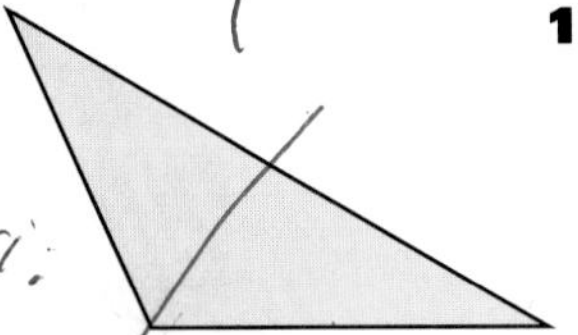 *tri.*   **14.**

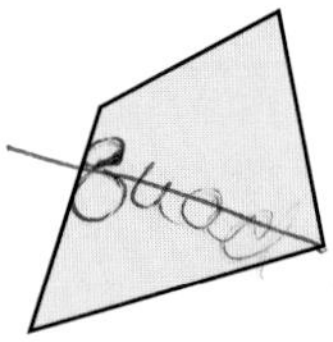

State if each figure will tessellate. Make a drawing to show your answer.

15. 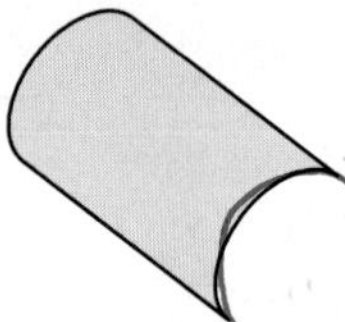   **16.**    **17.**    **18.**

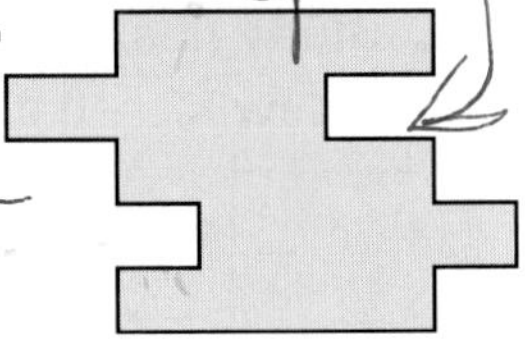

State the angle that is supplementary to each given angle.

19. $76°$ **20.** $152°$ **21.** $99°$ **22.** $48°$ **23.** $90°$ **24.** $179°$

Test Prep

Rotating a figure 180° clockwise is the same as rotating the figure 180° counterclockwise.

25. How has the figure been rotated?

Ⓐ 180° clockwise   Ⓑ 180° counterclockwise

Ⓒ Either of the above   Ⓓ None of the above

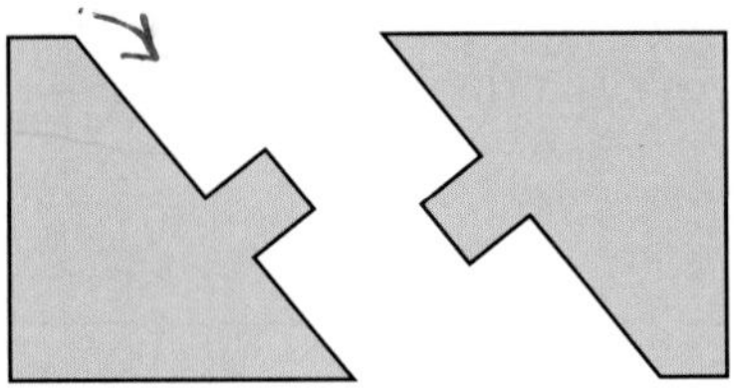

Extend Key Ideas ● Geometry

Constructions

A construction is a drawing of a geometric figure that is made using two instruments, a compass and a straightedge. *Bisecting*, which means dividing a figure into two congruent parts, is one kind of construction.

Bisecting a Line

1. Open the compass more than half the length of the segment. Place the compass point on *A* and draw an arc.

2. Without changing the opening of the compass, place the point on *B* and draw an arc.

3. Using the straightedge, draw a line through the two points where the arcs intersect. This line bisects the original segment $\overline{AB}$.

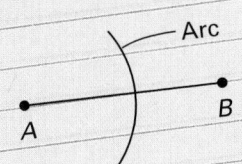

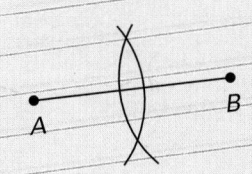

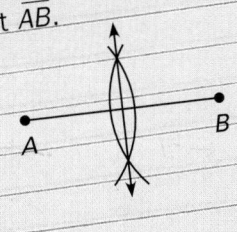

Bisecting an Angle

1. Place the compass point on the vertex and draw an arc. Label the points where the arc crosses the angle as *D* and *E*.

2. Using a smaller opening, place the point on *D* and draw an arc. Without changing the opening, place the point on *E* and draw an arc.

3. Draw a line through the point of intersection of the two new arcs and the vertex. This line bisects ∠*ABC*.

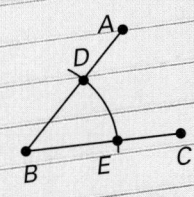

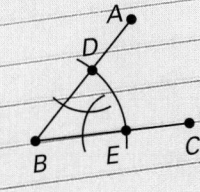

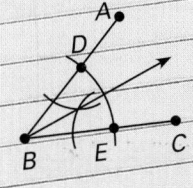

Try It

Trace and bisect each figure.

a.

b.

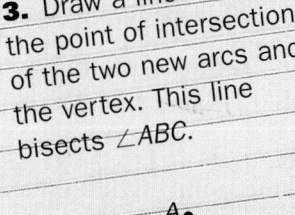

459

Graphic Organizer

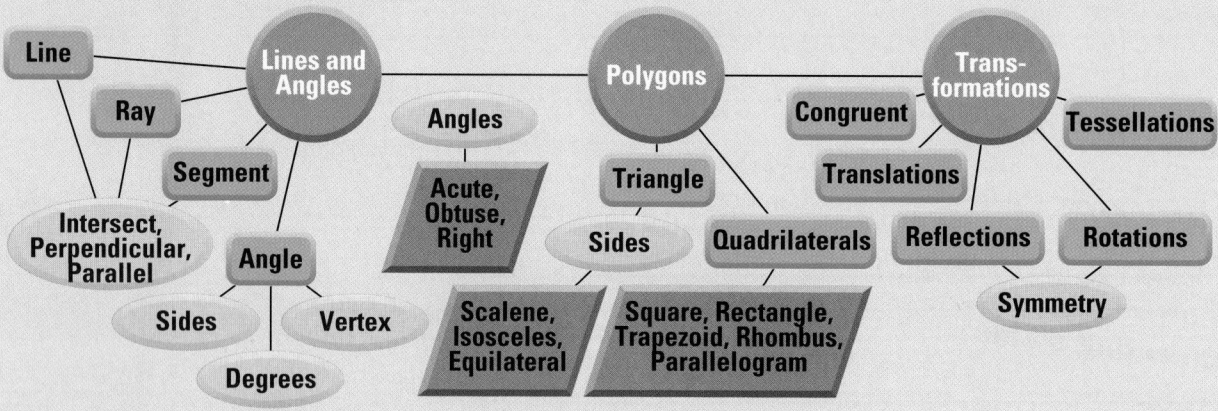

Section 8A   Lines and Angles

Summary

- **Segments** and **rays** are parts of **lines**. They can **intersect**. They can be **perpendicular** or **parallel**.

- An **angle** is formed from two rays that meet at the **vertex**. Angles are classified by size as **acute, right, obtuse,** or **straight.**

- You can use a **protractor** to measure the **degrees** in an angle.

Review

1. Draw and label a line with points *A* and *B*.

3. Draw and label:

   a. Two rays that are parallel.   **b.** $\overleftrightarrow{CD}$

2. Draw and label an obtuse angle through points *M*, *N*, and *O*, with *N* as the vertex.

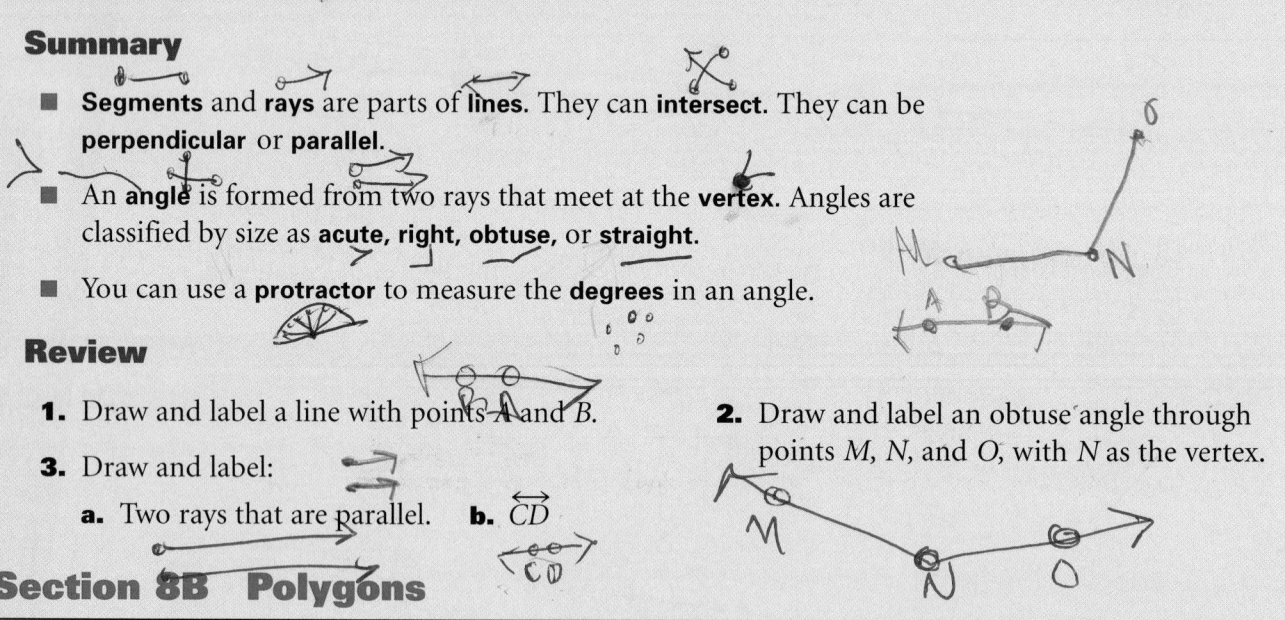

Section 8B   Polygons

Summary

- **Triangles** can be classified by the measures of their angles as **acute, obtuse,** or **right,** or by the lengths of their sides as **scalene, isosceles,** or **equilateral.**

- **Polygons** are **regular** if their sides and angles are equal. If not, they are **irregular. Quadrilaterals** have four sides. Some side pairs may be parallel.

Section 8B Polygons *continued*

Review

4. Classify the triangle whose angles measure 82°, 14°, and 84°. *acute*

5. Explain why all rectangles are parallelograms, but not all parallelograms are rectangles.

Section 8C Transformations

Summary

- **Congruent** figures have the same size and shape.

- If you flip a figure over a line, its **reflection** is the mirror image of the figure. The original figure and its reflection have **line symmetry**.

- If you turn a figure as if it were on a wheel, the image of the figure is a **rotation**. If the image lands on itself before one full turn, it has **rotational symmetry**. Turns can be **clockwise** or **counterclockwise**.

- If you slide a figure, its image is called a **translation**.

- A pattern of congruent shapes, with no gaps or overlaps, is a **tessellation**.

Review

Is the second figure a reflection, translation, or rotation of the first?

6. 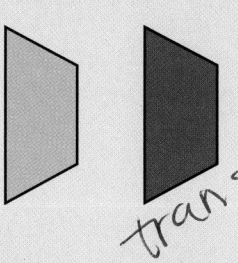 *trans*

7. 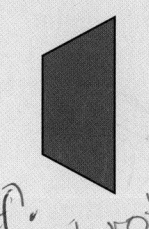 *ref. + rotation*

8. 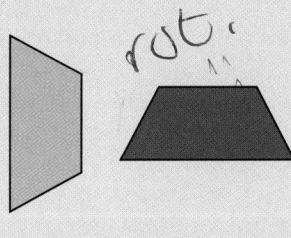 *rot.*

9. Are the figures in Exercises 6–8 congruent? Explain. *yes*

10. Trace the figure and draw its reflection over the line.

11. Tell whether the figure has line symmetry. If it does, draw its line(s) of symmetry.

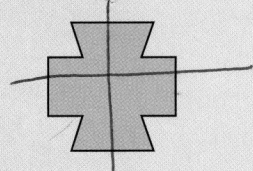

12. Give the number of degrees and the direction in which the figure has been rotated.

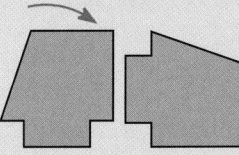 *90° clockwise*

For each group, describe the figures and their relationship.

1.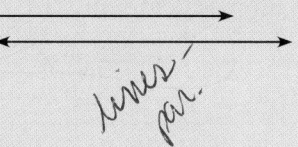

   lines par.

2.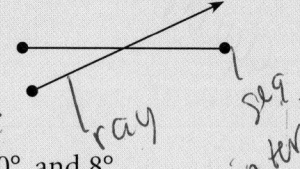

   ray   seg. inter.

3. Classify the triangle whose angles measure 82°, 90°, and 8°.

   right

4. Can you measure the length of a line? A segment? A ray? Explain.

   yes

5. **a.** Name the vertex of the angle. *S*

   b. Name the angle in three ways.

   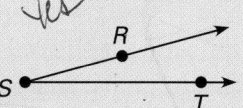

   *RST
   TSR
   S*

6. The sum of two angles of a triangle is 85°. What is the measure of the third angle?

7. Can the lengths of 4 m, 8 m, and 10 m form a triangle? If so, draw the triangle and classify it.   *yes*

8. Angles *A* and *B* are complements. If the measure of ∠*A* is 37°, what is the measure of ∠*B*?   ∠B = 143°

   *180
   37
   143*

9. Classify the triangle whose sides each measure 6 feet.

   equal.

Name each polygon and tell if it is regular or irregular.

10.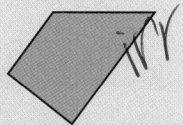

11.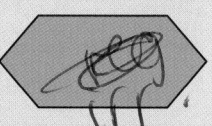

12. 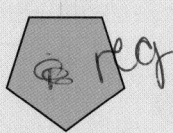   *reg*

13. Can you draw a triangle whose angles measure 62°, 63°, and 65°? Explain.

    *62
    63
    65*

14. Classify the figure in as many ways as possible.

    *quad.
    rec.   parrel.
    sq.*

Is the second figure a reflection, translation, or rotation of the first?

15.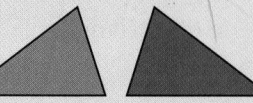

16.

17.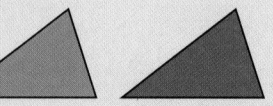

Performance Task

Make a list of 12 geometric concepts that are found in the design of the United Kingdom's flag. Four concepts must relate to lines and angles, four to polygons, and four to transformations and line or rotational symmetry.

Multiple Choice

Choose the best answer.

1. Which graph uses wedge-shaped pieces to represent the data? *[Lesson 1-1]*

   Ⓐ Bar   Ⓑ Circle

   Ⓒ Line   Ⓓ Pictograph

2. One business plan calls for a change in employees of 2^5. A second plan calls for a change that is twice as large as 2^5. What is the change in employees for the second plan? *[Lesson 2-4]*

   Ⓐ 2^6 Ⓑ 2^7 Ⓒ 2^{10} Ⓓ 4^5

3. What is the decimal form for seven and twenty-nine thousandths. *[Lesson 3-1]*

   Ⓐ 7029.0   Ⓑ 7.029

   Ⓒ 7.0029   Ⓓ 0.7029

4. Find the product of 0.001×32. *[Lesson 3-8]*

   Ⓐ 32000   Ⓑ 320   Ⓒ 0.032   Ⓓ 0.0032

5. What is the solution to the equation $0.01m = 25.2$? *[Lesson 3-12]*

   Ⓐ 2520   Ⓑ 252   Ⓒ 2.52   Ⓓ 0.252

6. Find the perimeter of the figure. *[Lesson 4-1]*

   Ⓐ 96 m

   Ⓑ 87 m

   Ⓒ 64 m

   Ⓓ 55 m

   16 m   7 m   22 m   10 m

7. What is the area of a rectangle 4 ft long and 6 ft wide? *[Lesson 4-5]*

   Ⓐ 20 ft   Ⓑ 24 ft   Ⓒ 20 ft²   Ⓓ 24 ft²

8. Write $\frac{29}{9}$ as a mixed number. *[Lesson 5-6]*

   Ⓐ $20\frac{1}{9}$ Ⓑ $4\frac{2}{9}$ Ⓒ $3\frac{2}{9}$ Ⓓ $3\frac{1}{9}$

9. Simplify $\frac{3}{7} - \frac{1}{4}$. *[Lesson 6-2]*

   Ⓐ $\frac{5}{28}$ Ⓑ $\frac{2}{11}$ Ⓒ $\frac{2}{3}$ Ⓓ $\frac{19}{28}$

10. Simplify $3\frac{2}{3} + 1\frac{3}{4}$. *[Lesson 6-5]*

    Ⓐ $4\frac{5}{7}$ Ⓑ $5\frac{5}{12}$ Ⓒ $5\frac{7}{12}$ Ⓓ None of these

11. Simplify $32 \times 1\frac{1}{2}$. *[Lesson 7-2]*

    Ⓐ 16   Ⓑ 32.5

    Ⓒ 48   Ⓓ None of these

12. Simplify $\frac{3}{5} \div 5$. *[Lesson 7-5]*

    Ⓐ $\frac{3}{55}$ Ⓑ $\frac{3}{25}$ Ⓒ $\frac{3}{10}$ Ⓓ 3

13. Solve for x, if $x \div \frac{3}{4} = \frac{8}{9}$. *[Lesson 7-6]*

    Ⓐ $\frac{3}{2}$ Ⓑ $\frac{27}{32}$ Ⓒ $\frac{2}{3}$ Ⓓ None of these

14. An angle that measures less than 90° is called a(n) _____ angle. *[Lesson 8-3]*

    Ⓐ Straight   Ⓑ Right

    Ⓒ Obtuse   Ⓓ Acute

15. What is the name of a triangle that has exactly two equal sides? *[Lesson 8-5]*

    Ⓐ Isosceles   Ⓑ Obtuse

    Ⓒ Right   Ⓓ Scalene

Integers and the Coordinate Plane

Entertainment Link
www.mathsurf.com/6/ch9/ent

Arts & Literature

Some photographs use the spaces in between objects to create interesting shapes. Photographers say that these kinds of shapes create "negative space."

Social Studies

The location of any place in the world can be described using the lines of longitude and latitude. Washington, DC, is located at 38° North, 77° West. The point at 0° latitude, 0° longitude is in the Gulf of Guinea, off the coast of Africa.

North Pole

EQUATOR

South Pole

Entertainment

Golf scores are often compared using *par*, the number of strokes it should take for a player to get the ball in a particular hole. A score of 3 under par means the player needed three strokes less than the expected number to sink the ball in the hole.

People of the World

In the Netherlands, the city of Amsterdam, near the North Sea, has an elevation of −22 feet. Since it is below sea level, canals and dikes line the city to prevent flooding.

KEY MATH IDEAS

An integer can be a whole positive number, the opposite of a whole positive number, or 0.

Integers can be added and subtracted.

When multiplying and dividing integers, the sign of the product or the quotient depends on the sign of the factors or divisor and dividend.

The coordinate plane can be used to locate any point on a flat surface.

Algebra equations can be represented on the coordinate plane.

Science

Sometimes when you walk across a carpeted floor, you collect electrons and develop a negative charge. If you touch something with a positive charge, the electrons move to the positively charged object. This causes a small electric shock.

CHAPTER PROJECT

Problem Solving

Understand
Plan
Solve
Look Back

In this project, you will create a drawing of a real country on a coordinate plane, and collect facts about the country that involve positive and negative numbers. Begin by thinking about a country that you find interesting and that has an interesting shape.

465

Solving Problems

You can solve most problems in more than one way. When solving a problem, you may find that one plan works more easily than another. An important part of good problem solving is choosing the easiest strategy to work with.

Problem Solving Focus

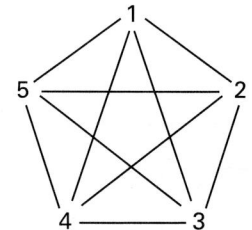

HELLO
my name is
Maritess Estrera

The following problem has already been solved using three different methods.

Five employees of the Carlson Company met at a meeting. These five employees had never met each other before, so each person shook everyone else's hand. How many handshakes were there?

Make a list	Number sense	Draw a picture

(Each pair represents one handshake.)
 	
1-2 1-3 1-4 1-5
   2-3 2-4 2-5
      3-4 3-5
         4-5
	There are five people. Each person shook four other hands.
	
	$5 \times 4 = 20$
	
	But this counts each handshake twice (once when 1 greets 2, and once when 2 greets 1). Therefore, you need to cut the number in half.
	
	$20 \div 2 = 10$
		
		Each line equals one handshake. There are ten lines.

There were 10 handshakes.	There were 10 handshakes.	There were 10 handshakes.

Solve the following problem. You may use one of the above methods, or a method of your own.

Three sets of twins met at the park. At first, each person knew only his or her twin. But by the end of the day, every person had met everyone else. How many introductions were there?

The Third Sphere From the Sun

How could you measure the height of a mountain?

PLAN A: Go to the top of the mountain, drill a hole to the bottom, and drop a long tape measure down the hole.

PLAN B: Build a gigantic ruler and have several hundred friends place it straight up into the air next to the mountain.

PLAN C: Find a mountain whose height you know and ask it to go stand back to back against the first mountain.

Nobody uses any of these methods, but many people do ask the question about how to measure and learn more about the earth. People who study the earth are collectively known as earth scientists. They include zoologists, who study animals; botanists, who study plants; geologists, who study rocks; meteorologists, who study weather; oceanographers, who study oceans; and many other types of scientists.

These scientists have to be able to describe how far a point is above or below sea level. They have to record temperatures above and below the freezing point of water. They have to keep track of how an animal population has grown or shrunk. All of these descriptions require a special set of numbers known as integers.

1 Other than the measurements mentioned above, what else could you measure about the earth?

2 Why is it useful for humans to have a better understanding of the earth?

Understanding Integers

▶ **Lesson Link** You've learned to locate whole numbers on a number line. Now you'll investigate a set of numbers that are related to the whole numbers and graph them on a number line. ◀

You'll Learn …

■ what an integer is

■ to order integers

… How It's Used

Hot-air balloon operators work with integers when determining how much ballast, or weight, is needed to maintain a certain altitude.

Vocabulary

positive numbers

negative numbers

integers

| **Explore** | **Integers** |

Connect the Debts

I owe John eleven dollars. I have fifteen dollars in my wallet.

Zack

I have eight dollars in my bank. My brother owes me four dollars.

Sonia

I owe my sister three dollars. I owe Molly nine dollars.

Tyreka

I have three dollars in my purse. I owe Tina eight dollars.

Peggy

I owe Raquel six dollars. I have six dollars in my bank.

Ricardo

1. Determine how much money each person will have or how much they will owe when all of the monies owed have been paid.

2. Rank the five friends from who has the most money to who owes the most money.

3. Copy this number line and indicate where each person is.

Owes ← Has →

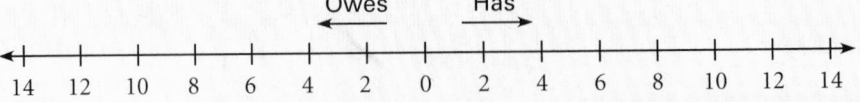

14 12 10 8 6 4 2 0 2 4 6 8 10 12 14

4. Without using words, how could you indicate if an answer of "6" meant "has 6 dollars" or "owes 6 dollars?"

Learn · Understanding Integers

> **Science Link**
>
> Most of the world uses degrees Celsius to measure temperature. In Celsius, water freezes at 0° and boils at 100°. People in the United States often use the Fahrenheit system, where water freezes at 32° and boils at 212°.

Most of the numbers you have seen so far have been greater than or equal to 0. Numbers greater than 0 are known as **positive numbers**. There is another set of numbers that are all *less than 0*. They are known as **negative numbers**.

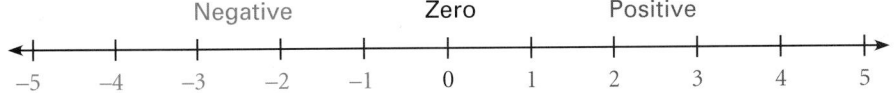

Negative numbers are used to keep track of values below a certain mark. They are used to describe debts, depths below sea level, and temperatures in degrees Celsius below freezing.

Negative numbers are always shown with a minus (−) sign. Positive numbers may or may not have a plus (+) sign. Whole numbers (1, 2, 3…), their negative counterparts (−1, −2, −3…), and 0 are

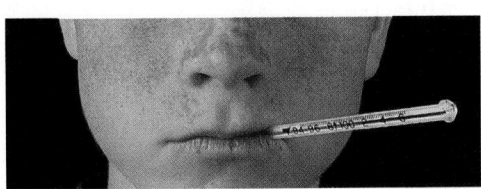

known as **integers**. On a number line, the further to the right a number is, the greater it is. The further to the left it is, the less it is.

Example 1

Order the integers from least to greatest: 1, −2, 4, −5, 0.

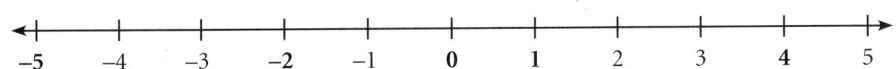

Locate the numbers on the number line. The least number, which is the one furthest to the left, is −5. It is followed by −2, 0, 1, and 4.

−5, −2, 0, 1, 4

Try It

Tell which Celsius temperature is greater. **a.** 4° or −4°   **b.** −7° or −6°

Order the integers from least to greatest. **c.** 1, −3, −10, 7, 10, 0

> **DID YOU KNOW?**
>
> Zero is the only integer that is neither positive nor negative.

Check · Your Understanding

1. What kinds of numbers are integers?

2. Is a negative number always less than a positive number? Explain.

Practice and Apply

Getting Started Tell if each number is an integer. If it is not, explain why.

1. -78 **2.** $\frac{1}{2}$ **3.** 56 **4.** -54.7 **5.** 0 **6.** $+33$

Draw a number line. Locate each integer on the number line.

7. -5 **8.** 2 **9.** 0 **10.** -4 **11.** 3 **12.** -2

Compare using $>$ or $<$.

13. $-8 \square -10$ **14.** $-6 \square 5$ **15.** $-1 \square 1$ **16.** $12 \square -42$ **17.** $-66 \square -68$

18. $-45 \square -49$ **19.** $-16 \square -26$ **20.** $-24 \square -18$ **21.** $5 \square -5$ **22.** $-55 \square -32$

Order from greatest to least.

23. $3, -4, -5, 2$ **24.** $-45, 67, -67, 45$ **25.** $-78, 13, -16, -56$ **26.** $-2, -42, -24, -4$

27. $16, -10, 12, 0$ **28.** $-45, -32, -59, -14$ **29.** $16, 17, -18, 19$ **30.** $-99, -100, -89, -47$

Write each number as an integer.

31. Ethanol freezes at 114°C below zero.

32. Bryan has a debt of $49.

33. Lori is 62 inches tall.

34. The picture is 37 in. wide.

35. Todd lost 7 pounds.

36. Chelsea hopped 5 ft backwards.

37. Kay completed five dives to the following depths below sea level: $-107, -52, -213, -211, -76$. Order these integers from smallest to largest.

38. Byron is making up a board game. He wants to write the following on the board spaces: Go back two spaces; Move ahead four spaces; Move ahead three spaces; Go back five spaces; Move ahead one space. If he writes these instructions using integers, will he have more negative numbers or more positive numbers?

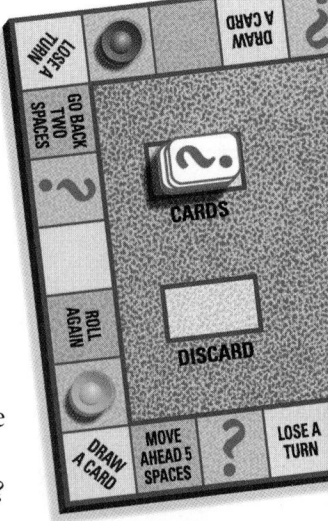

39. At the Spring Carnival Go-Fish booth, the 6th-grade class had expenses of $12. They took in $22. Write the money amounts as integers.

40. Lori is saving money to buy a new bicycle. She deposited $30 into a bank account. Later, she withdrew $25 to buy a new helmet. Write these amounts as integers.

41. Career Before a space shuttle takes off, astronauts count the time remaining in negative numbers. Order these takeoff times from earliest to latest: -4 minutes, -15 minutes, -3 minutes, -20 minutes, -5 minutes, -1 minute, -2 minutes.

42. **Test Prep** Choose the set of integers that is ordered from least to greatest.

Ⓐ $5, -6, 7, 8$ Ⓑ $-3, -1, 4, 0$

Ⓒ $-5, -3, 0, 7$ Ⓓ $9, 3, -6, -7$

Problem Solving and Reasoning

43. Communicate Is $\frac{1}{2}$ an integer? Is $-\frac{1}{2}$? Explain your reasoning.

44. Critical Thinking Like integers, decimals can be either positive or negative. Order each set of decimals from least to greatest.

a. $1.6, -2.7, -5.6$ **b.** $-7.3, -2.5, -5.8$ **c.** $-0.25, 0.5, -0.75$ **d.** $-0.3, -0.5, -0.4$

45. Journal What is the largest positive integer? The largest negative integer? Explain your reasoning.

46. Critical Thinking Order $-5, -26, 8, 19,$ and -20 from least to greatest. Then order these same numbers from closest to zero to furthest from zero. Explain the similarities and differences between your two lists.

Mixed Review

Estimate. *[Lesson 7-1]*

47. $6\frac{2}{3} \times 2\frac{1}{3}$

48. $11\frac{3}{4} \div 3\frac{5}{8}$

49. $2\frac{6}{7} \times \frac{1}{2}$

50. $15\frac{3}{7} \div 3\frac{1}{3}$

51. $4\frac{1}{4} \times 10\frac{4}{5}$

52. $9\frac{8}{9} \div 1\frac{7}{8}$

53. $20\frac{2}{5} \times 8\frac{5}{6}$

54. $5\frac{7}{8} \div 2\frac{8}{9}$

Describe the relationship between the lines, rays, or segments. *[Lesson 8-1]*

55.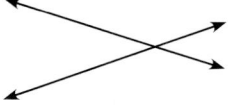

56.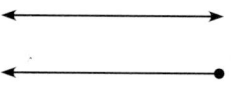

57.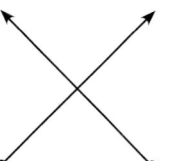

58.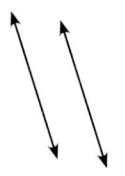

59.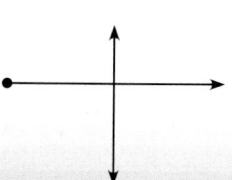

60.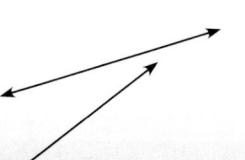

61.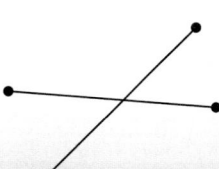

62.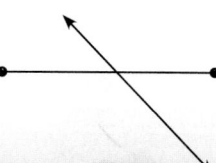

Adding Integers

You'll Learn ...

■ what an opposite is

■ to add integers

... How It's Used

Football referees add integers when determining how many yards a team must move the football in order to make it to first down.

▶ **Lesson Link**   In the last lesson, you learned that integers include positive and negative numbers. Now you'll add integers together. ◀

The **opposite** of an integer is the integer on the opposite side of zero but at the same distance from zero. 8 and −8 are the same distance from zero, so they are opposites.

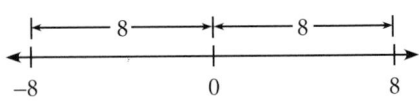

The sum of an integer and its opposite will always equal 0.

Explore   Adding Integers

Two Nothings Are Nothing!   **Materials:** 2-color counters

Adding Integers

• Count out enough counters to represent the first number. If the number is positive, put the yellow sides up. If it is negative, put the red sides up.

• Repeat the first step for the second number.

• Make as many opposite pairs of one yellow and one red counter as possible. Since each pair equals 0 when added together, remove each pair.

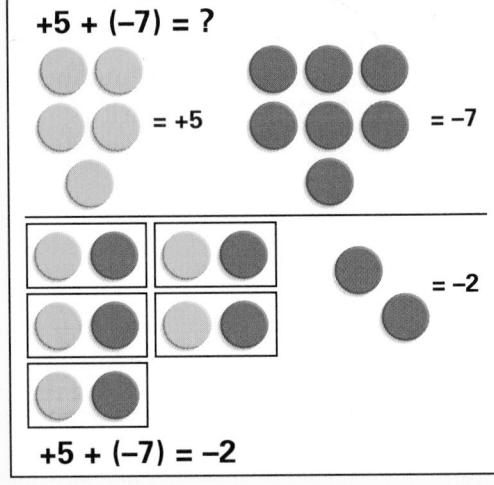

• Describe the number and color of the counters left over.

1. Model each problem, and state the answer.

    a. $10 + (-7)$ **b.** $-6 + 5$ **c.** $-3 + (-8)$ **d.** $6 + 2$

    e. $4 + (-12)$ **f.** $-5 + 0$ **g.** $-4 + 4$ **h.** $-7 + 7$

2. Is the sum positive or negative when you add two positive integers? Two negative integers? Explain.

3. How can you predict the sign of the sum when you add a positive integer to a negative integer?

Learn | Adding Integers

You can add integers using a number line. Find the first number on the line. Move *right* to add a positive number. Move *left* to add a negative number.

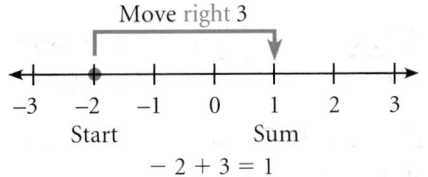

Move right 3

-2 + 3 = 1

Examples

1 Add: $-3 + 5$

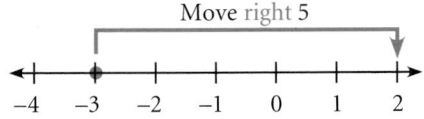

Move right 5

$-3 + 5 = 2$

2 Add: $2 + (-4)$

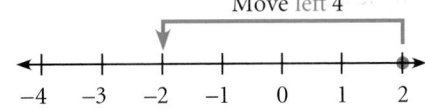

Move left 4

$2 + (-4) = -2$

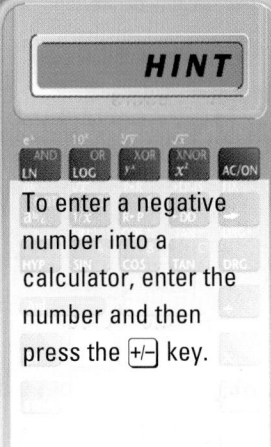
3 A geologist removed a rock sample from 12 feet below sea level. She then climbed 31 feet up and removed another rock sample. From what height was the second rock sample removed?

$-12 + 31$ Write an expression.

19 Add.

The rock sample was removed from 19 feet above sea level.

Try It

Add.

a. $6 + 4$ **b.** $-3 + (-5)$ **c.** $-7 + 8$ **d.** $2 + (-2)$

e. $10 + (-3)$ **f.** $-6 + 12$ **g.** $5 + (-2)$ **h.** $5 + (-8)$

> **Science Link**
>
> The skin that surrounds the surface of the Earth is called the *crust*. The crust varies in thickness, from 5 miles to 25 miles, and the deepest parts of the crust are hot enough to melt rocks.

Check | Your Understanding

1. If you add a positive integer to a negative integer, will the sum be positive or negative? Explain.

2. What is the sum of an integer and its opposite? Explain.

Practice and Apply

Getting Started State each equation that is modeled.

1.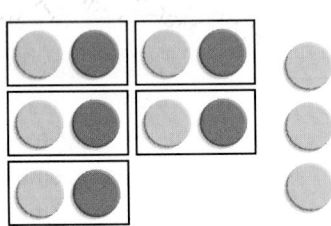

2.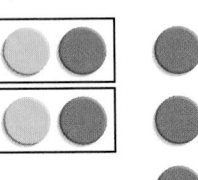

3.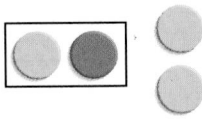

State each number's opposite.

4. 6   **5.** 12   **6.** -35 **7.** -40 **8.** 0   **9.** -1589

State if the sum is positive, negative, or zero.

10. $10 + 4$ **11.** $-7 + (-3)$ **12.** $-8 + 2$ **13.** $-3 + 7$ **14.** $5 + (-3)$

15. $21 + (-21)$ **16.** $63 + (-32)$ **17.** $-47 + 35$ **18.** $-15 + 15$ **19.** $-6 + (-22)$

Add.

20. $2 + (-6)$ **21.** $-8 + (-4)$ **22.** $-2 + 19$ **23.** $2 + (-4)$ **24.** $4 + (-4)$

25. $7 + (-1)$ **26.** $-7 + (-1)$ **27.** $-7 + (-5)$ **28.** $7 + (-5)$ **29.** $-14 + (-3)$

30. $-10 + (-2)$ **31.** $-6 + 7$ **32.** $-9 + 4$ **33.** $-10 + 12$ **34.** $5 + (-7)$

35. $-13 + 7$ **36.** $6 + (-3)$ **37.** $16 + (-3)$ **38.** $-17 + (-5)$ **39.** $-20 + 6$

40. $-8 + 9$ **41.** $11 + (-2)$ **42.** $18 + (-12)$ **43.** $-4 + 3$ **44.** $-5 + 2$

45. $-16 + (-15)$ **46.** $-13 + 16$ **47.** $-5 + (-9)$ **48.** $-6 + (-6)$ **49.** $8 + (-8)$

50. Leona runs a lemonade stand. One week she spent $7 on ingredients and sold $12 worth of lemonade. What was Leona's profit?

51. **Number Sense** Which depth is lower, -157 feet or the opposite of 211 feet?

52. **Measurement** Which number is farther from zero, -5 or the opposite of $+3$?

Sam wanted to buy a video game system. He recorded the change in price over several months on a line graph.

Price of Game System

53. How did the original price compare to the final price? Use numbers in your answer.

54. In what month did the price go up the most?

55. **Test Prep** For their booth at the Spring Fair, Mrs. Alvarado's class had expenses of $4, $2, and $1. The sales at the end of each of the shifts were $2, $5, $6, and $4. What was their total profit?

Ⓐ Lost $10　　Ⓑ Earned $10

Ⓒ Lost $12　　Ⓓ Earned $12

Problem Solving and Reasoning

56. Critical Thinking Jamie earns money by conducting nature hikes. She earned and spent the following dollar amounts: −3, +4, −3, +6, −2, +5, +12. How could you use number sense to determine if Jamie made money or lost money?

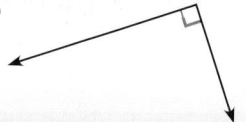

57. Critical Thinking Leon had the following test scores to average: 87, 91, 88, 95, and 89. He said, "I guess my average is about 90. My scores are off that by −3, +1, −2, +5, and −1. When I add those numbers, they add to zero. So I must be right." Do you agree with Leon? Explain.

58.  Does −5 + 3 equal 3 + (−5)? Use number lines to explain your answer.

Mixed Review

Simplify. *[Lesson 7-2]*

59. $5\frac{3}{4} \times 6$

60. $\frac{3}{7} \times 7$

61. $2 \times \frac{1}{2}$

62. $10 \times \frac{17}{19}$

63. $\frac{5}{6} \times 8$

64. $3\frac{2}{3} \times 6$

65. $8 \times 6\frac{1}{4}$

66. $6 \times \frac{5}{6}$

Classify each angle as acute, right, obtuse, or straight. *[Lesson 8-2]*

67.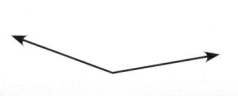

68.

69.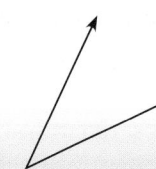

70.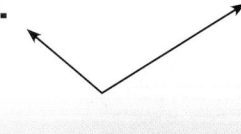

9-3

Subtracting Integers

▶ **Lesson Link** In the last lesson, you added integers. Now you'll subtract them. ◀

You'll Learn ...

■ to subtract integers

... How It's Used

Bank customers add and subtract integers when updating their checkbooks.

Explore   Subtracting Integers

They Have Nothing to Lose   Materials: 2-color counters

Subtracting Integers

- Count out several zero pairs. There should be as many pairs as the numerical value of the largest number in the problem.

- Count out counters to represent the first number. If the number is positive, put the yellow sides up. If negative, put the red sides up.

- Take away enough counters to represent the second number.

- Remove any zero pairs.

- Describe the number and color of the counters left over.

+3 – (–2) = ?

= 0   = 3

= 5

+3 – (–2) = +5

1. Model each problem, and state the answer.

   a. +4 – (–1)   b. –5 – (+3)   c. –4 – (–1)   d. +5 – (+3)

   e. +2 – (–2)   f. 0 – (–5)   g. –7 – (–7)   h. –7 – (+7)

2. When you subtract a positive number, is the difference smaller or larger than the original number?

3. When you subtract a negative number, is the difference less or more than the original number?

Learn   Subtracting Integers

Addition and subtraction are opposite operations. When you take a number and add a negative number to it, the result gets smaller. So when you take a number and *subtract* a negative number, the result gets *bigger*.

You can subtract integers on a number line by reversing the procedure you used for addition. Find the first number on the line. Move *left* to subtract positive numbers. Move *right* to subtract negative numbers.

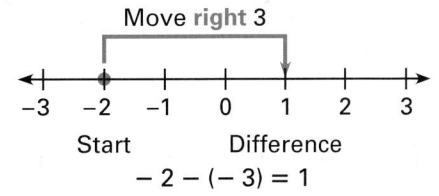

Move **right** 3

Start   Difference
$-2 - (-3) = 1$

Remember

The opposite of a number is the same number with the opposite sign, as in 4 and −4. The sum of two opposites is always 0.
[Page 472]

Examples

1 Subtract: $-1 - (-4)$

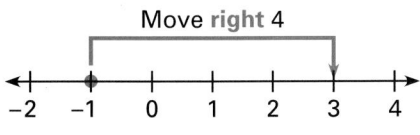

Move **right** 4

$-1 - (-4) = 3$

2 Subtract: $1 - 3$

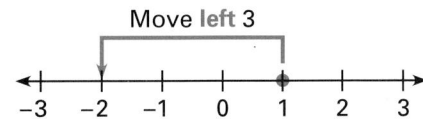

Move **left** 3

$1 - 3 = -2$

Try It

Subtract.

a. $5 - 7$ **b.** $-2 - 6$ **c.** $3 - (-1)$ **d.** $-4 - (-3)$

If you subtract $12 - 20$, the result will be -8. If you add $12 + (-20)$, the result will also be -8. This shows that you can subtract an integer by *adding its opposite*.

$$12 - (+20) = 12 + (-20)$$

Example 3

Jennifer earned $14 working in a hydroponics garden. She spent $16 buying shoes and gloves for the job. Find the amount of money she earned or lost.

$14 - 16$ Write an expression.

$14 + (-16)$ Rewrite the expression by adding the opposite.

-2 Add.

She had a $2 loss.

Try It

Subtract.

a. $5 - (-12)$ **b.** $-8 - (-13)$ **c.** $10 - (-16)$ **d.** $-24 - (-13)$

▶ **Science Link**

Hydroponics is the study of growing plants without soil. Hydroponic methods can be used to grow crops in places without soil, such as deserts or on ships at sea.

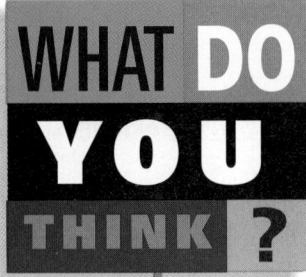

Van and Maritess operate a bicycle messenger service. They have one bicycle and $153 in profit. They want to buy a second bicycle from Van's brother. Van's brother is selling the bike for $210, but he's willing to take part of the money as an I.O.U. If Van and Maritess agree to purchase the bike, how much will they owe?

Maritess thinks ...

I'll take our $153 and add a $210 debt.

$153 + (-210) = -57$

We will still owe $57 for the bicycle.

Van thinks ...

I'll take the $210 debt and subtract the $153 that we have. The difference will be the amount we owe.

$210 - 153 = 57$

We will still owe $57 for the bicycle.

What do you think?

1. If you were solving the problem using pencil and paper, which method would be easier?

2. If you were solving the problem with a calculator, which method would be easier?

Check | Your Understanding

1. How is subtraction of integers like addition of integers?

2. When you subtract a negative number, why is the result greater than the original number?

Practice and Apply

Getting Started State each equation that is modeled.

1.

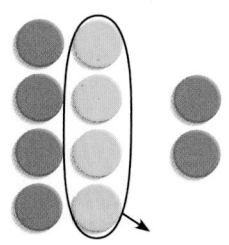

2.

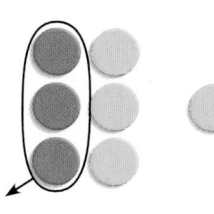

3.

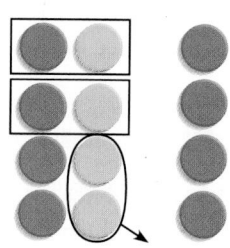

Write a subtraction equation that shows the difference between *P* and *Q* on each number line.

4.

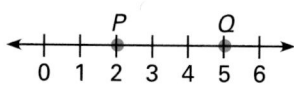

5.

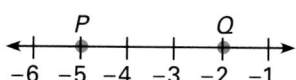

6.

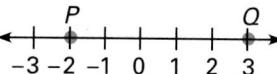

Subtract.

7. $-7 - 2$ **8.** $-7 - (-2)$ **9.** $7 - (-2)$ **10.** $-9 - 11$ **11.** $4 - (-8)$

12. $6 - (-3)$ **13.** $-3 - (-5)$ **14.** $7 - (-4)$ **15.** $-8 - 3$ **16.** $-9 - 7$

17. $14 - (-5)$ **18.** $10 - (-9)$ **19.** $-8 - 12$ **20.** $16 - (-1)$ **21.** $-13 - (-2)$

22. $-2 - 1$ **23.** $-5 - 3$ **24.** $-4 - (-6)$ **25.** $8 - (-5)$ **26.** $6 - (-12)$

27. $-9 - (-4)$ **28.** $0 - (-8)$ **29.** $9 - (-11)$ **30.** $-17 - (-2)$ **31.** $-5 - 8$

32. $-9 - 0$ **33.** $16 - (-6)$ **34.** $-3 - 1$ **35.** $2 - (-9)$ **36.** $8 - (-9)$

37. Estimation The lowest elevation on Earth is on the shore of the Dead Sea, 1,310 feet below sea level. The highest elevation on Earth is Mt. Everest in the Himalayas at 29,028 feet. Estimate the difference.

38. **Test Prep** The temperature outside is $-2°C$. It drops $5°$ at night. What is the new temperature?

   Ⓐ $-7°C$ Ⓑ $-3°C$

   Ⓒ $3°C$ Ⓓ $7°C$

Swimmers floating in the Dead Sea

Use the diagram for Exercises 39–40.

39. What is the distance from the bottom of the ship to the deck?

40. How many feet of the ship are under water?

41. Science In a magazine, John read that the average temperature on the surface of Earth is 15°C. The average temperature on the surface of Mars is −50°C. What is the difference between the two temperatures?

Problem Solving and Reasoning

42. Critical Thinking Nicki visited her dad at work and got lost in the building. She started on the first floor. She rode the elevator up 4 floors, then down 2 floors, then up 6 more floors, then down another floor.

a. Write an expression to represent this situation.

b. If Nicki started on the first floor, which floor did she end up on?

Draw a diagram.

43. Choose a Strategy At Kent Junior High, only 30 students can be in each room. Some classes have more than 30 students, and some have less. The principal used a spreadsheet to determine how many students had to be moved.

a. How many students need to be moved in Rooms 12 and 13? What integers should be in the Adjustment column? Explain.

b. How many students are currently in Rooms 14 and 15? Explain.

	A	B	C
	Room No.	Students	Adjustment
1	10	31	− 1
2	11	25	+5
3	12	27	
4	13	34	
5	14		−3
6	15		+4

Problem Solving

STRATEGIES

• Look for a Pattern
• Make an Organized List
• Make a Table
• Guess and Check
• Work Backward
• Use Logical Reasoning
• Draw a Diagram
• Solve a Simpler Problem

Mixed Review

Estimate the measure of each angle. Then measure each with a protractor. *[Lesson 8-3]*

44.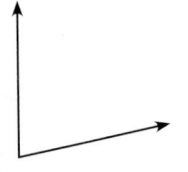

45.

46.

47.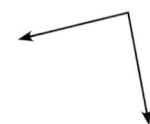

Multiply. *[Lesson 7-3]*

48. $4\frac{1}{3} \times 7\frac{9}{10}$

49. $\frac{4}{5} \times 5\frac{3}{4}$

50. $1\frac{2}{7} \times 3\frac{4}{7}$

51. $10\frac{3}{8} \times \frac{1}{5}$

Multiplying and Dividing Integers

▶ **Lesson Link** You've added and subtracted integers. Now you'll multiply and divide integers. ◀

Explore | Multiplying and Dividing Integers

What's Your Sign?

Materials: Spreadsheet software

... How It's Used

Artisans multiply and divide integers when keeping track of the money they've earned and the expenses they've paid for.

1. You can use a spreadsheet to create a multiplication table for positive and negative numbers. On a blank spreadsheet, enter the following information.

	A	B	C	D	E	F	G
1		− 3	− 2	− 1	0	1	2
2	− 4	=A2*$B$1	=A2*$C$1	=A2*$D$1	=A2*$E$1	=A2*$F$1	=A2*$G$1
3	− 3						
4	− 2						
5	− 1						
6	0						
7	1						
8	2						
9	3						
10	4						

2. In each column, copy the formula from row 2 down to row 10.

3. Study the signs of the products in the spreadsheet. Describe any patterns that you see.

4. Predict the sign of the product of two integers having the following signs.

    a. Positive, positive   **b.** Positive, negative

    c. Negative, positive   **d.** Negative, negative

5. Do you think the product of $(-3) \times (-3) \times (-3)$ will be a positive number or a negative number? Explain your reasoning.

Remember

Division can also be thought of as repeated subtraction. **[Previous course]**

Recall that multiplication is repeated addition. $2 \times 3 = 2 + 2 + 2$

This can help you find the product of a positive integer and a negative integer.

$(-2) \times 3 = (-2) + (-2) + (-2) = -6$

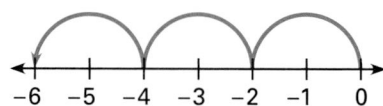

Example 1

Multiply: $3 \times (-3)$

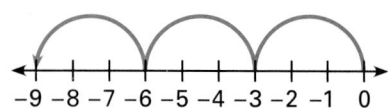 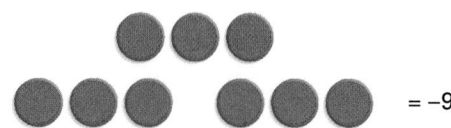
$= -9$

When two integers have *like* signs, the product or quotient will be positive.	$3 \times 4 = 12$ $-20 \div (-4) = 5$
When two integers have *unlike* signs, the product or quotient will be negative.	$-3 \times 4 = -12$ $20 \div (-4) = -5$

Examples

2 Multiply: $-7 \times (-9)$

The signs are alike, so the product is positive.

$-7 \times (-9) = 63$

3 Divide: $72 \div (-9)$

The signs are different, so the quotient is negative.

$72 \div (-9) = -8$

Study TIP

When solving a word problem, reread the problem and check to see that you answered the question being asked.

4 Over four consecutive hours, the temperature dropped from 0°F to −56°F. If the temperature dropped the same amount each hour, how much did the temperature change each hour?

$-56 \div 4$	Write an expression.
$-56 \div 4 = \boxed{?}\ 14$	Determine the numerical value of the quotient.
$-56 \div 4 = -14$	Determine the sign of the quotient.

The temperature dropped 14 degrees each hour.

Try It

Multiply. **a.** $4 \times (-9)$ **b.** $-15 \times (-6)$ **c.** 12×5 **d.** -10×1

Divide.   **e.** $-12 \div 3$ **f.** $24 \div 8$ **g.** $30 \div (-6)$ **h.** $-9 \div (-3)$

1. What do you know about the signs of two integers if their product is positive? If their quotient is negative?

2. Give a real-world example of multiplication involving a negative integer; of division involving a negative integer.

9-4 Exercises and Applications

Practice and Apply

Getting Started State the sign of the product or quotient.

1. $798 \times (-42)$ **2.** $-24 \times (-875)$ **3.** $-67 \div 46$ **4.** $-189 \div (-63)$ **5.** -51×49

Multiply.

6. $5 \times (-4)$ **7.** $-9 \times (-1)$ **8.** $-6 \times (-7)$ **9.** $-20 \times (-5)$ **10.** -5×8

11. $4 \times (-3)$ **12.** -9×9 **13.** $-2 \times (-9)$ **14.** $6 \times (-12)$ **15.** -10×2

16. -7×10 **17.** $8 \times (-6)$ **18.** $5 \times (-3)$ **19.** -8×4 **20.** $20 \times (-3)$

Divide.

21. $-6 \div 3$ **22.** $12 \div (-4)$ **23.** $8 \div (-2)$ **24.** $-16 \div (-4)$ **25.** $-21 \div 3$

26. $-14 \div (-2)$ **27.** $-60 \div 3$ **28.** $9 \div (-3)$ **29.** $4 \div (-2)$ **30.** $-18 \div (-9)$

31. $21 \div (-3)$ **32.** $-24 \div (-6)$ **33.** $-72 \div 9$ **34.** $-30 \div 10$ **35.** $-9 \div (-3)$

Patterns Complete each pattern.

36. $6 \div (-2) = -3$
$4 \div \square = -2$
$2 \div (-2) = \square$
$0 \div (-2) = \square$
$-2 \div \square = 1$
$-4 \div \square = \square$
$\square \div \square = \square$

37. $-4 \times 3 = \square$
$-4 \times \square = -8$
$-4 \times 1 = -4$
$-4 \times 0 = \square$
$\square \times -1 = 4$
$-4 \times \square = 8$
$\square \times \square = \square$

38. $(-2)^1 = -2$
$(-2)^2 = 4$
$(-2)^3 = -8$
$(-2)^4 = \square$
$(-2)^5 = \square$
$(-2)^6 = \square$
$(-2)^7 = \square$

39. $-9 \div 3 = -3$
$-6 \div 3 = \square$
$\square \div 3 = -1$
$\square \div 3 = 0$
$\square \div \square = 1$
$6 \div \square = \square$
$\square \div \square = \square$

40. Sal's business currently has expenses of $4 million and sales of $9 million. Sal wants to triple the size of his business. Express the new expenses, sales, and profit as integers.

PRACTICE 9-4

41. In 4 hours, the temperature dropped steadily from 0°C to −20°C. Using at least one negative integer, write an equation that shows how much the temperature dropped in 1 hour.

42. Which equations are correct?

I. $-10 \times -5 = 50$

II. $-10 \div -5 = 2$

III. $10 \times -5 = -50$

IV. $-10 \div 5 = -2$

Ⓐ Only I

Ⓑ Only II and III

Ⓒ Only II, III, and IV

Ⓓ I, II, III, and IV

Problem Solving and Reasoning

43. Critical Thinking Toby's game scores were −5, −10, 5, −20, and 15. Toby guessed his average score to be −5. State the difference between his guessed average and his actual average. Explain your reasoning.

44. Journal Does -6×4 equal $4 \times (-6)$? Use number lines to explain your answer.

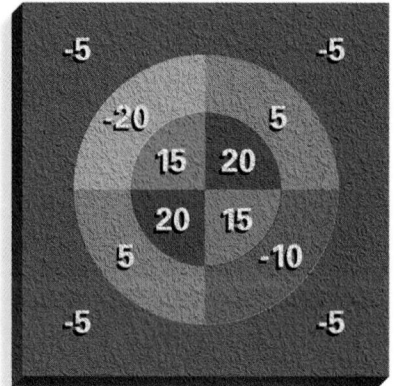

Mixed Review

Divide. *[Lesson 7-4]*

45. $4 \div \frac{6}{7}$

46. $1 \div 10\frac{1}{2}$

47. $7 \div \frac{3}{4}$

48. $9 \div 4\frac{3}{5}$

49. $8 \div \frac{2}{7}$

50. $3 \div \frac{7}{8}$

51. $5 \div 2\frac{4}{9}$

52. $6 \div \frac{5}{8}$

Find the measure of the missing angle in each triangle. *[Lesson 8-4]*

53. $m\angle S = 35°, m\angle D = 72°, m\angle F = \boxed{}°$

54. $m\angle J = 90°, m\angle C = 45°, m\angle M = \boxed{}°$

55. $m\angle D = 117°, m\angle G = 52°, m\angle H = \boxed{}°$

56. $m\angle B = 19°, m\angle N = 24°, m\angle M = \boxed{}°$

Project Progress

Gather information about the place you've chosen and list it in a facts chart.

Present some information as integers. You might average monthly temperatures, elevations of mountains or depths of lakes, and degrees of latitude.

Problem Solving

Understand

Plan

Solve

Look Back

In this section, you've seen how earth scientists use positive and negative numbers to study the earth. Now you'll use positive and negative numbers to record information about an earth science experiment.

The Third Sphere From the Sun

Becky's family took a two-week hiking vacation. On March 13, they hiked 320 feet up from an elevation of 5280 feet. During the vacation, Becky recorded how much the family's elevation changed.

Date	Change	Elevation
March 13	+320	5600
March 14	-500	
March 15		

1. Copy and complete Becky's chart, using the data below.

   a. March 13   up 320 ft
   b. March 14   down 500 ft
   c. March 15   up 460 ft
   d. March 16   up 120 ft
   e. March 17   down 240 ft
   f. March 18   down 170 ft
   g. March 19   up 570 ft
   h. March 20   down 400 ft
   i. March 21   down 130 ft
   j. March 22   up 220 ft
   k. March 23   up 40 ft
   l. March 24   down 290 ft
   m. March 25   up 200 ft

2. Becky's family started at an elevation of 5280 ft. On the last day, how many feet up or down must Becky's family hike to return to their starting elevation?

3. Did Becky's family ever hike above 6000 ft? 7000 ft? 8000 ft? Explain.

4. Create a data set of your own that shows a 7-day hike starting and ending at –1000 ft. Explain how you decided what numbers to choose to return to exactly –1000 ft.

Section 9A Review

Simplify.

1. -9×7 **2.** $25 \times (-4)$ **3.** $-6 - (-5)$ **4.** $12 + (-3)$ **5.** $16 \div (-4)$

6. $-7 + 2$ **7.** $-2 - (-4)$ **8.** $-2 \times (-1)$ **9.** $45 \div (-5)$ **10.** $-32 \div (-2)$

11. $7 \times (-6)$ **12.** $7 - (-6)$ **13.** $-7 + 6$ **14.** $-7 - (-6)$ **15.** $-16 \div 8$

16. $-8 + (-4)$ **17.** $-8 - (-2)$ **18.** $8 + (-2)$ **19.** $8 - (-2)$ **20.** $-5 + 9$

21. $8 \times (-5)$ **22.** $40 \div (-5)$ **23.** $-6 \times (-4)$ **24.** $24 \div (-4)$ **25.** $23 \div (-1)$

26. Whenever Jill buys new books, she sells back old ones. For each book returned, Jill gets a $2 refund. She pays $3 for every book she buys. How many books could Jill have bought if her bill was $4 after the refund?

Operation Sense For Exercises 27–30, solve each problem, state the operation you used, and explain your answer.

27. Ryan spent 12 dollars to go to a baseball game. He earned 8 the next day. What was the overall change in money for the two days?

28. On 4 plays, the Cardinals lost 10 yards. If they gained 2 yards on the first play, how many did they gain or lose on the other 3 plays?

29. In 3 hours, the temperature dropped steadily from 0°C to -12°C. How much did the temperature drop in one hour?

30. The Board of Directors reported that company stock gained 5 points each year for 6 years. What was the overall change in points for the stock?

Test Prep

Numbers other than zero that have neither a positive nor a negative sign are always positive.

31. On the second day of her descent, a mountain climber started at 12,500 feet above sea level. By the end of the day, she had gone down 2,500 feet. How far above sea level was she at the end of the day? Choose the correct answer(s).

I. $-10,000$ II. $10,000$ III. $+10,000$ IV. $-15,000$

Ⓐ Only I   Ⓑ Only IV   Ⓒ Only I, II, and III   Ⓓ Only II and III

A Hunting We Will Go...

In 1795, a teenager named Daniel McGinnis rowed out to Oak Island, off the coast of Nova Scotia. He knew the island had been a hideout for pirates in the 16th and 17th centuries. He noticed a sawed-off tree limb with rope burns and an old ship's tackle above a shallow hole. Two words came to his mind: "Pirate treasure!"

Daniel and a group of friends dug at the spot. They hit platforms of logs every 10 feet. At 90 feet, they uncovered a message saying they would find treasure in 40 more feet. Before they could dig that far, an underground tunnel filled their hole with water—too much to pump out. They abandoned their search.

Since then, other people have spent millions of dollars trying to find the treasure. So far, nobody has found it. Is there a treasure? If so, will it ever be found?

1 Other than the money itself, why do people search for buried treasure?

2 How can you use mathematics to describe the location of something like a buried treasure?

3 In what real-world situations is it important to describe a location exactly?

487

The Coordinate Plane

You'll Learn ...

■ to plot points on a coordinate plane

■ to read the coordinates of points on a coordinate plane

... How It's Used

Forest rangers use coordinates to describe the locations of forest fires.

Vocabulary

coordinate plane

x-axis

y-axis

origin

quadrant

ordered pair

coordinate

▶ **Lesson Link** You know how to locate points on a number line. Now you'll locate points using two number lines. ◀

Explore | **Locating Points on a Plane**

How Many Muldoons to the Green Monkey?

Materials: Graph paper

You have a map to the 9 treasures of Apple Island. You're at the apple tree in the middle of the island.

Apple Island

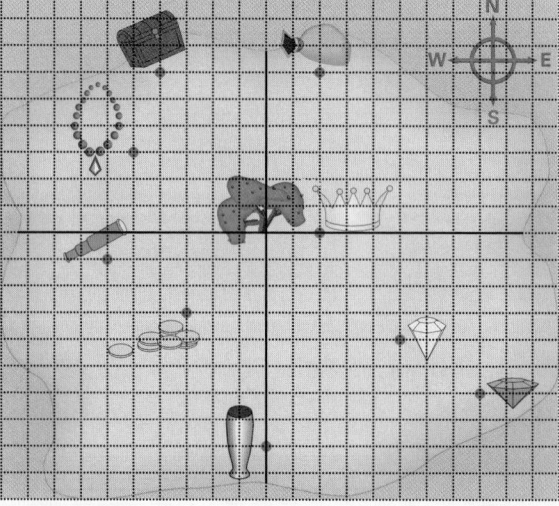

1. Write directions telling how to find each treasure, starting at the apple tree. You may use directions like up, down, left, and right, or compass directions such as north, south, east, and west, or other directions of your choosing. Each unit on the map equals 1 "muldoon."

2. Draw two perpendicular lines on grid paper. Note the location of four treasures of your own on your grid. When connected with lines, the four points should form a rectangle.

3. Write directions for three of the treasures and trade them with a partner. Try to locate your partner's fourth treasure. Describe its location, and explain your method.

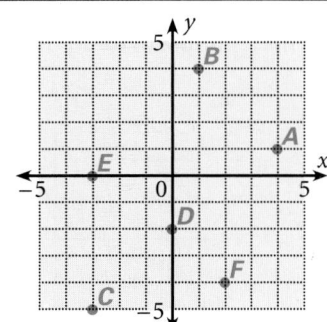

Learn | The Coordinate Plane

You can use a **coordinate plane** to locate points on the plane. The **x-axis** and the **y-axis** are number lines. They intersect at right angles at their zero points, the **origin** .

The two axes divide the plane into 4 **quadrants** , numbered I, II, III, and IV.

Any point can be located using an **ordered pair** . The first **coordinate** tells you how far to move on the x-axis from the origin. The second coordinate tells you how far to move on the y-axis from the origin.

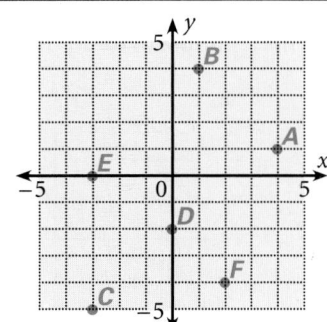

coordinate plane diagram showing points (−3, 4) labeled II, (4, 4) labeled I, (0, 0), (−1, −2) labeled III, IV, (0, −4), with y-axis and x-axis labeled, scale −5 to 5.

► History Link

The coordinate plane is also called the *Cartesian coordinate plane.* It is named after René Descartes, a 17th-century French philosopher and mathematician.

Examples

1 Give the coordinates of the points.

Starting at the origin, go right (+) or left (−) along the x-axis until you're above or below the point. Then, go up (+) or down (−) to the point.

Coordinates: $A(4, 1)$, $B(1, 4)$, $C(-3, -5)$, $D(0, -2)$, $E(-3, 0)$, $F(2, -4)$

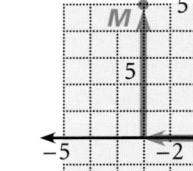
graph with points A, B, C, D, E, F plotted

Study TIP

You can remember that the second coordinate in an ordered pair is the y- coordinate by remembering that, in the alphabet, y comes after x.

2 On the map, plot the points $M(-2, 5)$ and $N(3, -3)$.

For M, start at the origin. Go left (−) 2 units. Go up (+) 5 units. Mark the point.

For N, start at the origin. Go right (+) 3 units. Go down (−) 3 units. Mark the point.

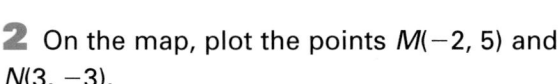

Try It

a. Give the coordinates of the points.

b. Plot and label each point on graph paper.

$H(-2, 2)$ $I(5, 3)$ $J(4, -3)$

$K(0, 1)$ $L(-1, -5)$ $M(5, 0)$

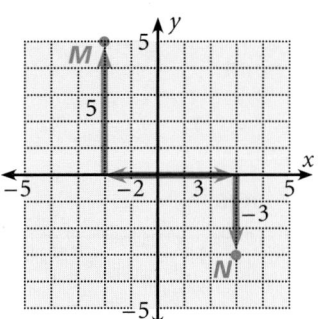
graph with points A, B, C, D, E, F, G plotted

1. How can you use the signs of the coordinates of a point to predict which quadrant the point is in?

2. Why do you need two coordinates to locate a point in the plane?

3. Are the points (2, 3) and (3, 2) the same? Explain.

9-5 Exercises and Applications

Practice and Apply

Getting Started State which quadrant each point lies in.

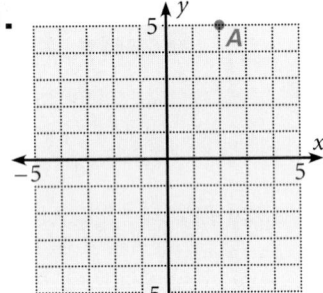

1.

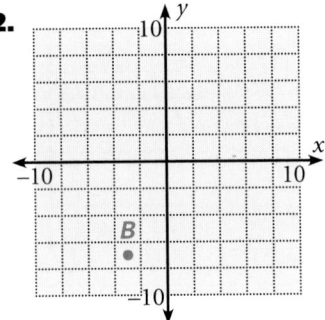

2.

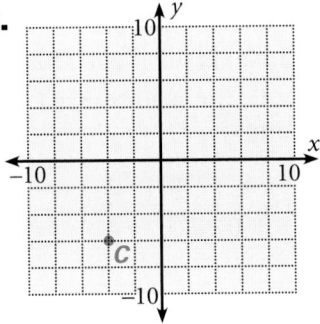

3.

Give the coordinates of each point.

4. Q **5.** W **6.** E **7.** D **8.** R

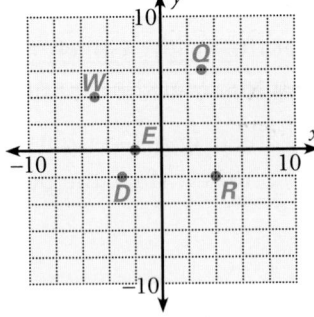

State which quadrant each point is in.

9. $(4, 10)$ **10.** $(-7, 18)$ **11.** $(32, -18)$

12. $(-52, -48)$ **13.** $(6, -45)$ **14.** $(-13, 17)$

Plot and label each point.

15. $M(4, 6)$ **16.** $R(0, 6)$ **17.** $K(3, 0)$ **18.** $N(-3, 7)$ **19.** $T(2, -5)$

20. $S(-4, -5)$ **21.** $J(0, -2)$ **22.** $Q(-6, -2)$ **23.** $P(0, 0)$ **24.** $H(5, 4)$

Describe how to locate each point.

25. $(-35, -18)$ **26.** $(0, -3)$ **27.** $(4, 10)$

28. $(-52, 63)$ **29.** $(88, -23)$ **30.** $(8, 0)$

31. Career Dan is a field geologist surveying drill holes in the Australian desert. He's mapped the location of the holes so that his truck is parked at the origin.

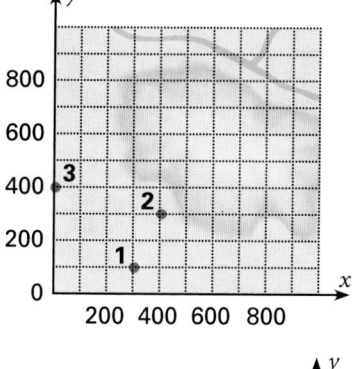

   a. What are the coordinates of the three drill holes?

   b. Estimate which drill hole is farthest away from Dan's truck.

   c. How far away from Dan's truck is the third drill hole?

32. **Test Prep** Choose the ordered pair for point *J*.

   Ⓐ $(8, -6)$ Ⓑ $(6, 8)$ Ⓒ $(-6, 8)$ Ⓓ $(-6, -8)$

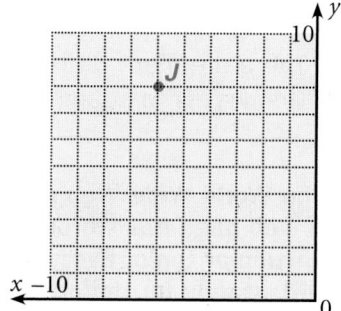

33. Geometry Plot these points: $(4, 3), (-2, 3), (6, -2),$ and $(-4, -2)$.

   a. Connect the points to form a quadrilateral.

   b. Classify the quadrilateral in as many ways as possible.

Problem Solving and Reasoning

34. **Journal** What are the signs of each of the coordinates of any point in the first quadrant? The second quadrant? The third quadrant? The fourth quadrant? Explain.

35. Critical Thinking Use the map and the directions given to find the coordinates of the Smallville School.

The school and the marketplace have the same *y*-coordinate. The *x*-coordinate of the school is twice the difference between the *y*-coordinate of the marketplace and the *y*-coordinate of the gas station.

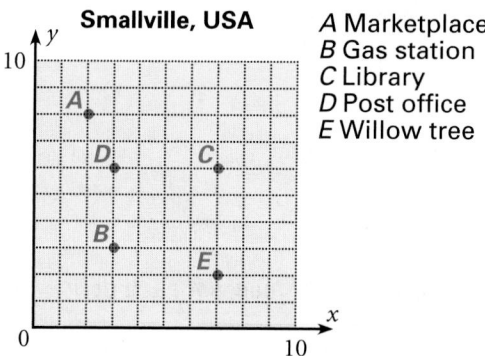

Smallville, USA

A Marketplace
B Gas station
C Library
D Post office
E Willow tree

36. Communicate When plotting an ordered pair, why is it important to always use the *first* number to describe the left/right location of the point and the *second* number to describe the up/down location of the point?

Mixed Review

Simplify. *[Lesson 7-5]*

37. $\dfrac{7}{16} \div \dfrac{16}{21}$ **38.** $\dfrac{3}{4} \div \dfrac{3}{4}$ **39.** $4\dfrac{7}{9} \div 2\dfrac{2}{7}$ **40.** $\dfrac{4}{7} \div \dfrac{21}{28}$

State whether the given lengths can form a triangle. *[Lesson 8-5]*

41. 7 m, 8 m, 14 m   **42.** 12 cm, 12 cm, 36 cm   **43.** 3 yd, 4 yd, 5 yd

TECHNOLOGY

Using Browser Software • Research on the World Wide Web

Problem: How can you find information about buried treasure?

There are many different ways of conducting research to learn more about a particular topic. One way is to search for information on the World Wide Web.

The World Wide Web is a series of web pages. A web page has words and pictures about a particular topic. Every page has a URL address. URL stands for Uniform Resource Locator.

| BACK | FORWARD | HOME | BOOKMARK | | SEARCH | RELOAD | PRI |

URL: http://www.piratenet/main_page

AHOY MATES

Welcome to the complete guide to Pirates on the web.

☠ Links to information on:

Famous pirates
Buried treasure
Sunken ships

1 If you know the URL address for the page you want to reach, you can type it into your browser software and press the return key.

The software will try to connect you to that page. Sometimes, a page cannot be reached because the computer connected to that page isn't working, or the page no longer exists.

2 You can also use a *search engine.* The search engine will ask you for a key word you want to research, such as *treasure.* It will list descriptions of the pages related to the key word. You can click on a description to go to the page it describes.

3 Many pages have *links* to other pages with related information. A link appears as an underlined word or phrase, and it is usually in a different color. You can go to these pages by clicking on the link.

ON YOUR OWN

▶ Try to find information about one of the following topics: pirates, explorers, archaeology, Antarctica.

▶ Use the World Wide Web to research a topic of your own choice.

Graphing Slides and Flips

▶ **Lesson Link** ▏ In the last chapter, you learned about translations and reflections. Now you'll graph translations and reflections on the coordinate plane. ◀

Explore ▏ Slides and Flips

The Temple of the Trapezoids

Materials: Graph paper

A team of treasure hunters knows the size, shape, and orientation of the ancient Temple of the Trapezoids. Unfortunately, they do not know where on Polygon's Island the temple is located.

1. The map shows the temple floor in one possible location. Copy the sketch onto graph paper and give the coordinates of its four corners.

2. Another possible location for the temple is where every point from the first location is moved 6 units east and 3 units south. Graph the temple at this possible location and give the coordinates of its corners.

3. The corners of the north wall of the actual Temple of the Trapezoids are located at (18, 23) and (20, 23). How can you find the coordinates of the other two corners without graphing the temple? What are they?

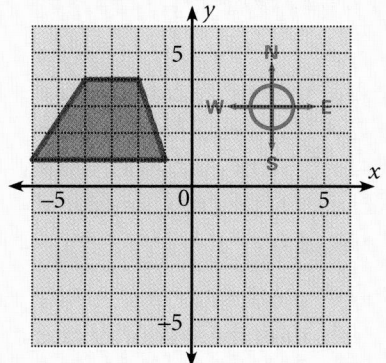

You'll Learn ...

■ to graph translations and reflections on the coordinate plane

... How It's Used

Computer animators slide and flip images on a coordinate plane when creating an animated sequence.

Learn ▏ Graphing Slides and Flips

Recall that a *translation* slides a figure to a new position without rotating the figure. You can graph translations on a coordinate grid. To translate △ABC, move each vertex right 4 units and up 4 units. The new triangle is △A'B'C', read as "triangle A prime B prime C prime."

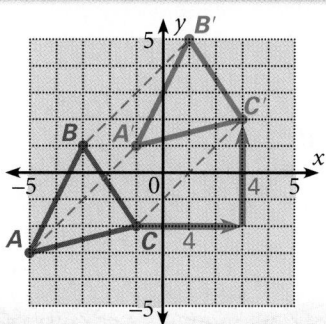

Example 1

Create △A'B'C' by translating △ABC 5 units left and 3 units up. Give the coordinates of A', B', and C'. Describe any patterns you find.

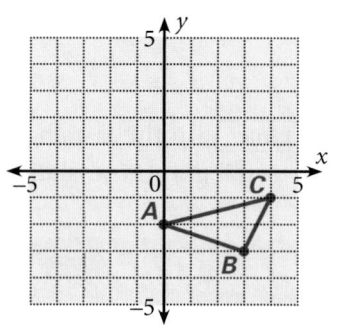

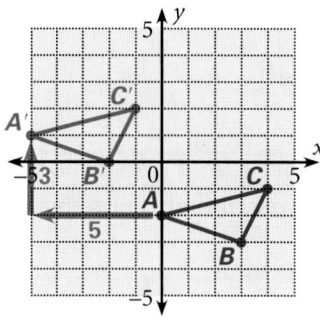

△ABC has coordinates A(0, −2), B(3, −3), and C(4, −1).

△A'B'C' has coordinates A'(−5, 1), B'(−2, 0), and C'(−1, 2).

Notice that the x-coordinates of △A'B'C' are 5 *less than* the x-coordinates of △ABC. That's because △ABC was translated 5 units *left* (−).

The y-coordinates of △A'B'C' are 3 *more than* the y-coordinates of △ABC. That's because △ABC was translated 3 units *up* (+).

$$\begin{array}{cc} \text{left 5} & \text{up 3} \\ \downarrow & \downarrow \end{array}$$

$$A(0, -2) \rightarrow A'(0 - 5, -2 + 3) = A'(-5, 1)$$

$$B(3, -3) \rightarrow B'(3 - 5, -3 + 3) = B'(-2, 0)$$

$$C(4, -1) \rightarrow C'(4 - 5, -1 + 3) = C'(-1, 2)$$

Try It

On the map, create △L'M'N' by translating △LMN 6 units right and 4 units down. Give the coordinates of L', M', and N'. Describe any patterns you find.

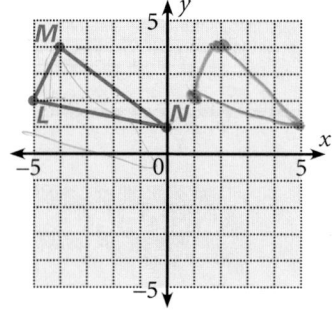

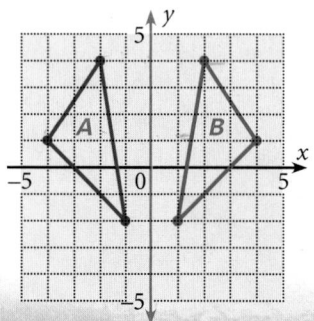

Recall that a *reflection* "flips" a shape over a line of symmetry. △A in the figure has been reflected across the y-axis to give △B. The y-axis is the line of symmetry. △A and △B are reflections of each other.

Example 2

Create △R'S'T' by reflecting △RST across the x-axis. Give the coordinates of R', S', and T'. Describe any patterns you find.

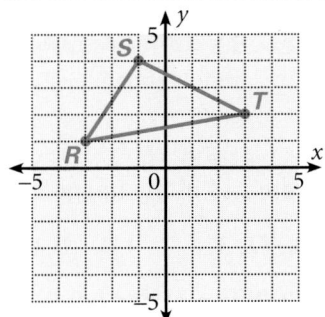

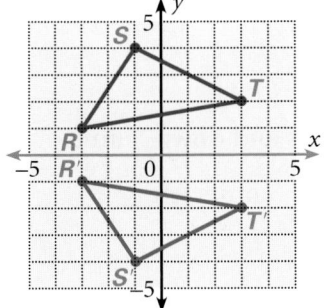

△RST has coordinates $R(-3, 1)$, $S(-1, 4)$, and $T(3, 2)$.

△R'S'T' has coordinates $R'(-3, -1)$, $S'(-1, -4)$, and $T'(3, -2)$.

Remember

In transformational geometry, there are three types of movement for a shape: reflection, rotation, and translation.

[Pages 444, 448, and 453]

Notice that the x-coordinates of △RST are the same as the x-coordinates of △R'S'T'. That's because a reflection across the x-axis does not move the triangle left or right.

Reflections across the x-axis change each y-coordinate into its *opposite*.

$$R(-3, \mathbf{1}) \rightarrow R'(-3, \mathbf{-1}) \quad S(-1, \mathbf{4}) \rightarrow S'(-1, \mathbf{-4}) \quad T(3, \mathbf{2}) \rightarrow T'(3, \mathbf{-2})$$

↑   ↑   ↑   ↑   ↑   ↑

    opposite   **opposite**   **opposite**

Try It

Create △X'Y'Z' by reflecting △XYZ across the y-axis. Give the coordinates of X', Y', and Z'. Describe any patterns you find.

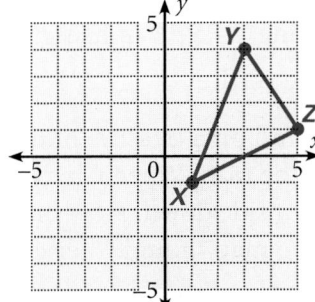

Check   Your Understanding

1. How are the coordinates of a point changed if the point is translated up or down? Right or left?

2. How are the coordinates of a point changed if the point is reflected across the x-axis? Across the y-axis?

Practice and Apply

Getting Started State the coordinates of the image of the point translated 1 unit up.

1. $(4, 5)$ **2.** $(2, 8)$ **3.** $(7, 3)$ **4.** $(0, 0)$ **5.** $(-3, 5)$ **6.** $(-7, -4)$

For Exercises 7–12, use the point $P(2, 3)$ to plot and label P'.

7. Slide P to the right 3 units

8. Reflect P across the y-axis

9. Slide P 1 unit right and 2 units up

10. Slide P to the left 2 units and down 3 units

11. Slide P 2 units down and 1 unit up

12. Slide P 3 units right and 3 units left

For Exercises 13–16, plot the image of quadrilateral $GHIJ$.

13. Translate $GHIJ$ 3 units up, 4 units right

14. Slide $GHIJ$ 2 units left, 5 units up

15. Slide $GHIJ$ 2 units right, 3 units down

16. Translate $GHIJ$ 5 units down

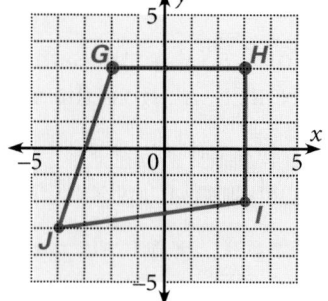

17. Geometry $\triangle RST$ has vertices at $R(-1, 1)$, $S(1, 3)$, and $T(4, -1)$.

   a. Draw the graph of $\triangle RST$.

   b. Create $\triangle R'S'T'$ by translating $\triangle RST$ 3 units right and 2 units up.

   c. State the coordinates of the vertices of $\triangle R'S'T'$.

18. One item that Cheryl had to find on a treasure hunt was located at the point $(3, 4)$ on the map. When Cheryl got there, she realized she had the map upside down. How many units left, right, up, and down on the map should Cheryl walk to find the correct location?

19. Geometry $\triangle XYZ$ has vertices at $X(-4, 2)$, $Y(4, 3)$, and $Z(2, 1)$.

   a. Draw the graph of $\triangle XYZ$.

   b. Create $\triangle X'Y'Z'$ by reflecting $\triangle XYZ$ across the x-axis.

   c. Give the coordinates of the vertices of $\triangle X'Y'Z'$.

PRACTICE 9-6

20. [Test Prep] Choose the graph that shows $\overrightarrow{KL}$ translated 3 units right and 1 unit down.

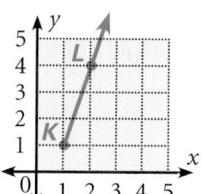

Ⓐ 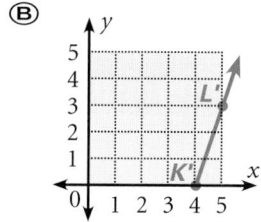   Ⓑ   Ⓒ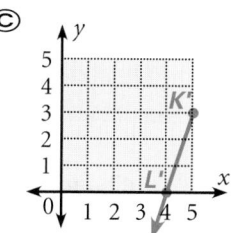

Problem Solving and Reasoning

21. Critical Thinking A polygon has vertices at $A(2, 5)$, $B(5, 5)$, $C(5, -1)$, and $D(2, -1)$. Reflect the polygon across the y-axis. Then translate the image 4 units to the right and 2 units down. Give the coordinates of the vertices of the new image. Explain your reasoning.

22. Choose a Strategy Can a reflection of a figure and a translation of the same figure be the same shape and have the same coordinates on a coordinate grid? Explain.

23. Communicate If the coordinates of the vertices of a figure are integers, will the translation or reflection always have integers as coordinates of the vertices?

Problem Solving STRATEGIES

- Look for a Pattern
- Make an Organized List
- Make a Table
- Guess and Check
- Work Backward
- Use Logical Reasoning
- Draw a Diagram
- Solve a Simpler Problem

Mixed Review

Solve. *[Lesson 7-6]*

24. $t \div \dfrac{2}{3} = \dfrac{9}{16}$ **25.** $\dfrac{1}{2}p = 2\dfrac{1}{5}$ **26.** $\dfrac{12}{15} \div j = \dfrac{4}{5}$ **27.** $\dfrac{8}{9}e = 1$

Name each polygon and tell if it is regular or irregular. *[Lesson 8-6]*

28. 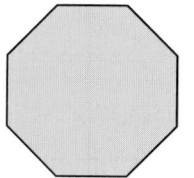   **29.** 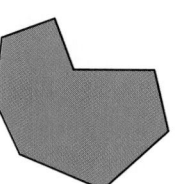   **30.** 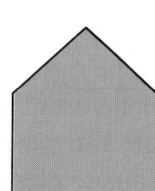   **31.**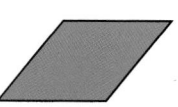

Graphing Equations

You'll Learn ...

■ to draw the graph of an equation

... How It's Used

Sound engineers graph equations when developing sound effects with computers.

Vocabulary

T-table

▶ **Lesson Link** You've learned how to graph translations and reflections on the coordinate plane. Now you'll learn how to graph equations on the plane. ◀

Explore | Graphing Equations

Catch My Drift

Materials: Graph paper

In 1705, the pirate ship Silver Legend sank in the Atlantic Ocean at the point (−5, −9) on the map. Every year, the Gulf Stream current moves the ship 1 unit east and 2 units north.

1. Draw an *x-y* coordinate system. Mark where the ship sank.

2. Draw the ship's location one year later, two years later, and three years later. Explain how you determined the location for each year.

3. Draw the ship's location $1\frac{1}{2}$ years after it sank. Explain how you determined the ship's location at that time.

4. Draw a line indicating the path the ship will travel over the years. Explain how you can determine where this line should be.

5. The year 2005 is 300 years after the sinking. Estimate the coordinates of the ship's location in 2005. Explain how you could determine the exact coordinates of the ship's location in 2005.

Learn | Graphing Equations

The algebraic equations you have seen so far have had one variable, as in $x + 3 = 7$. The coordinate plane uses two variables, x for the first coordinate and y for the second. You can use the coordinate plane to draw a picture of an equation.

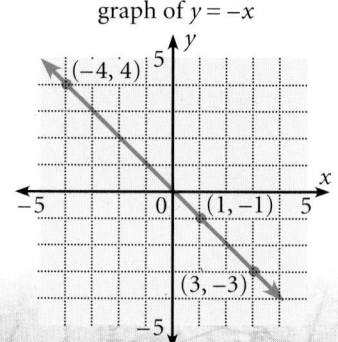

graph of $y = -x$

To draw the graph of an equation

$y = x + 1$

x	y
−1	0
0	1
1	2
2	3

1. Make a **T-table** like the one here. List three or four values for *x*. Choose easy numbers to work with, such as −1, 0 and 1.

2. For each value of *x*, use the equation to determine a value for *y*.

3. Plot the point for each pair of (x, y) values on a coordinate plane.

4. Draw a line connecting the points. This line represents all the other values you could have chosen for *x*, and the matching *y* values.

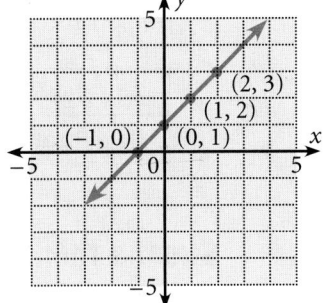

Examples

1 Graph the equation $y = x - 4$.

$y = x - 4$

x	y
−1	−5
0	−4
1	−3
2	−2

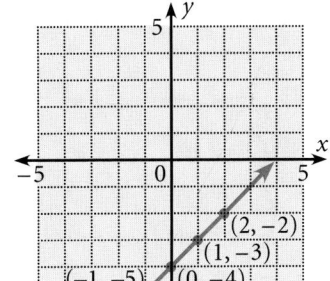

Problem Solving **TIP**

Look for a pattern in the *y* values.

2 Graph the equation $y = -2x$

$y = -2x$

x	y
−1	2
0	0
1	−2
2	−4

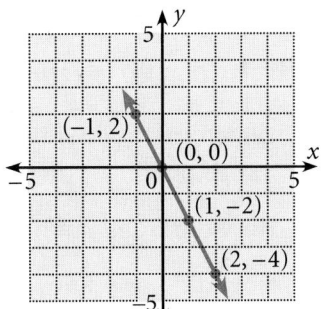

Remember

When multiplying integers, if the factors have like signs, the product will be positive. If they have unlike signs, the product will be negative.
[Page 482]

Try It

Graph each equation.

a. $y = x + 5$ **b.** $y = 2x$ **c.** $y = 8 - x$ **d.** $y = -1x$

WHAT DO YOU THINK?

A T-table and graph in a doctor's office give recommended maximum pulse rates during exercise, according to age.

Susana and Larry are 15 years old. What is their recommended pulse rate?

Recommended Pulse Rate

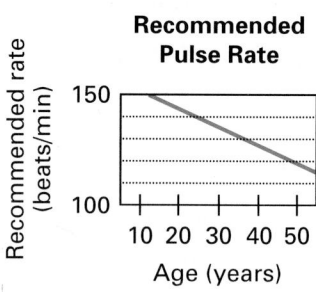

Recommended rate (beats/min) vs Age (years)

Age (years)	10	20	30	40	50
Rate (beats/min)	152	144	136	128	120

Susana thinks ...

I'll use the T-table. 15 is halfway between 10 and 20. 148 is halfway between 144 and 152.

So, 148 beats per minute is my recommended rate.

Larry thinks ...

I'll use the graph. The graph of the equation looks like it passes through (15, 148).

So, 148 beats per minute is my recommended rate.

What do you think?

1. Which method would you use to find the recommended rate for age 32? Explain.

2. How did Susana find the number halfway between 144 and 152?

3. How did Larry know that the graph passed through (15, 148)?

Check Your Understanding

1. How can you use the graph of an equation to find a *y*-value if you know the *x*-value? To find an *x*-value if you know the *y*-value?

2. Is the point (1, 3) on the graph of $y = x + 3$? Explain.

Practice and Apply

1. **Getting Started** Graph each equation on the same coordinate grid. Describe any patterns you see.

a. $y = x + 0$ **b.** $y = x + 1$ **c.** $y = x + 2$ **d.** $y = x + 3$

For Exercises 2–6, make a T-table with five (x, y) pairs for each.

2. $y = x - 53$ **3.** $y = x + 27$ **4.** $y = x - 106$ **5.** $y = -50x$ **6.** $y = 12x$

Graph each equation.

7. $y = x + 1$ **8.** $y = 1 + x$ **9.** $y = -5x$ **10.** $y = 3x$ **11.** $y = 3 + x$

12. $y = x$ **13.** $y = -1x$ **14.** $y = x - 3$ **15.** $y = 2 + x$ **16.** $y = 2x$

17. $y = x + 6$ **18.** $y = -2x$ **19.** $y = x - 4$ **20.** $y = 0x$ **21.** $y = 9$

22. $y = 6$ **23.** $y = 4 - x$ **24.** $y = 10 - x$ **25.** $y = 4 + x$ **26.** $y = -3$

Find the value of y when $x = 4$.

27. $y = 47 - x$ **28.** $y = 1 - x$ **29.** $y = -3 - x$ **30.** $y = x + 33$ **31.** $y = -2$

32. Pamela is a clerk in the receiving department of a company. When an order of computer paper comes in, she gives a ream to each of the four department administrators. The equation $y = x - 4$ gives the number of reams she has left after the distribution. Graph this equation.

33. **Consumer** A book at the Read It Again bookstore costs $3. Therefore, the equation for the cost of multiple books is $y = 3x$. Graph this equation.

x	-1	1	0	1	1	2	3
y	-4						

34. **Test Prep** Choose the graph of $y = x - 3$.

  Ⓐ 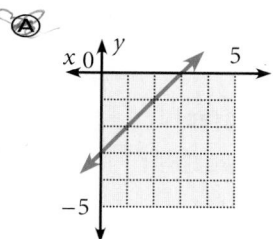   Ⓑ 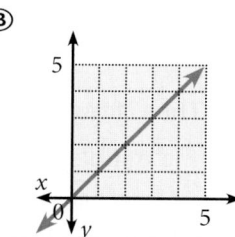   Ⓒ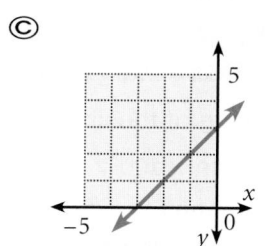

Problem Solving and Reasoning

35. Critical Thinking Shelley earns money bathing dogs. This month, her expenses were only $12. She collected x dollars from her customers.

a. Write an equation for Shelley's profit. Use y for the money she made and x for the money she collected from her customers.

b. Graph the equation.

c. Using the graph, how could you predict what Shelley's profit would be if she collected $25 from her customers?

d. Using the equation, how could you predict what Shelley's profit would be if she collected $25 from her customers?

36. Critical Thinking Graph the equations $y = 3x$ and $y = 5x$. Which line is steeper? Explain why you think this happens.

37. Critical Thinking Graph the equations $y = x + 3$ and $y = x + (-3)$ on the same coordinate plane. Describe the relationship between the lines.

38.  Explain how you can determine from an equation if the line will pass through the origin.

Mixed Review

Convert. *[Lesson 4-3]*

39. 72 feet = ☐ inches

40. 94 inches = ☐ feet

41. 3 feet = ☐ inches

42. 52 inches = ☐ feet

43. 0.75 feet = ☐ inches

44. 0.5 feet = ☐ inches

Draw an example of each. *[Lesson 8-7]*

45. Rhombus

46. Parallelogram

47. Trapezoid

48. Square

Classify each figure in as many ways as possible. *[Lesson 8-7]*

49.

50.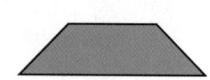

51.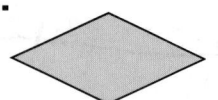

52.

Project Progress

Make a tracing of the shape of your country. Then, transfer the tracing onto graph paper. Draw an x and y axis with the origin in the middle of the country's shape. Start to determine the coordinates for the points that trace out the shape of the country.

Problem Solving

Understand
Plan
Solve
Look Back

At the beginning of this section, you learned that pirates may have buried treasure on Nova Scotia's Oak Island. Now you'll investigate how line graphs can be used to unscramble a system of tunnels and pinpoint the location of buried treasure.

A Hunting We Will Go ...

Materials: Graph paper

Pearl Island is shaped roughly like a square 10 leagues long and 10 leagues wide. The sides of the island run north-south and east-west. A 300-year-old treasure map gives the following instructions:

Lay out an east-west x-axis and a north-south y-axis. Have the axes intersect at the island's center point. Each unit on the graph will equal 1 league.

Draw these four tunnels:

The Emerald Tunnel $y = x - 7$

The Ruby Tunnel $y = \dfrac{x}{2}$

The Diamond Tunnel $y = -1x$

The Sapphire Tunnel $y = 2x$

Look for the intersection of exactly two tunnels. Mark that spot as T.

Find the reflection of T across the x-axis and mark it as T'.

From T', translate 3 leagues west and 2 leagues south. Dig in this spot, and you will find treasure.

Where was the intersection of exactly two tunnels? Where is the treasure? Explain your method.

Simplify.

1. $12 + (-4)$ 2. $-5 - (-9)$ 3. $6 \times (-2)$ 4. $-99 \div (-9)$ 5. $50 \div (-5)$

6. $4 \times (-10)$ 7. $-7 \times (-5)$ 8. $-9 - (-3)$ 9. $15 + (-10)$ 10. $8 \div (-1)$

For Exercises 11–15, use the coordinate grid.

11. What are the coordinates of each point?

12. If Point A were translated left 1 space and up 3 spaces, what would be the coordinates of A'?

13. If Point B were reflected across the y-axis, what would be the coordinates of B'?

14. If Point C were reflected across the y-axis and translated 3 points to the right and 2 points down, what would be the coordinates of its image?

15. If Point D were translated 3 spaces to the right and 5 spaces up, what would be the coordinates of its image?

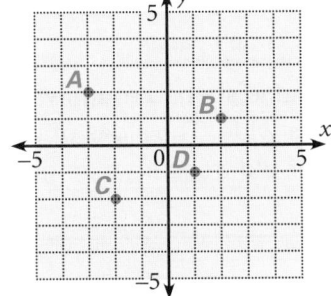

Graph each equation.

16. $y = -2x$ 17. $y = 6 + x$ 18. $y = x - 2$ 19. $y = x + (-2)$ 20. $y = 7$

21. **Geometry** The coordinates of two opposite vertices of a square are $(4, -4)$ and $(2, -2)$. If the square is reflected across the x-axis, what are the coordinates of the four vertices of its image?

22. Graph the equations $y = x + 1$ and $y = x - 1$. Do the lines have a point in common? Explain.

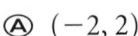 **Test Prep**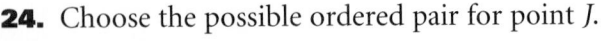

On the coordinate plane, numbers above the x-axis and numbers to the right of the y-axis are always positive.

23. Choose the possible ordered pair for point B.

Ⓐ $(-2, 2)$ Ⓑ $(2, -2)$ Ⓒ $(2, 2)$ Ⓓ $(-2, -2)$

24. Choose the possible ordered pair for point J.

Ⓐ $(0, -3)$ Ⓑ $(-3, 0)$ Ⓒ $(0, 3)$ Ⓓ $(3, 0)$

Negative Exponents

Remember that you can write large numbers using scientific notation. A number in scientific notation is a number between 1 and 10 multiplied by a power of 10.

$$2.4 \times 10^5 = 240,000$$

When converting a large number from scientific notation to standard form, the exponent tells you how many places to the right to move the decimal point. Small numbers can also be written using scientific notation. A small number written in scientific notation has a negative exponent. This negative exponent means "when converting to standard form, move the decimal point to the left."

$$2.4 \times 10^{-5} = 0.000024$$

When writing a number in scientific notation, first write down the nonzero part as a decimal number between 1 and 10. Then, write down the power of 10. The number of places the decimal moves will be the exponent. The sign of the exponent should be positive for numbers greater than 1 and negative for numbers less than 1.

$$0.00037 =$$
$$= 3.7 \times \square\square\square$$
$$= 3.7 \times 10 \,\square\square$$
$$= 3.7 \times 10 \,\square^4$$
$$= 3.7 \times 10^{-4}$$

Try It

Write the following numbers in standard form.

1. 5.6×10^{-3} **2.** 4.9×10^5 **3.** 2.8×10^{-2} **4.** 1.7×10^{-6}

5. 6.63×10^4 **6.** 5.14×10^{-5} **7.** 2.22×10^7 **8.** 8.35×10^{-4}

Write the following numbers in scientific notation.

9. 0.000056 **10.** 0.0000071 **11.** 43,000 **12.** 0.067

13. 64,500 **14.** 0.00891 **15.** 340,000,000 **16.** 0.00000022

Graphic Organizer

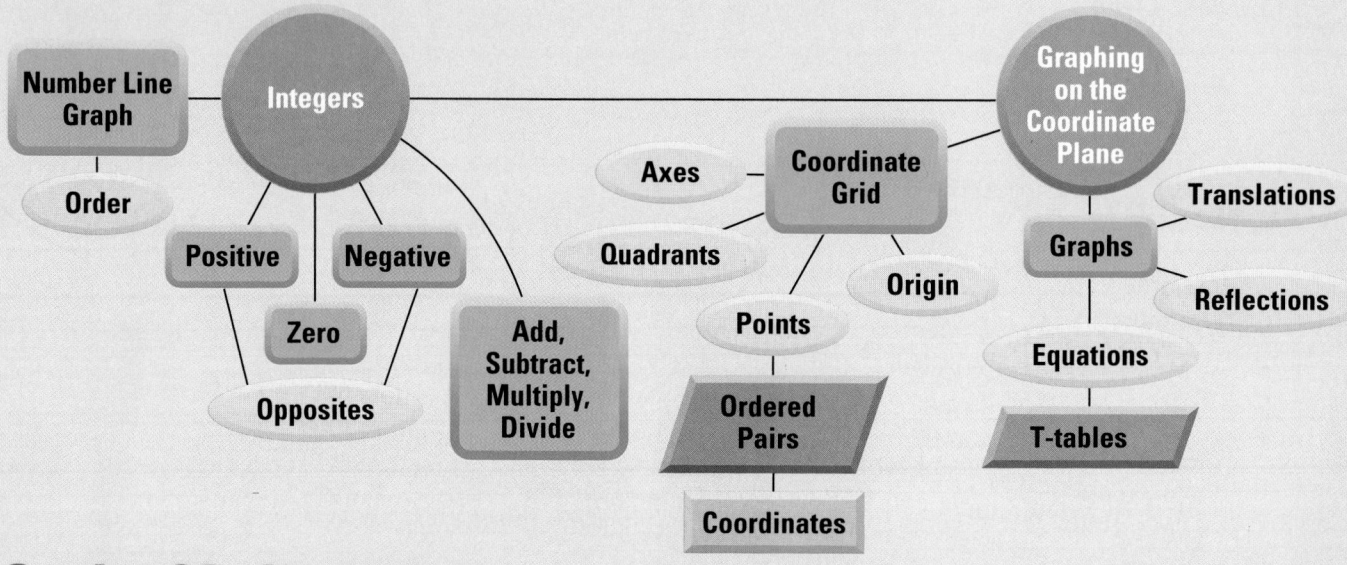

Section 9A Integers

Summary

- **Integers** include positive and negative whole numbers and zero.

- Integers can be graphed as points on a number line.

- Every integer has an **opposite**. The sum of an integer and its opposite is zero.

- You can add, subtract, multiply, or divide any combination of positive and negative integers.

Review

1. Locate the integers -4, 3, -2, -6, 1, and 0 on a number line.

2. What is the closest integer to the left of $-2\frac{1}{2}$ on a number line?

3. Is the sum of two negative numbers positive or negative?

4. Is the product of two negative numbers positive or negative?

Write a problem that is shown by each model.

5.

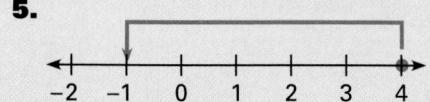

6.

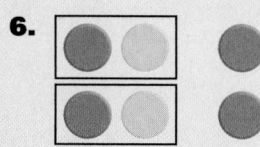

Simplify.

7. $-3 + 7$ **8.** $-1 + (-5)$ **9.** $8 + (-6)$ **10.** $-6 + 6$

11. $-4 - 2$ **12.** $-5 - 5$ **13.** $-3 - (-3)$ **14.** $7 - (-21)$

15. $3 \times (-7)$ **16.** $-4 \times (-9)$ **17.** $-16 \div 2$ **18.** $-27 \div (-9)$

Section 9B   Graphing on the Coordinate Plane

Summary

- You can use a **coordinate grid** with **x-** and **y-axes** to divide a plane into four **quadrants**.

- You can locate any point on the grid using two **coordinates**. A pair of coordinates is also called an **ordered pair**.

- The axes intersect at right angles at the point $(0, 0)$, called the **origin**.

- A figure can be translated or reflected on a coordinate grid.

- When a figure is reflected across the x-axis, only the y-coordinates of the image points change. When it is reflected across the y-axis, only the x-coordinates change.

- To graph an equation, you can first find pairs of values that are true for the equation using a **T-table**. Then, you can graph the points corresponding to these pairs on a coordinate grid.

Review

19. Name the ordered pair for the point 6 units left of the origin along the x-axis and 5 units down.

20. Name the quadrant where the point $(-3, 2)$ is located.

21. Name a point the same *distance* from the origin as $(-5, 0)$
    a. On the x-axis   **b.** On the y-axis

22. $\triangle RST$ has coordinates $R(-4, 2)$, $S(-3, 4)$, and $T(-2, 2)$. If $\triangle RST$ is reflected across the x-axis, name the coordinates of R', S', and T'.

23. Create $A'B'C'D'$ by translating the rectangle $ABCD$ 1 unit to the left and 3 units up. Give the coordinates of A', B', C', and D'.

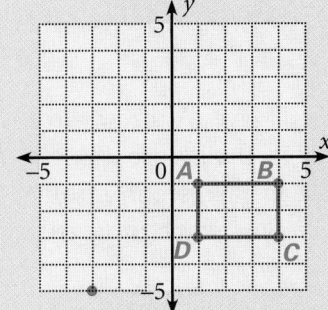

24. a. Graph the equation $y = x + 2$ and the equation $y = x - 1$ on the same coordinate grid.

    b. Explain why one of the graphs is a translation of the other.

Fill in each blank with the correct word.

1. The sum of an integer and its _____ is zero.

2. Numbers less than 0 are called _____ numbers.

3. You can subtract an integer by adding its _____.

4. The *x*- and *y*-axes of a coordinate grid divide a plane into four _____.

5. The point (0, 0) on a coordinate grid is called the _____.

6. The number −6 is the first _____ of the ordered pair (−6, 7).

7. It was 36°F at noon in Des Moines. Over the next 7 hours the temperature fell 48°. What integer would you use to represent the new temperature?

Simplify.

8. −10 + 7 **9.** 4 − (−6) **10.** 8 × (−6) **11.** −6 ÷ 6

12. −4 × (−2) **13.** −5 + 5 **14.** −5 − (−5) **15.** −21 ÷ (−21)

16. Create $\triangle D'E'F'$ by reflecting $\triangle DEF$ across the *y*-axis. Give the coordinates of D', E', and F'.

17. Create $\triangle R'S'T'$ by translating $\triangle RST$ 3 units to the right and 4 units down. Give the coordinates of R', S', and T'.

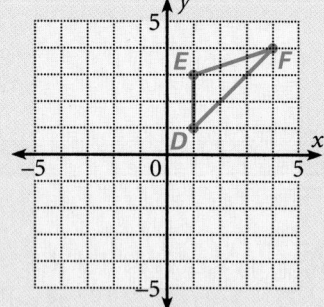

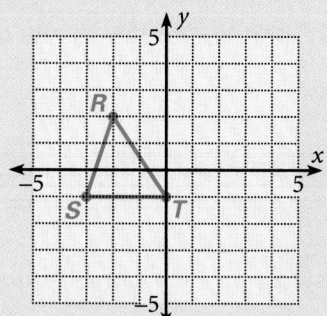

18. Use a T-table and graph the equation $y = -2x$.

Performance Task

Two players, A and B, started a dart game with 0 points. Player A threw three darts, and added the score in each section to his total. His final score was −5. Player B threw three darts, but she subtracted the score in each section from her total. Her final score was −1. On the dart board shown, which three darts belong to Player A, and which three to Player B?

Performance Assessment

Choose one problem.

Ups and Downs

Bar graphs may show negative as well as positive values.

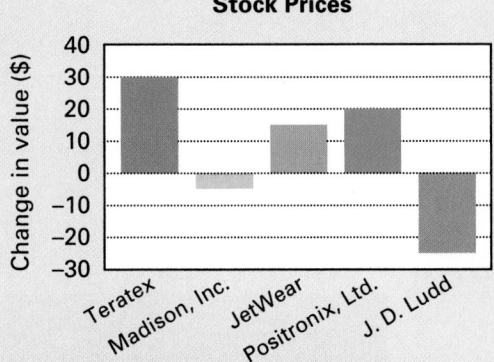

Stock Prices

Read the weather page in your newspaper or search the Internet and find the temperatures for five cities for the same date. At least two must be positive, and at least two must be negative. Graph the five temperatures on a bar graph. What was the median temperature for the cities?

The Powers of Negative Numbers

Write out a table showing the values of $2^2, 2^3, 2^4,$ $..., 2^{10}$. In another table, show the values for $(-2)^2, (-2)^3, (-2)^4, ..., (-2)^{10}$. Describe any patterns you see.

DECIMAL DELIGHTS

An ice cream store specializes in making very long sundaes for large groups. A plain, 1-scoop sundae with chocolate topping costs $1.40. Each additional scoop costs an additional $1.40. Write an equation that represents the situation and graph it. How much would a 25-scoop sundae cost? A 40-scoop sundae?

Point Me in the Right Direction

Graph the points (4, 3) and (4, −2) on a coordinate grid. Then state the coordinates of two points which could be connected to (4, 3) and (4, −2) to form each figure.

a. Trapezoid

b. Nonrectangular parallelogram

c. Rectangle

d. Quadrilateral that cannot be classified as a trapezoid or parallelogram

10 Ratio, Proportion, and Percent

▶ Cultural Link
www.mathsurf.com/6/ch10/people

▶ Arts & Literature Link
www.mathsurf.com/6/ch10/arts

People of the World

The Parthenon, built in Athens in the 400s B.C., incorporated the Greeks' ideal "Golden Ratio," which is approximately 0.618 to 1.

Arts & Literature

If one harp string is twice as long as another, the longer one will play the same note one octave lower. If one string is half as long as another, it will play the same note one octave higher.

Social Studies

Population density measures how many people there are for each square mile. New Jersey has a population density of 1042 people per square mile. Alaska has a population density of 1 person per square mile.

510

Entertainment

In 1930, less than 1% of the cars sold in the United States had a radio. By 1970, over 90% of them had a radio.

Science

The speed of a rotating object is often recorded in revolutions per minute (rpm) or revolutions per second.

KEY MATH IDEAS

Two quantities can be expressed as a ratio.

Two quantities with different units can be expressed as a rate.

A proportion is an equation made up of two ratios. If one value in the proportion is unknown, it can be found using the other three values.

Two figures are similar if their matching angles have the same measure and their side lengths are proportional.

A percent is a ratio that compares a quantity to the number 100.

CHAPTER PROJECT

Problem Solving

Understand
Plan
Solve
Look Back

In this project, you will choose a sport and find examples of ratios used in that sport. Start the project by thinking of a sport you enjoy and the kinds of quantities that get compared when discussing the sport.

Problem Solving Focus

Checking for a Reasonable Answer

Once you have solved a problem, it is a good idea to look back at your work to verify that you have done it correctly. One way to do this is to check your answer against the original situation to see if your answer is reasonable.

Each of these problems has an answer, but the answer is not exactly right. State if the answer is too low, too high, or close enough, and explain why.

1 A community garden is being designed for a vacant lot. The entire lot measures 127 feet by 160 feet. What is the area of the lot? *20,000 ft²*

2 The garden committee will build a fence around the lot. They will plant ivy to grow along the sides of the fence. How much fencing will they need for the 127- by 160-foot lot? *385 feet*

3 On the first day of planting, 144 people volunteered to help with the planting. One-fourth of the volunteers tilled the soil. How many volunteers tilled the soil? *45*

4 A space in the shape of a hexagon is set aside to be planted with marigolds. The perimeter of the hexagon will have a border of square tiles. Each side of the hexagon is $5\frac{1}{2}$ feet. Each tile is 1 square foot. How many tiles will the committee need? *36*

Ratios and Rates

Fire Alarm
October 8, 1871

8:30 p.m. According to one source, Catherine O'Leary milks her cow in her small barn. The cow knocks over her lantern, and the barn catches fire. Mrs. O'Leary starts a bucket brigade, but doesn't think to call the fire department.

9:05 p.m. William Lee goes to fire box 296 and pulls the lever, signaling a fire. The box is faulty, and the alarm does not get through.

9:10 p.m. Fire dispatcher William Brown ignores a red glow in the distance, assuming it is the rekindling of an earlier fire already under control.

9:21 p.m. Brown receives an alarm from fire box 342, a mile south of the fire. He sends seven fire-fighting vehicles to the wrong location.

By the time the fire crew arrived at the correct location, it was too late. The Great Fire of Chicago eventually destroyed over 17,000 homes, and over 300 people lost their lives. Every year, fire stations across the country remember this event by conducting Fire Prevention Week during the week of October 8.

1 The Great Fire of Chicago started out as a small fire. Why did it become so huge and devastating?

2 Do you think the Great Fire of Chicago could have been prevented? Why or why not?

3 How can mathematics help when trying to prevent fires?

Currier, N. and Ives, J., "The Great Chicago Fire"

513

10-1

What Is a Ratio?

You'll Learn ...

■ to express two quantities as a ratio

... How It's Used

Caterers use ratios to determine how much food to prepare for an event.

Vocabulary

ratio

▶ **Lesson Link**   You've learned how to work with fractions. Now you will work with a special kind of fraction called a ratio. ◀

Explore Ratios

What Happened at the Party?

Dear Joleen,

It's too bad you weren't in town for Rebecca's 12th birthday party. It was really great, except that there wasn't enough pizza. (There were only 2 slices for each kid.) She had an angelfood cake topped by 2 candles for each year of her age.

The guest list favored girls—3 out of every 5 guests were girls. Rebecca asked for jeans and got what she wanted—out of every 7 presents, 4 were jeans.

I hope you can make it to Rebecca's party next year!

Your friend,

Use the picture to determine which of the underlined statements are true and which are false. Give reasons for your answers.

A **ratio** is a comparison of two quantities. The ratio of erasers to pencils can be written as 5 to 3, 5:3, or $\frac{5}{3}$.

Example 1

Give a ratio comparing the number of cats and dogs that can be adopted at the animal shelter.

The ratio is 2 to 7, 2:7, or $\frac{2}{7}$.

Like fractions, ratios can sometimes be rewritten in lowest terms.

Examples

2 Six out of ten fire deaths occur in homes without fire detectors. Write this ratio in lowest terms.

$$\frac{6}{10} = \frac{6 \div 2}{10 \div 2}$$ Divide numerator and denominator by the same number.

$$= \frac{3}{5}$$ Simplify.

In lowest terms, the ratio is 3 to 5, 3:5, or $\frac{3}{5}$.

3 Give a ratio comparing the number of male soccer players and the total number of players in lowest terms.

$$\frac{\text{number of male players}}{\text{number of players}} = \frac{2}{6} = \frac{1}{3}$$

DID YOU KNOW?

It is recommended that the batteries in a smoke detector should be tested once a month, and replaced at least once a year.

Try It

Give a ratio comparing the quantities in lowest terms.

a. Number of triangles and number of squares

b. Number of squares and number of figures

1. How is a ratio like a fraction? How is it different?

2. Give an example of a ratio that compares a part to the whole. Give an example of a ratio that compares a part to a part.

PRACTICE 10-1

10-1 Exercises and Applications

Practice and Apply

Getting Started State if each is a ratio.

1. 6:13 **2.** 6×13 **3.** $\frac{6}{13}$ **4.** 13 to 6 **5.** $6 + 13$ **6.** $6 - 13$

Geometry For Exercises 7–10, use the shapes pictured.

7. What is the ratio of squares to hexagons?

8. Give the ratio of hexagons to squares.

9. What is the ratio of triangles to circles?

10. Give the ratio of hexagons to the whole group.

11. Industry Fire engines carry fire hoses. Fire trucks carry mainly ladders and fire-fighting equipment other than hoses. At one point, the city of San Francisco had 40 fire engines and 18 fire trucks.

a. Give the ratio of fire engines to fire trucks in lowest terms.

b. Give the ratio of fire trucks to total fire vehicles in lowest terms.

12. **Test Prep** Which of the following compares the number of pennies to the number of quarters?

Ⓐ 3:9 Ⓑ 9:4 Ⓒ 2:3 Ⓓ 9:3

A bag contains 3 red marbles, 8 blue marbles, and 10 yellow marbles. Give each ratio in three ways.

13. Red marbles to blue marbles

14. Yellow marbles to blue marbles

15. Red marbles to all marbles

16. Blue marbles to all marbles

17. At Midtown School, 24 out of the 49 sixth graders are in one of Ms. Campbell's classes. Write this as a ratio.

18. Mrs. Ng has 12 boys and 15 girls in her science class. Give each ratio.

    a. Boys to girls   **b.** Girls to boys   **c.** Boys to students   **d.** Girls to students

For Exercises 19–21, refer to the animals pictured.

19. The ratio of which animal to the whole group is 3:14?

20. The ratio of which animal to the whole group is 2:7?

21. Which two animals are compared in a ratio of 3:4?

Problem Solving and Reasoning

22. Critical Thinking Using ratios, three students described a cabinet containing 8 plates and 11 bowls. Helga used 8 to 11. Kendra used 11:8. Ka-fei used $\frac{8}{19}$. Explain how all three students could be correct.

23. Critical Thinking At the corner drug store, 32 out of 60 toothbrushes are red. How many are blue? Explain.

24. 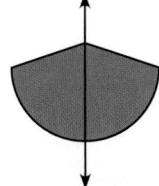 How is writing a ratio in lowest terms like writing a fraction in lowest terms?

Mixed Review

Tell if the line is a line of symmetry. *[Lesson 8-8]*

25.

26.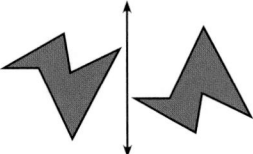

27.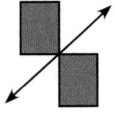

28.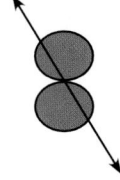

Find the missing measurement for each rectangle. *[Lesson 4-4]*

29. Area = 72 in²

Base = 8 in.

Height = ☐

30. Area = ☐

Base = 6.4 mm

Height = 2.3 mm

31. Area = 27.2 km²

Base = ☐

Height = 13.6 km

32. Area = ☐

Base = 3 ft

Height = 12 ft

▶ **Lesson Link**   You've used ratios to compare quantities. Now you will learn how to use tables to find equal ratios. ◀

Explore | Ratios

You Can Count On It

1. Copy and complete the table based on your own classroom. For the last two lines, choose your own items and count them.

Item	Number	Item	Number
Boys		Doors	
Girls		Windows	
Teachers		Pencil sharpeners	
Desks		Your choice #1	
Chairs		Your choice #2	

2. Write the following ratios.

    a. Boys to girls   **b.** Teachers to students

    c. Desks to chairs   **d.** Doors to windows

    e. Doors to people   **f.** People to pencil sharpeners

3. Write three ratios of your own. State the items being compared.

4. Find two quantities in your classroom whose ratio is about 2:1. How do you know the ratio is about 2:1? Repeat using 5:1 and 10:1.

5. Which ratios in Step 2 are important to people outside your class? Who might want to know these ratios? Why?

Learn | Equal Ratios

Sometimes you need to find ratios that are equal to a known ratio. You can create equal ratios by multiplying both quantities of the ratio by the same non-zero amount. A table can help organize the information.

Example 1

The city of San Francisco has 2 fire hydrants for every 3 city blocks. Find four ratios equal to this ratio.

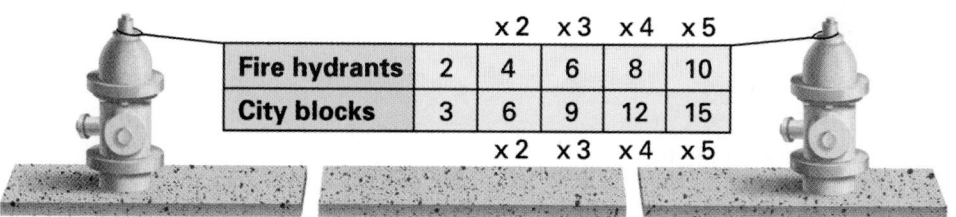

		x2	x3	x4	x5
Fire hydrants	2	4	6	8	10
City blocks	3	6	9	12	15
		x2	x3	x4	x5

San Francisco's ratio of fire hydrants to city blocks is equal to 4:6, 6:9, 8:12, and 10:15. Other answers are possible.

Remember

You can use either multiplication or division to find fractions equal to a given fraction.
[Page 294]

Division can also be used to find equal ratios. You can use any non-zero number, but numbers that go evenly into both quantities are the easiest to use.

Example 2

Using division, find three ratios that equal 40 to 60.

40			
60			

Set up a table.

$\div 2 \div 5 \div 10$

40	20	8	4
60	30	12	6

$\div 2 \div 5 \div 10$

Use division to find equal ratios.

Problem Solving TIP

When using division, try to choose numbers that are easy to divide by. Every whole number that ends in a zero is divisible by 2, 5, and 10.

Three ratios that equal 40 to 60 include 20 to 30, 8 to 12, and 4 to 6.

Try It

For each ratio, state another ratio equal to it.

a. 5:9   **b.** $\frac{3}{8}$ **c.** 60 to 100   **d.** 1:13

e. For every 12 pie slices sold at the Circus Cafe, 4 are cherry. Find one equal ratio using multiplication, and one equal ratio using division.

In Erica and Jamar's homeroom, 24 out of the 32 students want to go to Hillsdale Park for the school picnic. Erica and Jamar want to convince the teachers to choose Hillsdale Park. They plan to show three different ratios equal to $\frac{24}{32}$ in their presentation.

Erica thinks ...

I'll use a table, multiplying numerator and denominator by 2, 3, and 4.

		× 2	× 3	× 4
Numerator	24	48	72	96
Denominator	32	64	96	128
		× 2	× 3	× 4

Three equivalent ratios are $\frac{48}{64}$, $\frac{72}{96}$, and $\frac{96}{128}$.

Jamar thinks ...

I'll use a table, dividing the numerator and denominator by convenient numbers.

		÷ 2	÷ 4	÷ 8
Numerator	24	12	6	3
Denominator	32	16	8	4
		÷ 2	÷ 4	÷ 8

Three equivalent ratios are $\frac{12}{16}$, $\frac{6}{8}$, and $\frac{3}{4}$.

What do you think?

1. Erica and Jamar got different answers. Is each answer correct? Explain.

2. What does Jamar mean by "convenient numbers"?

1. For a given ratio, how many equal ratios can you create?

2. Is it possible to find a ratio that is equal to $\frac{2}{5}$, 2:5, and 2 to 5? Explain.

10-2 Exercises and Applications

Practice and Apply

Getting Started State if each ratio is in lowest terms.

1. $\frac{5}{6}$ 2. 2:10   3. 7 to 18   4. 4:3   5. $\frac{9}{3}$ 6. 6 to 2

Give two ratios equal to the given ratio.

7. 4 to 5   8. $\frac{10}{20}$ 9. 12:8   10. $\frac{25}{40}$ 11. $\frac{4}{6}$ 12. 3:7

13. $\frac{4}{8}$ 14. 7 to 1   15. $\frac{1}{8}$ 16. 5:10   17. $\frac{3}{4}$ 18. 2.1 to 4.2

State if the ratios are equal.

19. 7 to 21; 1 to 3   20. 6:9; 3:2   21. $\frac{5}{4}$; 10:8   22. 1 to 10; $\frac{2}{5}$

23. The circle graph shows the number of colored beads used in a hand-beaded bracelet. Carole wants to make a smaller bracelet using the same ratios of colors. Draw a circle graph that shows how many beads of each color Carole could use.

24. **Estimation** Mary jogs 5 laps in 7 minutes. Rikki jogs 11 laps in 15 minutes. Do Mary and Rikki jog at about the same speed?

25. **Test Prep** In order to control fires, some cities and counties require an indoor sprinkler system in each newly built house. If a sprinkler system goes on, 7 out of 10 times the fire will be controlled. How many fires out of 20 will be controlled?
    Ⓐ 14   Ⓑ 17   Ⓒ 20   Ⓓ 70

Colored Beads

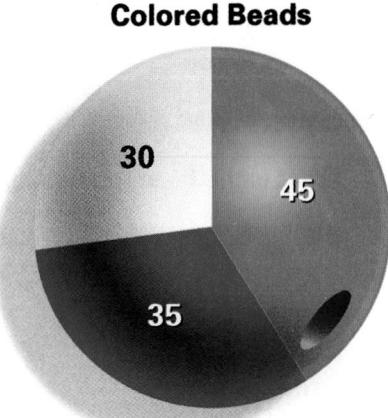

For Exercises 26–28, give three equal ratios.

26. Science In Oregon in 1995, for every forest fire caused by lightning, about 3 forest fires were caused by humans.

27. Seven out of ten calls to the fire department are for medical purposes.

28. A college residence hall has 7 students for every 2 bathrooms.

Complete each table of equal ratios.

29. 8 men to 10 women

Men	4			16
Women		10	15	

30. 5 fire fighters for each truck

Fire fighters				
Trucks	1	2	3	4

31. 6 triangles out of 15 figures

Triangles	2	4	6	8
Figures				

Problem Solving and Reasoning

32. Choose a Strategy How many whole-number ratios equal to 40:100 can you find using division? Explain your method.

33. Critical Thinking The ratios 1 to 2, 2 to 4, and 3 to 6 are equal ratios.

   a. Graph the ratios on the same coordinate grid. Use the first number in the ratio as the x-coordinate and the second as the y-coordinate

   b. Draw a straight line that connects the points.

   c. Repeat steps **a** and **b** using the ratios 2 to 3, 4 to 6, and 6 to 9.

   d. Do you think every set of equal ratios can be graphed as a straight line? Explain.

Problem Solving

STRATEGIES

- Look for a Pattern
- Make an Organized List
- Make a Table
- Guess and Check
- Work Backward
- Use Logical Reasoning
- Draw a Diagram
- Solve a Simpler Problem

Mixed Review

What is the least rotation that will land the figure on top of itself? *[Lesson 8-9]*

34. 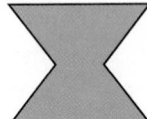   **35.**    **36.** 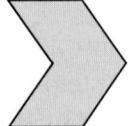   **37.**

Find the area if *b* is the base and *h* is the height of a parallelogram. *[Lesson 4-5]*

38. $b = 4, h = 5$ **39.** $b = 6$ in., $h = 3$ in.   **40.** $h = 12$ cm, $b = 3$ cm

41. $h = 10$ ft, $b = 88$ ft   **42.** $h = 10.5$ m, $b = 1.5$ m   **43.** $b = 67$ mm, $h = 100$ mm

What Is a Rate?

▶ **Lesson Link**   You've learned about ratios, and you've learned to find equal ratios. In this lesson you will use a special type of ratio called a rate. ◀

Explore   Rates

Doing It by the Book

Four students are in the Bookworm Club.

- Kevin reads 2 books every week.
- Joanna reads 7 books a month.
- Carlo reads 113 books a year.
- Noriko reads $\frac{1}{4}$ of a book each day.

1. Estimate how many books each student reads in a year. Explain how you made your estimates.

2. Estimate the number of books each student reads in a month.

3. There are approximately 4 weeks in a month. Estimate the number of books each student reads in a week.

4. Is it possible to find the number of books read per day? Per decade? Per any length of time? Explain.

5. Rank the students from the fewest books read to the most books read. Which set of estimates did you choose? Why?

Learn   What Is a Rate?

Some ratios are known as **rates** . A rate is a comparison of two quantities with different units of measure.

The average Dalmatian can run 15,400 feet in 5 minutes. The rate $\frac{15{,}400 \text{ feet}}{5 \text{ minutes}}$ compares the number of *feet* to the number of *minutes*. This can be read "15,400 feet *per* 5 minutes."

You'll Learn ...

■ to express two quantities with different units as a rate

... How It's Used

Tug boat captains use rates to determine how long it will take to sail to a particular destination.

Vocabulary

rate

unit rate

DID YOU KNOW?

Dalmatians were first used by firemen because the dogs developed a strong attachment to the firemen's horses. The dogs would bark if any thieves tried to steal the horses.

If the comparison is to 1 unit, the rate is called a **unit rate**.

$$\frac{15{,}400 \text{ feet} \div 5}{5 \text{ minutes} \div 5} = \frac{3080 \text{ feet}}{1 \text{ minute}} \leftarrow 1 \text{ unit}$$

The unit rate is **3080** feet per minute.

Examples

▶ History Link

The first fire engines were pumped by hand. They were replaced by steam-powered pumps, and finally by internal combustion engines, which use gasoline and diesel fuel.

1 A typical fire engine can hold 500 gallons of water. This water is used up in 10 minutes of continuous spraying. What is the rate of gallons per minute?

The rate that compares 500 gallons with 10 minutes is $\frac{500 \text{ gallons}}{10 \text{ minutes}}$. If you divide both numbers by 10, you get the unit rate of $\frac{50 \text{ gallons}}{1 \text{ minute}}$.

2 Every 3 hours, Henry's hamster eats 4 ounces of food. Use a table to find four rates describing this situation.

Since a rate is a ratio, you can find equal rates the same way you found equal ratios. Multiply or divide both quantities by the same number.

$$\times 2 \quad \times 3 \quad \times 4$$

Ounces of food	4	8	12	16
Number of hours	3	6	9	12

$$\times 2 \quad \times 3 \quad \times 4$$

Four rates that describe this situation are $\frac{4 \text{ oz}}{3 \text{ hr}}, \frac{8 \text{ oz}}{6 \text{ hr}}, \frac{12 \text{ oz}}{9 \text{ hr}}$, and $\frac{16 \text{ oz}}{12 \text{ hr}}$.

Try It

In 1987, Australian Greg Mutton paddled a bathtub 36 miles in 82 minutes, a world record. Use a table to find four rates describing this situation.

Check Your Understanding

1. Give an example of a ratio that is not a rate. Why isn't it a rate?

2. How can you tell if a rate is a unit rate?

3. A race car went 200 miles an hour. Is this a ratio? Is it a rate?

Practice and Apply

Getting Started State if the ratio is a rate.

1. 5 flowers in every square foot

2. $\dfrac{15 \text{ minutes}}{1 \text{ car wash}}$

3. 12 clips to 2 clips

4. 7:1

State if the ratio is a unit rate.

5. $\dfrac{3 \text{ in.}}{1 \text{ year}}$

6. $\dfrac{5 \text{ apples}}{7 \text{ oranges}}$

7. $\dfrac{3 \text{ inches}}{1 \text{ inch}}$

8. $\dfrac{5 \text{ dollars}}{1 \text{ pound}}$

For each situation, give two equal rates.

9. Margaret rode her bicycle 14 miles in 2 hours.

10. Randy bought fabric with a pattern of 5 shapes in every 3 feet.

11. Justen did 30 jumping jacks in 40 seconds.

For Exercises 12–14, use the bar graph.

12. Give three different rates that describe the speed of the cheetah.

13. Give a rate that uses the number 10.

14. Give a rate that compares a distance to $\dfrac{1}{2}$ hour.

15. **Estimation** Jo drove her car 98 miles and used 4 gallons of gas. Estimate how many miles she can go on 1 gallon of gas.

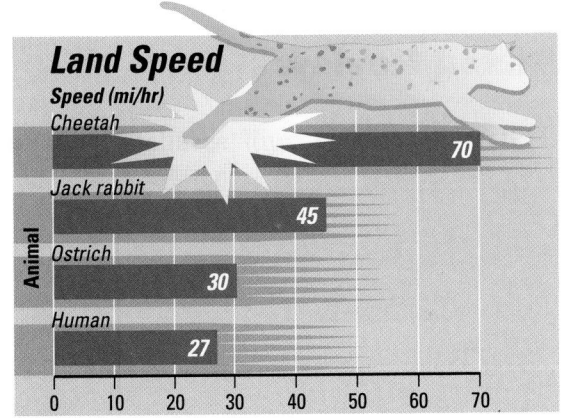

Land Speed

Speed (mi/hr)

Animal	Speed
Cheetah	70
Jack rabbit	45
Ostrich	30
Human	27

0 10 20 30 40 50 60 70

Use the table for Exercises 16–17.

16. **Industry** The table shows the maximum rate of water flow from fire hydrants of different colors. The rates are written in liters per minute. How many liters of water flow from each fire hydrant in five minutes?

17. **Industry** If a fire hydrant pumped 227,040 liters in 60 minutes, what color would the fire hydrant be?

Color	Rate (L/min)
Green	5677
Orange	3784
Red	1892

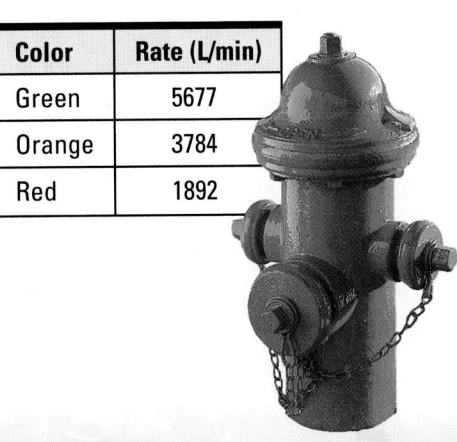

18. Raul checked his pulse, and counted 27 beats in 15 seconds. At that rate, how many beats would he have counted in 45 seconds?

19. [Test Prep] Doug needs 800 tiles for a new bathroom floor. The tiles cost $16 per 100. At that rate, how much will Doug spend on tiles?
Ⓐ $20   Ⓑ $50   Ⓒ $100   Ⓓ $128

20. A grocery store checker can total the purchases for about 3 average customers in 10 minutes. At this rate, how many customers can the checker serve in one hour?

Problem Solving and Reasoning

21. Critical Thinking Cameron is making decorations for "Back to School Night." He can make 2 posters in an hour. At this rate, how long will it take him to make 5 posters? Explain.

22. [Journal] Describe the similarities and differences between ratios and rates.

23. Communicate Describe how you could change a rate of meters per second to meters per minute.

Mixed Review

State if each figure will tessellate. If it tessellates, make a sketch to show how. *[Lesson 8-10]*

24. 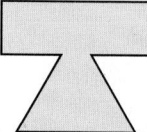 **25.** 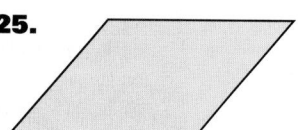 **26.**  **27.**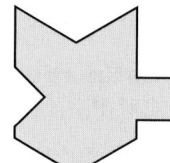

Find the area of the triangle if *b* is the base and *h* is the height. *[Lesson 4-6]*

28. $b = 7$ ft, $h = 6$ ft   **29.** $b = 1.6$ m, $h = 3$ m   **30.** $h = 5$ in., $b = 50$ in.

31. $h = 0.3$ cm, $b = 0.8$ cm   **32.** $h = 12$ yd, $b = 3$ yd   **33.** $b = 600$ mi, $h = 400$ mi

Project Progress

List some ways that ratios can be used in the sport you've chosen. Here are some examples: number of hits compared to times at bat, number of games won compared to number of games played; number of people on a team compared to number on the field. Explain the meaning of each ratio.

Problem Solving

Understand
Plan
Solve
Look Back

Section 10A Connect

At the beginning of this section, you learned how important it is to be prepared for fires. Now you will investigate to see how quickly your classroom and school cafeteria can be evacuated.

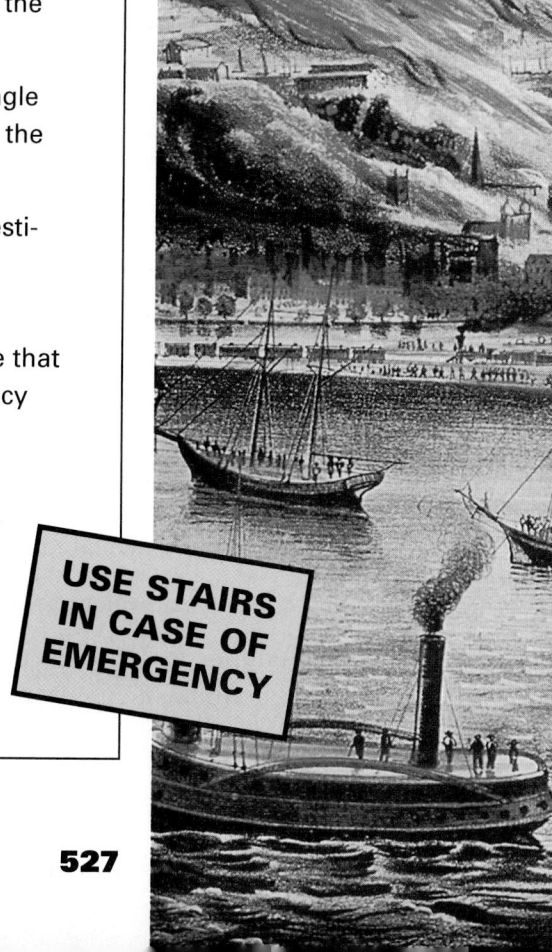

Fire Alarm

Materials: Watch with second hand, Yardstick or Meter stick

1. Have everyone in your class exit through one class-room door in an orderly fashion as if evacuating for an emergency. Time how long this takes.

2. Write a rate giving the number of people that can exit through the door per minute.

3. Compare the width of a classroom door with the width of a single cafeteria door. Then estimate the rate at which people can exit the cafeteria through the door.

4. Check the number and size of the other cafeteria doors. Then estimate the rate at which people can exit the cafeteria through all its doors.

5. The "maximum occupancy" of a room is the number of people that can be evacuated in 1 minute. Estimate the maximum occupancy of your cafeteria.

6. Write a report to the principal evaluating the cafeteria design in terms of emergency evacuation. Is the maximum occupancy you calculated in Step 5 a good recommendation? How could the cafeteria be improved to allow for a faster and safer evacuation?

MAX OCCUPANCY 150

USE STAIRS IN CASE OF EMERGENCY

EXIT

1. 23,000 of the 30,000 fire departments in the United States are staffed by volunteers. Write this ratio in lowest terms.

2. Last month the County Fire Department responded to 8 home fires and 6 brush fires. Give each ratio in lowest terms.

    a. Home fires to brush fires   **b.** Brush fires to home fires

    c. Home fires to all fires   **d.** Brush fires to all fires

3. Tamara has 3 red marbles, 5 blue marbles, and 4 green marbles. Give 5 ratios in lowest terms to describe the situation.

4. Complete each table of equal ratios.

Squares	3	6		12
Circles	5		15	

Binders	3	9	27	300
Books			18	

5. Give three ratios equal to 6:16.

6. There are 6 dogs and 5 cats. Write the ratio of dogs to cats in three ways.

For Exercises 7–9, use the stones pictured.

7. Give the ratio of metallic stones to red stones.

8. What is the ratio of purple and blue stones to green stones?

9. Write a ratio which compares something to the total number of stones.

10. Alex made 24 phone calls in 18 days. Write this as a rate in lowest terms.

Test Prep

When asked to find an equal rate, make sure the units are correct.

11. Which rate is equivalent to 9 pounds in 4 hours?

    Ⓐ $\dfrac{8 \text{ pounds}}{18 \text{ hours}}$ Ⓑ $\dfrac{8 \text{ hours}}{18 \text{ minutes}}$ Ⓒ $\dfrac{27 \text{ ounces}}{12 \text{ minutes}}$ Ⓓ $\dfrac{27 \text{ pounds}}{12 \text{ hours}}$

A MONUMENTAL STORY

1 Statues can cost thousands of dollars and take years to construct. Why do people spend the time and money to build them?

2 Other than the Statue of Liberty, what are some examples of things with humanlike features that are not human-sized?

3 How could an artist use mathematics when designing a statue? Give three examples.

"I was born in Paris in 1884. I made my first and only overseas trip to New York City, that same year. In 1903, poet Emma Lazarus called me the 'Mother of Exiles.' I stand at 151 feet and 1 inch, and I haven't sat down for over 100 years. Who am I?"

The paragraph above describes none other than the Statue of Liberty. The designer, Frédéric Bartholdi, spent over 13 years planning this monument to freedom and hope. He started with a small clay model. Then he built three plaster models, each one larger than the one before. These models became the "blueprint" for the statue's construction.

When designing a statue, artists must pay careful attention to scale. If the nose is too big for the face, or the shoulders too narrow for the height, then the effect of the statue can be altered. A statue with the intended proportions is not only a work of art … it is a work of mathematics.

529

You'll Learn ...

■ what a proportion is

■ to test to see if two ratios form a proportion

... How It's Used

Clothing designers use proportions when designing clothes to fit people comfortably.

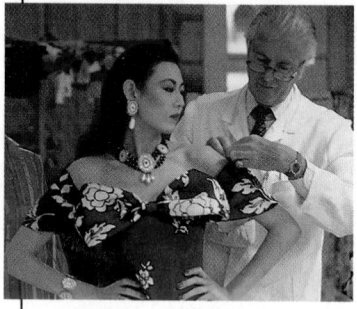

Vocabulary

cross product

proportion

▶ **Lesson Link** You've used tables to create equal ratios. Now you'll learn an easy way to check whether two ratios are equal. ◀

Explore Equal Ratios

Four Square

Each "four-square" below represents an equal ratio using four sets of shapes arranged in a particular order. One set of shapes in each four-square is missing.

A.

△	●
△△	??

B.

△△	△△△△
●●	??

C.

●	△△
●●●	??

D.

●●	●●●●
△△△△	??

1. These are the missing shapes from the four-squares. Determine where each set of shapes belongs. Explain your answers.

   a. △△△△△△   b. ●●   c. △△△△△△△△   d. ●●●●

2. For the four-squares above, can the shape in the upper left corner match the shape below it? Can it match the shape to the right of it? Can it match the shape diagonal to it? Explain.

3. Create three four-square patterns of your own like the ones above.

Learn What Is a Proportion?

For two ratios, a **cross product** is the result of multiplying the top value in one ratio by the bottom value in the other.

$$\frac{2}{5} \qquad \frac{3}{10} \qquad 5 \times 3 = 15 \qquad 2 \times 10 = 20$$

A **proportion** is a pair of equal ratios. In a proportion, the cross products of the two ratios are equal.

$$\frac{2}{5} = \frac{6}{15} \qquad 5 \times 6 = 30 \qquad 2 \times 15 = 30$$

Proportions often include different units of measurement. Units must be the same across the top and bottom *or* down the left and right sides. If the units only match diagonally, then the ratios do not form a proportion.

Examples

1 Decide if the ratios form a proportion.

a. $\frac{6 \text{ ft}}{10 \text{ sec}} \stackrel{?}{=} \frac{9 \text{ ft}}{15 \text{ sec}}$ **b.** $\frac{4 \text{ ft}}{6 \text{ ft}} \stackrel{?}{=} \frac{12 \text{ sec}}{18 \text{ sec}}$ **c.** $\frac{5 \text{ ft}}{10 \text{ sec}} \stackrel{?}{=} \frac{4 \text{ sec}}{8 \text{ ft}}$

The units are the same across the top and bottom. The cross products are equal.

6 × 15 = 90.
10 × 9 = 90.

It is a proportion.

The units are the same down the left and right sides. The cross products are equal.

4 × 18 = 72.
6 × 12 = 72.

It is a proportion.

The units are not the same across or down.

It is not a proportion.

2 The Golden Gate Bridge is 6480 ft long, with 756 ft tall towers. The model of the bridge used in *Superman* was 60 ft long with 7 ft tall towers. Was the model proportional to the actual bridge?

$\frac{60}{7} \stackrel{?}{=} \frac{6480}{756} \leftarrow \frac{\text{bridge length}}{\text{tower height}}$ Write terms of the ratios in the same order.

60 × 756 = 45,360

7 × 6,480 = 45,360   Determine the cross products.

The cross products are equal, so the ratios form a proportion. The model was proportional.

Try It

Decide if the ratios form a proportion.

a. $\frac{6}{8} \stackrel{?}{=} \frac{9}{12}$ **b.** $\frac{2}{3} \stackrel{?}{=} \frac{7}{10}$ **c.** $\frac{5 \text{ mi}}{2 \text{ hr}} \stackrel{?}{=} \frac{15 \text{ hr}}{6 \text{ mi}}$ **d.** $\frac{\$12}{32 \text{ min}} \stackrel{?}{=} \frac{\$3}{8 \text{ min}}$

1. How can you tell if two ratios form a proportion? Give an example.

2. What does it mean to say that quantities are "proportional"?

10-4 Exercises and Applications

Practice and Apply

1. **Getting Started** Match the ratio pairs to their cross products.

   a. $\frac{3}{4}$ and $\frac{30}{40}$ **b.** $\frac{5}{6}$ and $\frac{3}{5}$ **I.** 14 and 8   **II.** 120 and 120

   c. $\frac{1}{2}$ and $\frac{7}{8}$ **d.** $\frac{2}{3}$ and $\frac{6}{9}$ **III.** 18 and 25   **IV.** 18 and 18

State whether or not each pair of ratios forms a proportion.

2. $\frac{4}{3} \square \frac{12}{9}$ 3. $\frac{8}{5} \square \frac{11}{7}$ 4. $\frac{8}{3} \square \frac{32}{12}$ 5. $\frac{27}{4} \square \frac{20}{3}$ 6. $\frac{45}{81} \square \frac{5}{9}$

7. $\frac{6}{25} \square \frac{4}{117}$ 8. $\frac{7}{2} \square \frac{21}{6}$ 9. $\frac{3}{23} \square \frac{6}{50}$ 10. $\frac{3}{16} \square \frac{5}{30}$ 11. $\frac{29}{4} \square \frac{24}{6}$

12. $\frac{2 \text{ tsp}}{1 \text{ oz}} \square \frac{4 \text{ oz}}{8 \text{ tsp}}$ 13. $\frac{75 \text{ mi}}{3 \text{ hr}} \square \frac{125 \text{ mi}}{5 \text{ hr}}$ 14. $\frac{6 \text{ acres}}{10 \text{ acres}} \square \frac{15 \text{ ft}}{25 \text{ ft}}$

For Exercises 15 and 16, choose the proportion that is written correctly.

15. **a.** $\frac{1 \text{ cat}}{2 \text{ dogs}} = \frac{4 \text{ dogs}}{8 \text{ cats}}$ **b.** $\frac{1 \text{ cat}}{2 \text{ dogs}} = \frac{4 \text{ cats}}{8 \text{ dogs}}$ **c.** $\frac{1 \text{ cat}}{8 \text{ cats}} = \frac{4 \text{ dogs}}{2 \text{ dogs}}$

16. **a.** $\frac{24 \text{ inches}}{2 \text{ feet}} = \frac{48 \text{ inches}}{4 \text{ feet}}$ **b.** $\frac{24 \text{ inches}}{2 \text{ feet}} = \frac{48 \text{ feet}}{4 \text{ inches}}$ **c.** $\frac{24 \text{ inches}}{2 \text{ feet}} = \frac{4 \text{ feet}}{48 \text{ inches}}$

17. **Fine Arts** Here is a picture of the *Motherland* in Volgograd, Russia. In the photo, 1 cm is about 49 feet. How tall is the actual statue?

18. Cedrick earned $209 for 38 hours of work last week. This week he earned $176 for 32 hours of work. Do these rates form a proportion?

19. **Test Prep** Which of the following is a proportion?

   Ⓐ $\frac{25}{15} = \frac{15}{9}$ Ⓑ $\frac{6}{10} = \frac{7}{12}$ Ⓒ $\frac{18}{5} = \frac{9}{3}$ Ⓓ $\frac{10}{3} = \frac{16}{6}$

20. **Test Prep** Which of the following is proportional to $\frac{3}{5}$?

Ⓐ $\frac{4}{6}$ Ⓑ $\frac{10}{6}$ Ⓒ $\frac{5}{3}$ Ⓓ $\frac{12}{20}$

21. For which two classes are the ratios of boys to girls proportional?

22. For which two classes are the ratios of girls to total students proportional?

23. **Consumer** A 16 oz drink at Tito's Sandwich Shop costs 99¢. A 20 oz drink costs $1.19. Are these prices proportional?

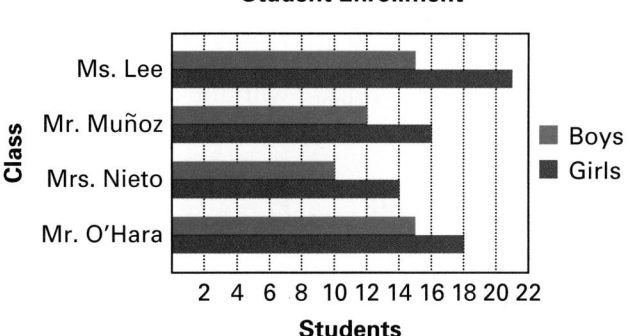

Problem Solving and Reasoning

24. **Communicate** How do you use multiplication to determine if two ratios are proportional?

25. **Choose a Strategy** Janice can run 100 meters in 12 seconds. Carl can run 500 meters in 48 seconds. Susan runs at a rate of 10 meters per second. Phillip can run 200 meters in 24 seconds. Which two students run at the same rate? Explain how you found your answer.

26. **Critical Thinking** The following ratios do not form a proportion: $\frac{3}{8}$ and $\frac{6}{9.5}$. How can you determine this without actually finding the cross products?

27. **Journal** Explain why the following is not a proportion.
$$\frac{\$0.25}{1 \text{ lb of apples}} \text{ and } \frac{3 \text{ lb of apples}}{\$0.75}$$

Problem Solving

STRATEGIES

- Look for a Pattern
- Make an Organized List
- Make a Table
- Guess and Check
- Work Backward
- Use Logical Reasoning
- Draw a Diagram
- Solve a Simpler Problem

Mixed Review

Order from greatest to least. *[Lesson 9-1]*

28. $4, -7, -2, -9$ **29.** $31, -55, 55, -13$ **30.** $2, 22, -22, -222$ **31.** $-17, -53, -31, -9$

32. $18, 0, -5, 22$ **33.** $41, -14, -41, 44$ **34.** $26, -6, -2, 62$ **35.** $-178, 133, 0, -100$

Find the missing measurement(s) for each circle, where r = radius, d = diameter, and C = circumference. Use 3.14 for π. *[Lesson 4-7]*

36. $r \approx 4$ mm, $d = 8$ mm, $C \approx \boxed{}$ **37.** $r = 2.1, d = \boxed{}, C \approx 13.188$

38. $r \approx 1.1$ in, $d = \boxed{}, C \approx \boxed{}$ **39.** $r = \boxed{}, d = \boxed{}, C \approx 27.632$ yd

10-5 Solving Proportions Using Cross Products

You'll Learn ...

■ to solve proportions using cross products

... How It's Used

Special-effects artists use cross products when determining how large or small something should be on a model to look realistic when filmed.

▶ **Lesson Link**   In the last lesson, you learned what a proportion is. Now you will find a missing number in a proportion. ◄

Explore   Solving Proportions

Truth or Dare Revisited

Each proportion is followed by two statements. Only one of the statements is true. For each problem, use your number sense to choose the correct statement, and explain how you know it's true.

1. Proportion: $\frac{6}{10} = \frac{w}{5}$

   a. If w is replaced with 3, the proportion will be true.

   b. If w is replaced with 3, the proportion will be false.

2. Proportion: $\frac{5}{7} = \frac{x}{8}$

   a. The value of x cannot be 6 because 6 is too large.

   b. The value of x cannot be 6 because 6 is too small.

3. Proportion: $\frac{3}{4} = \frac{y}{3}$

   a. The value of y is a whole number.

   b. The value of y is a decimal number.

Learn   Solving Proportions Using Cross Products

People use proportions to determine the value of an unknown measurement. If you know one measurement and the ratio that the known and unknown measurement should have, you can use a proportion to determine the unknown measure.

Example 1

Use cross products to solve the proportion $\frac{x}{15} = \frac{3}{5}$.

$5x = 15 \times 3$ Write the cross products.

$5x = 45$ Multiply.

$x = 9$ Think: What number times 5 equals 45?

If the numbers in a proportion are so complex that you can't use mental math to determine the value of a variable, you can use division. Division is the opposite of multiplication, and can be used to undo multiplication.

MENTAL MATH

Since the denominator in the first fraction is three times bigger than the denominator in the second fraction, the numerator must also be three times bigger.

Example 2

A 24 ft tall statue of the Sioux Indian chief Sitting Bull, in Denmark, is made entirely of Lego blocks. If the real Sitting Bull stood 6 ft and his head was 0.875 ft tall, find the height of the statue's head.

Let h be the height of the statue's head.

$$\frac{\text{head height}}{\text{total height}} \rightarrow \quad \frac{h}{24} = \frac{0.875}{6} \quad \text{Write a proportion.}$$

$6h = 24 \times 0.875$ Write the cross products.

$6 \times h = 21$ Think: What number times 6 equals 21?

$h = 21 \div 6$ Use division to undo multiplication.

$h = 3.5$

The statue's head is 3.5 ft tall.

Remember

For decimal multiplication, the number of digits after the decimal point in the product should be the same as the total number of digits after the decimal points in the factors.

[Page 181]

Try It

Solve each proportion.

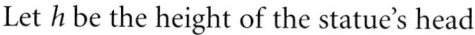

a. $\frac{8}{12} = \frac{6}{x}$ **b.** $\frac{4}{x} = \frac{6}{15}$ **c.** $\frac{5}{20} = \frac{x}{6}$ **d.** $\frac{4}{x} = \frac{10}{18}$

Check | Your Understanding

1. If all the numbers are different, how many numbers do you need in a proportion to be able to solve the proportion using cross products? Why?

2. Can you solve a proportion without using cross products? Explain.

PRACTICE 10-5

Practice and Apply

Getting Started Use the cross products to write an equation.

1. $\dfrac{9}{12} = \dfrac{3}{x}$

2. $\dfrac{78}{3} = \dfrac{26}{d}$

3. $\dfrac{j}{5} = \dfrac{55}{44}$

4. $\dfrac{6}{g} = \dfrac{42}{36}$

5. $\dfrac{7}{16} = \dfrac{s}{8}$

Solve each proportion.

6. $\dfrac{6}{8} = \dfrac{x}{12}$

7. $\dfrac{x}{8} = \dfrac{21}{14}$

8. $\dfrac{45}{m} = \dfrac{5}{3}$

9. $\dfrac{10}{14} = \dfrac{c}{35}$

10. $\dfrac{15}{14} = \dfrac{210}{l}$

11. $\dfrac{6}{11} = \dfrac{9}{x}$

12. $\dfrac{a}{7} = \dfrac{5}{3}$

13. $\dfrac{2.4}{4.5} = \dfrac{u}{1.8}$

14. $\dfrac{8.4}{y} = \dfrac{11.2}{6.8}$

15. $\dfrac{m}{3} = \dfrac{10}{5}$

16. $\dfrac{16}{c} = \dfrac{24}{3}$

17. $\dfrac{y}{7} = \dfrac{9}{21}$

18. $\dfrac{7}{10} = \dfrac{v}{20}$

19. $\dfrac{10}{g} = \dfrac{15}{4}$

20. $\dfrac{18}{k} = \dfrac{14}{3}$

21. $\dfrac{5}{6} = \dfrac{3}{a}$

22. $\dfrac{6}{16} = \dfrac{w}{12}$

23. $\dfrac{5}{22} = \dfrac{35}{m}$

24. $\dfrac{p}{12} = \dfrac{5}{15}$

25. $\dfrac{12}{20} = \dfrac{14}{x}$

26. Yesterday Stu earned $31.50 for 5 hours of work. Today he worked for 7 hours at the same pay rate. How much did he earn today?

27. Measurement If the rectangles shown are proportional to each other, what are the lengths of the unknown sides?

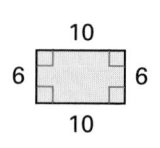
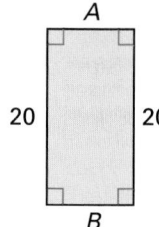

28. A factory uses 25 pounds of steel for every 37 pounds of copper. Last week the factory used 1820 pounds of steel. How much copper was used?

29. History In 1885, U.S. citizens living in Paris gave France a model of the Statue of Liberty. The model now stands on an island in the Seine River in Paris. The Statue of Liberty is about 150 feet tall, and the model in Paris is about 40 feet tall. If the torch of the taller statue measures about 20 feet and the statues are proportional to each other, how tall is the model's torch?

30. Geography One stone statue on Easter Island is 12 meters high. The nose of the statue is 3.3 meters long. If a proportional statue is only 10 meters high, how long would the nose be?

31. [Test Prep] Maria designs flags and banners. She always makes a flag proportional to the flagpole it hangs from. If one flag is 6 feet wide and its pole is 24 feet long, how wide would a flag with a 20-foot pole be?

    Ⓐ 5 feet   Ⓑ 8 feet

    Ⓒ 50 feet   Ⓓ 80 feet

32. The pictographs show the number of students playing a sport in the fall, and what sport they played. In the spring, 400 students played a sport. If the proportion of students playing soccer to students playing sports was the same in the fall and in the spring, how many students played soccer in the spring?

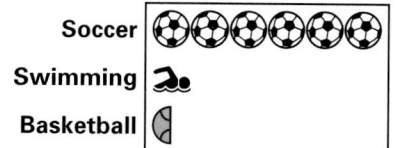

Fall Sports

Soccer ⚽⚽⚽⚽⚽⚽

Swimming 🏊

Basketball 🏀

⚽ = 20 students

🏊 = 20 students

🏀 = 20 students

Problem Solving and Reasoning

33. Choose a Strategy Darius thought that you could solve proportions only when three of the values are given, and one value is missing. Then he saw the proportion $\frac{4}{x} = \frac{x}{9}$, where two values are given and two are missing. Darius was able to solve the problem. What is the value of x? Explain your method.

34. [Journal] Explain how to use cross products to find the missing value in a proportion.

35. Critical Thinking In the proportion $\frac{-4}{10} = \frac{z}{-20}$, will the value of z be greater than or less than 0? Explain.

> **Problem Solving**
> ### STRATEGIES
> • Look for a Pattern
> • Make an Organized List
> • Make a Table
> • Guess and Check
> • Work Backward
> • Use Logical Reasoning
> • Draw a Diagram
> • Solve a Simpler Problem

Mixed Review

Add. *[Lesson 9-2]*

36. $4 + (-7)$ **37.** $-8 + (-10)$ **38.** $-12 + 11$ **39.** $3 + (-9)$ **40.** $6 + (-2)$

Find the area of each circle, where *r* = radius and *d* = diameter. Use 3.14 for π. Round to the nearest hundredth. *[Lesson 4-8]*

41. $r = 2$ cm   **42.** $d = 6.6$ feet   **43.** $d = 14$ cm   **44.** $r = 11$ feet

45. $r = 12$ inches   **46.** $r = 40$ mm   **47.** $d = 9.1$ yards   **48.** $r = 0.4$ miles

Solving Proportions Using Unit Rates

You'll Learn ...

■ to solve proportions using unit rates

... How It's Used

Divers use unit rates when determining the water pressure at a given depth.

> **▶ Lesson Link** You've learned how to solve proportions using cross products. Now you will learn another method for solving proportions. ◀

Explore **Unit Rates**

Food for Thought

Brand	Price	Size
Nuts 'n Flakes	$4.60	20 oz
Mighty Pops	$3.84	16 oz
Toastie Oaties	$4.05	15 oz
Nature's Finest	$4.00	16 oz
Cornies	$3.00	12 oz
Raisin Wheats	$4.20	14 oz

1. Rank the cereals from least expensive to most expensive in terms of total price.

2. For each brand of cereal, estimate the price for 1 ounce.

3. Rank the cereals from least expensive per ounce to most expensive per ounce.

4. If you're looking for the "best buy," is it more important to look at the price per box or price per ounce? Explain.

5. List three reasons why you might buy a cereal that's not the best buy.

Recall that a unit rate is a ratio where one quantity is compared to exactly one unit of another quantity. You can find the unit rate by using division.

Example 1

Market Supreme sells granola by the pound. Tammy's granola weighed 8 pounds. The cashier charged her $12. What was the price per pound?

$$\frac{\$12}{8 \text{ pounds}} = \frac{\$12 \div 8}{8 \text{ pounds} \div 8} \qquad \text{Write a ratio. Divide by the unit quantity.}$$

$$= \frac{\$1.50}{1 \text{ pound}}$$

The price of granola is $1.50 per pound.

HINT

You can also use a calculator to find a unit rate by entering numerator $\div$ denominator $=$.

Unit rates can be used to solve proportions. Find the unit rate of the given proportion, and use multiplication to find the unknown value.

Example 2

The *Tian Tan* (Temple of Heaven) *Buddha* on Lantau Island, Hong Kong, weighs 275 tons and cost $9,000,000 to build. If the cost of the statue is proportional to the weight, about how much would the statue have cost if it weighed 300 tons?

DID YOU KNOW?

At 112 feet tall, the *Tian Tan Buddha* is one of the ten tallest free-standing statues in the world.

$$\frac{\$9,000,000 \div 275 \text{ tons}}{275 \text{ tons} \div 275 \text{ tons}} \approx \frac{\$32,727}{1 \text{ ton}} \qquad \text{Find the unit rate.}$$

The statue cost about $32,727 per ton. Now, multiply by the new number of tons.

300 tons × $32,727 per ton = $9,818,100

It would have cost about $9,818,100.

Try It

a. A zebra can run 420 ft in 7 seconds. Find the zebra's rate per minute.

b. Veronica bought 20 pencils for $1.60. At that rate, how much would 35 pencils cost?

WHAT DO YOU THINK?

Aaron and Lauren want to read *The Lion, The Witch, and The Wardrobe*. The book is 216 pages long. Yesterday, they each read the first 12 pages in about 18 minutes. How long will it take to read the entire book?

Aaron thinks ...

I'll use cross products.

$$\frac{18 \text{ minutes}}{12 \text{ pages}} = \frac{x \text{ minutes}}{216 \text{ pages}}$$

The cross products are 3888 and 12x.

If 12x equals 3888, then x is 3888 divided by 12, or 324.

It will take 324 minutes, or about $5\frac{1}{2}$ hours, to read the book.

Lauren thinks ...

I'll use unit rates.

$$\frac{18 \text{ minutes}}{12 \text{ pages}} = \frac{18 \text{ minutes} \div 12}{12 \text{ pages} \div 12}, \text{ or } 1.5 \text{ minutes per page}$$

216 pages × 1.5 minutes per page = 324 minutes

It will take 324 minutes, or about $5\frac{1}{2}$ hours, to read the book.

What do you think?

1. Whose method do you prefer? Why?

2. Did both Aaron and Lauren have to use multiplication? Did they both have to use division? Explain.

Check   Your Understanding

1. How does solving a proportion by unit rates differ from solving by cross products?

2. Give an example of how shoppers use unit rates.

Practice and Apply

Getting Started State what number you should divide the numerator and denominator by to find the unit rate.

1. $\dfrac{16 \text{ miles}}{3 \text{ hours}}$ 2. $\dfrac{17 \text{ cats}}{4 \text{ square feet}}$ 3. $\dfrac{9 \text{ holes}}{7 \text{ inches}}$ 4. $\dfrac{5 \text{ feet}}{12 \text{ seconds}}$ 5. $\dfrac{2 \text{ minutes}}{8 \text{ problems}}$

Find the unit rate for each.

6. $\dfrac{6 \text{ mi}}{12 \text{ sec}}$ 7. $\dfrac{10 \text{ houses}}{5 \text{ mi}}$ 8. $\dfrac{12 \text{ pencils}}{3 \text{ boxes}}$ 9. $\dfrac{62 \text{ holes}}{12 \text{ in}^2}$

10. $\dfrac{\$18}{4 \text{ lb}}$ 11. $\dfrac{6 \text{ waves}}{10 \text{ sec}}$ 12. $\dfrac{17 \text{ people}}{37 \text{ ft}^2}$ 13. $\dfrac{9 \text{ slices}}{3 \text{ people}}$

14. $\dfrac{7 \text{ in. rain}}{3 \text{ days}}$ 15. $\dfrac{6 \text{ m}}{18 \text{ hr}}$ 16. $\dfrac{14 \text{ kg}}{3 \text{ bags}}$ 17. $\dfrac{11 \text{ cups}}{22 \text{ servings}}$

18. $\dfrac{16 \text{ shapes}}{5 \text{ boxes}}$ 19. $\dfrac{3 \text{ turtles}}{2 \text{ mi}^2}$ 20. $\dfrac{62 \text{ lines}}{1 \text{ sheet}}$ 21. $\dfrac{15 \text{ m}}{2 \text{ sec}}$

Solve each proportion using unit rates.

22. $\dfrac{24 \text{ lb}}{12 \text{ ft}} = \dfrac{?}{28 \text{ ft}}$ 23. $\dfrac{?}{6 \text{ hr}} = \dfrac{210 \text{ mi}}{5 \text{ hr}}$ 24. $\dfrac{?}{3 \text{ lb}} = \dfrac{\$3.50}{7 \text{ lb}}$ 25. $\dfrac{6.6 \text{ points}}{3 \text{ games}} = \dfrac{?}{1 \text{ game}}$

26. $\dfrac{62 \text{ m}}{20 \text{ sec}} = \dfrac{?}{32 \text{ sec}}$ 27. $\dfrac{?}{3 \text{ sec}} = \dfrac{21 \text{ drips}}{7 \text{ sec}}$ 28. $\dfrac{?}{9 \text{ m}} = \dfrac{16 \text{ kites}}{0.25 \text{ m}}$ 29. $\dfrac{3 \text{ apples}}{5 \text{ lunches}} = \dfrac{?}{2 \text{ lunches}}$

30. **Geography** The *Colossi of Memnon* in Karnak, Egypt, are 21 meters tall. They also measure 70 feet tall. Using these measurements, find the number of meters in a foot.

31. **Estimation** Emma estimates that she collected about 70 apples from the orchard and put an equal number of apples into each of 6 baskets. Mrs. Sanders wants 3 baskets of apples. Set up and solve a proportion to determine about how many apples Mrs. Sanders would receive.

32. **Science** The speed of sound through water is 1460 m/sec. Is this a unit rate? How far does sound travel through water in 2 seconds?

33. **Number Sense** Which is a better value, 2 pounds of bananas for 50¢ or 3 pounds of bananas for 72¢?

34. **Test Prep** Which animal is moving the fastest?

Ⓐ A cat at 660 ft per 15 sec. Ⓑ A greyhound at 616 ft per 12 sec.

Ⓒ A zebra at 645 ft per 11 sec. Ⓓ An elephant at 1100 ft per 30 sec.

35. Literature Janet wants to make a wooden carving of Artemis, Greek goddess of the hunt. She imagines that Artemis is 7 feet tall. If her carving is 12 inches tall, how many feet does 1 inch represent?

Problem Solving and Reasoning

36. **Journal** Describe a situation where you could use mental math to find the unit rate of a ratio.

37. Communicate If 7 square feet of carpet cost $4.50, how can you find the rate of square feet per dollar? How can you find the rate of dollars per square foot? If you were carpeting a room, which rate would be the most sensible rate to use?

38. Critical Thinking Fiona is filming a 6-inch lizard to represent a 48-foot monster. The lizard moves at a rate of 5 inches per second.

a. If Fiona films a 20-inch-tall movie set, how tall does the set look in the movie? Explain.

b. How long will it take for the small lizard to move 35 inches? Explain how you found your answer.

c. Is there any numerical information in the problem that isn't needed to answer the first two questions? Explain.

39. Communicate Name five unit rates that people use every day. For example, there are 60 minutes in 1 hour.

Mixed Review

Find the area of the irregular shape. *[Lesson 4-9]*

40.
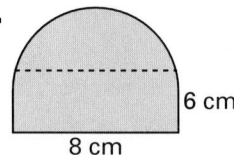
8 cm 6 cm

41.
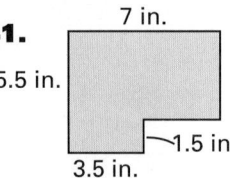
7 in.
5.5 in.
3.5 in. 1.5 in.

42.
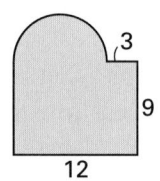
3
9
12

43.
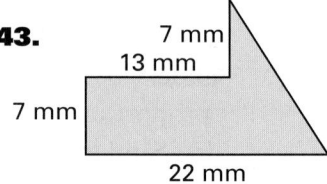
7 mm
13 mm
7 mm
22 mm

Subtract. *[Lesson 9-3]*

44. $12 - (-7)$ **45.** $-8 - 9$ **46.** $-16 - 10$ **47.** $11 - (-3)$

48. $-5 - (-9)$ **49.** $-4 - (-1)$ **50.** $0 - (-13)$ **51.** $2 - (-4)$

Similar Figures

▶ **Lesson Link** You've learned about geometric figures. Now you'll explore a class of figures whose dimensions are proportional. ◀

Explore Similar Figures

The Same ... But Different!

Materials: Centimeter ruler, Protractor

1. Draw a large triangle, △A, with three unequal sides. Measure and label the length of each side and the width of each angle.

2. Draw a smaller triangle whose angles have the same measures as the angles of △A. Call the new triangle △B. Measure and label the length of each side.

3. Find these ratios:

  a. $\dfrac{\text{longest side of } \triangle A}{\text{longest side of } \triangle B}$ **b.** $\dfrac{\text{mid-length side of } \triangle A}{\text{mid-length side of } \triangle B}$

  c. $\dfrac{\text{shortest side of } \triangle A}{\text{shortest side of } \triangle B}$

4. Are the longest sides proportional to the shortest sides? Explain.

5. Are the longest sides proportional to the mid-length sides? Explain.

6. Are the mid-length sides proportional to the shortest sides? Explain.

You'll Learn ...

■ what similar figures are

■ to use proportions to find lengths in a similar figure

... How It's Used

Drivers use similar figures when calculating the actual distance between two locations on a road map.

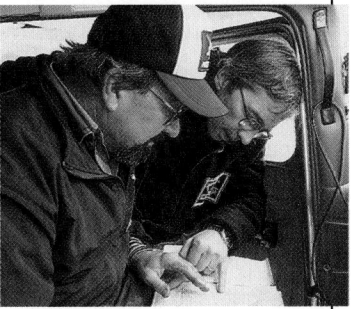

Vocabulary

similar

Learn Similar Figures

Recall that figures with the same size and shape are *congruent*. The symbol ≅ means "is congruent to."

Figures that have the same shape but not necessarily the same size are **similar** figures. The symbol ~ means "is similar to."

The objects pictured are similar because their shapes are the same, even though their sizes are different.

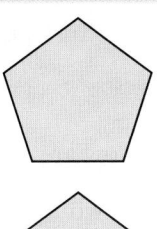

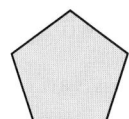

Example 1

Remember

Congruent figures have the same shape and the same size. **[Page 444]**

State whether the polygons appear to be congruent, similar, or neither.

a.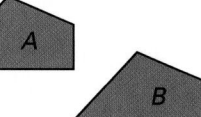

The figures are the same shape and size. $A \cong B$.

b.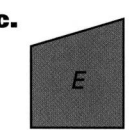

The figures are the same shape but different sizes. $C \sim D$.

c.

The figures are not the same shape or size. They are neither congruent nor similar.

If two figures are similar, their matching angles have the same measure and their matching sides are proportional.

Example 2

Problem Solving TIP

Some problems give you information that isn't needed to solve the problem. In this example, you don't need to know that the length of the right side of △A is 18.

$\triangle A \sim \triangle B$. Find the length of the side labeled x.

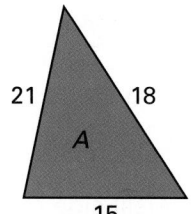

The triangles are similar, so the matching sides are proportional.

$\dfrac{21}{x} = \dfrac{15}{5}$ Write a proportion using the sides that match each other.

$15x = 21 \times 5$ Write the cross products.

$15 \times x = 105$ Multiply. Think: What number times 15 equals 105?

$x = 105 \div 15$ Use division to undo multiplication.

$x = 7$

Try It

Find the length of the side labeled y in Example 2.

Check | Your Understanding

1. How are similar figures and congruent figures alike? How are they different?

2. If two figures are congruent, are they similar? Explain.

3. Give an example of similar figures you see in everyday life.

Practice and Apply

Getting Started State whether the polygons are congruent, similar, or neither.

1.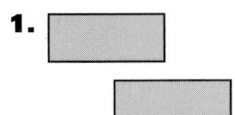

2.

3.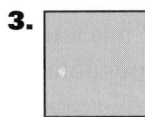

4.

For Exercises 5–10, find the missing side lengths.

5.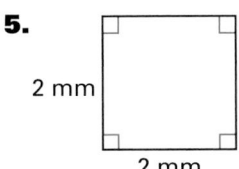

6.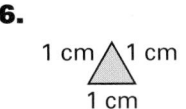

7.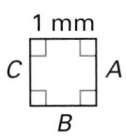

8.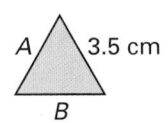

9.

10.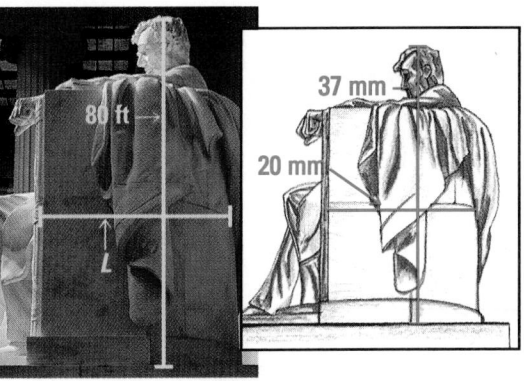

11. Geography On the map, 1 inch equals 250 actual miles.

a. Estimate the actual distances of the triangular flight plan indicated on the map.

b. Are the triangle shown on the map and the life-size triangle similar figures?

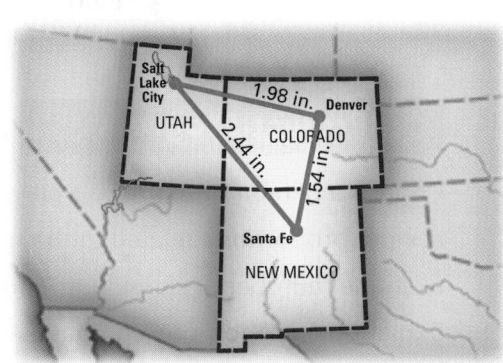

12. **Test Prep** Which triangles are similar?

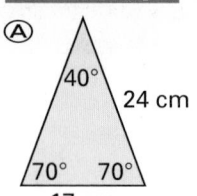 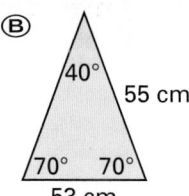 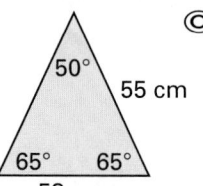 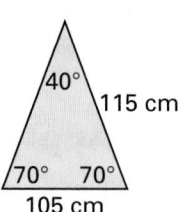 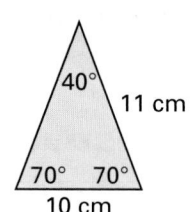

Ⓐ 40° 24 cm / 70° 70° 17 cm   40° 2.4 cm / 70° 70° 1.7 cm

Ⓑ 40° 55 cm / 70° 70° 53 cm   50° 55 cm / 65° 65° 53 cm

Ⓒ 40° 115 cm / 70° 70° 105 cm   40° 11 cm / 70° 70° 10 cm

13. **Geometry** A rectangle has sides of 5 ft and 8 ft. A similar rectangle has two sides of 40 feet. There are two possible answers for the length of the other side of the larger rectangle. What are they?

Problem Solving and Reasoning

14. **Choose a Strategy** Gigi's house and the blueprint for her house are similar figures. Her house is shaped like a rectangle. On the blueprint, the base and height of the rectangle are 4 inches and 5 inches. If the shorter side of her house is 40 feet, what is the perimeter? Explain.

15. **Critical Thinking** Is every pair of similar figures congruent? Is every pair of congruent figures similar? Explain.

16. **Critical Thinking** If two triangles are equilateral, are they similar? Explain.

> **Problem Solving**
> ## STRATEGIES
> • Look for a Pattern
> • Make an Organized List
> • Make a Table
> • Guess and Check
> • Work Backward
> • Use Logical Reasoning
> • Draw a Diagram
> • Solve a Simpler Problem

Mixed Review

Simplify. *[Lesson 9-4]*

17. $7 \times (-3)$ **18.** $18 \div (-9)$ **19.** $-8 \times (-2)$ **20.** $-22 \div 11$ **21.** -10×7

22. $-14 \div 7$ **23.** $-2 \times (-13)$ **24.** $6 \div (-3)$ **25.** $-36 \div (-3)$ **26.** $-25 \times (-4)$

Tell whether the first number is divisible by the second. *[Lesson 5-1]*

27. 65, 5   **28.** 33, 11   **29.** 57, 6   **30.** 106, 10   **31.** 882, 9   **32.** 116, 2

33. 36, 4   **34.** 59, 3   **35.** 49, 7   **36.** 81, 8   **37.** 100, 25   **38.** 1265, 5

Project Progress

Choose a person or team who plays the sport you selected. Research or invent several proportions related to the number of your player or team's wins. For example: number of home games/number of wins; attendance/number of wins. Explain the proportions you have written.

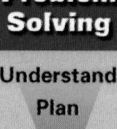

> **Problem Solving**
> Understand
> Plan
> Solve
> Look Back

In this section, you've seen how artists use proportions to convert actual measurements to model measurements. Now you'll use that process to create a blueprint for a model of a totem pole.

A Monumental Story

Materials: Centimeter ruler, Protractor

America's Northwest Coast Native Americans live along the Pacific coast from northern Oregon to southern Alaska. They include the Tlingit, Haida, and Bella Coola tribes. They use cedar wood to carve totem poles, some as tall as 7-story buildings. The poles are carved with fantastic figures relating to the family histories of the Native Americans.

You will design a proportional sketch for a totem pole. Here are the specifications for the totem pole:

1. The totem pole will be 15 m tall.

2. The totem pole will have 5 geometrically-shaped sections.

    a. A rectangle, 5 m tall

    b. A square, 3 m tall

    c. A trapezoid, 3 m tall

    d. A circle, 2 m in diameter

    e. A triangle, 2 m tall

3. The totem pole will have enough artistic detail so that the sections tell a story.

Your sketch should be a rectangle 24 cm tall and 4 cm wide. It should list all the "sketch lengths" in one color and the "actual totem pole lengths" they correspond to in another color.

You should also attach a paragraph explaining the story told by your totem pole.

1. Use a table to find three rates equal to $\frac{25\text{ cm}}{10\text{ sec}}$.

Find the unit rate for each ratio.

2. $\frac{51\text{ people}}{142\text{ ft}^2}$

3. $\frac{\$39}{60\text{ min}}$

4. $\frac{59\text{ pretzels}}{10\text{ servings}}$

5. $\frac{18\text{ commercials}}{30\text{ min}}$

Solve each proportion.

6. $\frac{32}{15} = \frac{?}{33}$

7. $\frac{42}{?} = \frac{20}{24}$

8. $\frac{7\text{ lb}}{18\text{ hr}} = \frac{?}{24\text{ hr}}$

9. $\frac{\$6}{20\text{ oz}} = \frac{?}{1\text{ oz}}$

10. Geography The statue shown is a 14-ft statue of King Kamehameha. It stands outside Aliiolani Hale, the state supreme court building, in Honolulu, Hawaii. The base of the statue is 6 feet tall, and the body is 8 feet tall. If the entire statue was 20 feet tall, how tall would the base and body be? Round your answers to the nearest tenth of a foot.

11. If Danielle can wash 2 cars in 24 minutes, how many cars could she wash in an hour?

In each pair of similar figures, find the missing side lengths.

12.

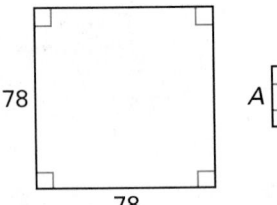

13.

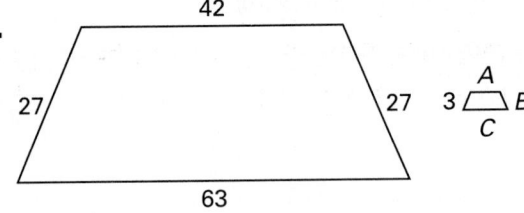

Test Prep

When solving a proportion on a multiple choice test, you can find the cross products for each choice. The correct answer will give equal cross products.

14. Solve: $\frac{2}{65} = \frac{6}{x}$

  Ⓐ 390 Ⓑ 195 Ⓒ 780 Ⓓ 290

15. Solve: $\frac{4}{5} = \frac{6}{x}$

  Ⓐ 9 Ⓑ 7.5 Ⓒ 9.5 Ⓓ 7

Touring the Rain Forest

"**G**ood morning, everyone. I'll be your guide for today's tour through the rain forest.

"That sound you're hearing is a howler monkey. They call most often in the morning, when the air is cool and sound travels better. Birds at different forest levels use different kinds of chirps to communicate. Butterflies communicate using their own perfumes.

"Have you seen any animals yet? They are there. Many look like plants to help them hide. That vine up there is really a snake. That flower is an orchid mantis. And those leaves on the tree ... they're butterflies.

"Oh, be careful! Don't disturb that poison dart frog. It has enough poison to paralyze a monkey.

Some frog poisons are strong enough to kill six people.

"I hope you've enjoyed the tour. Yes, I know I didn't get to everything. But there is such diverse animal life here that we could never describe it all in one tour. Please come back soon! There's still so much to learn!"

1 What sorts of things can people hope to learn by studying the rain forest?

2 How can mathematics be used when learning about the rain forest?

What Is a Percent?

▶ **Lesson Link** You've used ratios throughout this chapter. Now you will compare the ratio of a number to 100. ◀

You'll Learn ...

■ to express a quantity as a percent

... How It's Used

Accountants use percents in circle graphs to represent sources of a company's income.

Vocabulary

percent

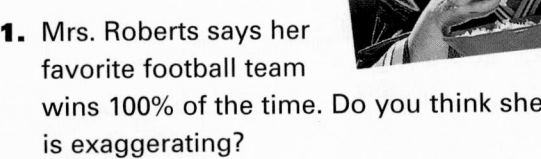

Explore **Percents**

Just Be Reasonable!

Read each statement and answer the question that follows. Explain your reasoning.

1. Mrs. Roberts says her favorite football team wins 100% of the time. Do you think she is exaggerating?

2. Kevin says that about 50% of the students in his school are males. Does Kevin's estimate seem reasonable?

3. The weather report predicts a 90% chance of rain. Would it be a good idea to take an umbrella?

4. Donna read 20% of a book last night. Randall read 30% of a magazine last night. Did Randall read more pages than Donna?

5. A local store's sale ad says, "Everything Must Go—Prices Slashed By 2%." Do you think you would find good bargains at this sale?

6. Write three percent statements like the ones above.

Learn **What is a Percent?**

A **percent** is a ratio that compares a part to a whole using the number 100. The percent is the number of hundredths that the part is equal to.

Examples

Give the percent for the portion of each figure that is shaded.

1

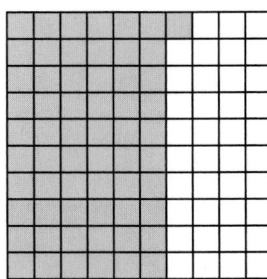

61 of the 100 squares are shaded.

$\frac{61}{100} = 61\%$

2

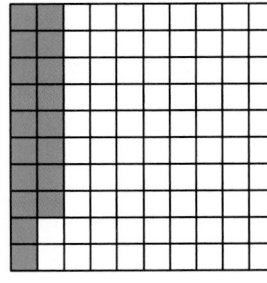

18 of the 100 squares are shaded.

$\frac{18}{100} = 18\%$

If a quantity is broken into 100 pieces, it is easy to describe using percents. It is also easy to use percents when working with fourths or tenths.

$\frac{1}{10} = \frac{10}{100}$, or 10% $\frac{1}{4} = \frac{25}{100}$, or 25% $\frac{1}{2} = \frac{50}{100}$, or 50% $\frac{3}{4} = \frac{75}{100}$, or 75%

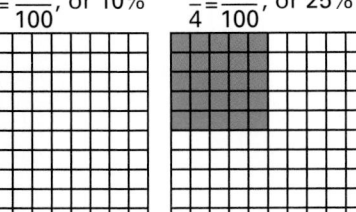 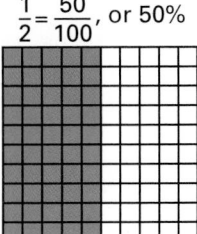 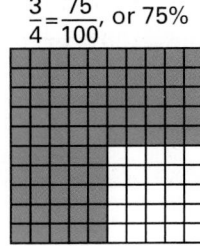

> ▶ **Science Link**
>
> The toucan is one of the best-known bird species from the rain forest. Each toucan's beak is colored in a slightly different way, allowing toucans to recognize one another.

Example 3

The shaded portion of the figure represents the portion of the world's bird species that live in rain forests. What percent of the bird species live in rain forests?

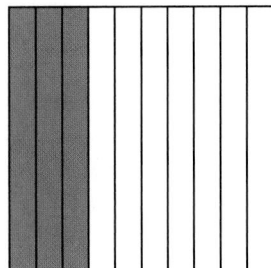

Each shaded section is $\frac{1}{10}$, or 10%, of the figure. Three sections are shaded, so the percent is 3 × 10%, or 30%.

30% of the world's bird species live in rain forests.

Try It

Give the percent of each figure that is shaded.

a.

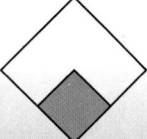

b.

Check Your Understanding

1. What is 100% of something? What is 0% of something?

2. Can a quantity be *more than* 100% of another quantity?

3. Can 25% of something be bigger than 50% of something else? Explain.

10-8 Exercises and Applications

Practice and Apply

Getting Started | Tell if each ratio is greater than or less than 50%.

1. $\frac{56}{100}$ **2.** $\frac{23}{100}$ **3.** $\frac{5}{100}$ **4.** $\frac{80}{100}$ **5.** $\frac{45}{100}$ **6.** $\frac{98}{100}$

Give the percent of each figure that is shaded.

7. 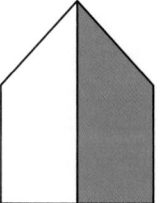   **8.** 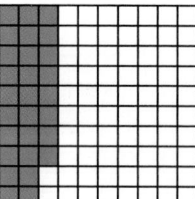   **9.** 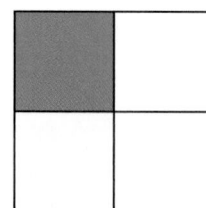   **10.**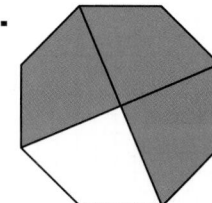

11. 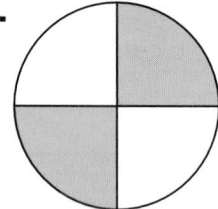   **12.** 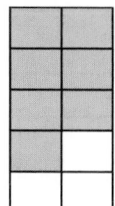   **13.**    **14.**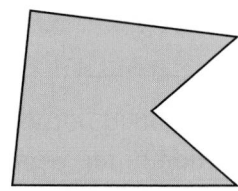

Geography The circle graph shows the percent of Asia's rain forest that is located in each country. Use the graph for Exercises 15–17.

15. About what percent of Asia's rain forest is located in Myanmar? Outside of Myanmar?

16. Which country has the highest percent of Asia's rain forest? Estimate the percent.

17. What three parts of the graph combined account for about 50% of Asia's rain forest?

Asia's Rain Forests

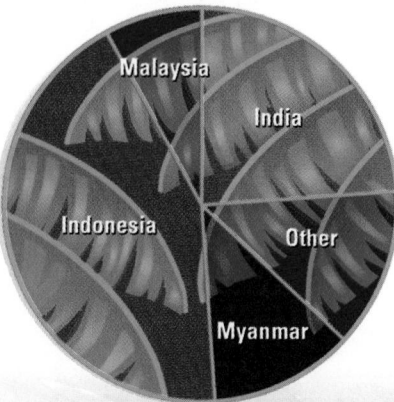

18. Geometry What percent of the shapes are quadrilaterals?

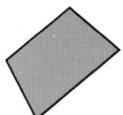  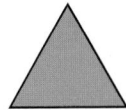

19. Number Sense Kwi and Park are building a model out of sugar cubes. Each has half of a box. If Kwi has used half of his sugar cubes, what percent of the box has he used?

20. | Test Prep | What percent of the figure is shaded?

Ⓐ 15%   Ⓑ 17%

Ⓒ 85%   Ⓓ 170%

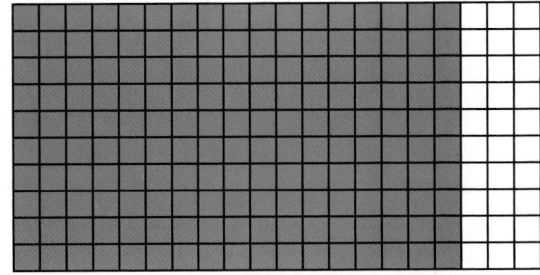

21. Crista's end-of-the-year math test had 100 problems.

a. If she got 89 of them correct, what percent of the problems did she get correct?

b. Is it possible for her to get 113% of the problems correct?

Problem Solving and Reasoning

22. Communicate A corporation says that its 1997 earnings were 120% of its 1996 earnings. Explain how this percent can be greater than 100%.

23. Communicate Do you think every ratio can be written as a percent? Explain your reasoning.

Critical Thinking Tell if the situations in Exercises 24–26 are possible or not. Explain your reasoning.

24. 62% of the students in Mrs. Chen's class are boys, and 48% are girls.

25. 48% of the students in Mr. Davis' class are wearing blue jeans, and 27% are wearing T-shirts.

26. Students in Mr. O'Malley's class showed an improvement in their test scores of 110%.

Mixed Review

On a coordinate grid, plot and label each point. *[Lesson 9-5]*

27. $Y(-5, 2)$ **28.** $K(3, 9)$ **29.** $A(6, -2)$ **30.** $M(-4, -5)$ **31.** $P(-3, 4)$

Find the prime factorization. [Lesson 5-2]

32. 58   **33.** 25   **34.** 26   **35.** 95   **36.** 405   **37.** 125

38. 56   **39.** 6   **40.** 288   **41.** 88   **42.** 87   **43.** 72

10-9 Estimating Percents

You'll Learn ...

■ to estimate percents

... How It's Used

Emergency planners work with percent estimates when preparing for earthquakes, floods, and tornadoes.

▶ **Lesson Link** In the last lesson, you learned the meaning of percent. Now you will estimate percents. ◀

Explore | Estimating Percents

The Percent Scavenger Hunt

1. Find a ratio or comparison in your classroom that is equal to about 10%. For example, about 10% of the students may be left-handed. Explain why you think the percent is about 10%.

2. Repeat Step 1 for the following percents.

   a. 25% **b.** 50% **c.** 60% **d.** 75% **e.** 90% **f.** 100%

3. Describe circumstances where it would be best to overestimate or underestimate a percent. Describe a circumstance where it would be best to get an exact percent.

Learn | Estimating Percents

Recall that $\frac{1}{2}$ of something is 50%, $\frac{1}{4}$ is 25%, and $\frac{1}{10}$ is 10%. When estimating a percent, think of a fraction close to the given value that uses halves, fourths, or tenths. These fractions can easily be expressed as percents.

Example 1

The map shows the rain forest in Indonesia. Estimate the percent of Indonesia that is made up of rain forest.

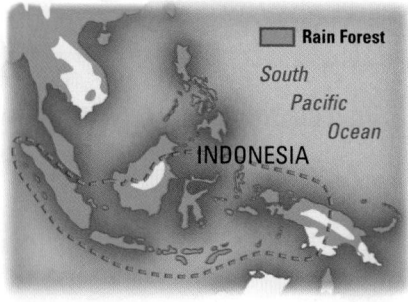

The shaded part of the map is more than $\frac{3}{4}$, but less than $\frac{4}{4}$. It is about $\frac{8}{10}$.

Your estimate should be more than 75% but less than 100%. You might estimate 80%.

About 80% of Indonesia's land is made up of rain forest.

Examples

2 Estimate the percent of the figure that is shaded.

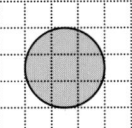

The circle covers 5 squares completely or almost completely. It covers about $\frac{1}{2}$ of 4 more squares. The combined number of covered squares is about

$$5 + \frac{1}{2} + \frac{1}{2} + \frac{1}{2} + \frac{1}{2}, \text{ or } 7.$$

The total number of squares is 5×5, or 25.

The part shaded is about $\frac{7}{25}$, which is about $\frac{1}{4}$, or 25%.

About 25% of the figure is shaded.

3 Of Mr. Niemeyer's 80 students, 71 wore Halloween costumes. Estimate the percent of Mr. Niemeyer's students who did *not* wear costumes.

$80 - 71 = 9$, so 9 students did *not* wear costumes.

9 is about $\frac{1}{10}$ of 80, or about 10% of 80. About 10% did *not* wear costumes.

Problem Solving TIP

When estimating area on a grid, a shaded part sometimes fills up part of a square, but not all of it. One way to estimate the area is to count a square with more than half shaded as 1 and to count a square with less than half shaded as 0.

Try It

a. Estimate the percent of the figure that is shaded.

b. 32 out of the 45 dentists surveyed recommend GlowBrite Toothpaste. Approximately what percent recommend GlowBrite?

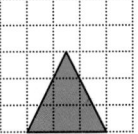

Check Your Understanding

1. If you know 10% of a number, how can you use estimation to find 5% of the number? 20% of the number? 80% of the number?

2. Describe a situation where you could use mental math to find a percent exactly, instead of having to estimate.

3. If you are describing a pizza that's been partially eaten, is it easier to estimate the fraction not eaten, or the percent not eaten? Explain.

10-9 Exercises and Applications

Practice and Apply

Getting Started Estimate what percent of each grid is shaded.

1.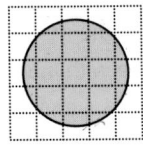

2.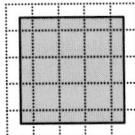

3.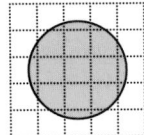

4.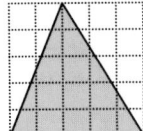

Estimate what percent of each figure is shaded.

5.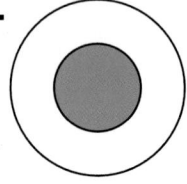

6.

7.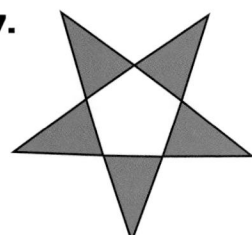

8.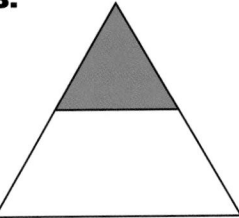

9.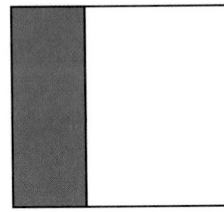

10.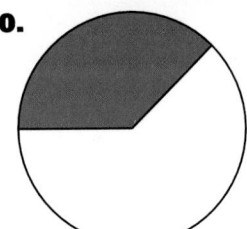

11.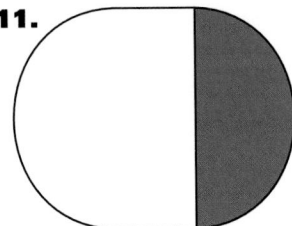

12.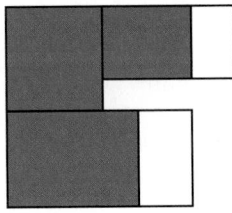

Estimate the percent.

13. 8 out of 72 **14.** 12 out of 77 **15.** 93 out of 187 **16.** 318 out of 965 **17.** 12 out of 16

18. $\frac{39}{150}$ **19.** $\frac{57}{90}$ **20.** $\frac{14}{109}$ **21.** $\frac{6}{657}$ **22.** $\frac{474}{489}$

23. Estimation One researcher estimates that rain forests cover about 3,536,342 square miles of the earth's 50,500,000 square miles of land. About what percent of the earth's land is covered by rain forests?

24. Estimation Of the 7800 known species of birds, about 2600 live in rain forests. What percent of bird species live in rain forests?

25. **Test Prep** Estimate what percent of the figure is shaded.

Ⓐ 45% Ⓑ 50%

Ⓒ 65% Ⓓ 95%

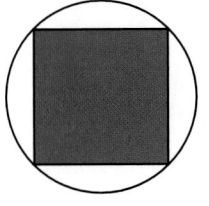

Geography A rain forest is an example of a *biome,* or a particular type of environment. Use the map showing the major biomes of South America for Exercises 26–28.

26. About what percent of South America is desert?

27. About what percent of South America is rain forest?

28. About what percent of the South American rain forest is above the equator?

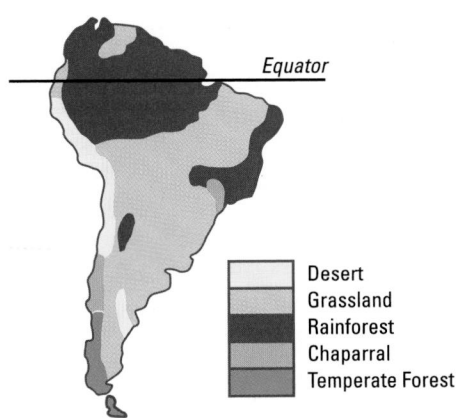

Equator

Desert
Grassland
Rainforest
Chaparral
Temperate Forest

Problem Solving and Reasoning

29. **Communicate** Is it easier to estimate the percent for $\frac{7}{200}$ or $\frac{7}{310}$? Explain.

30. **Critical Thinking** If a shirt was originally $20, went on sale for 15% off, and then was put on clearance with an additional 45% off, estimate the clearance price of the shirt. Explain your reasoning.

31. **Critical Thinking** In a right triangle, estimate the percent of the number of angles that are **not** right angles. Explain your reasoning.

32. Journal Explain two different ways you can estimate what percent 75 is of 200.

Mixed Review

For Exercises 33–36, plot the image of trapezoid *JKML*. *[Lesson 9-6]*

33. Translate *JKML* 2 units down, 6 units right

34. Slide *JKML* 5 units right, 1 unit down

35. Slide *JKML* 3 units up, 4 units left

36. Translate *JKML* 2 units down

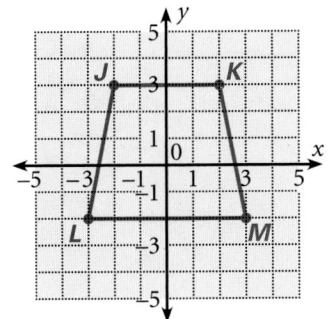

Find the LCM of each pair. *[Lesson 5-3]*

37. 1, 6   **38.** 10, 12   **39.** 6, 4   **40.** 8, 8   **41.** 5, 10   **42.** 25, 75

43. 5, 6   **44.** 12, 8   **45.** 14, 3   **46.** 12, 14   **47.** 3, 2   **48.** 13, 1

Connecting Percents to Fractions and Decimals

You'll Learn ...

■ to express percents as fractions and decimals

■ to express fractions and decimals as percents

... How It's Used

Travel agents use percents to compare the costs of different travel packages.

▶ **Lesson Link**   You've seen that a percent compares a number to 100. Now you'll use this relationship to rewrite percents as fractions and decimals. ◀

Explore   Percents as Fractions and Decimals

Materials: 10 x 10 grids, Colored pencils (or markers)

Grid-dle Me This

Modeling a Percent

• Color in a number of squares equal to the percent.

1. Model these percents:

   a. 21%   **b.** 55%   **c.** 4%   **d.** 75%

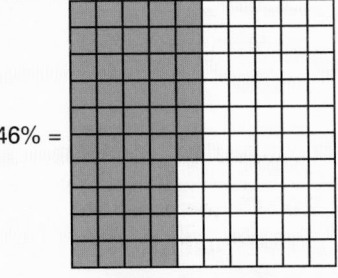

46% =

Modeling a Decimal

• Color in one column for each tenth.

• Color in one square for each hundredth.

2. Model these decimals:

   a. 0.66   **b.** 0.75   **c.** 0.02   **d.** 0.49

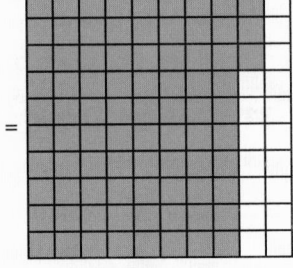

0.83 =

Modeling a Fraction

• Divide the grid into groups of equal size. The number of groups should equal the denominator.

• Color in as many groups as the numerator.

3. Model these fractions:

   a. $\frac{3}{4}$ **b.** $\frac{3}{5}$ **c.** $\frac{7}{10}$ **d.** $\frac{1}{2}$

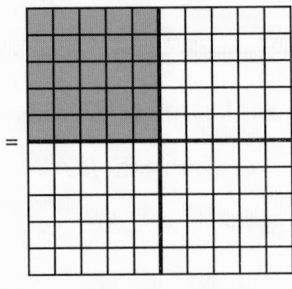

$\frac{1}{4}$ =

4. Rank the 12 values from steps 1–3 from least squares colored to most squares colored.

5. For a given grid, can you describe the number of squares colored using either a percent or a decimal? Explain.

6. For a given grid, can you describe the number of squares colored using either a percent or a fraction? Explain.

Remember

If a fraction does not have a power of 10 as a denominator, you can still convert it to a decimal by dividing the numerator by the denominator. **[Page 303]**

Fractions, percents, and decimals all describe parts of a whole. To convert a percent into a fraction or decimal, rewrite the percent as a fraction over 100.

Examples

1 Write 53% as a fraction.

$$53\% = \frac{53}{100}$$

2 Write 91% as a decimal.

$$91\% = \frac{91}{100} = 0.91$$

If you want to convert a fraction into a percent, you can do so with a proportion.

$$\frac{\text{part}}{\text{whole}} = \frac{\text{percent value}}{100}$$

Example 3

The White's tree frog is $\frac{5}{8}$ the length of the flying gecko. Rewrite this fraction as a percent.

▶ **Science Link**

The flying gecko does not actually fly, but it can glide from tree to tree by spreading its webbed feet apart as much as possible.

$\frac{5}{8} = \frac{x}{100}$ Write a proportion using the fraction and 100.

$8x = 500$ Find the cross products.

$x = 500 \div 8$ Use division to undo multiplication.

$x = 62.5$ Divide.

The White's tree frog is 62.5% of the length of the flying gecko.

Try It

Write the following as fractions and decimals:

a. 83%   **b.** 7%   **c.** Write $\frac{3}{8}$ as a percent.

A table of common percents and their equivalents is given below.

Percent	10%	20%	25%	30%	$33\frac{1}{3}\%$	40%	50%	60%	$66\frac{2}{3}\%$	70%	75%	80%	90%	100%
Decimal	0.1	0.2	0.25	0.3	$0.\overline{3}$	0.4	0.5	0.6	$0.\overline{6}$	0.7	0.75	0.8	0.9	1.0
Fraction	$\frac{1}{10}$	$\frac{1}{5}$	$\frac{1}{4}$	$\frac{3}{10}$	$\frac{1}{3}$	$\frac{2}{5}$	$\frac{1}{2}$	$\frac{3}{5}$	$\frac{2}{3}$	$\frac{7}{10}$	$\frac{3}{4}$	$\frac{4}{5}$	$\frac{9}{10}$	1

WHAT DO YOU THINK?

Alaska, our largest state, has just $\frac{6}{25}$ the area of the South American rain forest. For their social studies report, Jamar and Susana want to express this fraction as a percent.

Jamar thinks ...

I'll find the value of n in the proportion $\frac{6}{25} = \frac{n}{100}$.

The cross products are equal, so $6 \times 100 = 25n$. This means $600 = 25n$.

I can find n by using division to undo multiplication.

$600 \div 25 = 24$

Alaska is 24% of the size of the South American rain forest.

Susana thinks ...

I'll use equivalent fractions.

Since $25 \times 4 = 100$, I can multiply the numerator and the denominator by 4 to get an equivalent fraction with a denominator of 100.

$\frac{6}{25} = \frac{6 \times 4}{25 \times 4} = \frac{24}{100}$

Alaska is 24% of the size of the South American rain forest.

What do you think?

1. Which method do you prefer? Why?

2. Why did Jamar use the proportion $\frac{6}{25} = \frac{n}{100}$?

3. Why did Susana multiply both 6 and 25 by 4?

1. Which is easier, converting a fraction to a percent or converting a percent to a fraction? Explain.

2. Newspaper articles sometimes express relationships as percents and sometimes as fractions. Why?

10-10 Exercises and Applications

Practice and Apply

Getting Started Convert to a decimal.

1. 37%	**2.** 87.2%	**3.** 100%	**4.** 3%	**5.** 10%	**6.** 112%
7. 234%	**8.** 678%	**9.** 67.3%	**10.** 5%	**11.** 88.87%	**12.** 13.8%

Convert to a fraction in lowest terms.

13. 56%	**14.** 15%	**15.** 75%	**16.** 66%	**17.** 150%	**18.** 125%
19. 89%	**20.** 136%	**21.** 90%	**22.** 43%	**23.** 234%	**24.** 78%

Convert to a percent.

25. 0.84 **26.** 0.95 **27.** 0.04 **28.** 0.9 **29.** $\frac{55}{50}$ **30.** $\frac{14}{200}$

31. $\frac{17}{20}$ **32.** $\frac{39}{100}$ **33.** 0.53 **34.** $\frac{4}{5}$ **35.** $\frac{3}{10}$ **36.** 0.453

37. 0.56 **38.** 0.32 **39.** $\frac{12}{25}$ **40.** $\frac{98}{100}$ **41.** 0.75 **42.** 0.23

43. 0.675 **44.** $\frac{5}{100}$ **45.** 0.333 **46.** $\frac{3}{5}$ **47.** $\frac{76}{200}$ **48.** 0.01

Give the shaded part of each figure as a percent, fraction, and decimal.

49. 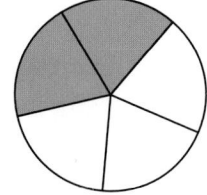 **50.** 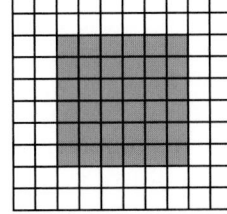 **51.** 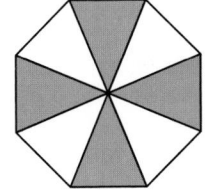 **52.**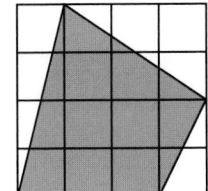

53. Two-thirds of the students at the Liberty Academy use the bus on the weekends. Convert this value to a percent.

54. Health 25% of all medicines in use today come from plant sources, many of which are found in rain forests. Convert this value to a decimal.

55. | Test Prep | Which of the following is equal to $\frac{23}{50}$?

Ⓐ 23%   Ⓑ 50%   Ⓒ 46%   Ⓓ 217%

56. Number Sense Chandra has $\frac{1}{3}$ of the marbles, and Liu has 30%. Who has more? Can you tell how many each person has?

Problem Solving and Reasoning

57. Critical Thinking 45% of the students at Suburban High School are boys. 30% of the boys at Suburban High School have curly hair. What fraction of the students at Suburban High School are boys with curly hair?

58. Critical Thinking Fanny's Fashion Center is advertising a sale. Everything is $\frac{1}{5}$ off. What percent of full price should you expect to pay?

59. Communicate How can you determine without converting to a percent if a decimal is less than 10%? Greater than 100%?

60. Journal In what situations would it be easier to work with fractions? With decimals? With percents? Explain.

Mixed Review

Graph each equation. *[Lesson 9-7]*

61. $y = x - 6$ **62.** $y = 6 + x$ **63.** $y = 8x$ **64.** $y = -2x$ **65.** $y = -5 + x$

Name an equivalent fraction. *[Lesson 5-4]*

66. $\frac{5}{6}$ **67.** $\frac{14}{20}$ **68.** $\frac{10}{32}$ **69.** $\frac{19}{50}$ **70.** $\frac{2}{7}$ **71.** $\frac{6}{10}$

72. $\frac{7}{29}$ **73.** $\frac{6}{24}$ **74.** $\frac{12}{96}$ **75.** $\frac{50}{75}$ **76.** $\frac{150}{200}$ **77.** $\frac{10}{80}$

Project Progress

For each ratio you have written so far, express the ratio as a percent and also as a decimal. Explain how you can use proportions to do this.

Problem Solving

Understand
Plan
Solve
Look Back

Finding a Percent of a Number

▶ Lesson Link You've learned to find percents by working with fractions. Now you'll work with percents by using decimals. ◀

Explore | Finding Percents

What's for Sale?

Donna's Discount World is having a sale.

Item	Regular Price	Discount
Blouse	$30	20% off
Jeans	$50	1/3 off
Belt	$15	10% off
Skirt	$40	1/4 off
Dress	$60	2/3 off
Jacket	$80	25% off
Shoes	$70	1/2 off

1. Estimate the amount discounted from each item.

2. Estimate the sale price of each item.

3. Rank the items from least expensive to most expensive both before and after discount. Are both rankings the same? Explain.

4. Why might a store manager want to represent a discount as a percent? Why might he or she want to represent it as a fraction?

... How It's Used

Community pool managers estimate percents to determine the right amount of chlorine to add to a pool.

Learn | Finding a Percent of a Number

Recall that you can use proportions to convert fractions into percents. You can also use proportions when looking for a percent of a whole number.

$$\frac{\text{part}}{\text{whole}} = \frac{\text{percent value}}{100}$$

Example 1

Find 53% of 62.

$$\boxed{\text{Estimate: } \frac{1}{2} \times 60 = 30}$$ 53% is slightly more than $\frac{1}{2}$, and 62 is close to 60.

$$\begin{array}{c}\textbf{part} \rightarrow \\ \textbf{whole} \rightarrow\end{array} \quad \frac{x}{62} = \frac{53}{100} \quad \begin{array}{c}\leftarrow \textbf{percent value} \\ \leftarrow \textbf{100}\end{array}$$ Write a proportion.

$100x = 3286$ Find the cross products.

$x = 3286 \div 100$ Use division to undo multiplication.

$x = 32.86$ Divide.

32.86 is close to the estimate of 30, so the answer is reasonable.

You can also convert the percent to a decimal and multiply.

Example 2

► **History Link**

Ynez Mexia, a self-taught plant collector, documented several thousand plant species from North and South America. In one two-year trip, she collected over 65,000 plant specimens from the Amazon rain forest.

Pharmacologists have identified about 3000 types of plants that have cancer-fighting properties. 70% of them grow in the rain forest. How many types of cancer-fighting plants grow in the rain forest?

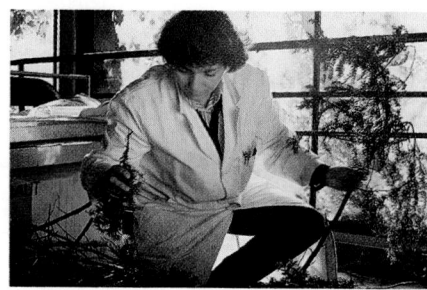

70% of 3000 = ?

70% of 3000 = 0.70 × 3000   Rewrite the percent as a decimal.

= 2100   Multiply.

2100 types of cancer-fighting plants grow in the rain forest.

Try It

a. 65% of the 940 students at Tyler Academy have attended at least one other school. How many students have attended more than one school?

b. Winston scored about 83% on a 160-point test. About how many points did he receive credit for?

HINT

Some calculators have a [%] key that will change the percent into a decimal. You can find 70% of 3000 by entering 70 [%] [×] 3000 [=].

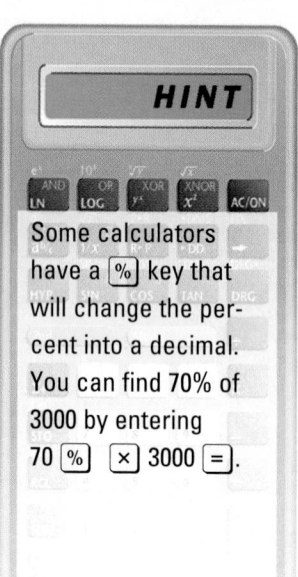

In some situations, you know the percent and the value of the percent, but you need to determine how big the "whole" is. You can also solve these problems using a proportion.

Example 3

The sales tax in Pennsylvania is 6%. Reuben had to pay $9 in sales tax on his purchase of a glockenspiel at Pennsylvania Percussion. Find the cost of the glockenspiel.

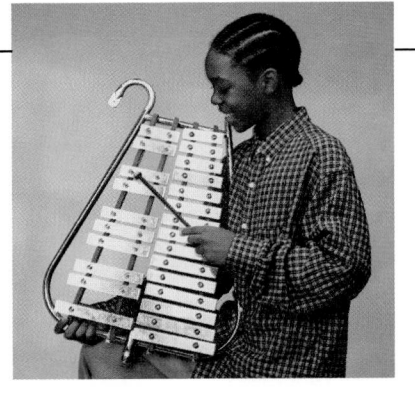

Let x represent the cost of the glockenspiel.

$$\begin{array}{l} \text{part} \rightarrow \\ \text{whole} \rightarrow \end{array} \quad \dfrac{9}{x} = \dfrac{6}{100} \quad \begin{array}{l} \leftarrow \textbf{percent value} \\ \leftarrow \textbf{100} \end{array}$$ Write a proportion.

$6x = 900$ Find the cross products.

$x = 900 \div 6$ Use division to undo multiplication.

$x = 150$ Divide.

The glockenspiel cost $150.

Try It

a. 28 is 40% of what number?

b. According to the Yukon Tourism Board in Canada, there are about 30,000 people in the Yukon Territory. That's 60% of the number of moose in the territory. How many moose are there in the Yukon?

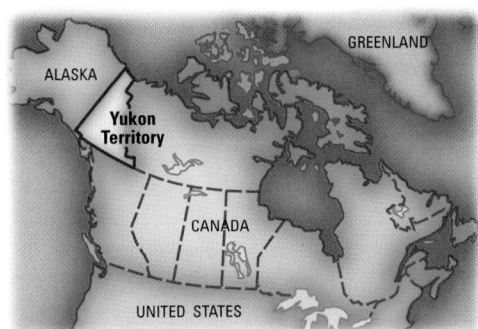

Check Your Understanding

1. What happens to a percent of a whole when the whole increases?

2. Give an example of a percent you might want to find outside of the classroom. Use the word *of* in your example to indicate multiplication.

Practice and Apply

Getting Started Simplify.

1. 50% of 100   **2.** 25% of 100   **3.** 20% of 10   **4.** 62% of 1000

Simplify. Round your answer to the nearest hundredth.

5. 34% of 65   **6.** 68% of 63.2   **7.** 22% of 84   **8.** 25% of 64

9. 99% of 106   **10.** 140% of 50   **11.** 100% of 54.3   **12.** 9% of 525

13. 33% of 68   **14.** 19% of 2.34   **15.** 2% of 18.8   **16.** 83% of 34

17. 76% of 20   **18.** 50% of 66   **19.** 25% of $10.99   **20.** 15% of $20.13

21. 13.6% of 45   **22.** 4.5% of $12.02   **23.** 37% of 23   **24.** 6% of 294

Find the total amount.

25. 30% of ☐ is 75   **26.** 45% of ☐ is 90   **27.** 4.3% of ☐ is 8.6   **28.** 90% of ☐ is 63

29. 7% of ☐ is 6.16   **30.** 22% of ☐ is 0.22   **31.** 7.5% of ☐ is 13.2   **32.** 115% of ☐ is $69

33. A test has 24 multiple choice questions. How many do you need to answer correctly to score at least 80%?

34. Consumer The sales tax on the items shown is 5.25%. For each item, find the sales tax amount and the total price.

35. Shalini earned $34,000 in 1997. If her 1998 income was 108% of her 1997 income, how much did she earn in 1998?

36. **Test Prep** Find 52% of 780.

Ⓐ 390   Ⓑ 40,560

Ⓒ 405.6   Ⓓ 520

37. Of the estimated 300 species of hummingbirds, 83% can be found in rain forests. About how many species can be found in rain forests?

38. Industry Argentina produced 11,100 passenger cars in 1991 and 21,000 in 1992. What percent of the number of 1992 cars was the number of 1991 cars?

39. Geography At the beginning of 1994, Ethiopia had a population of 55,200,000. If the population was growing at a rate of 3% per year, how much did the population increase that year?

40. Chance Gloria plays a game 100 times, and her chances of winning are 60%. Esmerelda plays the same game 50 times, and her chances of winning are 49%. Who will win more games?

Problem Solving and Reasoning

41. Critical Thinking Penelope explained how she calculated a 5% discount for a $22 meal. "First, I moved the decimal point over one place, and got $2.20. Then, I took half of that, which was $1.10. The meal is $22 minus $1.10, or $20.90." Do you agree with her answer? Will her method always work? Explain.

42. Choose a Strategy A new student's score on a spelling test was about 72% of Catherine's score. Catherine's score was about 98% of Tom's score. Tom's score was about 94% of Luanna's score. Luanna got 93 out of 100 points. How many points did the new student get?

43. Critical Thinking Hank bought some stock at $15 per share and later sold it at $30 per share. He told Robin his stock had gone up by 100%. Robin said he sold it for 200% of the original price. Who was right?

44. Communicate If you know the percent and the part, and you want to know the whole, explain how you can use division instead of proportions.

> **Problem Solving**
> # STRATEGIES
> - Look for a Pattern
> - Make an Organized List
> - Make a Table
> - Guess and Check
> - Work Backward
> - Use Logical Reasoning
> - Draw a Diagram
> - Solve a Simpler Problem

Mixed Review

Write in lowest terms. *[Lesson 5-5]*

45. $\dfrac{7}{14}$ **46.** $\dfrac{5}{25}$ **47.** $\dfrac{20}{30}$ **48.** $\dfrac{6}{18}$ **49.** $\dfrac{12}{36}$ **50.** $\dfrac{8}{10}$

51. $\dfrac{6}{8}$ **52.** $\dfrac{9}{15}$ **53.** $\dfrac{3}{21}$ **54.** $\dfrac{4}{24}$ **55.** $\dfrac{21}{35}$ **56.** $\dfrac{6}{9}$

Write each as an improper fraction or mixed number. *[Lesson 5-6]*

57. $6\dfrac{4}{5}$ **58.** $\dfrac{6}{5}$ **59.** $2\dfrac{8}{9}$ **60.** $\dfrac{10}{3}$ **61.** $5\dfrac{1}{7}$ **62.** $\dfrac{16}{7}$

63. $\dfrac{21}{2}$ **64.** $11\dfrac{3}{4}$ **65.** $3\dfrac{1}{2}$ **66.** $\dfrac{65}{8}$ **67.** $\dfrac{14}{5}$ **68.** $9\dfrac{11}{12}$

T E C H N O L O G Y

Using a Spreadsheet • Creating a Circle Graph

Problem: The data below represents the grades a math class received on a test. What would the data look like in a circle graph?

You can use your spreadsheet to organize the data and draw a circle graph.

C	A	C	B	C	B	A	B	A	D	C	B	A
B	D	C	A	B	A	C	C	B	A	C	B	C
F	A	B	C	C	A	B	C	B	C	A	C	F

1 Enter the data into the spreadsheet as shown.

2 Select cells A2 to B6. These cells contain the grades and the number of students earning each grade.

	A	B	C	D
1	Grade	Number		
2	A	10		
3	B	11		
4	C	14		
5	D	2		
6	F	2		
7				
8				
9				
10				

D 5% F 5% A 26%
C 36%
B 28%

3 Using the graph option, choose a circle graph that shows labels and percents.

TRY IT

a. Collect data from students about their favorite class. Use a spreadsheet to make a circle graph of the data.

b. Collect data from students about the kind of pet they have. Use a spreadsheet to make a circle graph of the data.

ON YOUR OWN

▶ What would a circle graph look like if all the categories in column A had the same number in column B?

▶ Is it easier to create a circle graph by hand or with a spreadsheet? Explain.

In this section, you've been given many percent facts related to the world's rain forests. Now you'll begin with the facts and use them to create some percents of your own.

Touring the Rain Forest

Write a short report on rain forests, based on some of the following information. Choose information that interests you. Your report should contain at least 5 percents, all of which you must calculate yourself.

A. Tropical rain typically falls at a rate of 1 inch per hour. However, rates as high as 16 inches per hour have been recorded in Liberia.

B. Tropical Costa Rica has an area of 20,000 square miles and has 8,000 species of plants. Nontropical Great Britain has an area of 94,000 square miles and has 1,600 species of plants.

C. A 3-square-mile section of Costa Rica's La Selva rain forest has 394 species of birds. Nontropical Pennsylvania has an area of 45,000 square miles and has 197 species of birds.

D. Tropical temperatures generally vary between 68°F and 85°F day and night year-round. Tropical rain forests get about 200 inches of rain per year. Northern Alaska has an average temperature of 40°F and gets 50 inches of rain each year.

E. The tallest trees are about 150–200 ft tall. Beneath these are a canopy of 60–90 ft vines and trees. Beneath this is an understory of 15–45 ft shrubs. Leaves average 6 inches in length, although the corozo palm has 30 ft leaves. Some bamboo shoots grow 3 ft per day.

F. In the rain forests of the Malay Archipelago, 25,000 plant species have been identified. These include orchids (4,000 species), large trees (2,500 species), heathers (700 species), and figs (500 species).

1. For every 4 carrots that Rennie grows, she grows 3 lettuce plants.

    a. What is the ratio of lettuce to carrots?

    b. Write this ratio in lowest terms and as a unit rate.

    c. What percent of Rennie's vegetables are carrots?

Tell if each is a proportion. If it is not, explain why.

2. $\frac{5}{9} \square \frac{10}{9}$ **3.** $\frac{7}{3} \square \frac{21}{9}$ **4.** $\frac{20}{45} \square \frac{4}{9}$ **5.** $\frac{5}{7} \square \frac{5}{7}$ **6.** $\frac{16}{4} \square \frac{60}{15}$

Solve each proportion.

7. $\frac{2}{7} = \frac{x}{14}$ **8.** $\frac{x}{28} = \frac{3}{6}$ **9.** $\frac{35}{m} = \frac{14}{4}$ **10.** $\frac{63}{27} = \frac{c}{40}$ **11.** $\frac{1}{2} = \frac{600}{l}$

Find the missing side lengths on these similar figures.

12.

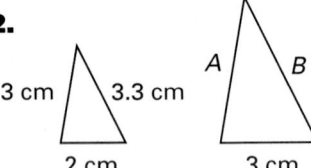

13.

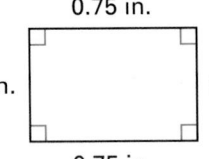

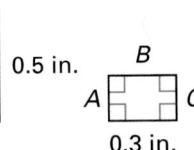

14.

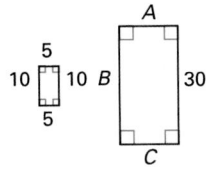

Simplify.

15. 78% of 37   **16.** 8% of 46.3   **17.** 12% of 146   **18.** 230% of 57

19. Number Sense Estimate the percent of each figure that is shaded.

    a.

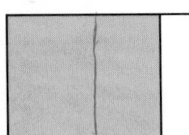

    b.

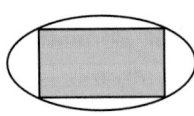

20. Convert 64% to a decimal and a fraction.   **21.** Convert 0.95 and $\frac{3}{5}$ to percents.

Test Prep

When asked to find a percent of a number, you can sometimes use estimation to eliminate wrong answers.

22. Find 68% of 328.

    Ⓐ 223.04   Ⓑ 22,304   Ⓒ 2230.4   Ⓓ 2.2304

Calculating Tips

In the United States, when people are served at a restaurant by a waiter or waitress, it is customary to leave a tip. The tip is equal to a percent of the bill for the food. Most tips range from 10% to 20%, based on the quality of the service. Leaving a 15% tip is common. You can easily calculate 15% of the bill using mental math.

CHECK	00131
taco platter	4.50
tostada salad	4.00
veggie burrito	3.15
2 med. root beers	1.50
1 large iced tea	1.00
	14.15
tax	0.93
	15.08

Thank You for Visiting Us

1. First, calculate 10% of the bill. Since this is the same as $\frac{1}{10}$ of the bill, you can divide the bill by 10, or move the decimal point one place to the left.

10% of $15.08 is about $1.50.

2. Next, calculate 5% of the bill. Since 5% is half of 10%, you can divide your result from Step 1 by 2.

5% of $15.08 is about $0.75.

3. Add the amounts for 10% and 5%.

15% is $1.50 + $0.75, or $2.25.

Try It

Determine what 15% of each amount is.

1. $10.62   **2.** $4.67   **3.** $13.59

4. $20.31   **5.** $47.53   **6.** $28.47

If service is exceptional, people sometimes leave a 20% tip. Use the ideas above to find 20% of each amount.

7. $9.81   **8.** $14.63   **9.** $16.67

10. $23.31   **11.** $27.20   **12.** $37.14

Chapter 10 Summary and Review

Graphic Organizer

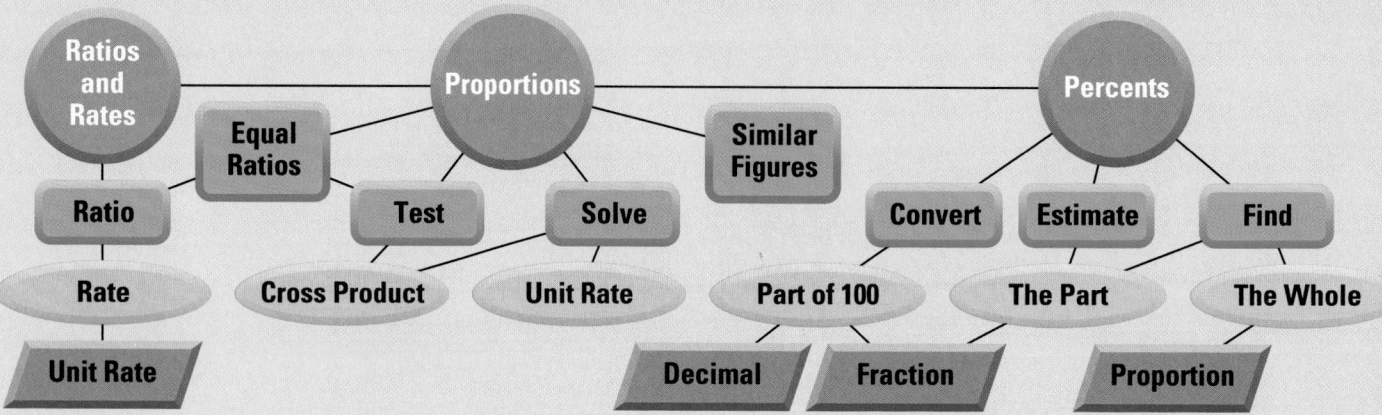

Section 10A Ratios and Rates

Summary

- A **ratio** compares two quantities.

- You can create equal ratios by multiplying or dividing each quantity by the same number.

- A **rate** is a ratio that compares two quantities that have different units. A **unit rate** is a rate that compares a quantity to 1 unit of measure.

Review

1. Show three ways to write the ratio of six yams to eleven potatoes.

2. Write the ratio $\frac{12}{16}$ in lowest terms.

3. Assume there are 5 fingers on each person's hand. In a group of six people, what is the ratio in simplest form:

   a. Of fingers to people?

   b. Of people to fingers?

   c. Of fingers to hands?

   d. Of hands to people?

4. What is the ratio of Elk School students to Rhodes students? Elk School students to total students?

5. Which of the following ratios is *not* equal to the ratio 14 to 21?

   Ⓐ $\frac{3}{2}$ Ⓑ $\frac{2}{3}$ Ⓒ 60:90   Ⓓ $\frac{12}{18}$

6. Which of the following is a rate?

   Ⓐ $\frac{7 \text{ hr}}{1 \text{ hr}}$ Ⓑ $\frac{3 \text{ mi}}{7 \text{ hr}}$ Ⓒ $\frac{3 \text{ mi}}{1 \text{ mi}}$ Ⓓ $\frac{3}{1}$

Section 10B Proportions

Summary

- You find a **cross product** by multiplying the top value of one ratio by the bottom value of another ratio.

- If the cross products of two ratios are equal, the two ratios form a **proportion**.

- You can use cross products or a unit rate to solve proportions.

- **Similar figures** have the same shape, but different sizes. Their angles have the same measure, and their sides are proportional.

Review

7. Can the ratios $\frac{7 \text{ mi}}{10 \text{ hr}}$ and $\frac{21 \text{ hr}}{30 \text{ mi}}$ form a proportion? Explain.

8. Use cross products to solve the proportion $\frac{9}{m} = \frac{3}{5}$.

9. Red ribbon costs $0.96 a foot. Use a unit rate to find out how much 54 in. cost.

10. Explain why the two triangles are similar.

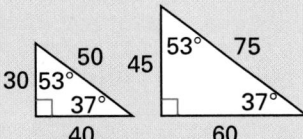

Section 10C Percents

Summary

- A **percent** is a ratio of a number to 100. It is written using the % symbol.

- To estimate a percent, think of a fraction you can easily write as a percent that's roughly equal to the amount being estimated.

- When using a percent to find a part or a whole, use a proportion to find the missing value. To find a part, you can also convert the percent to a decimal and multiply.

Review

Write each percent as a ratio of a number to 100, as a fraction in lowest terms, and as a decimal.

11. 35%   **12.** 20%   **13.** 8%   **14.** 75%

15. In Texas in 1995, about 25% of the population over 5 years old spoke a language other than English at home. If this population was 18,723,991, about how many people spoke a language other than English at home?

16. Use a table to find four equal rates that describe saving $6 for every 4 days of work.

17. What is the unit rate of the firefighters' response time of 7.5 minutes to a fire 5 miles away?

Chapter 10 Assessment

Write the ratio as a fraction in lowest terms.

1. 4 out of 32 dentists
2. One chaperone for every 6 students.
3. Ninety of the 100 students passed the test.

For Exercises 4–7, determine whether the statement is true or false. If it is false, rewrite it as a true statement.

4. Cross products and unit rates are used to solve proportions.

5. A percent can be written as a fraction and compares a quantity to the number 1.

6. If two triangles are similar, they are congruent.

7. Two figures are similar if their shapes are the same and their side lengths are proportional

8. Write four equal ratios for the ratio 5:7.

9. Write the ratio of 7 triangles to 8 squares in three ways.

10. Why is $\dfrac{8 \text{ mi}}{5 \text{ hr}} = \dfrac{20 \text{ hr}}{32 \text{ mi}}$ not a correct proportion? Rewrite it correctly.

11. Fuji apples cost \$2.10 for 3 lb. Use a proportion to find how much it would cost to buy 7 lb.

12. Valencia oranges cost \$3.16 for 4 lb. Use a unit rate to find how much it would cost to buy 5 lb.

13. Are the two figures congruent, similar, or neither? Explain.

Write the percent as a ratio of a number to 100, as a fraction in lowest terms, and as a decimal.

14. 70%
15. 27%
16. 40%
17. 5%

18. Jonah had 84 baseball cards. He threw 25% of them away. How many did he throw away?

19. Jessica had 6 Florida Marlin cards, which was 3 percent of her total collection. How many cards did she have in her collection?

Performance Task

A bicycle shop advertised a 30% discount on their bikes. After two weeks, they gave an additional 20% off the sale prices. John bought a bike the last day of the sale. Its original price was \$245. What did it cost him? What percent of its original price was the final price?

Multiple Choice

Choose the best answer.

1. A graph that shows separately the tens place values and ones place values of the data is a *[Lesson 1-6]*

Ⓐ Bar graph   Ⓑ Circle graph

Ⓒ Pictograph   Ⓓ Stem-and-leaf plot

2. Supply the next three numbers in the number pattern: 15, 25, 23, 33, 31, *[Lesson 2-9]*

Ⓐ 29, 39, 37   Ⓑ 41, 39, 49

Ⓒ 41, 51, 49   Ⓓ None of these

3. Find the quotient of 88.88 ÷ 44. *[Lesson 3-10]*

Ⓐ 2.02   Ⓑ 2.2   Ⓒ 20.2   Ⓓ 22

4. How many millimeters are there in 3 meters? *[Lesson 4-2]*

Ⓐ 30   Ⓑ 300   Ⓒ 3000   Ⓓ 30,000

5. What is the approximate area of a circle with a diameter of 10 ft? *[Lesson 4-8]*

Ⓐ 15.7 ft^2 Ⓑ 31.4 ft^2

Ⓒ 78.5 ft^2 Ⓓ 314 ft^2

6. Tell whether 495 is divisible by 2, 3, 5, 9, or 10. *[Lesson 5-1]*

Ⓐ 5   Ⓑ 3, 5, 9   Ⓒ 3, 5   Ⓓ 2, 3, 5, 9

7. Order from smallest to largest: $\frac{1}{4}, \frac{4}{5}, \frac{2}{3}$ *[Lesson 5-8]*

Ⓐ $\frac{4}{5}, \frac{1}{4}, \frac{2}{3}$ Ⓑ $\frac{4}{5}, \frac{2}{3}, \frac{1}{4},$

Ⓒ $\frac{1}{4}, \frac{4}{5}, \frac{2}{3}$ Ⓓ $\frac{1}{4}, \frac{2}{3}, \frac{4}{5}$

8. Solve the equation $x - \frac{3}{5} = \frac{2}{3}$. *[Lesson 6-3]*

Ⓐ $1\frac{4}{15}$ Ⓑ $\frac{5}{8}$ Ⓒ $\frac{2}{5}$ Ⓓ $\frac{1}{15}$

9. Estimate $5\frac{3}{5} + 7\frac{1}{3}$. *[Lesson 6-4]*

Ⓐ 12   Ⓑ 13

Ⓒ 14   Ⓓ None of these

10. How many $\frac{2}{3}$-cup servings are contained in 12 cups of juice? *[Lesson 7-4]*

Ⓐ 6   Ⓑ 8

Ⓒ 18   Ⓓ None of these

11. The sum of two angles of a triangle is 37°. What is the third angle's measure? *[Lesson 8-4]*

Ⓐ 143°   Ⓑ 106°   Ⓒ 53°   Ⓓ 16°

12. What is the least rotation clockwise that will land the figure on top of itself? *[Lesson 8-9]*

Ⓐ 360°

Ⓑ 270°

Ⓒ 180°

Ⓓ 90°

13. Simplify: $-3 - (-5)$. *[Lesson 9-3]*

Ⓐ −8   Ⓑ −2   Ⓒ 2   Ⓓ 8

14. The cross products for $\frac{m}{7} = \frac{12}{21}$ are *[Lesson 10-5]*

Ⓐ $21m = 84$ Ⓑ $7m = 252$

Ⓒ $12m = 147$ Ⓓ None of these

Solids and Measurement

Cultural Link
www.mathsurf.com/6/ch11/social

Arts & Literature Link
www.mathsurf.com/6/ch11/science

People of the World

Many African tribes build cylindrical houses with cone-shaped roofs such as the ones in this craft village near Victoria Falls, Zimbabwe.

Arts & Literature

Cubism is a style of art that often shows objects and scenes as basic geometric shapes.

Gris, Juan. "Femme Dans Un Fauteuil". Christie's, London

Entertainment

A standard basketball and a 16-pound bowling ball have approximately the same surface area (283 in^2 and 227 in^2). A basketball weighs about 22 ounces, about $8\frac{1}{2}\%$ of the weight of a bowling ball.

Science

In zero gravity, water "drops" are shaped like spheres. This is because the water molecules can form the most compact shape possible for their volume, which happens to be a sphere.

Social Studies

The Great Pyramid in Giza, Egypt, is made from over 2,000,000 stones. Each stone weighs 2,500 pounds.

CHAPTER PROJECT

Problem Solving

Understand
Plan
Solve
Look Back

In this project, you will determine what would be a good size for an aquarium in your classroom. Begin the project by recording how many fish you want in the aquarium. Also record how many inches long you want each fish to be.

Problem
Solving

Understand
Plan
Solve
Look Back

Checking the Rules of the Problem

When solving problems, it's important to look back to verify that your answer is appropriate. For example, check the facts in the problem and verify that your solution agrees with all of them.

Problem Solving Focus

Each problem has three answers. State which answer is correct, and which sentences in the problem the other two answers don't agree with.

❶ Kareem, Chris, Maggie, and Sid spent $31.25 at the diner. Kareem spent $2.00 more than Chris. Sid spent $3.00 less than Kareem. Maggie spent 25% of the total spent by Kareem, Chris, and Sid. How much did each person pay?

Answer #1	Answer #2	Answer #3
K = $ 8.00	K = $12.00	K = $10.00
C = $10.00	C = $14.00	C = $ 8.00
S = $ 5.00	S = $15.00	S = $ 7.00
M = $ 8.25	M = $10.25	M = $ 6.25

❷ After leaving the diner, Sid met Mai, Julio, and Danielle at Videorama to play Pinball Whiz. Every player gets a free turn when he or she scores over 25,000 points on a game. Sid played five more games than Julio. Julio played $1\frac{1}{2}$ times as much as Mai. Mai played three fewer games than Danielle. All together they played 88 games. How many games did each person play?

Answer #1	Answer #2	Answer #3
D = 19	D = 13	D = 24
J = 24	J = 8	J = 19
S = 29	S = 13	S = 16
M = 16	M = 16	M = 29

The Grapes of Wrap

Which package of grapes would you be most likely to buy?

When you shop, each product competes for your attention. To catch your eye, package designers create containers in a variety of shapes, sizes, designs, and color combinations. But designing a package is not as easy as it sounds.

◆ Consumers notice large containers, but store owners like small containers, so that they can stock as many items as possible.

◆ Consumers notice fancy packaging materials, but they are expensive to manufacture.

◆ Consumers notice unusual shapes, but these are difficult to pack and transport.

Geometry plays a critical role in designing packages with the most appeal for the least money.

1 Why did you choose the package of grapes that you picked?

2 In what ways might a package designer use mathematics?

Classifying Solids

You'll Learn ...

■ to classify different solids

... How It's Used

Art instructors use solid classifications when describing to students how to draw a particular object.

Vocabulary

solid

face

edge

polyhedron

prism

base

pyramid

net

cylinder

cone

sphere

cube

▶ **Lesson Link** You know how to classify flat figures, like circles and polygons. Now you'll classify three-dimensional shapes. ◀

Explore | Solids

Shape Up and Ship Out!

Materials: Prisms, Pyramids, Spheres, Cones, Cylinders

1. Choose several of the available shapes.

2. Describe each shape so that someone reading your description could tell which solid you were describing.

3. Which figures remind you of shapes used to package familiar products? Name some of the products. Why might the manufacturers have chosen those shapes?

4. Which package shapes would be easiest to make and transport? Which would be most difficult? Explain.

Learn | Classifying Solids

A **solid** is a three-dimensional figure or a figure that takes up space. The flat surfaces of a solid are called **faces**. The line where two faces come together is an **edge**. The point where several edges come together is a *vertex*.

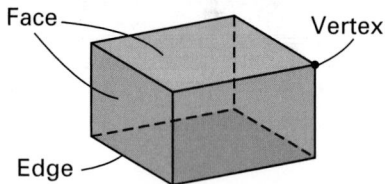

A solid whose faces are polygons is called a **polyhedron**. If two of the faces are parallel and congruent, the polyhedron is a **prism**. The parallel faces of a prism are the **bases**.

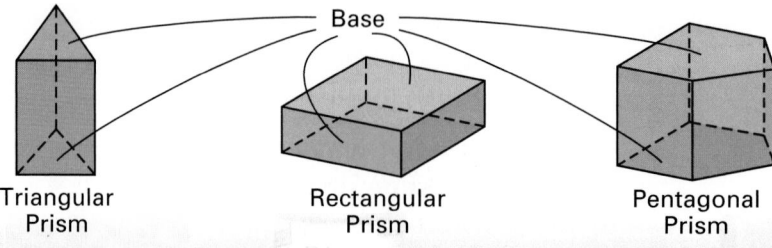

Triangular Prism

Rectangular Prism

Pentagonal Prism

A **pyramid** is a solid with one base. All the other faces are triangles. Both prisms and pyramids can be named by the shapes of their bases.

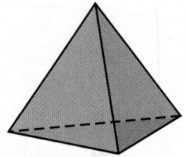

Triangular pyramid

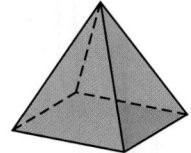

Rectangular pyramid

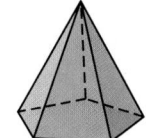

Pentagonal pyramid

Solids with curved surfaces are not polyhedrons.

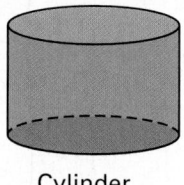

Cylinder

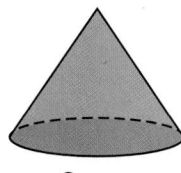

Cone

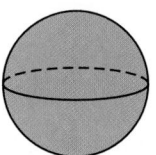

Sphere

Examples

Classify each solid. If the solid is a polyhedron, tell how many faces, edges, and vertices it has.

1

The solid is a triangular prism with 5 faces, 9 edges, and 6 vertices.

2

The solid is a square (or rectangular) pyramid with 5 faces, 8 edges, and 5 vertices.

3

The solid is a cylinder. It is not a polyhedron.

A flat pattern that can be folded into a solid is called a **net** . A solid may have several different nets. Both nets in the figure can be folded to make a **cube** (a square prism).

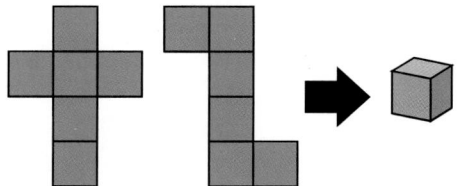

1. Is a pyramid a prism? Is a sphere a polyhedron? Explain.

2. In a prism, what shapes appear as the bases?

11-1 Exercises and Applications

Practice and Apply

Getting Started For each figure, state the shape of each face.

1.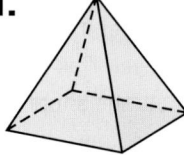

2.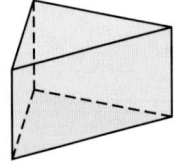

3.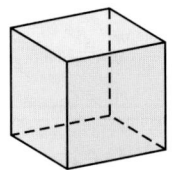

4.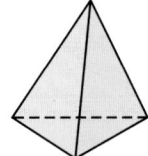

Geometry Classify each solid. If it is a polyhedron, tell how many vertices, edges, and faces it has.

5.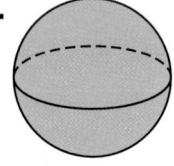

6.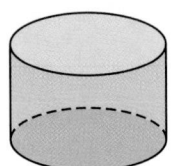

7.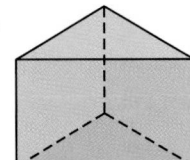

8.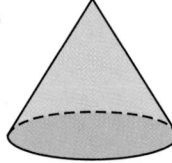

9.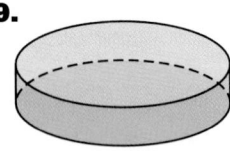

10.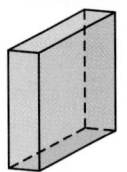

11.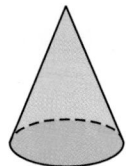

12.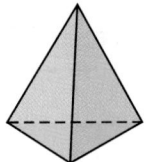

Geometry Draw an example of each.

13. Sphere   **14.** Triangular prism   **15.** Cylinder   **16.** Cone

Classify each group of figures.

17.

18.

19.

20. **Test Prep** How many edges and vertices does the given figure have?

Ⓐ 6 edges and 4 vertices

Ⓑ 7 edges and 6 vertices

Ⓒ 6 edges and 5 vertices

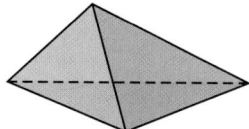

Name the solids in each figure.

21.

22.

Rickey, George. "Cluster of Four Cubes," 1992, stainless steel. National Gallery of Art, Washington D.C. Gift of George Rickey and Patrons Permanent Fund.

Problem Solving and Reasoning

23. **Critical Thinking** Use what you know about triangular, rectangular, and pentagonal prisms to draw a hexagonal prism. Classify each of the faces and explain your drawing.

24. **Critical Thinking** Heidi is mailing a set of building blocks to her cousin. She needs to decide which box to use. Most of the blocks are rectangular or triangular prisms, and the types of boxes she can use are shown. Explain to Heidi what shape box she should use and why.

25. **Communicate** Can you classify a polyhedron if you know only how many edges it has? Vertices? Faces? Explain your reasoning.

Mixed Review

26. What is the ratio of vowels to letters in the alphabet? *[Lesson 10-1]*

27. Give the ratio of pennies in a dollar to dimes in a dollar. *[Lesson 10-1]*

Write each as a decimal. *[Lesson 5-7]*

28. $\frac{3}{8}$ **29.** $\frac{10}{4}$ **30.** $3\frac{1}{2}$ **31.** $\frac{3}{4}$ **32.** $\frac{24}{12}$ **33.** $\frac{5}{6}$

Exploring Surface Area

▶ Lesson Link
In the last lesson you learned how to name solids. Now you'll find the area of the net for a polyhedron. ◀

You'll Learn ...

■ to find the surface area of a polyhedron by using a net of the solid

... How It's Used

Upholsterers use surface area when designing covers for furniture.

Vocabulary

surface area (SA)

Explore Areas of Solids

Wrap Artists

Materials: Cuisenaire rods, Centimeter graph paper

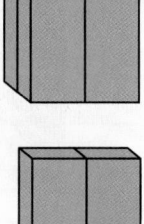

1. Choose four Cuisenaire rods of the same color. Create a rectangular prism by putting the rods together as shown. Draw a net for your rectangular prism. How many squares will it take to cover the prism?

2. Using the same four rods, put them together as shown. Draw a net for this prism. How many squares will it take to cover this prism?

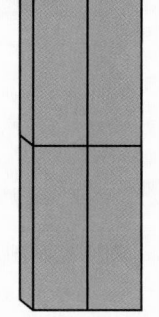

3. Repeat Steps 1 and 2 with a different set of four rods.

4. When you change the way four rods are arranged to make a prism, does that change the number of squares needed to cover the prism? Explain.

Learn Surface Area

The **surface area (SA)** of a polyhedron is the sum of the areas of all of its faces. To find the surface area of a polyhedron such as this rectangular prism, unfold it into a net of polygons and then add their areas.

Like the area for a single polygon, surface area is measured in square units, such as cm^2.

Examples

1 For the solid, count the number of faces and state the shape of each face.

The solid has five faces. The top and the bottom are triangles. The other three faces are rectangles.

2 Find the surface area of the pyramid.

The net consists of a 5-by-5 square and 4 triangles with bases of 5 and heights of 6.

SA = area of square + area of 4 triangles

$$
\begin{aligned}
SA &= (5 \times 5) &&+ 4 \times (5 \times 6 \div 2) \\
&= 25 &&+ 4 \times (15) \\
&= 25 &&+ 60 \\
&= 85
\end{aligned}
$$

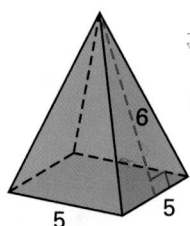
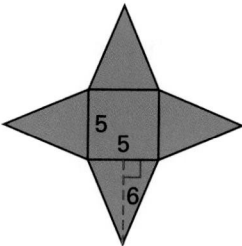

The surface area is 85 square units.

> **HINT**
>
> The [STO▸] button stores numbers in the calculator's memory. Press 5 [×] 5 [=] [STO▸] to store the area of the square. When you know the area of the four triangles, press [+] [RCL] [=] to add this to the number in memory.

Try It

a. Count the number of faces, and state the shape of each face.

b. Find the surface area.

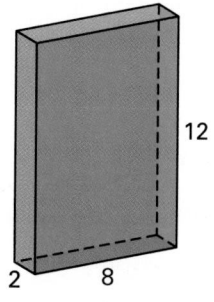

Check Your Understanding

1. Why must you be able to find areas of polygons in order to find surface areas of polyhedrons?

2. Describe a shortcut for finding the surface area of a cube.

11-2 Exercises and Applications

Practice and Apply

Getting Started Find each area.

1.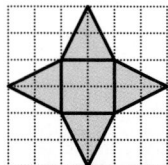

2.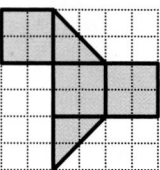

3.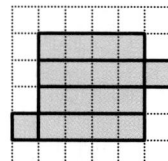

4.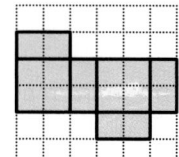

Geometry Find the area of each net. Classify the solid.

5.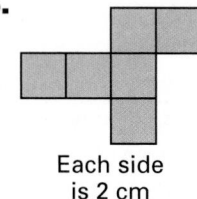

Each side
is 2 cm

6.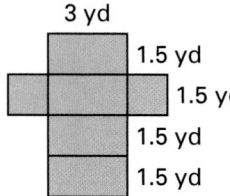

3 yd
1.5 yd
1.5 yd
1.5 yd
1.5 yd

7.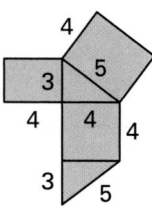

4
3 5
4 4 4
3 5

8.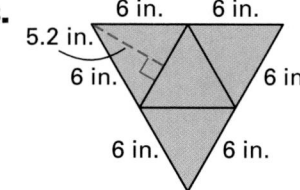

6 in.   6 in.
5.2 in.
6 in.   6 in.
6 in.   6 in.

Geometry For exercises 9–11, state the number of faces. Then classify each face and find the total surface area.

9.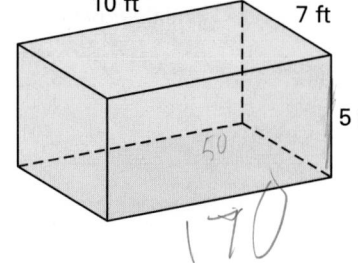

10 ft   7 ft
5 ft

10.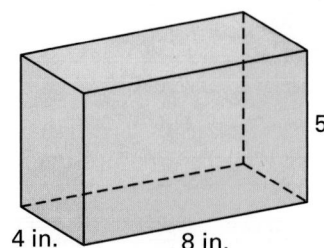

5 in.
4 in.   8 in.

11.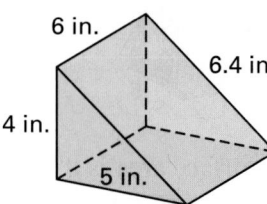

6 in.
6.4 in.
4 in.
5 in.

12. A box of spaghetti measures $1\frac{1}{2}$ in. wide, 4 in. long and 12 in. high. What is the total surface area of the package?

13. If wrapping paper costs $0.29 a square foot, how much would it cost to cover the box shown?

1 ft
0.3 ft   1 ft

586 *Chapter 11 • Solids and Measurement*

14. **Test Prep** Which net can form a cube?

Ⓐ 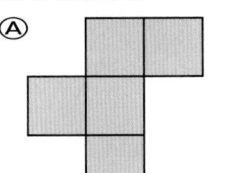   Ⓑ 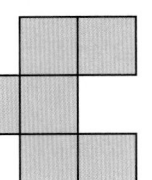   Ⓒ   Ⓓ

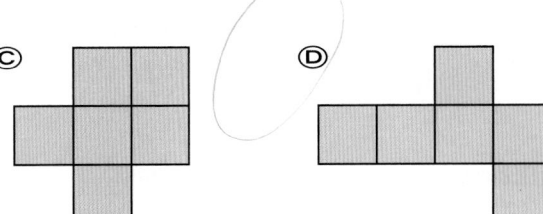

15. Industry The United States Post Office only delivers mail that is at least 0.007 in. thick. If a piece is between 0.007 and 0.25 in. thick, it must also be at least 3.5 in. long and 5 in. wide. What is the surface area of the thinnest piece of mail that the U.S. Post Office will deliver?

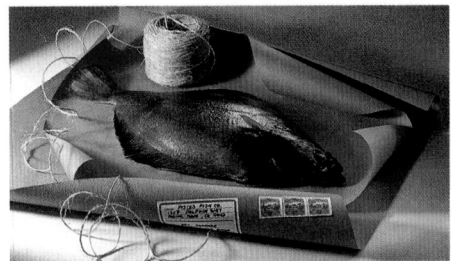

Problem Solving and Reasoning

16. **Journal** List some differences between the perimeter of a rectangle, the area of a rectangle, and the surface area of a rectangular prism. Can any of the quantities be negative? Explain.

17. Critical Thinking Regan has enough foil to cover half of the larger box shown. Since the dimensions of the smaller box are half those of the larger box, she thinks she can completely cover the smaller box instead. Do you agree with Regan? Explain.

18. Communicate Can a polyhedron have more than one net? Can one net form more than one polyhedron? Explain your reasoning.

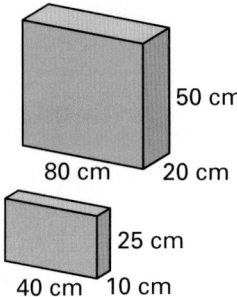

50 cm

80 cm   20 cm

25 cm

40 cm   10 cm

Mixed Review

For each ratio, give two equivalent ratios. *[Lesson 10-2]*

19. $\frac{3}{4}$ **20.** 6:24   **21.** $\frac{4}{10}$ **22.** 7 to 9   **23.** $\frac{11}{12}$ **24.** 3:8

Order from smallest to largest. *[Lesson 5-8]*

25. $\frac{1}{2}$, 0.23, 1.23   **26.** 6.7, $\frac{1}{6}$, $\frac{5}{6}$ **27.** 8.2, $8\frac{1}{4}$, 8.75   **28.** $\frac{1}{3}$, $\frac{3}{3}$, 3.3

Project Progress

A fish needs at least 20 square inches of water surface on the top of the tank for each inch of body length. Based on the total length of all of your fish, find out what the area of the water surface in your aquarium should be. Use this number to figure out a possible length and width for the tank.

Problem Solving

Understand
Plan
Solve
Look Back

11-3 Surface Area Formulas

You'll Learn ...

■ to use surface area formulas

... How It's Used

Set designers calculate surface area when determining the cost to construct a given set.

▶ **Lesson Link** You know how to use a net to find the surface area of a polyhedron. Now you will use formulas to find surface areas. ◀

Explore Surface Area

It's All on the Surface

A.
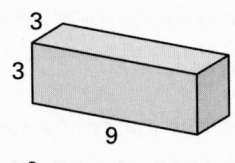

B.
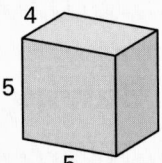

C.
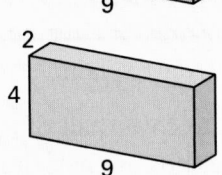

D.
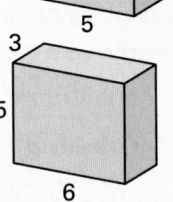

1. Each figure below is a net of one of the prisms above. (Figures not drawn to scale.) The areas of the faces are marked on the nets. Match each prism with its net.

I.
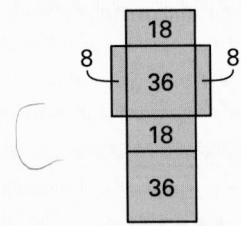

II.
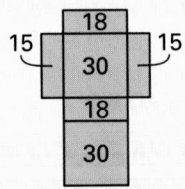

III.
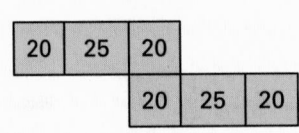

IV.
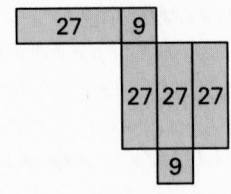

2. Find the surface area of each prism. Describe patterns you see in the areas of the faces.

3. If two prisms have the same surface area, are they the same prism? Explain.

4. Suppose you unfolded one of the above prisms into a net different from the one shown. Would the surface area be different? Explain.

You've seen that you can find the surface area of any polyhedron by adding the areas of its faces. When a polyhedron is a rectangular prism, you can use a shortcut to find its surface area.

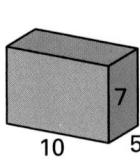

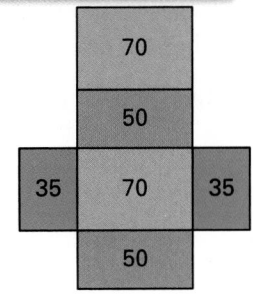

Notice that opposite each face is a "twin" with the same area.

$$l \times w \quad l \times w \quad l \times h \quad l \times h \quad w \times h \quad w \times h$$

$$50 \longleftrightarrow 50 \quad 70 \longleftrightarrow 70 \quad 35 \longleftrightarrow 35$$

The total surface area is the sum of the areas of three sets of twins:

$$\mathbf{SA = (2 \times 50) + (2 \times 70) + (2 \times 35)}$$

> SA (rectangular prism) $= (2 \times l \times w) + (2 \times l \times h) + (2 \times w \times h)$

Example 1

Find the surface area of the box.

$l = 7, w = 2, h = 6$

6 in.

2 in.

7 in.

$SA = (2 \times l \times w) + (2 \times l \times h) + (2 \times w \times h)$

$\quad = (2 \times 7 \times 2) + (2 \times 7 \times 6) + (2 \times 2 \times 6)$

$\quad = 28 + 84 + 24$

$\quad = 136$

The surface area is 136 in^2.

If a rectangular prism is a cube with side s, the length, width, and height all equal s. This simplifies the surface area formula.

> SA (cube) $= 6s^2$

s

s

s

Example 2

Find the surface area of the baseball box.

The box is a cube 3 in. on a side.

$$SA = 6s^2 = 6 \times 3^2$$

$$= 6 \times 9$$

$$= 54$$

3 in.

3 in.

3 in.

The surface area is 54 in².

Remember

According to the order of operations, you should multiply in an expression *before* you add. **[Page 99]**

If the triangular faces of a pyramid are congruent, you can use this shortcut to find the surface area of the pyramid:

SA = area of base + [(number of triangular faces) × (area of each face)]

Example 3

Find the surface area of the pyramid.

The base is a square 8 units on a side. Each face is a triangle with base 8 and height 6.

$$SA = (8 \times 8) + [4 \times (8 \times 6 \div 2)]$$

$$= 64 \quad + [4 \times \quad (24) \quad]$$

$$= 160$$

6

8

8

The surface area is 160 units².

HINT

The parentheses keys can help you use the order of operations. Enter (8 × 8) + 4 × (8 × 6 ÷ 2) = . The calculator should show the correct answer of 160.

Try It

Find the surface area of each solid.

a.

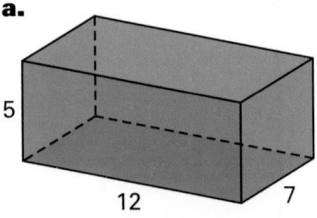

5

12

7

b.

4

4

4

c.

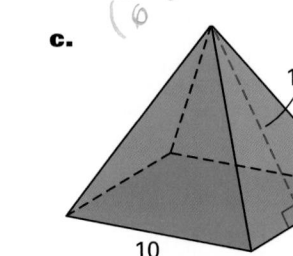

14

10

10

1. Can you use the formula for the surface area of a rectangular prism to find the surface area of a cube? Explain.

2. Suppose you couldn't remember the formula for the surface area of a rectangular prism. What would you do to find the surface area?

11-3 Exercises and Applications

Practice and Apply

Getting Started Find the surface area of each cube.

1.
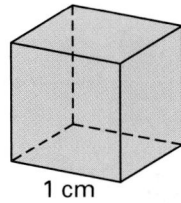
1 cm

2.
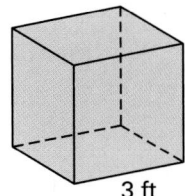
3 ft

3.
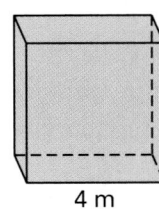
4 m

4.
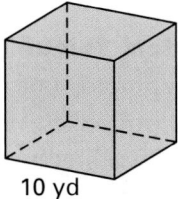
10 yd

Find the surface area.

5.
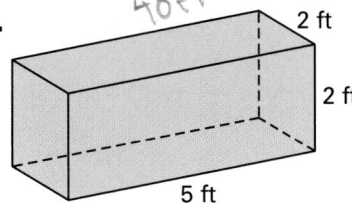
40 ft²
2 ft
2 ft
5 ft

6.
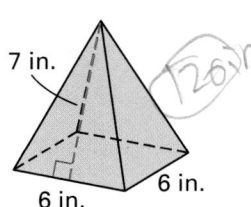
120 in²
7 in.
6 in.
6 in.

7.
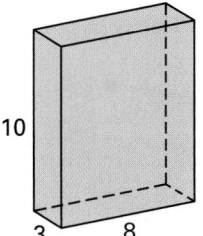
10
3   8

8.
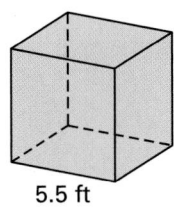
5.5 ft

9.
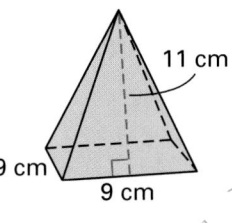
11 cm
9 cm   9 cm
279 cm²

10.
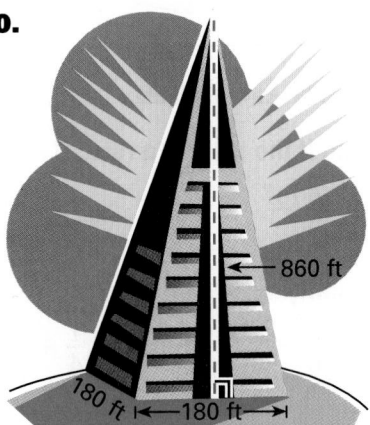
860 ft
180 ft ⟵180 ft⟶

Geometry Find the surface area of each rectangular prism.

11. $l = 4.1$ cm, $w = 3$ cm, $h = 6$ cm

12. $l = 10$ in., $w = 15$ in., $h = 12$ in.

13. The side of a number cube measures 1.5 cm. What is its surface area?

14. A trailer is 23 ft by 9 ft by 8 ft. How much aluminum siding is used for the trailer, including the top and the bottom?

15. **Test Prep** What is the surface area of a cube with 4-in. sides?

   Ⓐ 48 in²   Ⓑ 64 in²

   Ⓒ 96 in²   Ⓓ 144 in²

16. Mariana wants to cover the pyramid shown with gold foil.

   a. How many square feet of foil does she need?

   b. If the foil costs $0.02 per square foot, estimate how much Mariana should plan to spend.

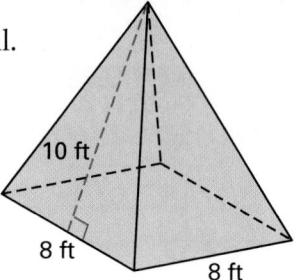

Problem Solving and Reasoning

17. **Critical Thinking** The Wrap'n'Pack gift wrapping company has three different-sized medium boxes. What is the average surface area for a medium box?

Medium Boxes (in.)		
	A	**B**	**C**
Length	12	20	8
Width	12	16	6
Height	12	24	2

18. **Critical Thinking** Which solid has the greater surface area? Explain.

   a.

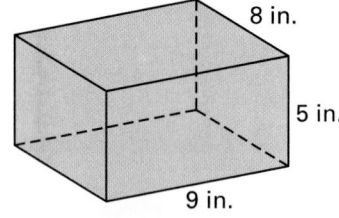

8 in.

5 in.

9 in.

   b.

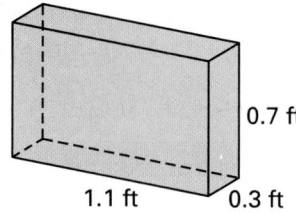

0.7 ft

1.1 ft   0.3 ft

Mixed Review

State if the ratio is a rate. *[Lesson 10-3]*

19. $\dfrac{6 \text{ mi}}{4 \text{ hr}}$ **20.** $\dfrac{1 \text{ kitten}}{7 \text{ ounces}}$ **21.** $\dfrac{6 \text{ in.}}{11 \text{ in.}}$ **22.** 7:9

Simplify. *[Lesson 6-2]*

23. $\dfrac{5}{6} - \dfrac{2}{3}$ **24.** $\dfrac{1}{4} + \dfrac{7}{11}$ **25.** $\dfrac{3}{4} - \dfrac{2}{7}$ **26.** $\dfrac{10}{12} + \dfrac{1}{6}$ **27.** $\dfrac{4}{9} - \dfrac{2}{7}$

Surface Area of a Cylinder

▶ **Lesson Link** You've found the surface areas of several polyhedrons. Now you'll find surface areas of a type of solid with curved surfaces. ◀

You'll Learn ...

■ to find the surface area of a cylinder

... How It's Used

Aluminum can manu-facturers calculate surface area when determining the amount of aluminum needed for a given size can.

Explore   Cylinders

Caution: Curves Ahead!

Materials: Cans of food (e.g., soup can, juice can) without labels, Graph paper

1. What is the shape of a can's label after it has been removed and flattened? Draw a "label" for your can. It should be sized to fit exactly on your can.

2. What is the shape of a can's bases? Add two bases to your label to make a net for your can.

3. Cut your net out and tape it together to form a solid. Does your solid have the same size and shape as the can?

4. Describe the relationship between the circumference of the base of your can and what you drew in Steps 1 and 2.

5. Estimate the surface area of your can.

Learn   Surface Area of a Cylinder

A cylinder has two bases. Each base is a circle. The side can be unrolled to form a rectangle. Notice that the length of the rectangle equals the circumference of the circle.

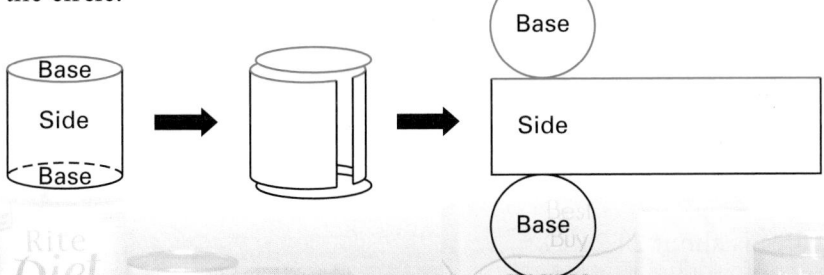

11-4 • Surface Area of a Cylinder **593**

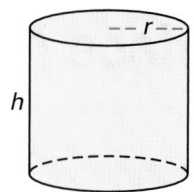

Remember

The area formula for a circle is $\pi \times radius^2$. You can use 3.14 as an approximation for π.

[Pages 247 and 250]

You can use these relationships to find the surface area of a cylinder whose height is h and whose bases have a radius of r.

SA = (2 × area of base) + (**area of rectangular side**)

= (2 × area of base) + (**height of side** × **length of side**)

= (2 × area of base) + (**height of cylinder × circumference of base**)

= (**2 × πr^2**) + (**h** × **$2\pi r$**)

$$SA = (2 \times \pi r^2) + (h \times 2\pi r)$$

Example 1

Find the surface area of the ice cream container. Use 3.14 for π.

$r = 2.5$ in. $h = 6.5$ in.

SA = (2 × πr^2) + (h × $2\pi r$)

SA ≈ (2 × 3.14 × 2.5 × 2.5) + (6.5 × 2 × 3.14 × 2.5)

≈ **39.25** + **102.05**

≈ **141.3**

The surface area is about 141.3 in².

If you know the diameter of the base of a cylinder, you can find the radius by dividing the diameter by 2.

Example 2

Find the surface area. Use 3.14 for π.

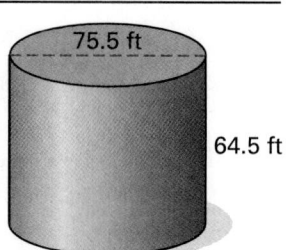

If the diameter is 75.5, the radius is half of that, or 37.75.

SA =   (2 × πr^2)   +   (h × $2\pi r$)

≈ (2 × 3.14 × 37.75 × 37.75) + (64.5 × 2 × 3.14 × 37.75)

≈   8,949.4   +   15,291

≈   24,240.4

The surface area is about 24,240.4 ft².

Chip's Cheesesticks are sold in half-cylinder packages like the one shown. Ricardo and Maritess want to know the surface area of a package.

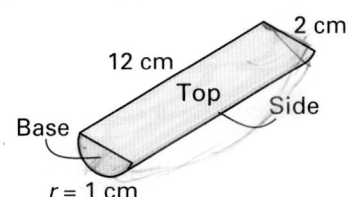

2 cm

12 cm

Top

Base   Side

r = 1 cm

Maritess thinks ...

I'll add the areas up one at a time.

The rectangular top is 12 × 2, or **24 cm²**.

The 2 half-circles can be put together to make one full circle. The full circle is $\pi \times 1^2$, or about **3.14 cm²**.

The curved side is a rectangle with a height of 12 and a base of half the circle's circumference. Half of the circle's circumference is π × diameter ÷ 2, or about 3.14 × 2 ÷ 2, or 3.14. The curved side is 12 × 3.14, or about **37.68 cm²**.

The total surface area is about 24 + 3.14 + 37.68 = **64.82**.

The surface area is about 65 cm².

Ricardo thinks ...

I'll use the formula SA = $(2 \times \pi r^2) + (h \times 2\pi r)$ to find the surface area of a complete cylinder, and then divide by 2.

SA ≈ [(2 × 3.14 × 1²) + (12 × 2 × 3.14 × 1)] ÷ 2

=   81.64   ÷ 2 = 40.82 cm².

The rectangular top is 12 cm by 2 cm, for an area of 24 cm².
I'll add that to the half cylinder. 40.82 cm² + 24 cm² = 64.82 cm².

The surface area is about 65 cm².

What do you think?

1. Which method do you think is easier? Why?

2. How would the solution change if the package had no top?

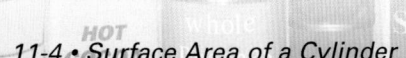

1. Describe how you could make a cylinder.

2. How would you find the surface area of a cylinder with a bottom base but no top base? With no bases?

11-4 Exercises and Applications

Practice and Apply

Getting Started Find the circumference of each cylinder. Use 3.14 for π.

1.
5 cm

2.
5 in.

3.
2 ft

4.
3 m

Find the surface area of each cylinder. Use 3.14 for π.

5. 1.5 m   5 m

6.

5 in.
6 in.

7. 1 in.
5 in.

8. 7 mm
7 mm

9.
4 ft
2 ft

Given the radius and the height of each cylinder, find the surface area. Use 3.14 for π.

10. $r = 7, h = 10$ **11.** $r = 1, h = 21$ **12.** $r = 5, h = 3.5$ **13.** $r = 12, h = 16$

14. Industry A can of cake frosting is 4.5 inches tall and has a 3 inch diameter.

  a. If there is no overlap, what is the area of the can's label?

  b. What is the surface area of the entire can?

15. If a cylindrical gift box costs $0.01 per square inch to produce, how much does it cost to make each box?

a.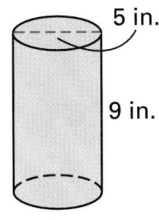
5 in.
9 in.

b.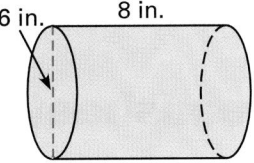
6 in. 8 in.

16. **Test Prep** Choose the best estimate of the surface area of the cylinder shown.

Ⓐ 90 cm²   Ⓑ 110 cm²

Ⓒ 360 cm²   Ⓓ 540 cm²

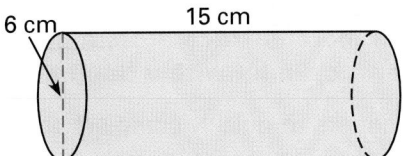
6 cm   15 cm

Problem Solving and Reasoning

17. **Choose a Strategy** Tito has found the surface area of 4 cylinders and recorded the data in the bar graph. The surface area of a 5th cylinder is greater than the 2nd but less than the 3rd. Find a possible height and diameter for the 5th cylinder.

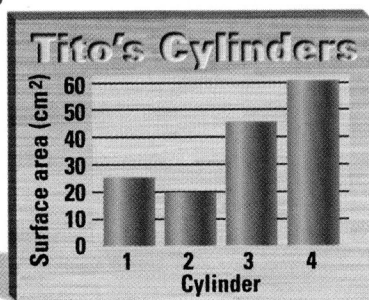

Tito's Cylinders

18. **Critical Thinking** How much advertising space is there on the label of a can with a diameter of 3 in. and a height of 4 in.? Explain.

19. **Critical Thinking** Some doll collectors display their dolls in cases like the one shown. The back of the case is a 12 in. by 5 in. rectangle. The bottom and top pieces are both half-circles. The front is clear plastic. What is the surface area of the entire case? Describe how you found it and explain your reasoning.

Mixed Review

State if the pair of ratios form a proportion. *[Lesson 10-4]*

20. $\frac{2}{9}$ and $\frac{9}{2}$ **21.** $\frac{5}{10}$ and $\frac{1}{2}$ **22.** $\frac{4}{7}$ and $\frac{2}{3}$

23. $\frac{7}{27}$ and $\frac{21}{54}$ **24.** $\frac{4}{10}$ and $\frac{110}{27}$

25. $\frac{1}{2}$ and $\frac{32}{16}$ **26.** $\frac{1}{8}$ and $\frac{3}{24}$ **27.** $\frac{10}{16}$ and $\frac{2}{4}$ **28.** $\frac{9}{4}$ and $\frac{36}{36}$ **29.** $\frac{12}{5}$ and $\frac{60}{144}$

Simplify. *[Lesson 10-11]*

30. 62% of 200   **31.** 30% of 58   **32.** 78% of 24   **33.** 12% of 2

TECHNOLOGY

Using a Spreadsheet • Finding the Surface Area of a Cylinder

Problem: Which has more surface area, a cylinder with a height of 5 cm and a radius of 2 cm, or a cylinder with a height of 2 cm and a radius of 5 cm?

You can use spreadsheets to quickly complete the calculations.

	A	B	C	D	E
1	Height	Radius	Lateral SA	Base area	Total SA
2					

1 Enter the information into the spreadsheet as shown.

	A	B	C	D	E
1	Height	Radius	Lateral SA	Base area	Total SA
2	5	2	62.8	12.56	87.92
3	2	5	62.8	78.50	219.80

2 In cell A2, enter 5. In cell B2, enter 2. In cell C2, enter the formula =2*3.14*A2*B2. In cell D2, enter the formula =3.14*(B2)^2. In cell E2, enter the formula =C2+2*D2.

3 Copy the contents of row 2 down to row 3. Then, change the height value to 2 and the radius value to 5.

Solution: A cylinder with a height of 2 cm and a radius of 5 cm has more surface area than a cylinder with a height of 5 cm and a radius of 2 cm.

TRY IT

a. Which has more surface area, a cylinder with a height of 3 cm and a radius of 4 cm, or a cylinder with a height of 4 cm and a radius of 3 cm?

b. If the height and radius of a cylinder must be whole numbers whose sum is 10, how much should the height and radius be to get the cylinder with the largest surface area?

ON YOUR OWN

▶ Why do you think it's necessary to type an = at the beginning of each formula?

▶ Why might a person want to set up a spreadsheet to calculate the surface area of a cylinder instead of using a calculator or pencil and paper?

In this section, you've used the dimensions of solids to find their surface areas. Now you'll answer a question that often faces package designers: If you know the surface area of a solid, how do you find the dimensions?

The Grapes of Wrap

Materials: Ruler

The Play-Brite Company has invented a new toy, known as a Squidge. The Squidge is a foam cylinder that can be decorated with different plastic legs, hands, mouths, eyes, and hair. You must design and decorate a package for the Squidge. Begin by drawing a net that meets the following conditions:

- It must fold together into a rectangular prism.

- It must have a surface area that is as close to 100 cm² as possible.

1. If your first try is too far below 100 cm², how could you increase the surface area? If it is too far above 100 cm², how could you decrease the surface area?

2. When you have a net that is between 90 cm² and 110 cm², cut it out. Label the lengths of each edge on each face.

3. Add designs and color to the package to make it as attractive as possible. Don't forget to show on the box why the Squidge is an ideal toy.

Classify each solid. If it is a polyhedron, tell how many vertices, edges, and faces it has.

1.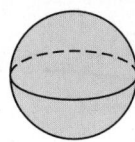

2.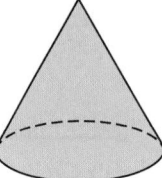

3.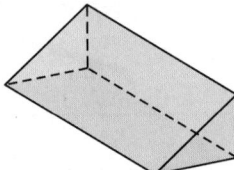

4.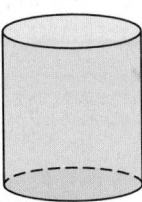

5.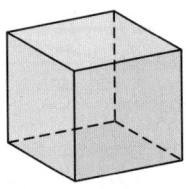

6.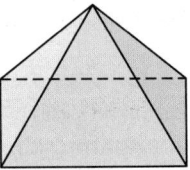

7. 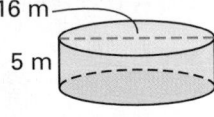 Describe the difference between a rectangular pyramid and a rectangular prism.

Find the surface area of each figure.

8. 16 m
5 m
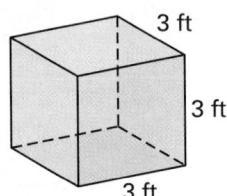

9. 3 ft
3 ft
3 ft
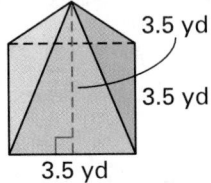

10. 3.5 yd
3.5 yd
3.5 yd

11. Find the surface area of a rectangular prism that measures 20 cm by 40 cm by 60 cm.

Test Prep

In order for a shape to be a prism, it must have two congruent bases that are both polygons.

12. Which of the following is **not** a prism?

Ⓐ 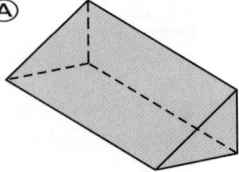   Ⓑ 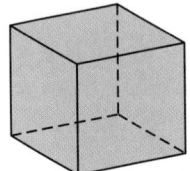   Ⓒ   Ⓓ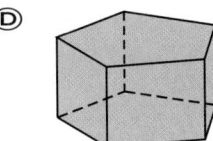

A Pet From a Different World

What would it be like having a pet from another planet? Would it breathe a different kind of air? Live at a different temperature? Need different kinds of light? Would you need a self-contained room where the environment could be carefully controlled? It might be more trouble than keeping a gerbil, but think of how much fun it would be to watch.

In many ways, keeping fish is like having an alien pet. An aquarium is a self-contained room with a controlled environment. Aquariums often need equipment to maintain the air, the temperature, and the light. But fish can be so interesting to watch that many people enjoy the challenge of putting together an interesting aquarium.

The kind of aquarium you need depends upon the number and types of fish you have. One thing you'll need for certain is an understanding of surface area and volume. After all, what aquarium can be complete without a little mathematics?

1 What does it mean to have a room with a "controlled environment"?

2 Why might it be interesting to watch fish?

3 How could a person who is putting together an aquarium use mathematics?

Three-Dimensional Figures

► Lesson Link In the last section, you learned to calculate surface areas of solids. Now you'll draw pictures of solids. ◄

You'll Learn ...

■ to draw the front, side, and top views of a solid

... How It's Used

Technical artists make drawings of the front, side, and top views of objects when explaining how complex machines work.

Explore Three-Dimensional Figures

Something's Fishy!

Materials: Centimeter cubes

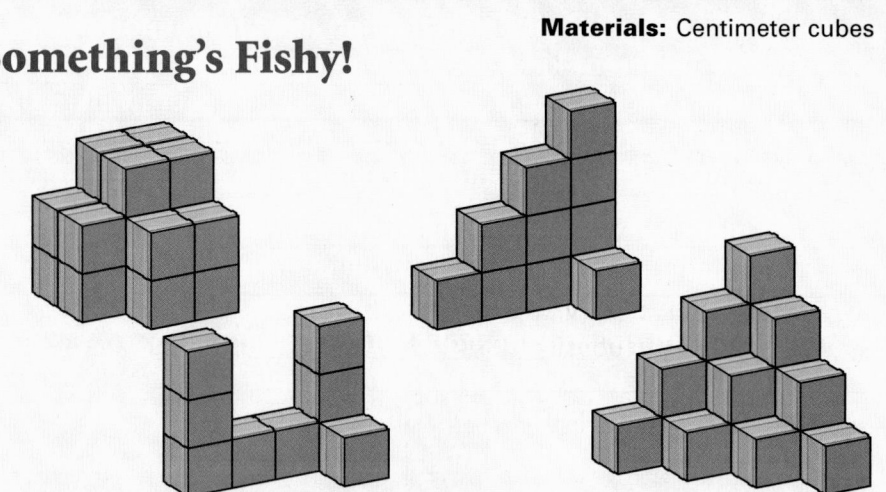

The stacks of crates pictured are stored in the Fish Farm warehouse. The manager records each stack by drawing what the crates look like from above and using numbers to show how many crates are in each stack.

Stack of crates

Manager's drawing

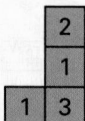

1. Build each stack of crates using centimeter cubes. Draw the crates as seen from above, as the manager did. Be sure to write in the number of crates for each square in your sketch.

2. Can you determine the number of cubes needed to build a stack from the manager's drawing? Explain.

3. Can you determine the number of cubes needed to build a stack from a picture of the stack? Explain.

4. Is it harder to draw a diagram of a stack with a small number of cubes, or a large number of cubes? Explain.

Recall that a solid is a three-dimensional figure. Solids are often drawn in perspective to show that they are three-dimensional.

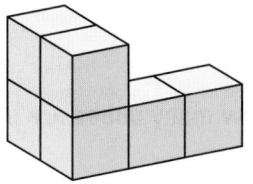

Solids can also be drawn using a flat view. Flat drawings show the solid from one view only. In order to record what the solid looks like, you usually need to show three views: front, side, and top.

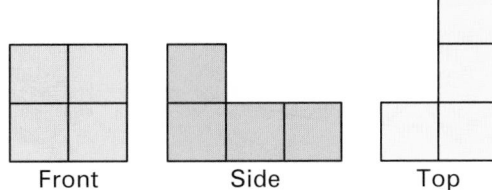

▶ **Language Link**

The flat drawings that show the front, side, and top views of a solid are also known as *orthographic projections*. A three-dimensional picture of a solid is an *isometric projection*.

Example 1

Draw front, side, and top views of the solid. There are no hidden cubes.

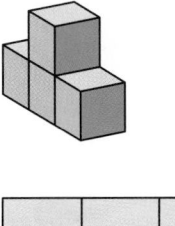

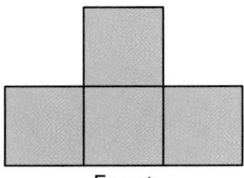

Front

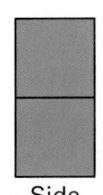

Side

Top

Try It

Draw front, side, and top views of the solid. There are no hidden cubes.

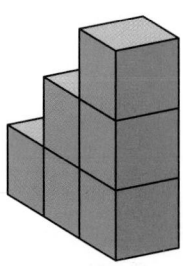

A solid also has other views, such as the back view and the bottom view. Because these views are mirror images of the front, side, and top views, they are not necessary when drawing a solid.

Check | **Your Understanding**

1. Describe a solid with the same front, side, and top views.

2. Could you use the front, side, and top views of a solid to build it? Explain.

Practice and Apply

Getting Started State how many cubes are in each solid.

1.

2.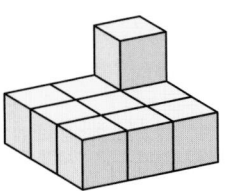

3.

4.

Draw the front, side, and top views of each solid.

5.

6.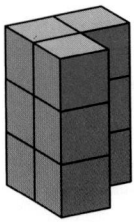

7.

8.

9.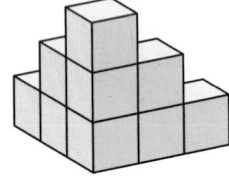

10.

11.

12.

Patterns Describe each pattern. How many cubes are in the eighth solid of each pattern?

13.

14.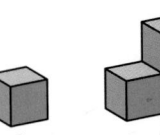

15. **Problem Solving** Each cube in the solid shown is 1.7 cm by 1.7 cm by 1.7 cm.

   a. How many cubes are in the solid?

   b. How tall is the solid at its highest point?

   c. How wide is the solid at its widest point?

16. **Test Prep** How many cubes are in the tower?

(A) 6   (B) 10

(C) 14   (D) 18

Problem Solving and Reasoning

17. Critical Thinking Tell if each set of views makes a prism. Explain.

a.

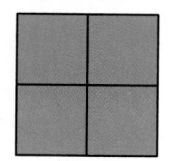

Front   Side   Top

b.

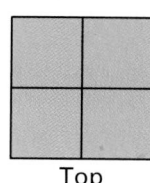

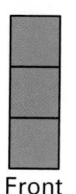

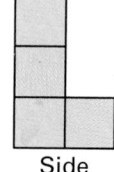

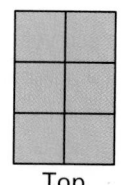

Front   Side   Top

18. Critical Thinking Each solid is made up of 1-centimeter cubes. Find the surface area of each. Explain your reasoning.

a. 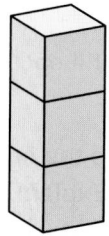   **b.**    **c.**    **d.**

19. Communicate Suppose you have 24 cubes. Describe or draw the dimensions of three different rectangular prisms you can make with the cubes. Explain.

Mixed Review

Solve each proportion. *[Lesson 10-5]*

20. $\frac{4}{6} = \frac{8}{x}$ **21.** $\frac{86}{f} = \frac{43}{24}$ **22.** $\frac{5}{y} = \frac{42}{35}$ **23.** $\frac{9}{21} = \frac{r}{7}$ **24.** $\frac{p}{11} = \frac{33}{27}$

Convert each to a percent. *[Lesson 10-10]*

25. 1.56   **26.** 0.723   **27.** $\frac{11}{20}$ **28.** 0.34   **29.** $\frac{7}{25}$ **30.** $1\frac{3}{10}$

Convert each to a fraction or mixed number in lowest terms. *[Lesson 10-10]*

31. 67%   **32.** 83.4%   **33.** 250%   **34.** 99%   **35.** 1%   **36.** 0.6%

Exploring Volume

You'll Learn ...

■ to calculate the volume of a rectangular prism

... How It's Used

Paramedics use volume to determine the amount of oxygen in an oxygen tank.

Vocabulary

volume

cubic units

▶ **Lesson Link** You've learned to sketch the different views of a solid. Now you'll find how many cubes it takes to fill the space inside a solid. ◀

Explore | Volume

How Many Beans in a Box?

Materials: Graph paper, Dried beans, Centimeter cubes, Scissors, Tape

1. Using graph paper and tape, build an open box with a 6-by-6 cm base and a height of 6 cm. Build another open box with a 5-by-12 base and a height of 5. Do not make lids for the boxes.

2. Fill each box with beans. Record the number of beans that fit in each box.

3. Determine the number of centimeter cubes needed to fill each box. Which box holds the least? Explain.

4. Which material do you think most accurately measures the space inside each box? Which measures it least accurately? Explain.

Learn | Exploring Volume

Recall that two-dimensional figures are measured by their *area*. You can find a figure's area by counting the number of *square units* it contains.

Three-dimensional objects can be measured by their **volume** . The volume of an object is the number of **cubic units** it contains. You can find the volume of a rectangular prism by counting cubes.

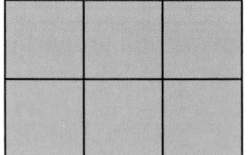

Area = 6 square units

Recall that the exponent 2 means to multiply the base number by itself.

$$6^2 \text{ (read "6 } squared\text{")} = 6 \times 6 = 36$$

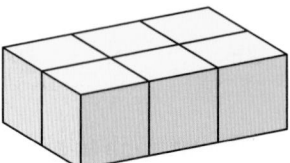

Volume = 6 cubic units

The exponent 3 means to use the base number as a factor 3 times.

$$5^3 \text{ (read "5 } cubed\text{")} = 5 \times 5 \times 5 = 125$$

Examples

1 Find the volume of the rectangular prism.

Each layer of the prism is 6 cubes by 2 cubes. This equals 6 × 2, or 12 cubes.

There are 4 layers in the prism. At 12 cubes per layer, this equals 4 × 12, or 48 cubes.

The volume is 48 cubic units. A shorthand way of writing this is 48 units³.

2 Tropical Tanks received the shipment of cubical aquarium tanks shown. Each tank measures 1 m by 1 m by 1 m. Find the volume of the shipment.

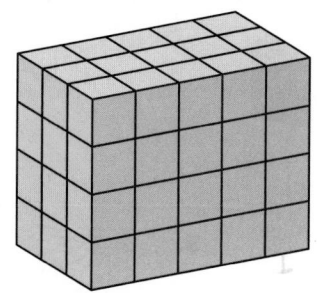

One layer is 5 m by 3 m. That's 5 × 3, or 15 m². There are 4 layers. At 15 m² per layer, this equals 15 × 4, or 60 m³.

Try It

Find the volume of the prisms.

a.

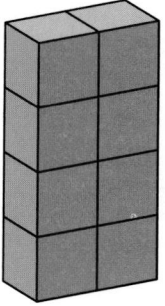

b.

c.

d.

▶ **Science Link**

There are two types of aquarium tanks: glass and acrylic. Glass tanks are cheaper and harder to scratch. Acrylic tanks are lighter, harder to break, and don't distort images of the fish as much as glass tanks. Most pet store owners recommend glass tanks.

Check | Your Understanding

1. Why is area measured in square units and volume measured in cubic units?

2. Is the volume of a solid the same as its surface area? Explain.

Practice and Apply

Getting Started Find the volume of each solid.

1.

2.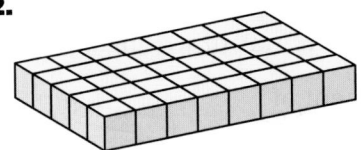

3.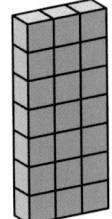

Find the volume of each solid.

4.

5.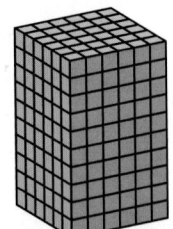

6.

7.

8.

9.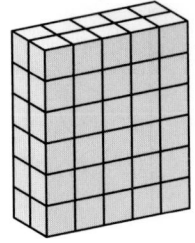

10. Geometry What is the volume of a rectangular prism that measures 8 cubes by 5 cubes by 4 cubes?

11. Consumer When sugar cubes are produced, they are put into tightly packed boxes for purchasing. If the box of sugar cubes shown is 3 cubes high, how many sugar cubes are in the box?

12. **Test Prep** Each cube in the aquarium shown measures 1 ft by 1 ft by 1 ft. What is the aquarium's volume?

Ⓐ 1 ft³

Ⓑ 24 ft³

Ⓒ 26 ft³

Ⓓ 52 ft²

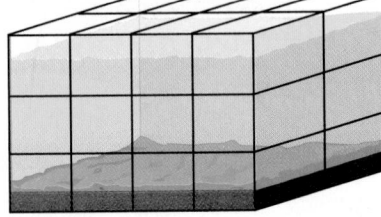

13. Sonjay has 32 1-inch cubes and a box that is 5 in. by 4 in. by 2 in. Will all of Sonjay's blocks fit into the box?

Problem Solving and Reasoning

14. Critical Thinking Each cube in each solid shown measures 1 cm by 1 cm by 1 cm. Order the solids from least to greatest according to their volumes. Would your list be different if you ordered the solids by surface areas? Explain.

a.  **b.** 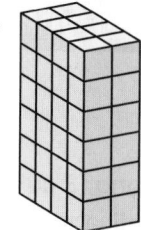 **c.**

15. Choose a Strategy Raquel is selling cookies for a school fund-raiser. The Raisin Delight variety comes in square packages. Each shipment of Raisin Delights is made up of 12 square packages. How many different ways can the 12 packages be arranged to form a rectangular shipment? List the different ways.

16. Critical Thinking Use the views shown to find the volume of each solid.

Problem Solving

STRATEGIES

- Look for a Pattern
- Make an Organized List
- Make a Table
- Guess and Check
- Work Backward
- Use Logical Reasoning
- Draw a Diagram
- Solve a Simpler Problem

a.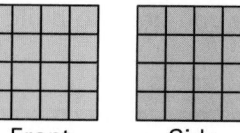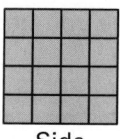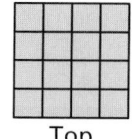
　　Front　　Side　　Top

b.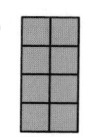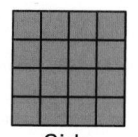
　　Front　　Side　　Top

c.
　　Front　　Side　　Top

Mixed Review

Find the unit rate for each. *[Lesson 10-6]*

17. $\dfrac{9 \text{ mi}}{3 \text{ min}}$ 　　**18.** $\dfrac{15 \text{ yd}^2}{5 \text{ rooms}}$ 　　**19.** $\dfrac{45 \text{ bananas}}{\$9}$ 　　**20.** $\dfrac{14 \text{ lb}}{4 \text{ sacks}}$

21. $\dfrac{19 \text{ m}}{60 \text{ sec}}$ 　　**22.** $\dfrac{28 \text{ elephants}}{27 \text{ mi}^2}$ 　　**23.** $\dfrac{9 \text{ worms}}{2 \text{ in}^2}$ 　　**24.** $\dfrac{4 \text{ dots}}{34 \text{ sec}}$

Estimate what percent of each figure is shaded. [Lesson 10-9]

25. 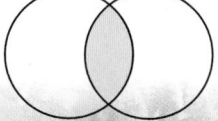 　　**26.** 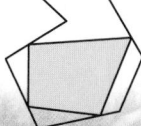 　　**27.** 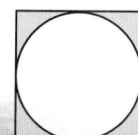 　　**28.**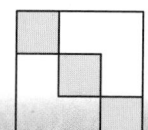

Calculating Volume

You'll Learn ...

■ to use the volume formula for rectangular prisms

... How It's Used

Phlebotomists use volume to determine how much blood they have drawn from blood donors.

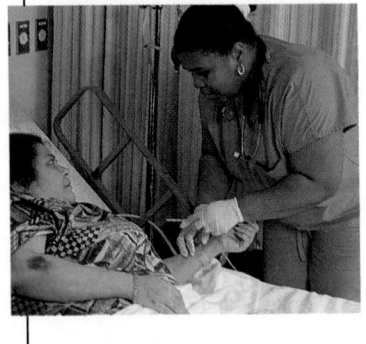

▶ **Lesson Link**   You know how to find the volume of a prism by counting the number of cubes that fill the space inside. Now you'll find the volume using a formula. ◀

Explore | Calculating Volume

Materials: Centimeter cubes

Toy Stories

1. Build a prism 4 cubes long, 3 cubes wide, and 1 cube high. Write an expression using multiplication for the total number of cubes needed.

2. Build a second 4-cube-by-3-cube "story" on top of the first. Write an expression using multiplication that gives the total number of cubes needed for the entire prism.

3. Add a third story and write an expression using multiplication for the total number of cubes needed for the entire prism.

4. If you know the length, width, and height of a prism, what is the fastest way to determine how many cubes you need to build the prism? Explain.

Learn | Calculating Volume

The volume of a rectangular prism is measured by the number of cubic units that can fit inside it. One way to find the volume is to count the number of cubes inside the prism.

You can also use a formula. The volume of a rectangular prism is the product of the prism's length, width, and height.

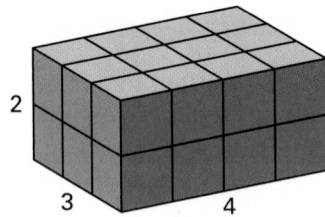

| Volume = length × width × height |

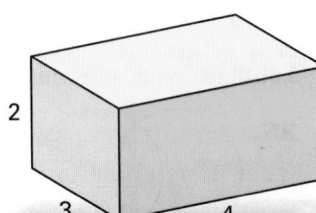

Examples

1 Find the volume of the rectangular prism.

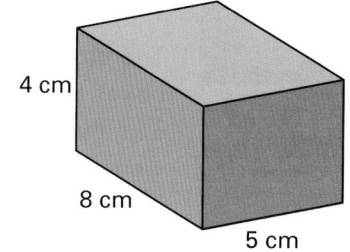

$V = l \times w \times h$ Write the formula.

    $= 8 \times 5 \times 4$ Substitute known values.

    $= 160$ Multiply.

The volume is 160 cm^3.

2 One gallon of water has a volume of 231 in^3. Find the volume of the tank in cubic inches and in gallons.

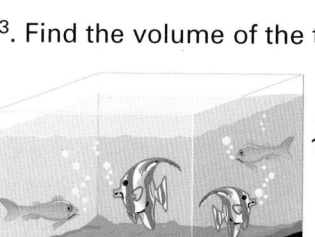

$V = l \times w \times h$ Write the formula.

    $= 35 \times 15 \times 11$ Substitute known values.

    $= 5775$ Multiply.

The volume is 5775 in^3.

Every 231 in^3 of water in the tank represents 1 gallon.

Therefore, the total number of gallons in the tank is $5775 \div 231 = 25$.

The tank has a volume of 25 gallons.

> ► **Science Link**
>
> The amount of space a fish needs varies from species to species. In general, saltwater fish require more space than freshwater fish of the same size.

If you know the volume of a rectangular prism and two of its dimensions, you can find the third dimension.

Example 3

Becky built an 8 ft by 6 ft sandbox for her best friend. She bought 48 ft^3 of sand for the box. How deep was the sand?

$V = l \times w \times h$ Write the formula.

$48 = 8 \times 6 \times h$ Substitute known values.

$48 = 48h$ Simplify. Think: What number times 48 equals 48?

$1 = h$ Use mental math.

The sand was 1 ft deep.

Try It

a. Find the volume of a rectangular prism measuring 7 in. by 5 in. by 3 in.

b. Find the length of a rectangular prism with a width of 15 in., a height of 8 in., and a volume of 2160 in^3.

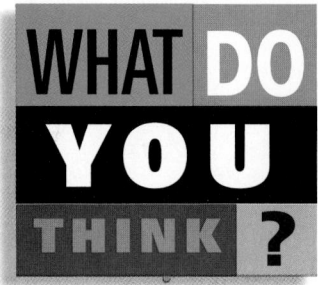

WHAT DO YOU THINK?

A toy manufacturer makes 1 in. cubical building blocks. The blocks are packed in boxes measuring 12 in. by 6 in. by 4 in. Tyreka and Larry want to know how many blocks are in a box.

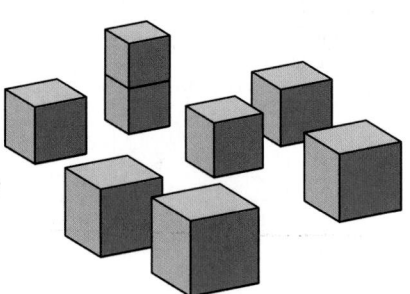

Tyreka thinks ...

I'll find the volume by counting the blocks and using multiplication.

The top layer has 6 rows with 12 blocks in each row. This equals 6×12, or 72 blocks.

There are 4 layers with 72 blocks in each layer. That equals 4×72, or 288 blocks.

There are 288 blocks in each box.

Larry thinks ...

I'll use the volume formula.

$V = l \times w \times h$

$V = 12 \times 6 \times 4 = 288$

There are 288 blocks in each box.

What do you think?

1. Tyreka says her method uses multiplication. Did Larry's method also involve multiplication? Explain.

2. Which method is the easier method to understand? Why?

Check | Your Understanding

1. Can you use the formula $V = l \times w \times h$ to find the volume of any solid? Explain.

2. Describe an easy way to find the volume of a cube.

Practice and Apply

Getting Started Find the volume of each solid.

1.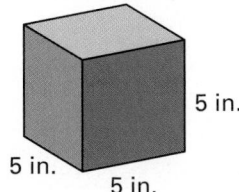
5 in.
5 in.
5 in.

2.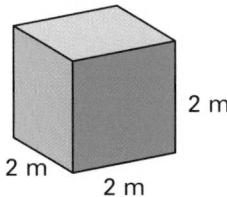
2 m
2 m
2 m

3.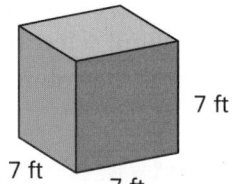
7 ft
7 ft
7 ft

Find the volume of each solid.

4.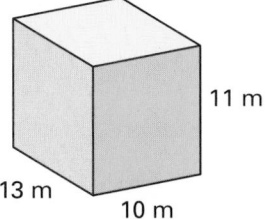
11 m
13 m
10 m

5.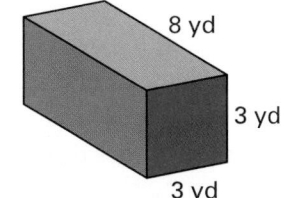
8 yd
3 yd
3 yd

6.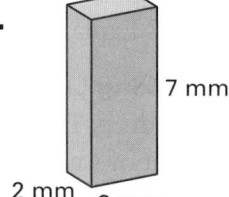
7 mm
2 mm
3 mm

7.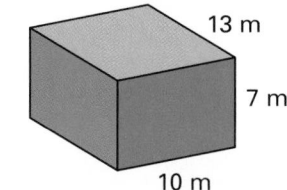
13 m
7 m
10 m

8.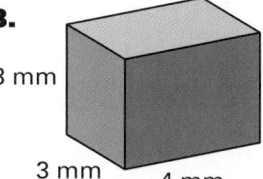
3 mm
3 mm
4 mm

9.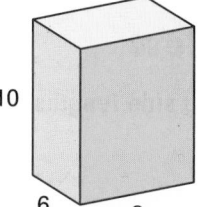
10
6
8

10.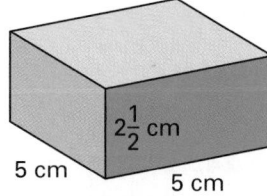
$2\frac{1}{2}$ cm
5 cm
5 cm

11.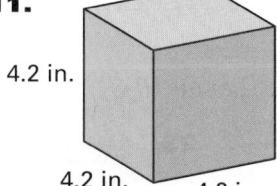
4.2 in.
4.2 in.
4.2 in.

12.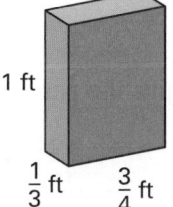
1 ft
$\frac{1}{3}$ ft
$\frac{3}{4}$ ft

13. Geography The Great Barrier Reef along the east coast of Australia is the world's largest coral reef. The coral reef tank at The Great Barrier Reef Aquarium in Townsville, Australia, is 38 meters long, 17 meters wide, and 4.5 meters deep. What is the volume of the tank?

14. Number Sense The volume of an aquarium is 5000 cubic inches. If the width is 20 inches and the height is 10 inches, what is the length?

15. **Test Prep** The length of a box is 28 inches. The width is 10 inches. What other information about the box do you need in order to find its volume?

Ⓐ The weight   Ⓑ The height

Ⓒ The contents   Ⓓ The surface area

16. The size of a goldfish depends on the size of the pond or tank it is in. A small pond for a dozen 4-inch goldfish should be about 6 feet long, 4 feet wide, and 1.5 feet deep. What is the volume of this pond?

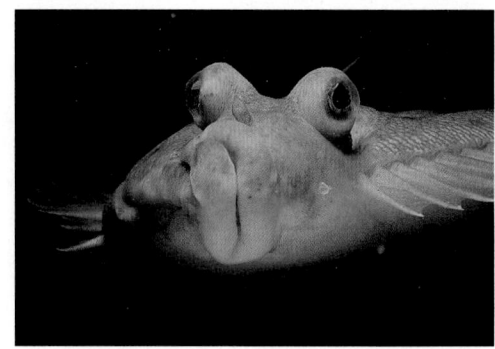

Problem Solving and Reasoning

17. **Critical Thinking** The volume of a gallon of water is about 231 cubic inches. If a 25-gallon aquarium is 32 inches long and 15 inches wide, how deep is it? Explain.

18. **Critical Thinking** One area in Water-Play Park has a 15 ft by 20 ft pool that is 12 feet deep. The pool is filled at the start of summer at the rate of 1200 cubic feet of water per hour. How many hours does it take to fill the pool? Explain.

Mixed Review

Find the missing side lengths for each pair of similar figures. *[Lesson 10-7]*

19.

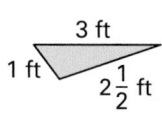
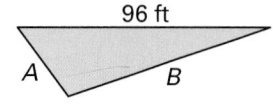

20.

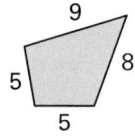
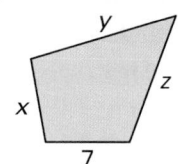

For each figure, give the percent that is shaded. *[Lesson 10-8]*

21.

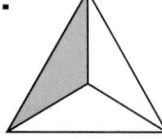

22.

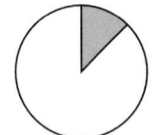

23.

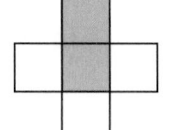

24.

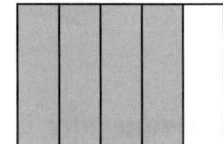

Project Progress

Multiply the length, width, and height of your aquarium to find its volume. Find the volume of your classroom in cubic inches. Decide if your aquarium will fit comfortably in the classroom or if you will have to make adjustments.

Problem Solving

Understand
Plan
Solve
Look Back

In this section, you've learned to find the volume of a rectangular prism given its dimensions. Now you'll determine what dimensions you should choose for an aquarium tank with a given volume.

A Pet from a Different World

Materials: Ruler

You've decided to build a 50 gal tank for tropical fish. A 50 gal tank has a volume of 11,550 in^3.

1. You want your tank to have a height of 22 in. Find a possible length and width for your tank. Make sure the length and width are reasonable.

2. Draw a net of your tank. (Remember, it's open-topped.)

3. You need to know how much glass to buy, so find the surface area of your tank, including the bottom.

4. Repeat Steps 1–3, finding a *different* possible length and width for your tank.

5. Would your two possible tanks cost the same amount to build? Explain.

6. Some aquarium owners use the rule "1 inch of fish per gallon of water." You've decided to stock your aquarium with the following species.

Species	Length (in.)
White Cloud Mountainfish	1
Zebra Danios	2
Red-Striped Rasboras	3
Cherry Barbs	$1\frac{1}{2}$

Choose the largest possible collection of fish for your aquarium. You should have at least 6 of each species. Explain how you determined how many of each species of fish should be in your collection.

Geometry Classify each solid. If it is a polyhedron, tell how many vertices, edges, and faces it has.

1. 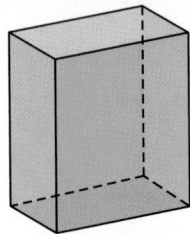　**2.** 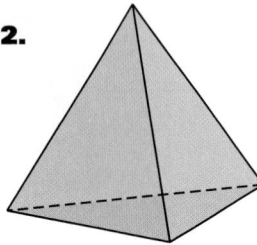　**3.** 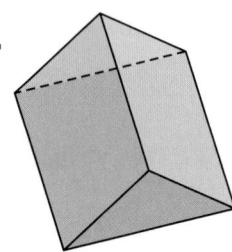　**4.**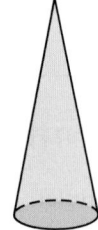

5. **Test Prep** Which of the following is **not** true of all polyhedrons?

Ⓐ The volume is usually measured in cubic units.

Ⓑ All of the faces are flat.

Ⓒ There are two bases that are the same size and shape.

Ⓓ None of these.

Draw the front, side, and top views of each solid. There are no hidden cubes.

6. 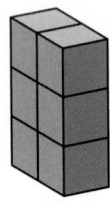　**7.** 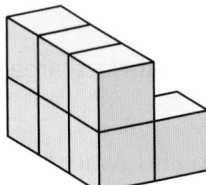　**8.** 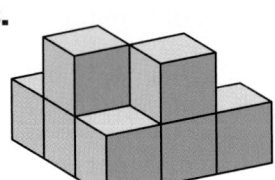　**9.**

Test Prep

You only need to multiply two numbers together to find the area of one face of a rectangular prism. If a problem asking for the area of one face gives you three numbers, at least one of the numbers is unnecessary information.

10. A good fish tank has a large surface at the top to provide the most oxygen possible. Which fish tank has the greatest area on top?

Ⓐ 24 in. deep, 24 in. long, 14 in. wide

Ⓑ 32 in. deep, 23 in. long, 13 in. wide

Ⓒ 20 in. deep, 22 in. long, 12 in. wide

Ⓓ 22 in. deep, 26 in. long, 11 in. wide

REVIEW 11B

Euler's Formula

Leonhard Euler, a Swiss mathematician who lived from 1707 to 1783, revised almost every branch of mathematics known at the time. He discovered a relationship among the faces (*F*), the vertices (*V*), and the edges (*E*) of polyhedrons.

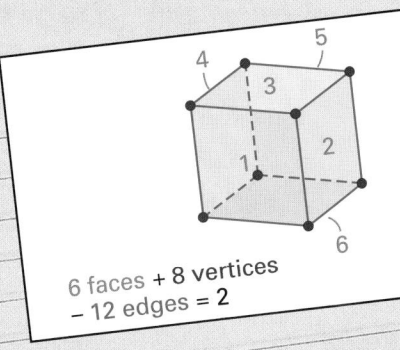

6 faces + 8 vertices
− 12 edges = 2

$$F + V - E = 2$$

If you know the numbers for two of the above values, you can use the formula to find the third.

Try It

For each polyhedron, count the number of faces, the number of vertices, and the number of edges. Verify that Euler's formula works for these polyhedrons.

1.
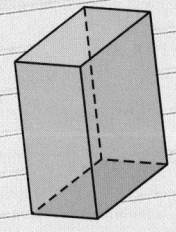

2.
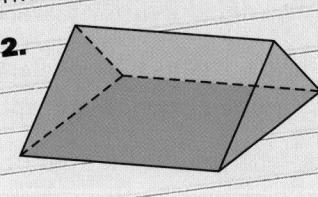

3.
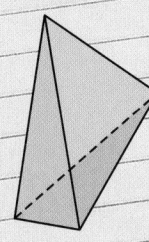

4.
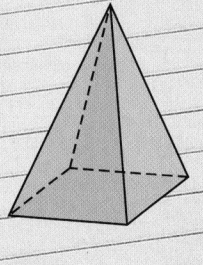

Use Euler's formula to complete the chart below.

	Number of faces	Number of vertices	Number of edges
5.	7	10	18
6.	8		24
7.		16	

Graphic Organizer

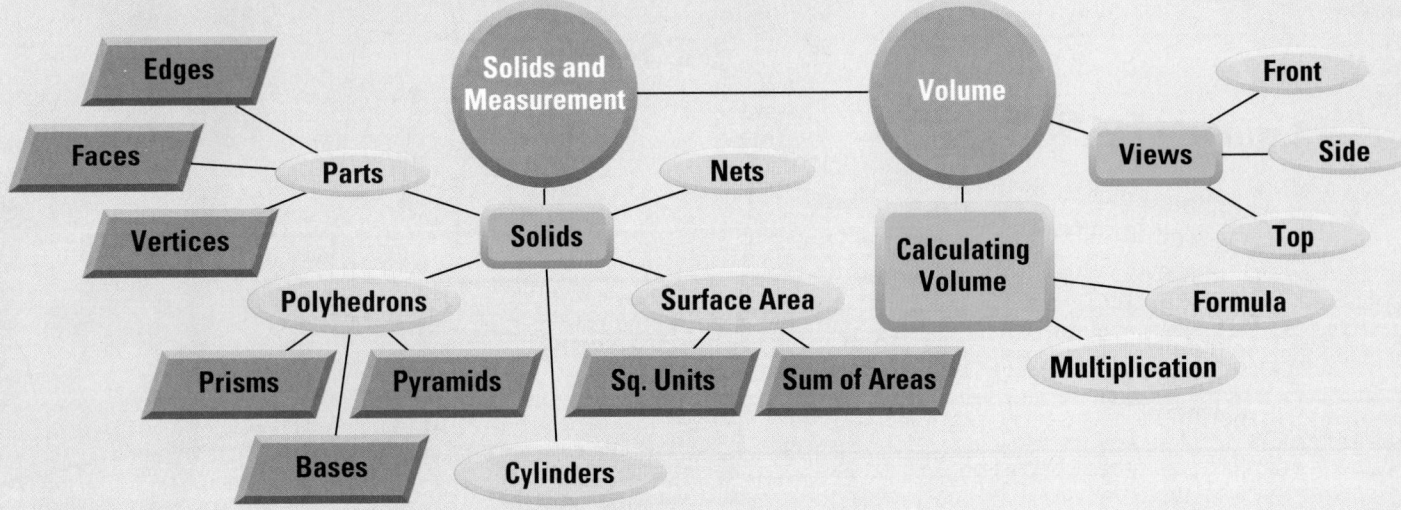

Section 11A   Solids and Surface Area

Summary

- A **solid** is a three-dimensional figure with **faces, edges,** and vertices.

- A solid whose faces are polygons is a **polyhedron.** Some polyhedrons are **prisms** or **pyramids. Cylinders, cones,** and **spheres** are not polyhedrons.

- The **surface area (SA)** of a solid is the sum of the areas of all of its faces.

- A **net** is a flat pattern that can be folded into a solid. You can use a net or a formula to find the surface area of a solid.

Review

Classify each solid. If it is a polyhedron, state the number of faces, edges, and vertices.

1.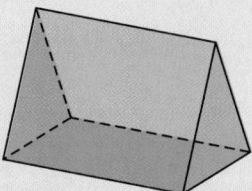

2.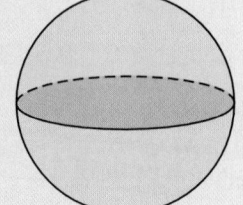

3.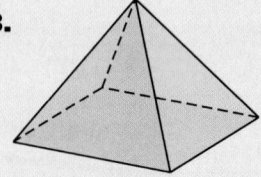

Find the surface area of each solid.

4.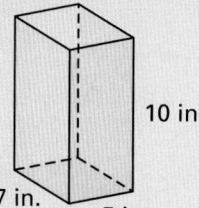

10 in.

7 in.   5 in.

5.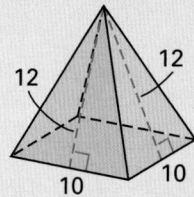

12   12

12

10   10

6.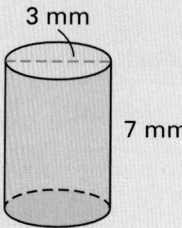

3 mm

7 mm

Section 11B Volume

Summary

- A solid can be drawn with a front view, a side view, and a top view.

- The **volume** of a solid is the number of **cubic units** needed to fill it.

- If the cubes in a rectangular prism have been drawn in, you can find the volume by counting the number of cubes in one layer and multiplying that by the number of layers.

- You can find the volume of a rectangular prism using the formula $V = l \times w \times h$, where l is the length, w is the width, and h is the height.

Review

For each solid, draw the front view, the side view, and the top view.

7.

8.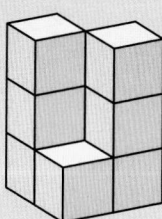

Find the volume.

9.

10.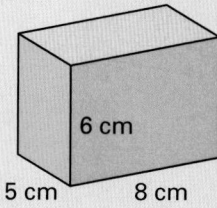

6 cm

5 cm   8 cm

11.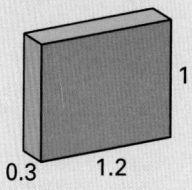

1

0.3   1.2

12. Prints Etc. uses tubes to mail posters to customers. Find the surface area of the tube shown. Use 3.14 for π.

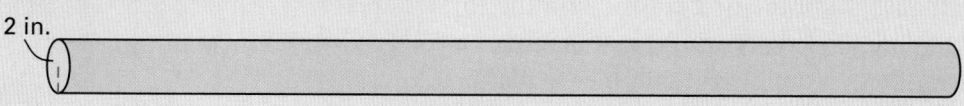

2 in.

36 in.

Fill in each blank with the correct word.

1. A _____ is a solid whose faces are polygons.

2. The number of cubic units needed to fill a solid is the _volume_

3. An _____ is a line formed where two faces of a solid come together.

4. A solid with one base where all the other faces are triangles is a _____.

5. The _____ of a solid is the sum of the areas of the faces.

6. Like a pyramid, a _____ can be named by the shape of the base.

7. Is a cone a polyhedron? Is a cube a polyhedron? Explain.

8. Draw the front, side, and top views of the solid. There are no hidden cubes.

Find the surface area of each solid.

9.
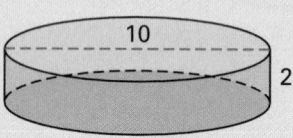

10.
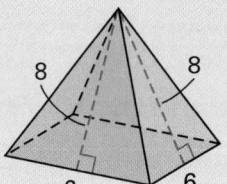

11.
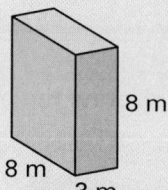

Find the volume of each solid.

12.

13.
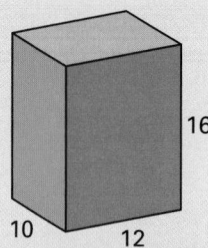

14.

Performance Task

Copy the sketch of a rectangular prism with a length of 10, a width of 5, and a height of 15. Find the surface area and volume of the prism. Then, draw a sketch of a rectangular prism with twice the length, twice the width, and twice the height of the first prism. Find the surface area and volume. Does doubling the length, width, and height of a solid double the surface area? Does it double the volume? Explain.

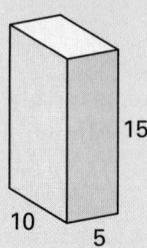

Performance Assessment

Choose one problem.

The Mystery Quadrilateral

On a coordinate plane, connect these four points in order: $(5,-3)$; $(2, 7)$; $(-4, 7)$; $(-7, -3)$. Classify the shape. Find the shape's area, and explain how you found the area.

A Change of Data

Using a centimeter ruler, measure the diameter of four different coins (for example, a penny, a nickel, a dime, a half-dollar). Find the circumference for each coin. Display the data in a bar graph.

Round Pegs and Square Holes

Draw a circle and a square. The length of the square should be the same as the diameter of the circle. Find the area of the circle and the square. What percent of the square's area is the circle's area? Repeat this for two more pairs of circles and squares. What patterns do you notice?

The One That Boasts the Most

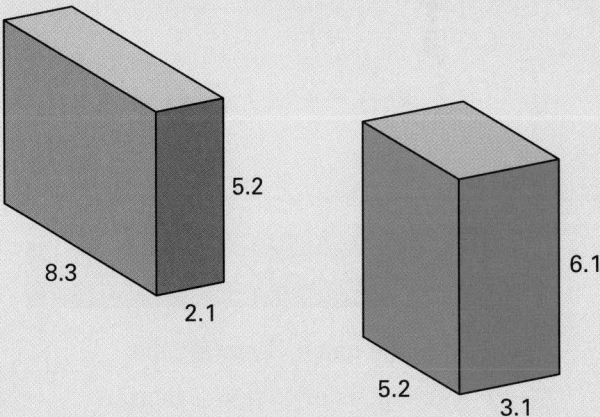

Calculate the surface area and volume for each of the two boxes. Which has more surface area? Which has the greater volume? Does the box with more surface area automatically have the greater volume? Explain.

People of the World

"Rock-paper-scissors," a game of chance, is played throughout the world. In Japan, it's known as "jan-ken-po."

Arts & Literature

In Frank Stockton's short story *The Lady or the Tiger*, a young man has to choose between two doors. Behind one is the woman he would marry. Behind the other is a ferocious tiger. He has a 50/50 chance of choosing the door with the tiger.

Entertainment

In the game *Yahtzee*®, the chances of getting a yahtzee, or five of a kind, on the first roll of the dice are 1 out of 1296, or approximately 0.08%.

622

Science

The chances of a person you meet being left-handed are about 13%.

Social Studies

When trying to predict which presidential candidate is most favored by the public, the polls give results that include a "margin of error." This is a measure of how inaccurate the prediction is.

Student Council Elections

	Votes
Susana Alcocer	32%
Van Nguyen	28%
Maritess Estrera	20%
Peter Michaels	

±5% margin of

KEY MATH IDEAS

The **probability** of an event is a mathematical description of the chances that the event will happen.

Sample data can be used to determine the probability of an event.

The possible outcomes of an event can be listed using a **tree diagram**.

In an **unfair** game of chance, one player is more likely to win than the other. In a **fair** game, all players are equally likely to win.

CHAPTER PROJECT

Problem Solving
Understand
Plan
Solve
Look Back

In this project, you will plan a game of chance for a school carnival. Begin by thinking about what kind of game you want, how many winners there should be for each round of the game, and what would be a fair price to charge for tickets.

Problem Solving Focus

Checking for a Reasonable Answer

When you have finished solving a problem, it may be helpful to look back to make sure your solution is reasonable. Estimation is a useful tool for determining if the answer is reasonable. If your estimate is very different from your answer, you may need to recheck your plan and your arithmetic.

Each of the problems below has an answer, but it is not exactly right. State if the answer is "too low," "too high," or "close enough," and explain why.

❶ The Chelsea Flea Market raised money to help remodel the Chelsea Public Library. The market manager rented 31 booths at $150 a booth. She put aside 10% of the rental fee for clean-up expenses. How much did she plan to spend on clean-up? *$15*

❸ The Flea Market raised a total of $10,345. Of that money, $2,586.24 went to cover the operating expenses of the Flea Market. The rest went to the library. How much went to the library? *$7800*

❷ Emilio's Pizzeria sold pizza for $1.10 a slice. Each pizza had 8 slices, and they sold 59 pizzas. Emilio's donated one-third of the money collected to the library. What was Emilio's donation? *$21.63*

❹ Martha's school is in the Chelsea neighborhood. The school rented a booth and sold $2469 worth of items. The school gave $\frac{1}{4}$ of the money to the library fund. How much did the school donate? *$1851.75*

Introduction to Probability

▶ **Science Link**   ▶ **Geography Link**   ▶ **www.mathsurf.com/6/ch12/disasters**

Decide if each statement about natural disasters is true *or* false.

1 *Four out of five fires are caused by nature. One out of five is caused by humans.*

2 *The center of a hurricane or tornado is known as the "eye." It's the most violent part of the storm.*

3 *Alaska, not California, is the state where the most earthquakes occur.*

4 *On the open ocean, the speed of a tsunami can reach 450 miles per hour.*

Force of Nature!

*N*aturaldisasters can be both expensive and deadly. Much of the loss of life and property can be prevented or avoided if the disaster can be anticipated. Scientists are constantly working to find better ways of predicting these disasters. Probability, a branch of mathematics, is one of their most useful tools.*

1 Why can't scientists predict disasters with 100% accuracy?

2 How do people use mathematics when trying to predict or prepare for disasters?

Probability

▶ **Lesson Link** You have looked at different ways things can happen. Now you'll describe the chance of something happening. ◀

You'll Learn ...

■ to find the probability of an event

... How It's Used

Safety inspectors use probability to determine the chances that a particular safety device will fail to work correctly.

Vocabulary

experiment

outcome

event

probability

Explore | Probability

What Are the Chances?

These words can describe the chances that something will happen.

impossible	rarely	probably not	even chance	possibly	probably	for certain

1. For each item, label where it belongs on the probability list.

   a. A quarter is tossed and it lands heads up.

   b. One of your parents wins the lottery.

   c. An earthquake will happen in your town in the next week.

   d. The sun will rise tomorrow morning.

   e. The President of the United States will visit your class today.

   f. There will be both boys and girls present in your next math class.

   g. Someone in the classroom owns a pet.

2. If you compared everyone's lists, do you think they would all be the same? Explain.

3. Why might a mathematician who studies chance have a difficult time using the chance line above?

Learn | Probability

A probability **experiment** is a situation that can happen in more than one way. The **outcomes** of an experiment are the ways it can happen.

 Outcomes: red, blue, green

 Outcomes: 1, 2, 3, 4, 5, 6

 Outcomes: heads, tails

An **event** is the particular outcome that you're looking for. You can describe the **probability** that a particular event will happen by using a ratio.

$$P(\text{event}) = \frac{\text{number of ways the event can happen}}{\text{number of possible outcomes}}$$

Example 1

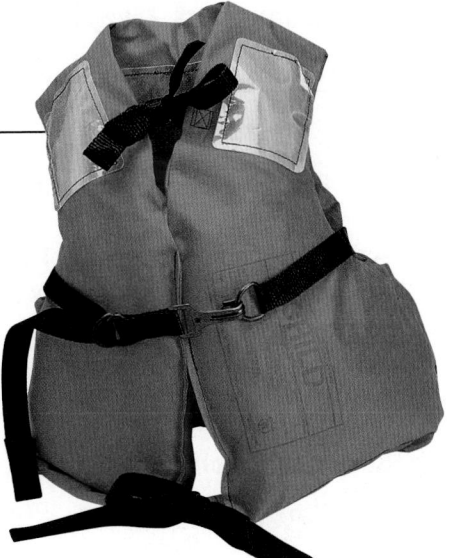

An ocean liner has 8 lifeboats, numbered 1 through 8. In the event of an emergency, every passenger is randomly assigned to one of the 8 boats. What is the probability of being assigned to a boat whose number is less than 6?

Possible outcomes: 1, 2, 3, 4, 5, 6, 7, 8

Number of ways the event can occur: 5 (boat 1, 2, 3, 4, or 5)

$P(\text{less than 6}) = \frac{5}{8}$.

It is sometimes helpful to express a probability as a decimal or percent.

Example 2

What is the probability of rolling an even number on a number cube? Express your answer as a decimal and a percent.

Possible outcomes: 1, 2, 3, 4, 5, 6

Number of ways the event can occur: 3 (rolling a 2, a 4, or a 6)

$P(\text{even number}) = \frac{3}{6}$. As a decimal, this is 0.50. As a percent, 50%.

Try It

For each spinner, what is the probability of the pointer landing in a section that is:

a. Red?

b. Blue or green?

i. 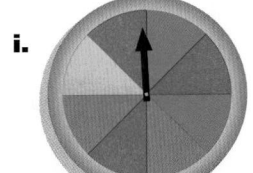 ii.

Check Your Understanding

1. Give an example of a situation with 4 outcomes.

2. If $P(\text{event}) = \frac{6}{6}$, what can you conclude about the event?

Practice and Apply

Getting Started Tell how many outcomes are possible for each experiment.

1. Flipping a quarter.

2. Answering a true/false question.

3. Rolling a standard number cube.

4. Choosing a month at random.

A set of ten cards is labeled 1 through 10. Suppose you choose one card at random. Find the probability of each event.

5. $P(1)$

6. P(multiple of 3)

7. P(2-digit number)

8. P(6 or 2)

9. $P(12)$

10. P(less than 11)

11. P(odd number)

12. $P(5)$

Suppose you roll a number cube. Find the probability of each event.

13. $P(6)$

14. P(even number)

15. P(less than 6)

16. $P(7)$

There are 6 cards that spell out C H A N C E. Suppose you choose one card at random. Find the probability of each event.

17. $P(A)$

18. $P(C)$

19. P(vowel)

20. P(consonant)

21. Janice's board game uses 8 playing tokens, each a different color. If she places the 8 tokens in a bag so that she can't see them, what is the probability that she picks the blue token? The red token?

22. **Test Prep** The probability of getting a winning game piece in a contest is 3 in 5. What is the probability of **not** winning?

  Ⓐ $\frac{1}{5}$ Ⓑ $\frac{2}{5}$ Ⓒ $\frac{3}{5}$ Ⓓ $\frac{4}{5}$

24. **Science** A group of scientists studying earthquakes plans to observe nine different devices that monitor seismic activity. If each scientist is assigned to a monitoring device at random, what is the probability that the first scientist will monitor either the laser reflector or creepmeter?

25. **Logic** Suppose the probability of an event is $\frac{7}{13}$. Which is greater, the probability that the event will occur or the probability that it will *not* occur?

23. At the Hamburger Hotline restaurant, each kid's meal comes with a dinosaur cup. The dinosaurs are Triceratops, Stegosaurus, Tyrannosaurus rex, Brontosaurus, and Parasaurolophus. What is the probability of getting the Tyrannosaurus rex cup?

26. History The first seismograph was built in the year 132 by the Chinese philosopher Zhang Heng. Eight bronze dragon heads were set around a large vessel above eight bronze toads. When an earthquake occurred, a ball fell out of a dragon's mouth and was caught by a toad. If the dragons were numbered 1 to 8, what was the probability that the ball would fall out of the mouth of a dragon with a prime number?

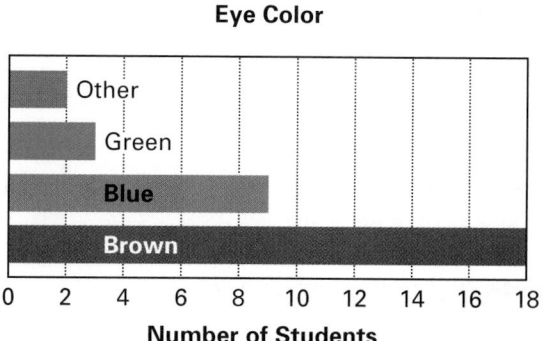

The bar graph shows the eye color of the 32 students in Patty's class. If a student is chosen at random, find the probability of each event.

27. $P(\text{blue})$

28. $P(\text{brown or green})$

Eye Color

Number of Students

Problem Solving and Reasoning

29. Communicate Can the probability of an event be greater than 1? Less than 0? Explain.

30. Critical Thinking Is it more likely that you could roll a number cube twice and get a 3 and then a 5, or a 3 and then a 3? Explain.

31. **Journal** The probability of getting red on a spinner is 80%. What is the probability of not getting red? How are these two probabilities related?

Problem Solving TIP

Sometimes, acting a problem out can help you solve it.

Mixed Review

Classify each solid. [Lesson 11-1]

32.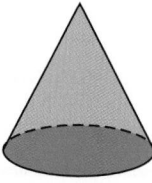

33.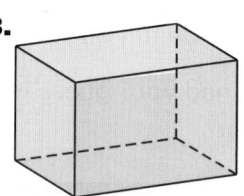

34.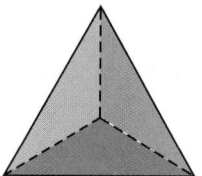

35.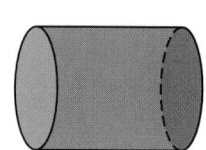

Find the surface area for each solid. [Lesson 11-2]

36.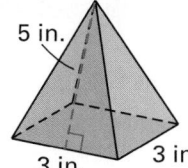
5 in.
3 in.   3 in.

37.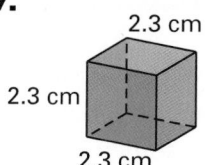
2.3 cm
2.3 cm
2.3 cm

38.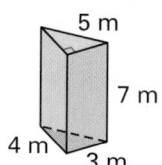
5 m
7 m
4 m   3 m

39.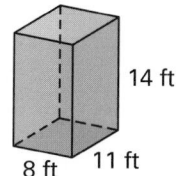
14 ft
8 ft   11 ft

▶ **Lesson Link** In the last lesson, you determined probability by counting the possible outcomes. Now you'll determine probability from data based on real-world situations. ◀

Explore | **Making Predictions**

Gaze Into the Crystal Bag

Materials: A bag with 2 cubes of color 1, 6 cubes of color 2, 5 cubes of color 3

1. Choose a partner, and record what colors you are using for color 1, color 2, and color 3. Give your bag to another set of partners and ask them to remove three cubes from the bag. They should not tell you or show you which three have been removed.

2. Without looking in the bag, remove a cube at random and record what color it is. Put the cube back in the bag.

3. Repeat Step 2 until you have drawn from the bag 20 times.

4. Based on your data, determine the following probabilities:

   a. *P*(drawing a color 1 cube)   **b.** *P*(drawing a color 2 cube)

   c. *P*(drawing a color 3 cube)

5. Guess which three cubes were removed by the other students. After you have guessed, look inside the bag and check your answer.

6. Explain how you determined your guess in Step 5. Was your guess accurate? Why or why not?

Learn | **Making Predictions**

Sometimes it is difficult to calculate the probability of an event because you don't know all the possible outcomes or you don't know how likely each outcome is. In these situations, you can sometimes collect data and predict the probability based on the data.

A **sample** is a set of data that can be used to predict how a particular situation might happen. You can use sample data to determine probability.

Examples

1 At Paolo's Pizzeria, the manager wanted to know what kind of pizza slices customers order during the lunch hour. He collected the following data during one lunch shift. Based on this data, what is the probability that a lunch customer will order a cheese slice?

Pizza	Slices Ordered
Pepperoni	31
Veggie	13
Combination	10
Cheese	7

There were 61 slices ordered. Of the 61 slices, 7 were cheese. The manager can expect $\frac{7}{61}$ of the customers to order cheese.

2 Which of the three spinners was most likely the spinner that produced the sample data?

Data: red, blue, blue, red, red, red, red, red, red, blue

Remember

When comparing fractions, you can determine which fraction is larger by rewriting both as equal fractions with common denominators.
[Page 308]

#1
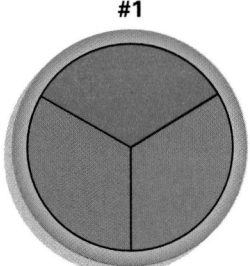
#2
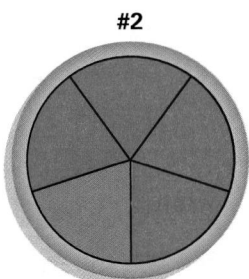
#3
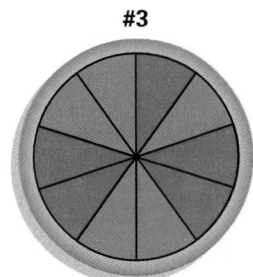

Red happened 7 out of 10 times, or $\frac{7}{10}$ of the time. On spinner #1, $\frac{1}{3}$ of the spinner is red. On spinner #2, $\frac{4}{5}$ are red. On spinner #3, $\frac{5}{10}$ are red. The fraction closest to $\frac{7}{10}$ is $\frac{4}{5}$. So, spinner #2 is the most likely spinner.

Try It

Using Example 1, what are the chances a customer orders the following:

a. A veggie slice?   **b.** A slice that's not a combination slice?

Check | Your Understanding

1. Is the probability calculated from sample data an estimate? Explain.

2. Why would it be a good idea to collect as large a set of sample data as possible before determining the probability of an event?

Practice and Apply

Getting Started Tell if you need sample data to determine the probability of each situation happening.

1. A tsunami striking Hawaii next year

2. Meeting a person from Peru tomorrow

3. Rolling a 2 on a number cube

4. Choosing a red crayon out of a box

Use the data recorded in the chart for Exercises 5–7.

Trial	1	2	3	4	5	6	7	8	9	10
Outcome	Blue	Pink	White	White	White	Pink	Blue	White	Pink	Pink
Trial	11	12	13	14	15	16	17	18	19	20
Outcome	Blue	White	White	Pink	White	Pink	White	White	Pink	White

5. How many different outcomes were there?

6. How many outcomes were blue?

7. What is the probability of the outcome being pink or white?

Estimation Ms. Shaw's 6th-grade class conducted an in-class survey.

Question	Result
Are you male or female?	15 female, 17 male
Do you have an emergency kit at home?	21 yes, 11 no
Is the day of your birth an odd or even number?	20 even, 12 odd
Have you experienced a flood?	27 no, 5 yes

If there are 102 6th graders in the school, use the survey results to estimate the number of 6th graders in the school who:

8. Are girls

9. Have an emergency kit at home

10. Have an even birth date

11. Have experienced a flood

12. **Test Prep** The following data comes from a spinner: A, C, E, B, A, B, C, E, B, A, A. Based on the data, which of the following has the lowest probability?

     Ⓐ $P(A)$ Ⓑ $P(B)$ Ⓒ $P(C)$ Ⓓ $P(D)$

Problem Solving and Reasoning

Critical Thinking The chart shows the average number of tornadoes in the United States per month over 10 years.

Month	Tornadoes	Month	Tornadoes	Month	Tornadoes	Month	Tornadoes
January	15	April	112	July	90	October	25
February	29	May	181	August	62	November	26
March	55	June	169	September	42	December	20

13. In what month is the probability of a tornado the greatest? If a tornado occurs, what is the probability that it occurs during that month?

14. Tornado season is from March through August. If a tornado occurs, what is the probability that it occurs during tornado season?

Critical Thinking Hurricane season in the United States is from June 1 to November 30. In an average season, there are ten tropical storms. Six are expected to reach hurricane strength and two of these are likely to strike the U.S. coast.

15. Is the probability that a tropical storm will turn into a hurricane more than 50%?

16. If a hurricane happens, what is the probability that the hurricane will hit the U.S. coast?

17. In 1995, there were 19 tropical storms, of which 11 reached hurricane strength. Why was 1995 considered an unusual year?

Mixed Review

Tell which solid of each pair has the greater surface area. *[Lesson 11-3]*

18.

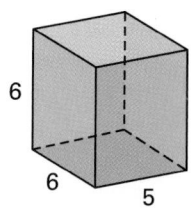

19.

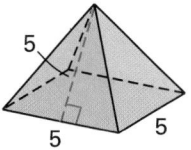 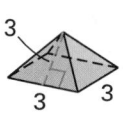

Find the surface area. Use 3.14 for π **.** *[Lesson 11-4]*

20.

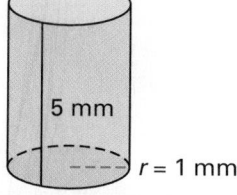

5 mm

$r = 1$ mm

21.

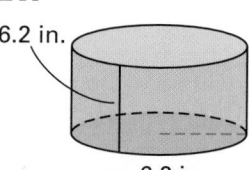

6.2 in.

$r = 6.2$ in.

22.

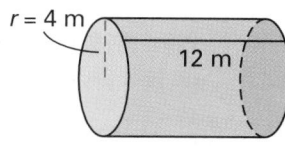

$r = 4$ m

12 m

TECHNOLOGY

Using a Spreadsheet • Using Random Numbers

Problem: What are the chances of rolling two number cubes and getting a sum of 10?

You can use spreadsheets to quickly generate random data.

1 Enter the information into the spreadsheet as shown.

	A	B	C
1	Roll 1	Roll 2	Sum
2			

2 In cell A2, enter =TRUNC(6*(RAND())+1). **Copy this formula into cell B2. Then copy the formula down to row 101. This will generate 100 random numbers from 1 to 6. (Your data may look different from the data shown here.)**

	A	B	C
1	Roll 1	Roll 2	Sum
2	3	5	
3	4	6	
4	6	3	
5	1	2	
6	2	1	
7	2	4	
8	3	5	
9	5	2	

3 In cell C2, enter the formula =(A2+B2). **Copy the formula down to row 101.**

4 Count the number of times 10 appears as the sum. This can easily be expressed as a ratio to 100, and as a percent.

Solution: Since the data is random, every spreadsheet can give a different answer. The answers should be close to 8%.

TRY IT

a. Repeat the experiment by recopying the formulas in row 2 down to row 101. How does your probability the second time compare to the first time?

b. Use the steps above to find the chances of getting a sum of 12.

ON YOUR OWN

▶ Can you roll two number cubes 100 times and record the results more quickly by hand or with a spreadsheet? Explain.

▶ Change the number in front of the "*RAND" to a different number, and copy the formula to row 101. How does this change the data?

Geometric Models of Probability

▶ **Lesson Link**   You know how to determine probability from lists and from data. Now you will see how to determine probabilities that involve the areas of figures. ◀

Explore | Geometric Models

Betting on a Blizzard

Materials: Paper clips

The spinners below represent models of the chances of a blizzard occurring.

B = blizzard occurs   N = no blizzard occurs

1. Trace each of the spinners onto a sheet of paper.

2. Unbend the end of a paper clip. Place the other end over the center of a spinner, and place your pencil point on the center of the spinner. Use the paper clip as the spinner pointer.

3. For each spinner, spin the pointer 20 times. Record the number of times a blizzard occurs, and the number of times it doesn't.

4. Which spinner is the least likely to have a blizzard? Explain.

5. Could you have determined which spinner would be most likely to have a blizzard without actually spinning the pointers? Explain.

6. Can two different spinners have the same chances of having a blizzard?

You'll Learn ...

■ to calculate probability from geometric models

... How It's Used

The Coast Guard uses probability when describing the chances of locating a particular ship lost at sea.

Remember

The area of a circle is $\pi \times \text{radius}^2$. **[Page 250]**

Learn | Geometric Models of Probability

Some events and outcomes are not single items that can be counted. For situations such as carnival games and dart boards, the probability of an event may depend upon the areas of portions of a figure. If you can determine each area within the figure, you can determine the probability of the situation.

Examples

1 A tornado has a very irregular path. When the funnel touches the ground, it might go straight, double back, or hop over places. If a tornado touches down in the area pictured, what is the probability that it will touch down in the shaded area?

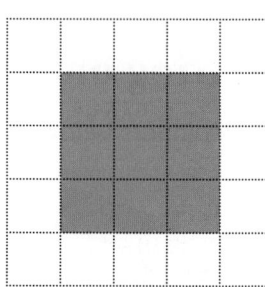

The total area is 25 square units. The shaded area is 9 square units.

The probability that the tornado will hit the shaded region is $\frac{9}{25}$.

2 If a coin is tossed onto the carnival game board at random, what is the probability that it will land in the circle?

$$P(\text{land in circle}) = \frac{\text{area of circle}}{\text{area of rectangle}}$$

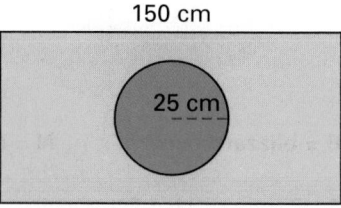

150 cm

25 cm

75 cm

$$\approx \frac{3.14 \times 25 \times 25}{75 \times 150}$$

$$\approx \frac{1962.5}{11250} \approx 0.17, \text{ or } 17\%.$$

The probability that the coin will land in the circle is approximately 17%.

Try It

Find the probability of tossing a dart at the dart board and hitting the shaded region.

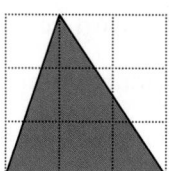

FIRST AID

1. When calculating the probability of a geometric model, why is it important to know how to calculate the areas of figures?

2. One dart board has a bull's-eye of 20 square centimeters. Another dart board of the same size has two bull's-eyes, each with an area of 10 square centimeters. Which dart board would you choose to play? Why?

12-3 Exercises and Applications

Practice and Apply

Getting Started | Use the figure shown for Exercises 1–3.

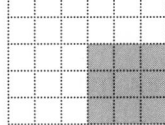

1. Find the area of the shaded square.   2. Find the area of the rectangle.

3. Find the probability that a token thrown at random will land on the shaded square.

Suppose you drop a token on each shape in Exercises 4–7. Find the probability of the token landing on the shaded area. Write your answer as a percent.

4.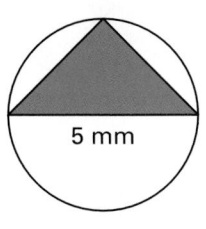
5 mm

5.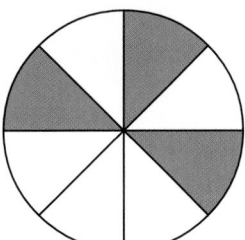

6.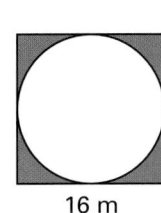
16 m

7.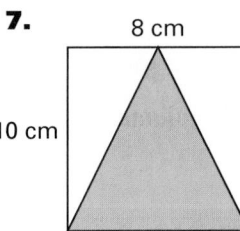
8 cm
10 cm

8. **Science** Hurricanes blow in a spiral around a circular center known as the "eye." If a storm covers a circular area 400 miles wide and its eye is 20 miles wide, what is the probability of an object in a hurricane being in the eye of the hurricane?

9. **Test Prep** A parachutist is scheduled to land somewhere in the open field shown. Which is the best estimate of the probability that she will land within the grassy area?

   Ⓐ $\frac{1}{4}$ Ⓑ $\frac{1}{2}$ Ⓒ $\frac{3}{4}$

Target area

10. Chance If you throw 200 darts at the dart board shown, how many should you expect to land in the shaded area?

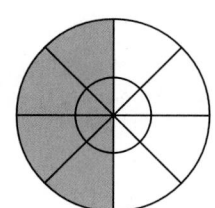

Problem Solving and Reasoning

11. Choose a Strategy On Jerome's game board, the probability of a coin randomly landing on a blue square is $\frac{1}{4}$, on a green square is $\frac{1}{3}$, and on a red square is $\frac{3}{14}$. What is the smallest number of squares that could be on Jerome's board?

12. Communicate In a geometric model of probability, if the entire model is reduced in size, what happens to the probability of randomly landing on the shaded area? Explain.

13. **Journal** Draw a dart board so that the probability of hitting the bull's-eye is $\frac{2}{3}$. Explain your drawing.

Problem Solving

STRATEGIES

• Look for a Pattern
• Make an Organized List
• Make a Table
• Guess and Check
• Work Backward
• Use Logical Reasoning
• Draw a Diagram
• Solve a Simpler Problem

Mixed Review

Draw front, side, and top views for each figure. There are no hidden cubes.
[Lesson 11-5]

14. 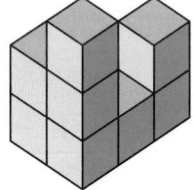 **15.**  **16.**  **17.**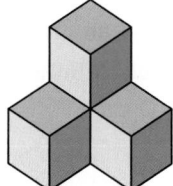

Find the volume. *[Lesson 11-6]*

18. 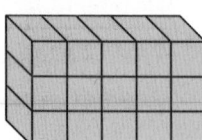 **19.** 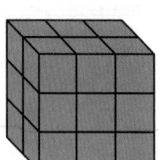 **20.** 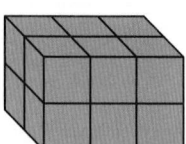 **21.**

Project Progress

Write instructions for each game at your fun fair. Decide how long it takes to play one round of the game, and how many players and winners there will be for each round. Then figure out the number of prizes you will need to have to keep the game open during the entire fun fair.

Problem Solving

Understand
Plan
Solve
Look Back

PROBLEM SOLVING 12-3

You have calculated probability in different situations. Now you will use these ideas to evaluate an emergency disaster plan.

Force of Nature! ...

The floor plan below details the Northrop City Branch Public Library.

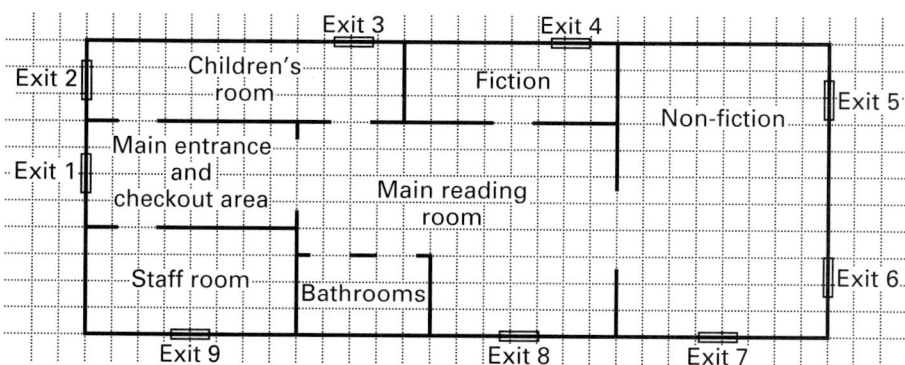

Time to evacuate patrons, in minutes, from 16 fire drills:

4	7	12	6	4	11	5	11
13	17	4	8	5	8	10	9

1. State the probability of each occurring and rank from least likely to most likely. Assume that it is equally likely that a fire will happen on any day.

   a. A fire will begin in the main reading room.

   b. A fire will begin in the children's room.

   c. A patron choosing an exit at random will choose Exit 3.

   d. A fire will occur on a Thursday.

   e. The patrons will evacuate the building in less than 5 minutes.

   f. The patrons will evacuate the building in 15 minutes or more.

2. Identify three different events like the ones above. The chances of the first event should be less than $\frac{1}{2}$, of the second should be exactly $\frac{1}{2}$, and of the third should be more than $\frac{1}{2}$.

A number cube is rolled. Find the probability of each event.

1. $P(1)$ **2.** $P(3 \text{ or } 4)$ **3.** $P(7)$ **4.** $P(< 7)$ **5.** $P(\text{not } 3)$

Use the spinner to find each probability.

6. $P(\text{red})$ **7.** $P(\text{not red})$

8. $P(\text{green})$ **9.** $P(\text{not yellow})$

10. The probability of winning a game is $\frac{7}{9}$. If there are no ties or draws, what is the probability of losing the game?

11. If $P(A) = \frac{3}{5}$, $P(B) = 0.52$, and $P(C) = 61\%$, which event has the greatest probability of occurring?

12. Which probability is greater, 1 out of 10 or 15 out of 15,000? Explain.

13. Estimation On average, there are 100,000 thunderstorms in the United States every year. The probability that a thunderstorm will develop into a tornado is approximately $\frac{1}{100}$. About how many *tornadoes* are there every year?

14. If 100 tokens were dropped on the figure shown, how many would you expect to hit the shaded region?

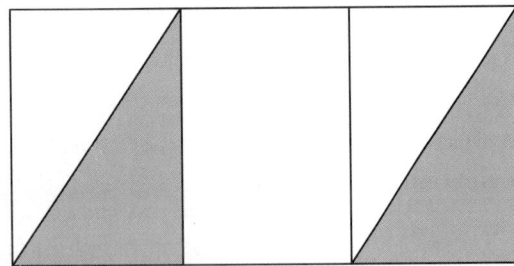

Test Prep

In order to determine the probability for one of two events happening, find the probability of each event and add the two probabilities together.

15. The probability of drawing a red marble out of a bag is $\frac{1}{5}$, for a green marble it is $\frac{1}{10}$, for a blue marble it is $\frac{3}{10}$, and for a yellow marble it is $\frac{2}{5}$. What are the chances of randomly drawing a marble that's either red or blue?

Ⓐ $\frac{4}{10}$ Ⓑ $\frac{5}{10}$ Ⓒ $\frac{11}{20}$ Ⓓ $\frac{6}{10}$

In 1929, Charles Darrow was unemployed. He wanted to find a hobby that didn't involve spending lots of money, so he developed a game in which people buy and sell property. He liked the idea of a game that uses large sums of "money," something he couldn't afford to do in real life. He called his game Monopoly®.

Darrow made several copies of the game for his friends. He tried to sell the game to Parker Brothers, but at first they felt the game took too long and the rules were too complicated. However, Parker Brothers changed their mind. They have now sold over 160 million sets, and Charles Darrow became the first millionaire game designer. Not such a bad ending for someone who developed the game because he didn't have lots of money.

To design a game that millions of people will enjoy, a game designer must think of many things. One of those things is how fair the game is. Fairness is a part of probability, and probability is a part of mathematics.

1 What makes a game good enough to sell millions of copies?

2 How can an understanding of probability help a person design a better game?

Tree Diagrams

You'll Learn ...

■ to make tree diagrams

... How It's Used

Botanists use charts based on tree diagrams to determine all the possible offspring for two varieties of plants.

Vocabulary

tree diagram

▶ **Lesson Link** You have counted the number of outcomes for a single experiment. Now you will count the number of outcomes for a series of experiments. ◀

Explore Tree Diagrams

All Roads Lead to the Finish Line

The three sketches below are diagrams for three board games. In each game, players start on the left side and move to the right side. Players always move from left to right.

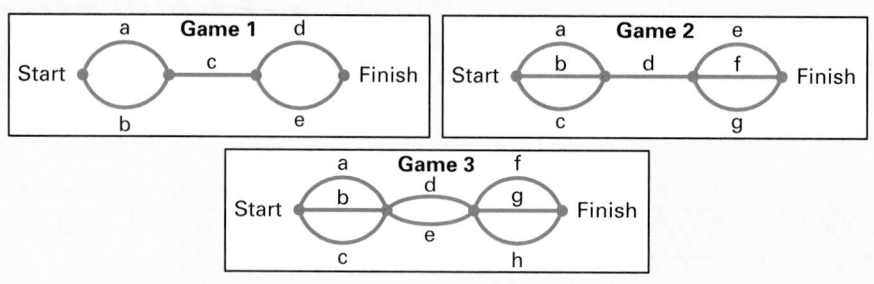

1. For each sketch, list all of the possible routes a player could take to get from start to finish. Use the letters next to each path to describe each route.

2. Can you be certain that you have found all possible routes for each game board? Explain.

3. Is it possible to move from start to finish using a set of paths that are not in alphabetical order? Explain.

4. Is it possible to determine the number of ways to go from start to finish without actually listing all of them? Explain.

Learn Tree Diagrams

It is often easy to list the outcomes for a single experiment. It can be more complicated to list the outcomes for a series of experiments. To list the outcomes for a series, you can use a **tree diagram** . This type of diagram shows one branch for each possible outcome.

Example 1

A sandwich shop has two choices for sandwiches (tuna or egg salad) and three for drinks (milk, juice, cider). If a "meal" is one sandwich and one drink, draw a tree diagram to show all of the possible meals.

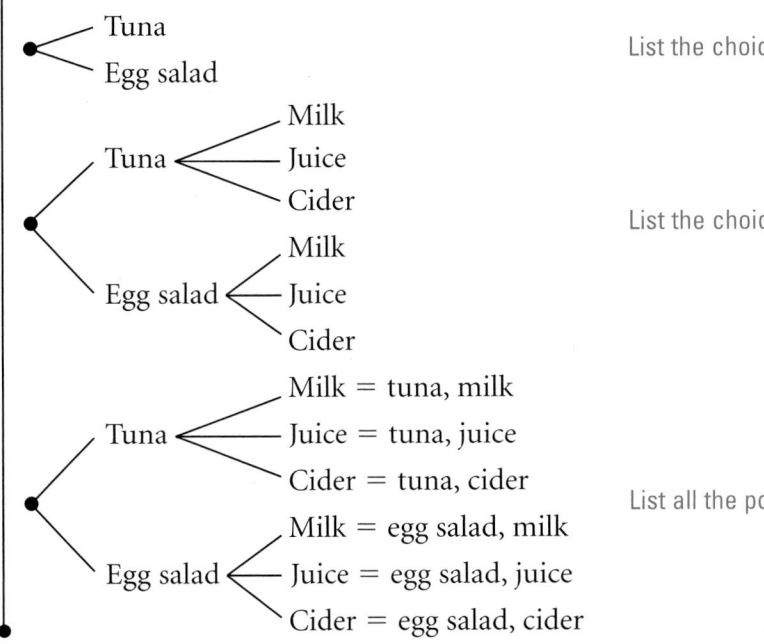

List the choices for sandwich.

List the choices for drink.

List all the possible choices.

You can use multiplication to find the *number* of possible outcomes. In the example above, there were 2 choices for sandwiches and 3 choices for drinks. All together, there were 2×3, or 6, possible combinations of choices.

Example 2

If you flip a penny, a nickel, and a dime, how many different ways can the three coins land?

There are two ways the penny can land: heads or tails. There are also two outcomes for the nickel, heads or tails, as well as for the dime. All together, there are $2 \times 2 \times 2$, or 8 possible outcomes.

Try It

a. Conway's Restaurant has three flavors of ice cream (chocolate, vanilla, and mint) and two toppings (hot fudge and butterscotch). Draw a tree diagram showing all the possible ice cream servings with one flavor of ice cream and one topping.

b. One spinner has the numbers 1, 2, 3, and 4 on it. Another spinner has the letters A, B, C, and D. If you spin both spinners, how many different outcomes are there?

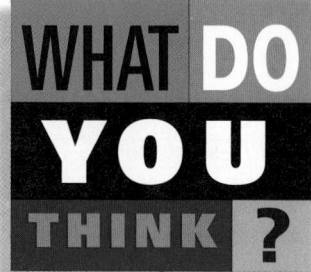

WHAT DO YOU THINK?

Catherine and Van are preparing lunches for a field trip. Each lunch will have one main dish (chicken, roast beef sandwich, or pita sandwich), one fruit (banana or apple), and one cookie (chocolate chip or oatmeal raisin). They want to know how many different lunches they can make.

Catherine thinks ...

I'll use a tree diagram.

There are 12 different possible lunches.

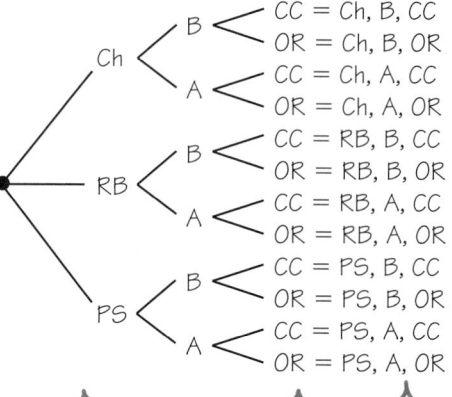

```
           B < CC = Ch, B, CC
     Ch <      OR = Ch, B, OR
           A < CC = Ch, A, CC
                OR = Ch, A, OR
           B < CC = RB, B, CC
     RB <      OR = RB, B, OR
           A < CC = RB, A, CC
                OR = RB, A, OR
           B < CC = PS, B, CC
     PS <      OR = PS, B, OR
           A < CC = PS, A, CC
                OR = PS, A, OR
```

Van thinks ...

I'll use multiplication. There are 3 choices for a main dish, 2 for fruit, and 2 for a cookie.
$3 \times 2 \times 2 = 12$.

There are 12 different possible lunches.

What do  you think?

1. Which method would work better if Catherine and Van had 11 different lunches and were trying to determine which combination they hadn't made? Explain.

2. If every lunch also had one bag of pretzels, would this change the number of different lunches? Explain.

Check | Your Understanding

1. What kind of information does a tree diagram give you?

2. Is a tree diagram helpful when determining the number of ways a single coin can be flipped once? Explain.

Practice and Apply

1. **Getting Started** Follow these steps to draw a tree diagram showing the possible outcomes of rolling a number cube and flipping a coin.

   a. Start the tree diagram by listing the outcomes of rolling a number cube.

   b. Draw the branches and list the outcomes of flipping a coin.

   c. List all of the possible outcomes.

   d. How many outcomes are possible for rolling a number cube and flipping a coin?

For Exercises 2–4, draw a tree diagram showing all possible outcomes for each situation.

2. The lunch choices of the day are bologna or peanut butter sandwich with either an apple, orange, or banana, and either juice or milk.

3. A softball team has five pitchers and three catchers. Only one pitcher and one catcher are on the field at the same time.

4. Each player gets two playing pieces for a board game: a cube (red, blue, green, or yellow) and a cylinder (1 in. high, 2 in. high, or 3 in. high).

5. **Test Prep** Mitzi has 3 sweaters, 8 blouses, 6 skirts, and 5 pairs of shoes. How many days can Mitzi wear a different outfit?

   Ⓐ 22   Ⓑ 68   Ⓒ 512   Ⓓ 720

6. If you spin both spinners at the same time, how many possible outcomes are there?

 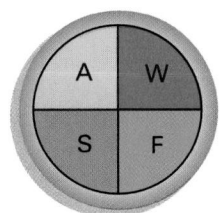

7. Prizes for first, second, and third place were wrapped in separate boxes. The labels identifying the prizes fell off.

   a. How many ways can the labels be put on the boxes?

   b. If one of the three labels is put on a box, what is the probability that it is the correct label?

8. **Problem Solving** The Wild Outback Resort has 10 different board games, 5 different card games, and 6 different water games for their guests to play. Sam wants to borrow 1 of each type of game for the weekend. How many combinations of board, card, and water games are there?

PRACTICE 12-4

FINISH

9. Industry A Texas license plate consists of "letter, letter, letter, number, number, letter." If all 26 letters of the alphabet and all 10 digits, 0–9, can be used, how many different license plates are possible?

10. The Wheel Shop sells five different brands of bikes. Each brand comes in three different models: 1-speed, 3-speed, or 10-speed. Each bike can also be red or blue. How many different kinds are there?

Problem Solving and Reasoning

11. Critical Thinking For his costume, Mike has to choose one wig and one scarf. The items he can choose are shown in the photo. What is the probability that Mike chooses the brown wig and the black scarf? Explain.

12. Choose a Strategy Each radio station in Kilkenney County has to have three call letters, with the first letter being K.

a. How many different radio stations can the county have? Explain.

b. If no two letters can be the same, are there more possibilities, or fewer possibilities? Explain.

Problem Solving

STRATEGIES

- Look for a Pattern
- Make an Organized List
- Make a Table
- Guess and Check
- Work Backward
- Use Logical Reasoning
- Draw a Diagram
- Solve a Simpler Problem

13. Communicate Jessie is drawing a tree diagram to show possible combinations. She has red, orange, yellow, and green blocks. They come in three shapes: triangles, squares, and circles. How many branches will her tree diagram have if Jessie first lists the choices for color? If she first lists the choices for shape? Explain.

Problem Solving **TIP**

Draw a partial tree diagram. You will probably not need to finish the diagram in order to solve the problem.

Mixed Review

Find the volume. *[Lesson 11-7]*

14.
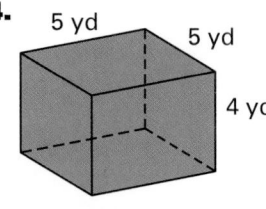
5 yd
5 yd
4 yd

15.
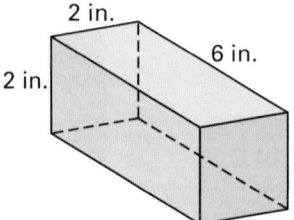
2 in.
6 in.
2 in.

16.
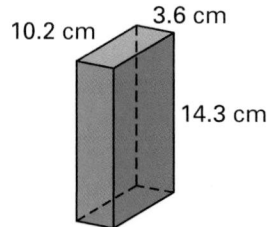
3.6 cm
10.2 cm
14.3 cm

Suppose you roll a 10-sided die with faces numbered 1–10. Find the probability of each event. *[Lesson 12-1]*

17. $P(1, 6, \text{ or } 9)$ **18.** $P(10)$ **19.** $P(5 \text{ or } 3)$ **20.** $P(12)$ **21.** $P(\text{factor of } 10)$

Compound Events

▶ **Lesson Link** You know how to find all of the possible outcomes for a series of experiments. Now you will find the probability of one of those outcomes. ◀

Explore | Compound Events

Counting On a Way Out

Materials: Number cubes

In the game Monopoly®, you can get out of Jail if you roll a 7, an 11, or doubles (the same number on both number cubes).

1. Predict the number of times out of 100 rolls that you can roll a 7. Also, predict the number of 11's and the number of doubles.

2. Roll the cubes 25 times. For each roll, write down the sum of the numbers. Circle the sum if it was a double.

3. Share your data with three other groups.

4. Based on your collected data, determine the probability of getting just a 7, just an 11, or just doubles. Also, determine the probability for getting either a 7, an 11, or doubles.

5. Did your data match your prediction? Explain.

6. Why might it be a good idea to add the data from three other groups to your own data?

You'll Learn ...

■ to find the probability of a compound event

... How It's Used

State lottery designers use compound events when determining the chances for winning a lottery prize.

Vocabulary

compound event

Learn | Compound Events

A single event is the outcome of a single experiment, such as tossing a coin and getting heads, or rolling a 6 on a number cube. A **compound event** is a combination of two or more single events, such as tossing a coin and getting heads *and* then rolling a 6 on a number cube.

 $P(\text{H}) = \frac{1}{2}$  $P(6) = \frac{1}{6}$

 and $P(\text{H and 6}) = ?$

FINISH

To find the probability for a compound event, first calculate the number of possible outcomes. Then, calculate the number of ways the compound event can happen. The probability is the ratio of these values.

Examples

1 What is the probability of spinning a consonant (B, C, or D) on Spinner 1 and a prime number on Spinner 2?

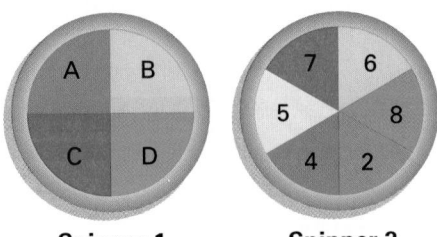

Spinner 1   Spinner 2

Recall that you can use multiplication to determine the number of possible outcomes. There are 4 outcomes on the first spinner, and 6 on the second. There are 4 × 6 or 24 possible outcomes.

There are 3 ways to get a consonant on the first spinner, and 3 ways to get a prime number on the second spinner. There are 3 × 3 or 9 ways to get a consonant and a prime number.

The probability of getting a consonant and a prime number is $\frac{9}{24}$, or 37.5%.

2 What are the chances of flipping three coins and getting all heads?

There are 2 outcomes for each of the three coins. There are 2 × 2 × 2 or 8 possible outcomes. There is 1 way of getting heads on each of the three coins. There is 1 × 1 × 1 or 1 way of getting three heads.

The probability of getting three heads is $\frac{1}{8}$, or 12.5%.

Try It

In Example 1, what is the probability of spinning a letter in the word "DAD" on Spinner 1 and an even number on Spinner 2?

Check | Your Understanding

1. How can multiplication help you find the probability of a compound event?

2. Give an example of a compound event in your life.

Practice and Apply

1. **Getting Started** Answer these questions to find the probability of rolling a number cube three times and getting a 4 each time.

   a. How many outcomes are there for each roll?

   b. How many possible outcomes are there?

   c. How many ways can you get a 4 on each roll?

   d. How many possible ways can you get three 4's?

   e. What is the probability of getting a 4 each time?

Three cards numbered 1, 4, and 7 are in a paper bag. Each time a card is drawn it is replaced. Find the probability of each event.

2. $P(\text{odd, then even})$

3. $P(\text{even, then even})$

4. $P(\text{odd, then odd})$

5. $P(\text{odd, even, odd})$

6. $P(\text{even, then odd})$

7. $P(\text{even, even, even})$

8. Use the menu shown to find the probability of a customer ordering an egg roll, sweet and sour pork, and juice.

9. **Science** The probability of a newborn child being a girl is about $\frac{1}{2}$. What is the probability of all 5 children in a family being girls?

Lunch Special:
1 side dish, 1 main dish, 1 drink

Side dishes	Main dishes
Egg roll	Sweet & Sour Pork
Soup	Chop Suey
Fried rice	Broccoli & Beef
White rice	

Drinks
Low-fat milk, Soda, Juice

For Exercises 10–12, the spinner is spun twice.

10. Find the probability of spinning white both times.

11. Find the probability of spinning white and then red.

12. Find the probability of not spinning red either time.

13. Two number cubes are tossed. What is the probability that the number on each cube is the same? Different?

14. **Test Prep** Marcos rolls 2 eight-sided dice with each side numbered 1-8. What is the probability that he rolls a 7 and then a 1?

    Ⓐ $\frac{1}{4}$ Ⓑ $\frac{1}{16}$ Ⓒ $\frac{1}{36}$ Ⓓ $\frac{1}{64}$

PRACTICE 12-5

FINISH

15. Chance The probability of Josh winning the 50-yard dash at the school track meet is 0.6 and his probability of winning the hurdles is 0.7. Which pair of outcomes listed in the chart does Josh have the greatest chance of accomplishing?

Dash	Hurdles
Win	Lose
Win	Win
Lose	Win
Lose	Lose

16. Suppose you have 26 cards, and each card has a different letter of the alphabet. Find each probability if you draw a card, put it back, and then draw another. The vowels are *A, E, I, O,* and *U.*

    a. *P*(vowel and then consonant)   **b.** *P*(vowel and then vowel)

    c. *P*(consonant and then consonant)   **d.** *P*(*X* and then *Y*)

Problem Solving and Reasoning

17. Critical Thinking Paul has 6 argyle socks, 8 green socks, and 4 brown socks in his drawer. While getting dressed, he picks out 1 sock at random, doesn't return it, and then picks out another. What is the probability that he picks an argyle sock on both tries?

18. Communicate If you flip a coin 4 times, which is greater, *P*(3 heads and then 1 tail) or *P*(2 heads and then 2 tails)? Explain.

19. Journal How can a tree diagram help when finding the probability of a two-step event? Explain.

20. Critical Thinking Zack has two spinners with numbers on them. The probability of spinning a "7" on both spinners is $\frac{3}{20}$. If the probability of getting a "7" on the first spinner alone is $\frac{1}{4}$, what is the probability of getting a "7" on the second spinner alone?

Mixed Review

21. Which of the three spinners is most likely to have produced the sample data? *[Lesson 12-2]*

Data:
green, green, yellow, yellow,
yellow, yellow, green, green,
yellow, green, yellow

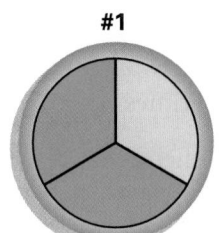
    #1

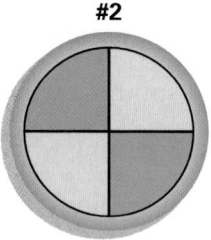
    #2

    #3

22. Suppose you drop a token on the rectangle shown. Find the probability of the token landing on the red area. *[Lesson 12-3]*

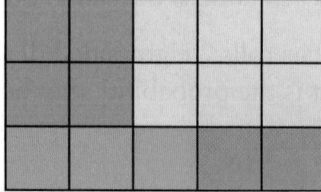

Fairness and Unfairness

▶ **Lesson Link** You know how to find the probability of an event. Now you'll use probability to determine if a game is fair or unfair. ◀

You'll Learn ...

■ to tell if a game is fair

... How It's Used

Bowlers use fairness when determining game handicaps that will make games more even for less experienced players.

Explore Fairness and Unfairness

But That's Not Fair!

Get together in groups of three. One person will need to record the data.

1. Decide who will be Player A, Player B, and Player C.

2. On the count of three, each person should form a hand into Rock, Paper, or Scissors. Player A gets a point if all three hands are the same. Player B gets a point if all three hands are different. Player C gets a point if two hands are the same and one is different.

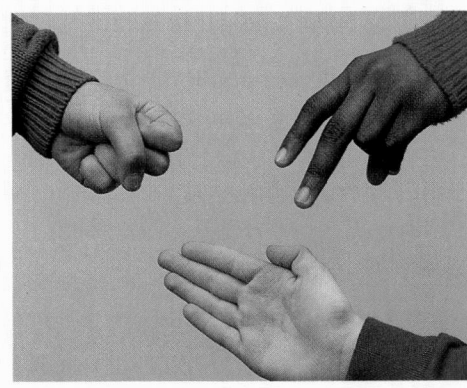

3. Play the game 20 times, and record how many points each player gets. Based on your data, determine the chances of each player winning.

4. Play the game again 20 times, and record your results. From the new set of data, find the probability of each person winning. Was your second set of data the same as your first set, or different? Explain.

5. Does every player have an equal chance of winning the game? Explain.

Vocabulary

fair

unfair

Learn Fairness and Unfairness

A game is **fair** if each player has the same probability of winning. The game is **unfair** if one player has a greater probability of winning. You can determine if a game is fair or unfair by comparing the probabilities for winning.

FINISH

Examples

1 In a game, two coins are flipped. If the coins match, Player A wins. If the coins don't match, Player B wins. Is the game fair?

There are 2 outcomes for each coin. There are 2 × 2 or 4 possible outcomes.

Player A wins if both coins are heads (H-H) or both are tails (T-T). The probability of Player A winning is $\frac{2}{4}$, or 50%.

Player B wins if the first coin is heads and the second tails (H-T) or if the first coin is tails and the second heads (T-H). The probability of Player B winning is $\frac{2}{4}$, or 50%. The game is fair.

2 In a game, each letter of the alphabet is written on a separate card. A card is drawn at random. If the letter is before the letter *M*, Player A wins. Otherwise, Player B wins. Is the game fair?

There are 26 possible outcomes. There are 12 ways for Player A to win (drawing an *A, B, C, D, E, F, G, H, I, J, K,* or *L*). The probability of Player A winning is $\frac{12}{26}$, or about 46%. There are 14 ways for Player B to win. The probability of Player B winning is $\frac{14}{26}$, or about 54%. The game is not fair.

Try It

a. Players A and B each write down a whole number less than 10. If one number is a factor of the other, Player A wins. If not, Player B wins. Is the game fair?

b. Players A and B each write down a whole number. If the *difference* between the numbers is even, Player A wins. If not, Player B wins. Is the game fair?

Check | Your Understanding

1. Why is it important to consider whether or not a game is fair?

2. Why would anyone be willing to play a game that is unfair?

Remember

You can use multiplication to determine the total number of outcomes. You can use a tree diagram to list all of the possible outcomes.

[Pages 642–643]

Practice and Apply

1. **Getting Started** In a game, two number cubes are rolled. If the product of the resulting numbers is less than 18, Player A wins. Otherwise Player B wins. Follow these steps to determine if the game is fair.

    a. Complete the chart to list the products of the numbers.

    b. Find the probability for getting a product less than 18.

    c. Find the probability for getting a product greater than or equal to 18.

    d. Use the probabilities you found to determine if the game is fair.

First Roll

Second Roll	1	2	3	4	5	6
1	1	2	3	4	5	6
2	2				10	
3	3			12		
4	4					
5	5	10				
6	6					36

Problem Solving For Exercises 2–5, determine if the game is fair. If it is *not*, tell which player has the higher probability of winning.

2. A blue number cube is labeled −3, 3, 3, −5, 6, 6 and a red number cube is labeled −1, 2, 2, 4, 4, 6. Sheila wins if the number on the blue cube is greater than the number on the red cube. Manda wins if the number on the red cube is greater, or if both numbers are the same.

3. A nickel and a dime are tossed. The winner is determined as shown.

  Tim wins

  Vern wins

  Maggie wins

  Urse wins

4. A number cube is tossed. Player 1 wins if the number is less than 3. Otherwise, Player 2 wins.

5. Edna and Charity played a number game 20 times. Charity won 35% of the time. Edna won 65% of the time.

6. **Test Prep** The probabilities for each player winning a game are listed. Which group does not represent a fair game?

    Ⓐ $\frac{3}{12}, \frac{2}{4}$ Ⓑ $\frac{4}{8}, \frac{5}{10}$ Ⓒ $\frac{1}{3}, \frac{1}{3}, \frac{1}{3}$ Ⓓ $\frac{7}{14}, \frac{7}{14}$

PRACTICE 12-6

7. Daryn rolled a number cube 50 times and recorded how many times he got each number. His bar graph is shown. Is it possible that Daryn is using a fair cube?

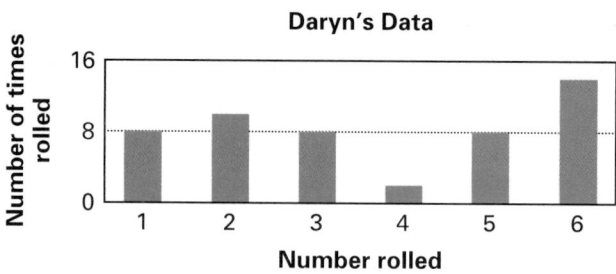

Daryn's Data

Problem Solving and Reasoning

8. Communicate In many games, the team or person that goes first is determined by flipping a coin. Heads goes first, tails goes second. Why do you think this is such a common method?

9. Critical Thinking You and a friend toss a coin to decide who will go first for a game. Your friends says, "Heads I win. Tails you lose." Is this method fair or unfair? Explain.

10. **Journal** In a game, the probability that Player A wins is 40%. The probability that Player B wins is 40%. The probability that neither player wins is 20%. Is this game fair? Explain your reasoning.

Mixed Review

11. Draw a tree diagram showing the following. *[Lesson 12-4]*

a. The possible outcomes for tossing 3 coins.

b. The possible pizza combinations using 5 different toppings, 2 different cheeses, and 3 different crusts. Assume each pizza has one topping, one cheese, and one crust.

12. What is the probability of spinning a number less than 5 on Spinner 1 and an A on Spinner 2? *[Lesson 12-5]*

Spinner 1

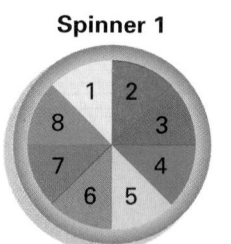

Spinner 2

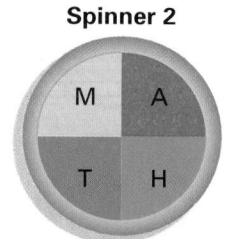

Project Progress

Make tickets for each game. On the tickets, state the probability of winning the game. Explain the probability of winning, and make sure that each game is fair. Decide on prizes for the winners, and describe the prizes on the tickets. Schedule a time for your fun fair.

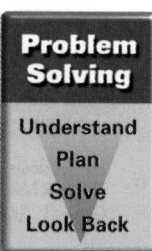

Problem Solving

Understand
Plan
Solve
Look Back

PROBLEM SOLVING 12-6

You learned how to find all possible outcomes by making tree diagrams, to calculate the probability of a compound event occurring, and to use probabilities to decide whether or not a game is fair. Now, you will use these ideas to design two games of chance.

Free Parking!

You will be designing two games of chance. When designing the games, you must follow these instructions:

1. Both games must be games of chance.

2. You can use any materials for either game, such as cards, number cubes, or spinners. You can use the same materials for both games, or a different set for each game.

3. One game should be a fair game. The other game should be an unfair game.

4. Each game should be accompanied by a set of rules clearly written, so that anyone could understand how to play the game.

5. Each game should have a written explanation of how you determined that the game was fair or unfair.

1. Suppose you toss three coins.

    a. How many possible outcomes are there?

    b. What is the probability for each outcome happening?

3. There is one of four different prizes inside each box of Toastie Oaties. If you buy three boxes, what is the probability of getting the same prize in each box?

5. A locker combination has three numbers. Each number is a whole number from 1 to 35.

    a. How many locker combinations are possible if the numbers can be repeated?

    b. What is the probability that someone could choose the correct combination in one try?

2. Laurel made 12 oatmeal cookies, 10 sugar cookies, and 15 chocolate chip cookies. Her brother took a cookie at random. What is the probability that he *didn't* take a chocolate chip cookie?

4. **Geometry** Suppose you toss a quarter onto a 2-foot square that has a 1-foot diameter circular region shaded. Does the probability of the quarter landing outside the circular region depend on the location of the circle? Explain.

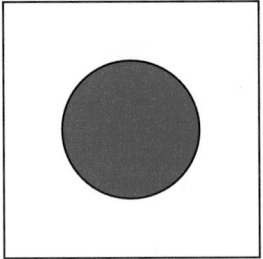

6. Two coins are tossed. Player A wins if they both land with the same side up. Player B wins if they land differently. Is the game fair? Explain.

7. One 8-sided die whose sides are numbered 1 through 8 is tossed. Player A wins if the number on top is less than 4. Player B wins if the number on top is greater than 3. Is the game fair? Explain.

Test Prep

In order for a game to be fair, all players must have an even chance of winning.

8. The following percentages list the chances of each player winning different 3-player games. Which game is fair?

    I. 20%, 30%, 40%   **II.** 40%, 40%, 20%   **III.** 50%, 50%, 0%

    Ⓐ Only I   Ⓑ II and III   Ⓒ I, II, and III   Ⓓ Not here

REVIEW 12B

Extend Key Ideas ● Probability

Odds

The chances of an event happening can be expressed in several ways. Two common ways are with fractions and percents. The chances of getting red on the spinner are $\frac{1}{4}$, or 25%. Both of these expressions are ratios that compare the ways of getting red to the total number of outcomes.

You can also express chance using *odds*. Odds are also ratios, but they don't compare the number of favorable outcomes to the total number of outcomes. They compare the number of favorable outcomes to the number of *unfavorable* outcomes.

When discussing the odds *for* an event, the number of favorable outcomes is listed first. For the spinner, the odds *for* getting red are 1 to 3. The odds for rolling a number cube and getting a 6 are 1 to 5.

When discussing the odds *against* an event, the number of unfavorable outcomes is listed first. For the spinner, the odds *against* getting red are 3 to 1. The odds against rolling a number cube and getting a 6 are 5 to 1.

Try It

Using the spinner, express the odds *for* each event.

1. Landing on a letter
2. Landing on a number
3. Landing on an even number

Using the spinner, express the odds *against* each event.

4. Landing on a two-digit number
5. Landing on the "?"
6. Landing on a number or letter that rhymes with "be"

Graphic Organizer

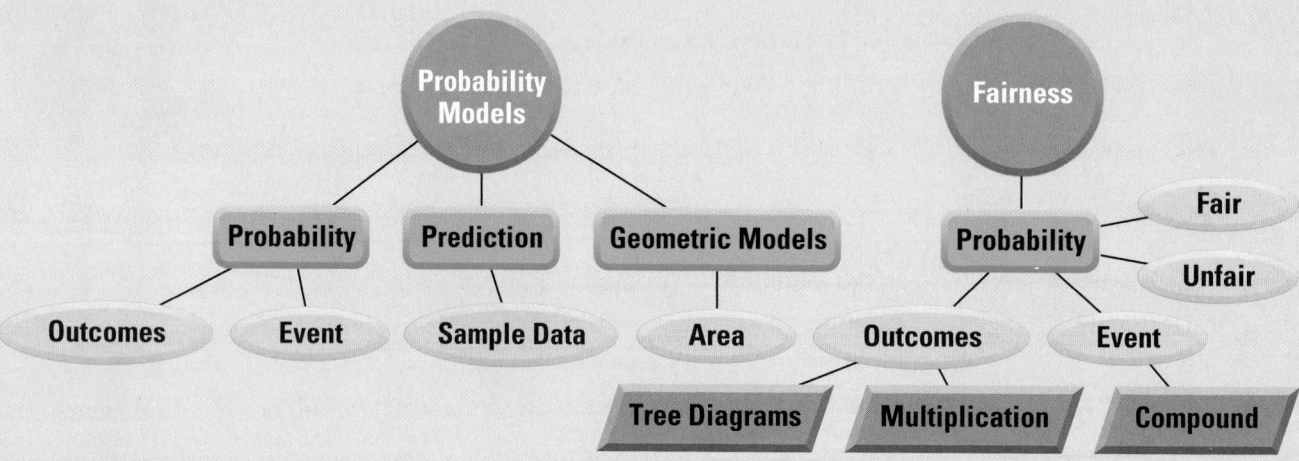

Section 12A Probability Models

Summary

- The **outcomes** of an **experiment** are all the results that can happen. The **probability** that an **event** or particular outcome will happen is a ratio.

$$P(\text{event}) = \frac{\text{number of ways an event can occur}}{\text{number of possible outcomes}}$$

- When you don't know all the possible outcomes or the number of ways an event can occur, you can use **sample** data and make a prediction.

- When the chance of an event happening depends on the size of an area inside a figure, you can determine its probability using a ratio.

Review

1. Estimate the probability of having a birthday in a month that begins with a *J*.

2. If $P(\text{event}) = \frac{5}{6}$, what can you conclude about the event?

3. Jim is on call at work one day each week. What are his chances of being called to work on Tuesday, Wednesday, or Friday?

4. Estimate the probability of hitting the shaded area with a dart.

5. Nine businesses out of 27 surveyed on Main Street were closed more than 5 days because of a recent flood. Predict how many of the 48 businesses on the street were closed more than 5 days.

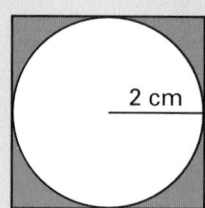

2 cm

Summary

- A **tree diagram** is used to list the outcomes of a series of experiments. You can also use multiplication to find the number of possible outcomes.

- You can find the probability of a **compound event** using a ratio:

  $$\frac{\text{the number of ways a compound event can happen}}{\text{the number of possible outcomes}}.$$

- A game is **fair** if each player has an equal probability of winning. Otherwise, it is **unfair**.

Review

6. Complete a tree diagram that shows how many different outfits can be worn if there are 2 kinds of shirts (T-shirts and sweatshirts), 4 types of pants (shorts, dress pants, jeans, and cutoffs), and 3 kinds of shoes (loafers, hiking boots, and sandals.)

7. Use multiplication to find the possible number of fishing-gear combinations that could be assembled using 5 poles, 3 kinds of spinners, 2 kinds of floaters, and a box of 6 hand-tied flies.

8. If you spin both of the spinners, how many possible outcomes are there?

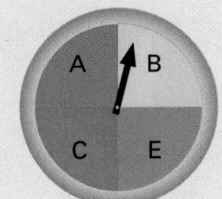

Spinner 1   **Spinner 2**

9. What is the probability of spinning a blue or red on Spinner 1 and a vowel on Spinner 2?

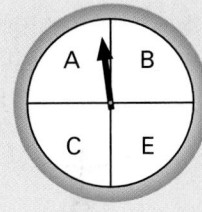

Spinner 1   **Spinner 2**

10. Jane rolls a six-sided number cube twice. What is the probability that she rolls a 3 and then a 1?

11. What is the probability of flipping four coins and getting all tails?

12.

5	10	15	20	25
30	35	40	45	50

In a card game, each card is labeled with one of the multiples of 5, from 5 to 50. Player A draws a card. If the number is 25 or less, Player A wins. Otherwise, Player B wins. Is the game fair? Explain.

13. Player A and Player B each roll a number cube. If the two numbers can be put together to make a 2-digit even number, Player A wins. Otherwise, Player B wins. Is the game fair? Explain.

Chapter 12 Assessment

For questions 1–3, tell whether the statement is true or false. If it is false, change the words in bold to make it true.

1. The probability of an event $= \dfrac{\text{number of possible outcomes}}{\text{number of ways an event can happen}}$.

2. The **outcomes** of a situation are all the ways something can happen.

3. A **compound event** lists the outcomes of a series of experiments.

4. One event has a probability of 65%, and one has a probability of $\frac{4}{5}$. Which is more likely to occur?

5. An airline randomly assigns passengers to seats in rows 15 through 32. What are the chances of being assigned to a row number higher than 21?

6. In an election poll, 320 out of 500 people said they would vote for a school bond issue. The bond issue needs 51% of the votes to pass. What are its chances of passing? Explain.

7. Two number cubes are tossed.

   a. How many outcomes are there?

   b. What is the probability that the number on each cube is a multiple of 3?

8. If a button lands on the game board, what is the chance it will land on a shaded triangle?

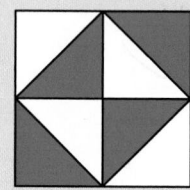

9. a. Name two methods of finding the number of possible kinds of sundaes that can be made with vanilla, chocolate, and strawberry ice creams; fudge, pineapple, raspberry, and cherry syrups; and toppings of peanuts, coconut, raisins, or candies.

   b. How many different sundaes can be made?

10. If you spin both spinners, what is the probability that the pointers will land on a circle and a triangle?

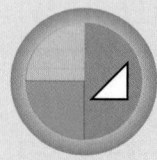

Spinner 1   Spinner 2

Performance Task

Roll two number cubes. If both numbers are prime, Player A gets a point. If both numbers are less than 5, Player B gets a point. If both numbers are even, Player C gets a point. Is the game fair or unfair? Explain.

Multiple Choice

Choose the best answer.

1. Divide 8.442 by 0.42. *[Lesson 3-11]*

ⓐ 0.021   ⓑ 0.201

ⓒ 20.1   ⓓ 21

2. What conversion factor do you multiply by to convert from quarts to pints? *[Lesson 4-3]*

ⓐ 4   ⓑ 2

ⓒ $\frac{1}{2}$ ⓓ $\frac{1}{4}$

3. Find the least common multiple of 36 and 54. *[Lesson 5-3]*

ⓐ 2   ⓑ 9   ⓒ 18   ⓓ 108

4. Subtract: $4\frac{3}{8} - 3\frac{1}{2}$ *[Lesson 6-6]*

ⓐ $\frac{7}{8}$ ⓑ $1\frac{1}{3}$

ⓒ $1\frac{7}{8}$ ⓓ $9\frac{7}{8}$

5. Multiply: $\frac{2}{3} \times 1\frac{5}{6}$ *[Lesson 7-3]*

ⓐ $1\frac{2}{9}$ ⓑ $1\frac{4}{9}$

ⓒ $2\frac{1}{3}$ ⓓ None of these

6. Which description best fits the pair of lines? *[Lesson 8-1]*

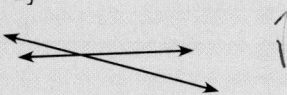

ⓐ Parallel   ⓑ Perpendicular

ⓒ Perpendicular and intersecting

ⓓ Intersecting

7. If a figure with point $A(-3, -4)$ is reflected over the x-axis, what is its image point? *[Lesson 8-8]*

ⓐ $(3, 4)$ ⓑ $(3, -4)$

ⓒ $(-3, 4)$ ⓓ None of these

8. Find the product of -7×4. *[Lesson 9-4]*

ⓐ 28   ⓑ 27   ⓒ −27   ⓓ −28

9. Which point does not lie on the graph of $y = -3x$? *[Lesson 9-7]*

ⓐ $(10, -30)$ ⓑ $(-30, 10)$

ⓒ $(-2, 6)$ ⓓ $(6, -18)$

10. The sides of one triangle measure 3 ft, 5 ft, and 6 ft. The shortest side of a similar triangle measures 18 ft. What are the lengths of its other two sides? *[Lesson 10-7]*

ⓐ 30 ft, 48 ft   ⓑ 30 ft, 36 ft

ⓒ 11 ft, 15 ft   ⓓ 6 ft, 10 ft

11. If Sandra saves 35% on the purchase of a $22 dress, how much does she save? *[Lesson 10-11]*

ⓐ $77.70   ⓑ $14.30

ⓒ $7.70   ⓓ None of these

12. Find the surface area to the nearest tenth of a cylinder whose base has a radius of 4 cm and whose height is 2 cm. *[Lesson 11-4]*

ⓐ 196.5 cm²   ⓑ 150.7 cm²

ⓒ 50.2 cm²   ⓓ 25.1 cm²

13. Find the volume of the box. *[Lesson 11-6]*

ⓐ 84 in³

ⓑ 66 in³

ⓒ 33 in³

ⓓ 84 in²

3 in.   7 in.   4 in.

14. Eleven cards spell MATHEMATICS. What is the probability of picking an A card? *[Lesson 12-1]*

ⓐ $\frac{2}{11}$ ⓑ $\frac{11}{2}$

ⓒ $\frac{1}{5}$ ⓓ None of these

Chapter Review

Chapter 1 Review

1. How much was spent on clothes and entertainment?

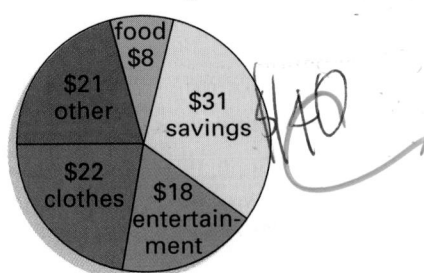

Tara's Budget

food $8
$21 other
$31 savings
$22 clothes
$18 entertainment

2. In which month did the sales of hot dogs increase the most when compared to the month before?

Hot Dogs Sold

May to June

3. Does the scatter-plot show a trend? Explain.

Price of Car and Number Sold

4. A pictograph's key shows that a symbol equals 10 bicycles. How many symbols would be needed to represent 115 bicycles?

11½ symbols

(10) 115

Use the Science Test Scores data to answer Exercises 5 and 6.

5. Use tallies to make a frequency chart of test scores in these groups: under 70; 70–79; 80–89; 90–100.

Science Test Scores									
86	72	98	79	84	63	72	86	89	72
98	92	75	81	76	93	94	88	64	77

—mode

6. Use the test score data to make a line plot.

7. Make a bar graph using the number of Supreme Court Justices appointed by these Presidents: Clinton, 2; Bush, 2; Reagan, 3; Carter, 0; Ford, 1; and Nixon, 4.

8. Make a stem-and-leaf diagram for the following data: 43, 41, 56, 37, 42, 48, 45, 43, 51, 54, 39, 44, 42, 47, 42, 40.

9. Find the median, mode, and mean for these stolen-base records: Henderson, 1117; Brock, 938; Cobb, 892; Raines, 777; Collins, 743; Carey, 738; Wagner, 703; Morgan, 689; Wilson, 661; and Campaneris, 649.

no mode

649
661
689
703
738
743
777
892
938
1117

need

10. For any data set, which of the three measures (mean, median, or mode) is most likely to be affected by an outlier? Explain.

mean,

median is just the middle # & sometimes is not affected much. mode is not 'cause no t often the outleir is same as another # in

set of data

Chapter 2 Review

1. Give the place value of 4 in 2,549,013.

2. Write 81,294,537 in word form.

3. Round 81,294,537 to the given place: **a.** Thousands   **b.** Millions

4. Use > or < and compare 593,293 and 593,392.

5. Order from least to greatest: 3,192,536; 31,925,006; 3,492,426

6. Give the base and exponent of 13^6.   **7.** Write 6^5 in expanded form.

8. Write 3 squared in exponential notation.

9. Write each in standard form:

   a. 7^2 **b.** 8 cubed   **c.** 12^1 **d.** 5 to the fourth power

Use mental math to solve each problem.

10. $170 + 30 + 64 + 36$ **11.** 8×303 **12.** 40×700 **13.** $54,000 \div 60$

Use estimation to solve each problem.

14. $592 - 128$ **15.** $4518 + 3179$ **16.** 47×712 **17.** $152 \times 9 \times 12$

Use the order of operations to solve each problem.

18. $7 \times 8 \div 2 + 3$ **19.** $(11 - 5)^2 \div 3 \times 7$

Find the next three numbers for each pattern.

20. 53, 49, 45, 41, 37, …   **21.** 24, 36, 35, 47, 46, …

22. State whether each phrase describes a constant or a variable.

   a. The number of quarters in a dollar

   b. The number of quarters in your pocket

Evaluate each expression for x = 3, 5, and 7.

23. $3x$ **24.** $x + 9$

25. Julio bought a roll of film with n pictures. He took 18 of them. Write an expression for the number of pictures left on the roll of film.

26. Is the equation $24 - x = 15$ true for $x = 9$? For $x = 11$?

27. Solve for x: **a.** $x + 6 = 27$ **b.** $\frac{x}{3} = 6$

1. Show each number in decimal form.

  a. 41 thousandths

  b.
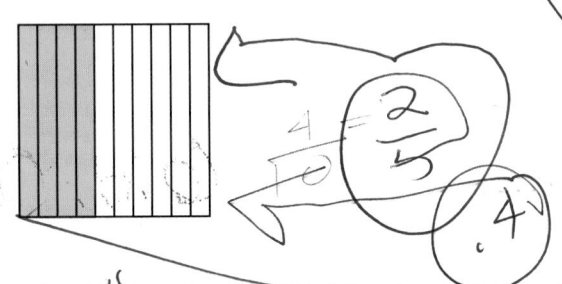

2. Give the fly's length to the nearest centimeter; the nearest tenth of a centimeter.

7cm
7.3cm

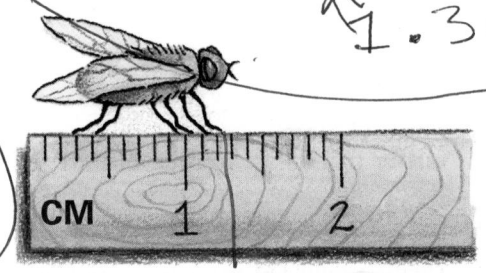

3. Round 0.6927 to the thousandths place.
  .693

4. On a ruler, is 3.34 closer to 3.3 or 3.4? Explain. *idc i'll tell you verbally*

5. Use the > symbol to order the decimals from greatest to least: 4.018; 4.179; and 4.0182

  4.0182 > 4.179 > 4.018

6. The state of New York has a population of about 17,990,000. Write this number in scientific notation.

  1.799 × 10⁷

Estimate.

7. 29.21 + 72.4 **8.** 451.8 − 93.507 **9.** 15.9 × 6 **10.** 46.4 ÷ 15

Simplify.

11. 8.4 + 421.93 **12.** 11.03 − 2.287 **13.** 7.3 × 4.1 **14.** 10.8 ÷ 2.7

15. The star Arcturus is about 10.3 light-years from Earth. The star Vega is about 7.5 light-years from Earth. How many more light-years away from Earth is Arcturus? *2.8 more lite years*

16. Solve.

  a. $h - 7.2 = 12.3$ **b.** $x + 6 = 19.3$

Simplify.

17. 3.68 × 0.01 **18.** 4.91 × 10,000 **19.** 83 ÷ 100 **20.** 638 ÷ 0.001

Solve.

21. $0.5k = 0.35$ **22.** $\dfrac{n}{0.9} = 5$

Chapter 4 Review

Find the perimeter of each figure.

1.

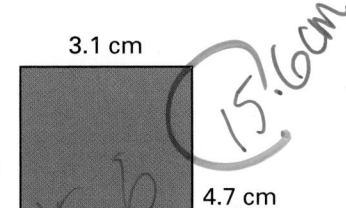

3.1 cm

4.7 cm

2.

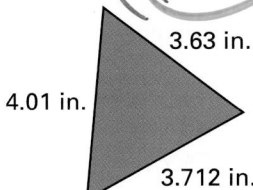

3.63 in.

4.01 in.

3.712 in.

3.

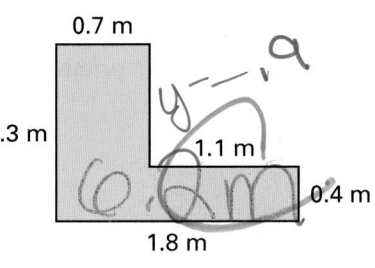

0.7 m

1.3 m

1.1 m

0.4 m

1.8 m

Use powers of 10 or conversion factors to find each measure.

4. 174 g = ☐ kg

5. 60 in. = ☐ ft

6. 6.5 lb = ☐ oz

7. 5 gal = ☐ qt

8. 24.913 km = ☐ m

9. 2.8 kg = ☐ g

10. A rectangular swimming pool is 25 m by 50 m. What is the perimeter of the pool in meters? In centimeters?

Find the area of each figure.

11.

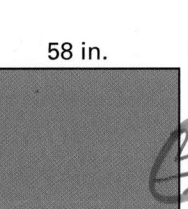

58 in.

51 in.

12.

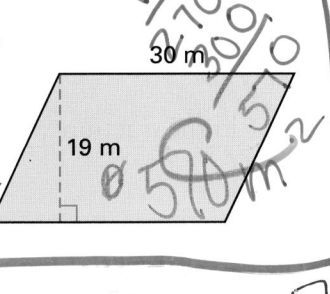

30 m

19 m

13.

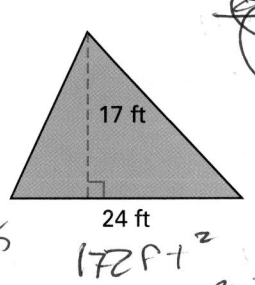

17 ft

24 ft

14. What is the area of a square with a side 12.5 m long?

15. What is the area of a rectangular desktop that is 2.5 ft long and 3 ft wide?

16. Find the base of a triangle whose height is 8.4 in. and area is 126 in².

17. The diameter of a circle is 12 mm.

a. Find the circumference. Use 3.14 for π.

b. Find its area.

18. Find the area of the irregular shape.

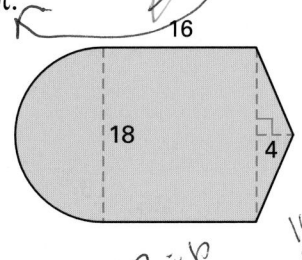

16

18

4

Chapter 5 Review

Test each number for divisibility by 2, 3, 5, 6, 9, and 10.

1. 104   **2.** 660   **3.** 450   **4.** 1200

handwritten: 2,   *handwritten: 2,3,5,6 9,10*

Label each number as prime or composite. If it is composite, find its prime factorization.

handwritten: 2²×19   *handwritten: 3⁵*

5. 76   **6.** 101   **7.** 243   **8.** 85

handwritten: com   *handwritten: com*

Find the least common multiple for each number pair.

9. 14, 24   **10.** 21, 35

What fraction does the shaded part of each model represent?

11.

12.

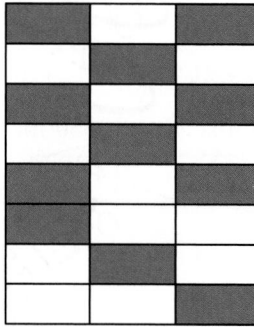

13. Identify the numerator and denominator in the fraction $\frac{7}{12}$.

Write each fraction in lowest terms.

14. $\frac{45}{60}$ **15.** $\frac{48}{128}$ **16.** $\frac{18}{63}$ **17.** $\frac{420}{480}$

handwritten 14: 9/12 3/4   *handwritten 16: = 2/7*

Rewrite each as a mixed number or as an improper fraction.

18. $\frac{43}{5}$ **19.** $3\frac{5}{6}$ **20.** $\frac{25}{4}$ **21.** $7\frac{2}{7}$

handwritten 18: 8 3/5   *handwritten 20: 6 1/4*

22. Draw a model of the fraction $\frac{3}{5}$ and name an equivalent fraction.

23. Four drawings have heights of $6\frac{1}{3}$, $\frac{15}{2}$, $7\frac{3}{4}$, and $\frac{15}{4}$ inches. List their heights in order from shortest to tallest.

Rewrite each fraction as a decimal.

24. $\frac{7}{8}$ **25.** $\frac{1}{6}$ **26.** $\frac{13}{4}$ **27.** $\frac{14}{5}$

1. Write the equation this model represents.

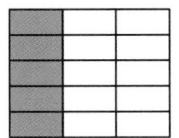 + 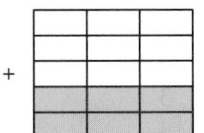 =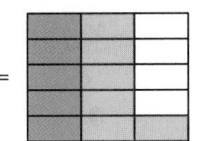

Find the least common multiple of each number pair.

2. $5, 8$ **3.** $6, 24$ **4.** $10, 14$ **5.** $12, 27$

Add or subtract. Write each answer in lowest terms.

6. $\dfrac{8}{9} - \dfrac{5}{9}$ **7.** $\dfrac{3}{8} + \dfrac{9}{8}$ **8.** $\dfrac{2}{11} + \dfrac{7}{11}$ **9.** $\dfrac{5}{6} - \dfrac{1}{6}$

10. $\dfrac{3}{19} + \dfrac{14}{19}$ **11.** $\dfrac{7}{16} - \dfrac{1}{4}$ **12.** $\dfrac{7}{8} + \dfrac{1}{3}$ **13.** $\dfrac{4}{7} - \dfrac{1}{2}$

14. $\dfrac{7}{9} + \dfrac{3}{4}$ **15.** $\dfrac{1}{6} + \dfrac{9}{10}$ **16.** $\dfrac{6}{7} - \dfrac{4}{5}$ **17.** $\dfrac{3}{4} - \dfrac{3}{5}$

Solve each equation.

18. $\dfrac{4}{15} + y = \dfrac{13}{15}$ **19.** $x - \dfrac{3}{10} = \dfrac{1}{5}$ **20.** $t + \dfrac{1}{4} = \dfrac{7}{8}$

Round each mixed number to the nearest whole number.

21. $7\dfrac{4}{5}$ **22.** $12\dfrac{1}{2}$ **23.** $23\dfrac{9}{19}$ **24.** $\dfrac{6}{11}$

Estimate each sum or difference.

25. $6\dfrac{3}{4} + 3\dfrac{1}{8}$ **26.** $11\dfrac{1}{5} - 5\dfrac{2}{7}$ **27.** $4\dfrac{7}{15} + 1\dfrac{2}{5}$ **28.** $8\dfrac{4}{5} - 2\dfrac{5}{11}$

29. Find the sum of $2\dfrac{7}{9}$ and $5\dfrac{1}{9}$.   **30.** Find the difference between $12\dfrac{10}{13}$ and $4\dfrac{2}{13}$.

31. Elena wanted to tie a $37\dfrac{1}{2}$ in. ribbon on a gift. She had a $42\dfrac{1}{4}$ in. ribbon. How much would she need to trim off the ribbon in order to use it on the gift?

Simplify each expression.

32. $2\dfrac{3}{4} + 5\dfrac{1}{4}$ **33.** $7\dfrac{1}{8} + 4\dfrac{1}{3}$ **34.** $10\dfrac{7}{9} - 3\dfrac{2}{9}$ **35.** $5\dfrac{11}{16} - 4\dfrac{3}{16}$

36. $7\dfrac{4}{15} - 5\dfrac{1}{9}$ **37.** $8\dfrac{2}{5} + 7$ **38.** $6\dfrac{4}{5} - 2\dfrac{1}{3}$ **39.** $19 - 4\dfrac{7}{12}$

1. Write the problem the model represents.

Estimate.

2. $3\frac{1}{2} \times 7\frac{1}{8}$

3. $15\frac{5}{7} \div 3\frac{3}{4}$

Simplify.

4. $\frac{2}{5} \times 6$

5. $\frac{3}{7} \times \frac{3}{8}$

6. $\frac{2}{3} \times \frac{2}{3}$

7. $\frac{3}{10} \times \frac{1}{4}$

8. $\frac{1}{6} \times \frac{5}{6}$

9. $4\frac{3}{5} \times \frac{8}{13}$

10. $1\frac{1}{4} \times 1\frac{7}{8}$

11. $2\frac{7}{10} \times 3\frac{1}{3}$

12. The distance between Joaquin's house and the store is $1\frac{1}{4}$ miles. If he walks $\frac{1}{3}$ of the way to the store, how far has he walked?

13. Is the product of two mixed numbers always larger than either number? Explain.

14. Write the equation that the model represents.

State the reciprocal.

15. $\frac{4}{11}$

16. 5

Simplify.

17. $4 \div \frac{3}{4}$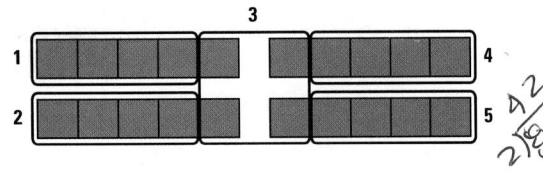

18. $\frac{1}{3} \div \frac{6}{5}$

19. $\frac{10}{7} \div \frac{12}{5}$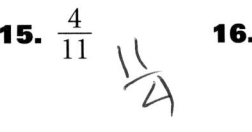

20. $\frac{5}{8} \div \frac{1}{4}$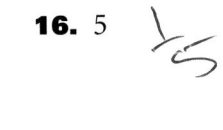

21. $\frac{5}{9} \div 4$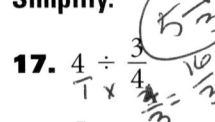

22. $\frac{1}{4} \div 8$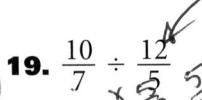

23. $\frac{3}{12} \div 6$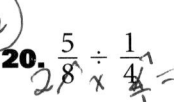

24. $\frac{5}{6} \div 3\frac{1}{2}$

For each equation, state if the given value will make the equation true.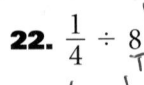

25. $\frac{3}{4}u = \frac{3}{10}$; $u = \frac{3}{5}$

26. $t \div \frac{1}{4} = \frac{5}{3}$; $t = \frac{20}{3}$

27. $\frac{5}{6}r = \frac{25}{36}$; $r = \frac{5}{6}$

Solve.

28. $\frac{2}{3}x = \frac{5}{6}$

29. $\frac{3}{4}t = \frac{15}{20}$

30. $\frac{4}{5}j = \frac{8}{35}$

31. $\frac{3}{10}h = \frac{21}{80}$

1. Draw and label a segment with end points *C* and *D*.

2. Draw and label an acute angle through points *A*, *B*, and *C* with *B* as the vertex.

3. Which angle sum has the same number of degrees as a right angle, two <u>complementary</u> angles or two supplementary angles?

4. Draw and label:
   a. Two rays that are perpendicular
   b. $\overleftrightarrow{AB}$

5. Classify the triangle whose angles measure 73°, 24°, and 83°.

6. What kind of triangle has <u>two sides with length 4 cm</u> and one side with length 5 cm?

7. Which quadrilaterals have two pairs of parallel sides?

8. Explain why all squares are rectangles, but not all rectangles are squares.

Tell whether each transformation is a reflection, translation, or rotation.

9.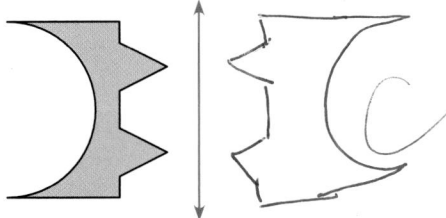

10.

11.

12. Are the figures in Exercises 9–11 congruent? Explain.

13. Trace the figure and draw its reflection over the line.

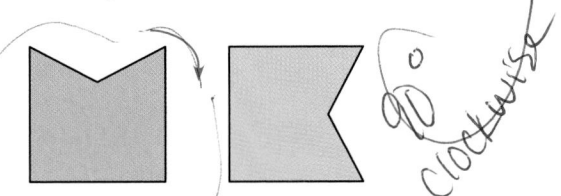

14. Tell whether the figure has line symmetry. If it does, draw its line(s) of symmetry.

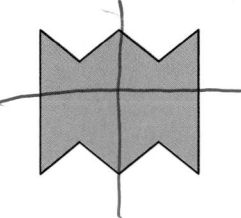

15. Give the number of degrees and the direction the figure has been rotated.

16. What is the least rotation that will land the rectangle on top of itself?

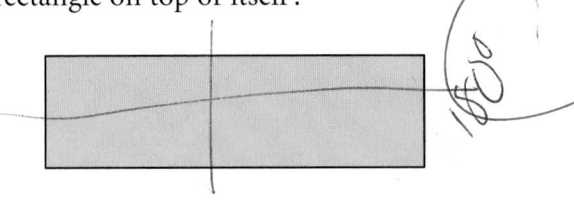

17. If a figure has rotational symmetry, can it also have line symmetry? Explain.

18. Do all parallelograms tessellate? If not, what type of parallelograms tessellate?

1. Locate the integers $-3, 2, -5, 6, 1,$ and -1 on a number line.

2. What is the closest integer to the right of $-5\frac{2}{3}$ on a number line?

3. Is the product of one positive and one negative number a positive or negative value?

4. Is the quotient of two negative numbers positive or negative?

Write the equation that is shown by each model.

5.

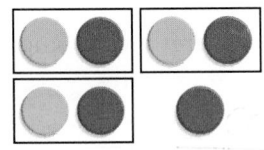

6.

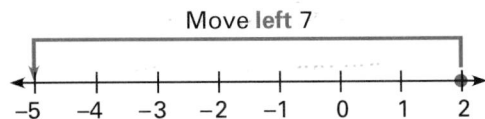

Simplify.

7. $-3 + (-9)$ **8.** $2 + (-6)$ **9.** $-4 + 11$

10. $-7 - 8$ **11.** $5 - (-2)$ **12.** $-6 - (-1)$

13. $-7 - (-7)$ **14.** $8 \times (-5)$ **15.** $-4 \times (-9)$

16. -7×3 **17.** $-24 \div 4$ **18.** $-45 \div (-9)$

19. Name the ordered pair for the point 2 units to the right of the origin and 7 units down.

20. Name the quadrant where the point $(-1, -4)$ is located.

21. Name a point the same *distance* from the origin as $(0, 3)$ and located:

  a. On the x-axis   **b.** On the y-axis

22. Create $A'B'C'$ by translating the triangle ABC 3 units to the left and 2 units down. Give the coordinates of A', B', and C'.

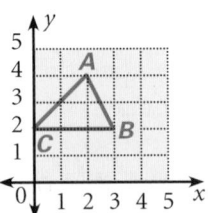

23. Rectangle $QRST$ has coordinates $Q(-5, 1)$, $R(-5, 3)$, $S(-1, 3)$, and $T(-1, 1)$. If $QRST$ is reflected across the y-axis, name the coordinates of Q', R', S', and T'.

24. a. Graph the equations $y = x - 2$ and $y = x + 3$ on the same coordinate grid.

  b. Explain why one of the graphs is a translation of the other.

1. Show three ways to write the ratio of four lemons to seven limes.

2. Write the ratio $\frac{35}{60}$ in lowest terms.

3. Each bag contains 8 red marbles and 11 blue marbles. If there are 4 bags, what is the ratio in lowest terms:
   a. Of red marbles to blue marbles?
   b. Of blue marbles to red marbles?
   c. Of red marbles to total marbles?
   d. Of bags to marbles?

4. According to the graph, what is the ratio of fiction books to nonfiction books? Of fiction books to total books?

Library Books

Fiction

Nonfiction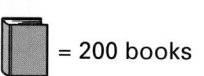

 = 200 books

5. Which of the following ratios is *not* equal to the ratio 8 to 24?

   (A) $\frac{5}{15}$ (B) $\frac{30}{10}$ (C) 7:21 (D) $\frac{1}{3}$

6. Which of the following is not a rate?

   (A) $\frac{5 \text{ ft}}{4 \text{ sec}}$ (B) $\frac{4 \text{ ft}}{1 \text{ sec}}$ (C) $\frac{4 \text{ sec}}{5 \text{ ft}}$ (D) $\frac{4 \text{ sec}}{5 \text{ sec}}$

7. Use a table to find four equal rates that describe boiling 2 gallons of water in 4 minutes.

8. What is the unit rate of a car's travel time if the car travels 240 miles in 5 hours?

9. Can the ratios $\frac{5 \text{ mi}}{8 \text{ s}}$ and $\frac{35 \text{ s}}{56 \text{ mi}}$ form a proportion? Explain.

10. Solve for a: $\frac{6}{15} = \frac{4}{a}$.

11. Apples cost $1.20 per pound. How much do 40 oz of apples cost?

12. Explain why the two triangles are similar.

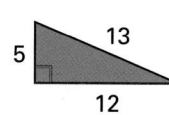 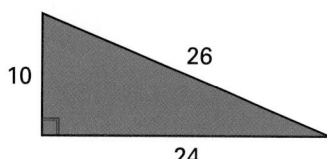

Write each percent as a ratio of a number to 100, as a fraction in lowest terms, and as a decimal.

13. 60%   14. 12%   15. 45%   16. 52%

17. In Denver, Colorado, in 1990, 23% of the population was Latino. If the total population was 467,610, about how many Latino people lived in Denver?

Classify each solid. If it is a polyhedron, state the number of faces, edges, and vertices.

1.

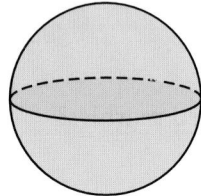

2.

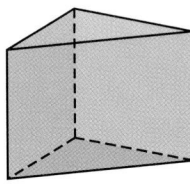

3.

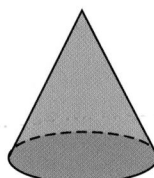

Find the surface area of each figure. Use 3.14 for π.

4.

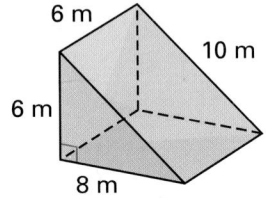

5.

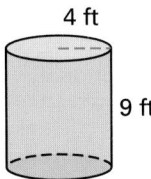

6.

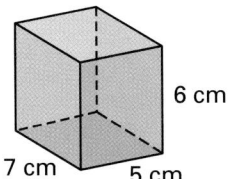

For each solid, draw the front view, the side view, and the top view.

7.

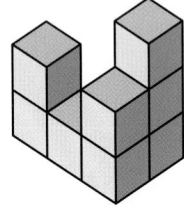

8.

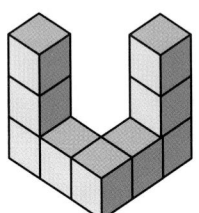

9.

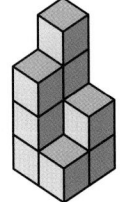

Find each volume.

10.

11.

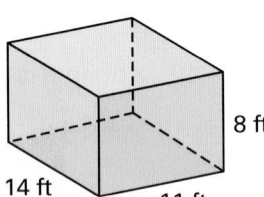

12.

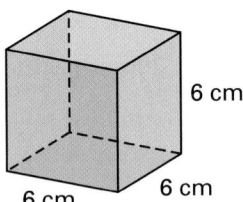

13. The Veggie Soup Co. sells its soup in cans like the one pictured. Find the surface area of the can. Use 3.14 for π.

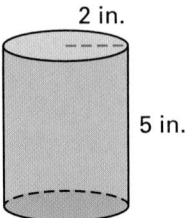

Chapter 12 Review

1. Estimate the probability of choosing a person at random whose birthday falls on a Monday next year.

2. If $P(\text{event}) = \frac{2}{3}$, what is the probability that the event will not occur?

3. Michiko bought 12 eggs. Three of them were brown. One was spotted. The rest were white. If she chooses an egg at random, what are the chances she will choose a white or brown egg?

4. In one neighborhood, 30 out of 45 people surveyed said they read at least one book each week. Predict how many of the 600 people in the neighborhood read at least one book each week.

5. A spinner has 6 equal sections labeled A, B, C, D, E, and F.

   a. What is the probability of landing in the "B" section?

   b. What is the probability of *not* landing in "B" section?

6. Estimate the probability of hitting the shaded area with a dart.

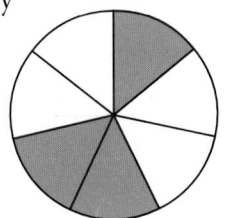

7. Complete a tree diagram that shows how many different kinds of lunches can be made if there are 4 kinds of sandwiches (tuna, peanut butter, turkey, and cheese); 2 kinds of snacks (chips and fruit); and 3 kinds of drinks (milk, juice, and soda.)

8. Use multiplication to find the possible number of stereo systems that could be assembled using one each of 3 tuners, 5 compact disc players, 4 cassette players, and 3 amplifiers.

9. If you spin both of the spinners, how many possible outcomes are there?

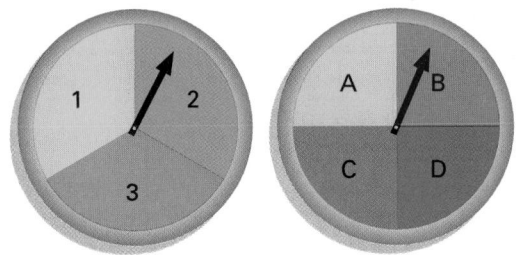

10. What is the probability of spinning A or B on Spinner 1 and an odd number on Spinner 2?

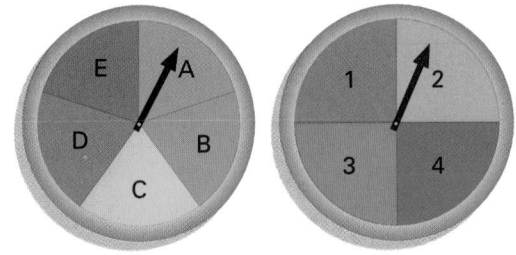

11. Emily rolls one six-sided number cube twice. What is the probability that she rolls an even number and then a 5?

12. What is the probability of flipping three coins and getting all heads?

13. Player A and Player B each roll a number cube. If the sum of the two numbers is greater than 5, Player A wins. Otherwise, Player B wins. Is the game fair? Explain.

Geometric Formulas

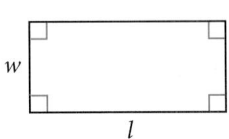

Rectangle

Area: $A = lw$

Perimeter: $p = 2l + 2w$

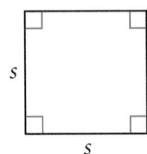

Square

Area: $A = s^2$

Perimeter: $p = 4s$

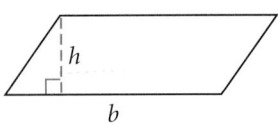

Parallelogram

Area: $A = bh$

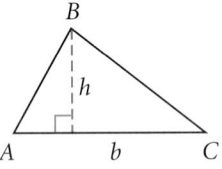

Triangle

Area: $A = \frac{1}{2}bh$

$m\angle A + m\angle B + m\angle C = 180°$

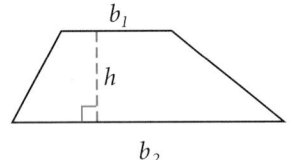

Trapezoid

Area: $A = \frac{1}{2}h(b_1 + b_2)$

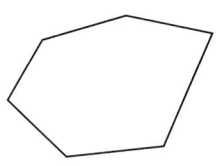

Polygon

Sum of angle measures for
n-sided polygon: $S = (n - 2)180°$

Perimeter: sum of measures of
all sides

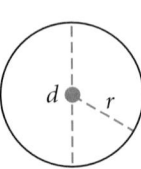

Circle

Area: $A = \pi r^2$

Circumference: $C = \pi d = 2\pi r$

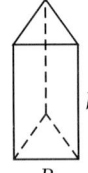

Prism

Volume: $V = Bh$

Surface Area: $SA = ph + 2B$

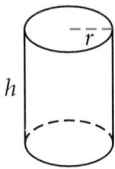

Cylinder

Volume: $V = \pi r^2 h$

Surface Area: $SA = 2\pi rh + 2\pi r^2$

Measurement Conversion Factors

Metric Measures of Length
1000 meters (m) = 1 kilometer (km)
100 centimeters (cm) = 1 m
10 decimeters (dm) = 1 m
1000 millimeters (mm) = 1 m
10 cm = 1 decimeter (dm)
10 mm = 1 cm

Area
100 square millimeters = 1 square centimeter
(mm^2) (cm^2)
10,000 cm^2 = 1 square meter (m^2)
10,000 m^2 = 1 hectare (ha)

Volume
1000 cubic millimeters = 1 cubic centimeter
(mm^3) (cm^3)
1000 cm^3 = 1 cubic decimeter (dm^3)
1,000,000 cm^3 = 1 cubic meter (m^3)

Capacity
1000 milliliters (mL) = 1 liter (L)
1000 L = 1 kiloliter (kL)

Mass
1000 kilograms (kg) = 1 metric ton (t)
1000 grams (g) = 1 kg
1000 milligrams (mg) = 1 g

Temperatures in Degrees Celsius (°C)
0°C = freezing point of water
37°C = normal body temperature
100°C = boiling point of water

Time
60 seconds (sec) = 1 minute (min)
60 min = 1 hour (hr)
24 hr = 1 day

Customary Measures of Length
12 inches (in.) = 1 foot (ft)
3 ft = 1 yard (yd)
36 in. = 1 yd
5280 ft = 1 mile (mi)
1760 yd = 1 mi
6076 ft = 1 nautical mile

Area
144 square inches = 1 square foot
(in^2) (ft^2)
9 ft^2 = 1 square yard (yd^2)
43,560 sq ft^2 = 1 acre (A)

Volume
1728 cubic inches = 1 cubic foot
(cu in.) (cu ft)
27 cu ft = 1 cubic yard (cu yard)

Capacity
8 fluid ounces (fl oz) = 1 cup (c)
2 c = 1 pint (pt)
2 pt = 1 quart (qt)
4 qt = 1 gallon (gal)

Weight
16 ounces (oz) = 1 pound (lb)
2000 lb = 1 ton (T)

Temperatures in Degrees Fahrenheit (°F)
32°F = freezing point of water
98.6°F = normal body temperature
212°F = boiling point of water

Symbols

$+$	plus or positive	$\llcorner$	right angle
$-$	minus or negative	$\perp$	is perpendicular to
$\cdot$	times	$\parallel$	is parallel to
$\times$	times	AB	length of $\overline{AB}$; distance between A and B
$\div$	divided by		
$\pm$	positive or negative	$\triangle ABC$	triangle with vertices A, B, and C
$=$	is equal to	$\angle ABC$	angle with sides $\overrightarrow{BA}$ and $\overrightarrow{BC}$
$\neq$	is not equal to	$\angle B$	angle with vertex B
$<$	is less than	$m\angle ABC$	measure of angle ABC
$>$	is greater than	$'$	prime
$\leq$	is less than or equal to	a^n	the nth power of a
$\geq$	is greater than or equal to	$|x|$	absolute value of x
$\approx$	is approximately equal to	$\sqrt{x}$	principal square root of x
$\%$	percent	π	pi (approximately 3.1416)
$a{:}b$	the ratio of a to b, or $\frac{a}{b}$	(a, b)	ordered pair with x-coordinate a and y-coordinate b
$\cong$	is congruent to	$P(A)$	the probability of event A
$\sim$	is similar to	$n!$	n factorial
$\circ$	degree(s)		
$\overleftrightarrow{AB}$	line containing points A and B		
$\overline{AB}$	line segment with endpoints A and B		
$\overrightarrow{AB}$	ray with endpoint A and containing B		

TABLES

Glossary

acute angle   An angle smaller than a right angle. [p. 413]

acute triangle   A triangle with three acute angles. [p. 424]

addend   A number added to one or more others.

addition   An operation that gives the total number when two or more numbers are put together.

algebra   A branch of mathematics in which arithmetic relations are explored using letter symbols to represent numbers.

algebraic expression   An expression that contains at least one variable. Example: $n - 7$.

angle   Two rays with the same endpoint. [p. 412]

area   The amount of surface a figure covers. [p. 229]

Associative Property   The fact that changing the grouping of addends or factors does not change the sum or product. Example: $(5 + 3) + 7 = 15$ and $5 + (3 + 7) = 15$. [p. 87]

average   See mean.

axes   See x-axis and y-axis.

bar graph   A graph using vertical or horizontal bars to display numerical information. [p. 7]

base [of an exponent]   A number multiplied by itself the number of times shown by an exponent. Example: $6^2 = 6 \times 6$, where 6 is the base. [p. 78]; **[of a figure]** On a two-dimensional figure, the distance across the bottom. [p. 230] On a prism, one of the two parallel and congruent faces. [p. 580]

binary number system   A base-2 place value system. [p. 201]

bisect   Dividing a geometric figure into two equal parts. [p. 459]

box-and-whisker plot   A graph showing the shape of a data set. [p. 57]

capacity   The volume of a figure, given in terms of liquid measure.

center   The point at the exact middle of a circle.

centi-   A prefix meaning $\frac{1}{100}$. [p. 216]

circle   See examples below. [p. 246]

circle graph   A round graph that uses different-sized wedges to show how portions of a set of data compare with the whole set. [p. 8]

circumference   The perimeter of a circle. [p. 246]

clockwise   The direction of rotation when the top of a figure turns to the right. [p. 448]

clustering   An estimation method where numbers that are approximately equal are treated as if they were equal. Example: $26 + 24 + 23$ is about $25 + 25 + 25$, or 3×25. [p. 91]

common denominator   A denominator that is the same in two fractions. [p. 309]

common factor   A number that is a factor of two different numbers. Example: 4 is a common factor of 8 and 12.

common multiple   A number that is a multiple of each of two given numbers. Example: 44 is a common multiple of 2 and 11. [p. 281]

Commutative Property   The fact that changing the order of addends or factors does not change the sum or product. Example: $4 \times 7 = 28$ and $7 \times 4 = 28$. [p. 87]

compatible numbers   Pairs of numbers that can be computed easily. Example: $30 + 70$. [p. 86]

compensation   Choosing numbers close to the numbers in a problem, and then adjusting the answer to compensate for the numbers chosen. [p. 87]

complementary angles   Two angles whose measures add up to $90°$. [p. 417]

composite number   A whole number greater than 1 that is not prime. [p. 276]

compound event   A combination of two or more single events. Example: getting heads on a coin toss and then rolling 4 with a number cube. [p. 647]

cone   See example below. [p. 581]

congruent   Having the same size and shape. [p. 444]

constant   A quantity that does not change. [p. 111]

conversion factor The number of measurement units that another unit is equal to. Example: to convert inches to feet, divide by the conversion factor 12 (12 inches = 1 foot). [p. 222]

coordinate One of the numbers in an ordered pair. [p. 489]

coordinate plane A set of lines used to locate points in a plane. [p. 489]

counterclockwise The direction of rotation when the top of a figure turns to the left. [p. 448]

cross product For two ratios, the product of the top value from one and the bottom value from the other. [p. 530]

cube A prism whose faces are all squares of the same size. [p. 581]

cubed Raised to the power of 3. Example: 2 cubed = 2^3 = 8. [p. 79]

cubic unit A unit measuring volume, consisting of a cube with edges one unit long. [p. 606]

customary system (of measurement) The measurement system often used in the United States, using inches, feet, miles, ounces, pounds, quarts, gallons, etc.

cylinder See example below. [p. 581]

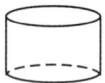

decagon A polygon with 10 sides. [p. 433]

deci- A prefix meaning $\frac{1}{10}$.
Example: 1 decimeter = 0.1 meter. [p. 217]

decimal system A base-10 place value system.

degree A unit of angle measure, $\frac{1}{360}$ of a complete circle. [p. 417]

deka- A prefix meaning 10.
Example: 1 dekameter = 10 meters. [p. 217]

denominator The bottom number in a fraction, telling how many parts the whole is divided into. [p. 289]

diameter A line connecting two points on a circle and passing through the circle's center. [p. 246]

difference The result of subtracting one number from another. [p. 114]

digit The symbols used to write the numerals 0, 1, 2, 3, 4, 5, 6, 7, 8, and 9.

Distributive Property The fact that numbers can be broken into smaller numbers for calculating. Example: (32 × 5) = (30 + 2) × 5 = (30 × 5) + (2 × 5) = 160. [p. 87]

dividend A number being divided by another number. Example: in 5 ÷ 3, 5 is the dividend. [p. 185]

divisible Can be divided by another number without leaving a remainder. Example: 18 is divisible by 6. [p. 271]

division An operation that tells how many equal sets or how many in each equal set.

divisor A number that another number is being divided by. Example: in 4 ÷ 9, 9 is the divisor. [p. 185]

dodecagon A polygon with 12 sides. [p. 433]

edge The line where two faces of a solid come together. [p. 580]

endpoint A point at the end of a segment or ray. [p. 409]

equality A mathematical relation of being exactly the same.

equation A mathematical sentence stating that two expressions are equal. Example: 14 = 2x. [p. 119]

equilateral triangle A triangle with three sides of the same length. [p. 428]

equivalent fractions Two fractions naming the same amount. [p. 289]

estimate An approximation for the result of a calculation.

Euler's formula A formula about edges, faces, and vertices of polyhedrons stating: E = F + V − 2. [p. 617]

evaluate To find the number that an algebraic expression names.

even number A whole number that has 0, 2, 4, 6, or 8 in the ones place.

event The particular outcome one is looking at in a probability experiment. [p. 627]

expanded form A way of writing an exponential number showing all of the factors individually. Example: 9 × 9 × 9. [p. 79]

experiment A situation that can turn out in more than one way. [p. 626]

exponent A raised number telling how many times another number, the base, is being multiplied by itself. Example: 9^3 = 9 × 9 × 9, where 3 is the exponent and 9 is the base. [p. 78]

exponential notation A way of writing repeated multiplication of a number using exponents. Example: 9^3. [p. 78]

expression A mathematical phrase containing variables, constants, and operation symbols. Example: 12 − x. [p. 111]

face A flat surface on a solid. [p. 580]

factor A number that divides another number without remainder. Example: 6 is a factor of 42. [p. 78]

factor tree A diagram showing how a composite number breaks down into its prime factors. [p. 276]

fair game A game in which each player has the same probability of winning. [p. 651]

flip See *reflection*.

foot A unit in the customary system of measurement equal to 12 inches. [p. 221]

formula A rule showing relationships among quantities. Example: $A = bh$.

fraction A number describing part of a whole when the whole is cut into equal pieces. [p. 288]

frequency chart A table listing each value that appears in a data set followed by the number of times it appears. [p. 25]

front-end estimation An estimation method where only the first digit of each number is used for computation, and the result is adjusted based on the remaining digits. [p. 91]

gallon A unit in the customary system of measurement equal to 4 quarts. [p. 221]

geometry A branch of mathematics in which the relations between points, lines, figures, and solids are explored.

gram The basic unit of mass in the metric system. [p. 215]

graph A diagram that shows information in an organized way.

• **greatest common factor (GCF)** The greatest whole number that divides two whole numbers. Example: 16 is the GCF of 32 and 48. [p. 295]

hecto- A prefix meaning 100. Example: the hectometer = 100 meters. [p. 217]

height The distance along a figure that is perpendicular to the base. [p. 230]

heptagon A polygon with 7 sides. [p. 433]

hexagon A polygon with 6 sides. [p. 433]

horizontal axis The horizontal line of the two lines on which a graph is built. [p. 29]

improper fraction A fraction whose numerator is greater than or equal to its denominator. Example: $\frac{22}{7}$. [p. 298]

inch A unit of length in the customary measurement system. [p. 221]

inequality A statement that two expressions are not equal. Example: 7 > 5.

integers The set of positive whole numbers, their opposites, and 0: ... –3, –2, –1, 0, 1, 2, 3, ... [p. 469]

intersect To cross through the same point. [p. 409]

interval One of the equal-sized divisions on a bar graph scale. [p. 29]

isosceles triangle A triangle with at least two sides of the same length. [p. 428]

kilo- A prefix meaning 1000. [p. 216]

least common denominator (LCD) The least common multiple (LCM) of two denominators. Example: 30 is the LCD of $\frac{1}{6}$ and $\frac{1}{15}$. [p. 330]

• **least common multiple (LCM)** The smallest multiple common to two numbers. Example: 60 is the LCM of 10 and 12. [p. 281]

like denominators Denominators that are the same in two fractions. [p. 325]

line A one-dimensional figure that extends forever in both directions. [p. 409]

line graph A graph in which a line shows changes in data, often over time. [p. 8]

line of symmetry The imaginary "mirror" in line symmetry.

line plot A plot that shows the shape of a data set by stacking x's above each value on a number line. [p. 26]

line symmetry The ability of a figure to be folded into congruent halves. [p. 444]

liter The basic unit of volume in the metric system. [p. 215]

• **lowest terms** The name for a fractional amount where the numerator and denominator have a greatest common factor of 1. [p. 294]

mass The amount of matter that something contains.

mean The sum of the values in a data set divided by the number of values. [p. 47]

median The middle value in a data set when the values are listed from lowest to highest. [p. 42]

mental math Performing calculations in your mind, without using pencil and paper or a calculator.

meter The basic unit of length in the metric system. [p. 215]

metric system (of measurement) A system of measurements used to describe how long, heavy, or big something is. [p. 215]

mile A unit in the customary system of measurement equal to 5280 feet. [p. 221]

milli- A prefix meaning $\frac{1}{1000}$. [p. 216]

mixed number A number combining a whole number with a fraction. Example: $2\frac{7}{8}$. [p. 298]

mode One of the values appearing most often in a data set. [p. 42]

multiple The product of a given number and any whole number. [p. 281]

multiplication An operation that combines two numbers, called factors, to give one number, called the product.

negative numbers Numbers less than 0. [p. 469]

net A flat pattern that can be folded into a solid. [p. 581]

nonagon A polygon with 9 sides. [p. 433]

number line A line that shows numbers in order.

number-word form A way of writing a number using digits and words. Example: 45 trillion. [p. 67]

numeral A symbol for a number.

numerator The top number in a fraction, telling how many parts of the whole are being named. [p. 289]

obtuse angle An angle greater than a right angle but smaller than a straight angle. [p. 413]

obtuse triangle A triangle with an obtuse angle. [p. 424]

octagon A polygon with 8 sides. [p. 433]

odd number A whole number that has 1, 3, 5, 7, or 9 in the ones place.

odds A ratio expressing the chances of an event happening that compares the number of favorable to unfavorable outcomes. [p. 657]

operation A mathematical procedure. Examples: addition, subtraction, multiplication, division.

opposite The integer on the opposite side of zero from a given number, but at the same distance from zero. Example: 7 and –7 are opposites of each other. [p. 472]

order of operations The rules telling what order to do operations in: (1) simplify inside parentheses, (2) simplify exponents, (3) multiply and divide from left to right, and (4) add and subtract from left to right. [p. 99]

ordered pair A pair of numbers, such as (3, –7), used to locate a point on a coordinate plane. [p. 489]

origin The point (0, 0), where the x- and y-axes of a coordinate plane intersect. [p. 489]

ounce A unit of weight in the customary measurement system. [p. 221]

outcome One of the ways an experiment can turn out. [p. 626]

outlier A number very different from the other numbers in a data set. [p. 51]

parallel Two lines, segments, or rays that do not cross, no matter how far they extend. [p. 409]

parallelogram A four-sided figure whose opposite sides are parallel and of the same length. [p. 234]

pentagon A polygon with 5 sides. [p. 433]

percent A ratio comparing a part to a whole using the number 100. The percent is the number of hundredths that the part is equal to. [p. 550]

perimeter The distance around the outside of a figure. [p. 210]

perpendicular Two lines are perpendicular if they cross at right angles. [p. 409]

pi (π) For any circle, the ratio of the circumference to the diameter. π equals 3.14159265... . [p. 247]

pictograph A graph using symbols to represent data. [p. 7]

place value The multiple of ten telling how much a digit represents. Example: in 374, the 7 is in the tens place. [p. 66]

polygon A closed figure made of line segments. [p. 432]

polyhedron A solid consisting entirely of flat faces. [p. 580]

positive numbers Numbers greater than 0. [p. 469]

pound A unit in the customary system of measurement equal to 16 ounces. [p. 221]

power An exponent. [p. 79]

● **prime factorization** The set of primes whose product is a given composite. Example: 70 = 2 × 5 × 7. [p. 276]

prime number A whole number greater than 1 with exactly two whole positive factors: 1 and itself. Examples: 2, 3, 5, 7, 11, ... [p. 276]

prism A polyhedron that has two faces congruent and parallel. See examples below. [p. 580]

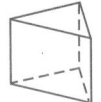 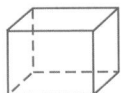

probability A ratio of the number of ways an event can happen to the total number of possible outcomes. [p. 627]

product The result of multiplying numbers. [p. 114]

proportion A pair of equal ratios. [p. 531]

protractor A tool that measures angles. [p. 417]

pyramid A solid with one base and whose other sides are all triangles. See examples below. [p. 581]

quadrants   The four regions into which the two axes of a coordinate grid divide the plane. [p. 489]

quadrilateral   A polygon with 4 sides. [p. 433]

quart   A unit of volume in the customary measurement system. [p. 221]

quotient   The result of dividing one number by another. [p. 114]

radius   A line from the center of a circle to any point on the circle. [p. 246]

range   The difference between the highest and lowest values in a data set. [p. 30]

rate   A ratio in which two quantities with different units of measure are compared. Example: 18 dollars per 2 hours. [p. 523]

ratio   A comparison of two quantities, often written as a fraction. [p. 515]

ray   A part of a line that has one endpoint and extends forever in the other direction. [p. 409]

reciprocal   A fraction whose numerator and denominator have been switched. [p. 383]

rectangle   A parallelogram with opposite sides the same length and all angles measuring 90°.[p. 437]

reflection   The mirror image of a figure that has been "flipped" over a line. [p. 444]

regular polygon   A polygon whose sides and angles all have the same measure. [p. 433]

remainder   The number less than the divisor that remains after the division process is completed.

repeating decimal   A decimal number that repeats a pattern of digits continuously on the right. Example: 6.141414 ... . [p. 304]

rhombus   A parallelogram with all sides the same length. [p. 437]

right angle   An angle like the corner of an index card. It measures 90°. [pp. 230, 413]

right triangle   A triangle with a right angle. [p. 424]

rotation   The image of a figure that has been "turned," as if on a wheel. [p. 448]

rotational symmetry   The ability of a figure to be rotated less than a full circle and exactly match its original image. [p. 449]

rounding   Adjusting a number to make it more convenient to use, according to a given place value. Example: 2571 rounded to the nearest hundred is 2600. [p. 71]

sample   A set of data used to predict how a particular situation might happen. [p. 631]

scale   The "ruler" that measures the heights of the bars in a bar graph. [p. 29]

scalene triangle   A triangle with no sides of equal length. [p. 428]

scatterplot   A graph showing paired data values. [p. 17]

scientific notation   Writing a number as the product of a number greater than or equal to 1 but less than 10 and a power of 10. Example: $350 = 3.50 \times 10^2$. [p. 153]

segment   Part of a line, with two endpoints. [p. 409]

side   Each of the rays forming an angle. [p. 412]

similar   Figures having the same shape but possibly different sizes. [p. 543]

slide   See *translation*.

solid   A three-dimensional figure. [p. 580]

sphere   See example below. [p. 582]

square   A quadrilateral with all sides the same length and all angles measuring 90°. [p. 437]

square centimeter   The area of a square with 1-centimeter sides. [p. 229]

square inch   The area of a square with 1-inch sides. [p. 229]

square root   The length of one side of a square with an area equal to a given number. [p. 261]

squared   Raised to the power of 2. Example: 3 squared = 3^2 = 9. [p. 79]

standard form   A way of writing a number using digits. Example: 45,000,000,000,000. [p. 67]

stem-and-leaf diagram   A graph showing the shape of a data set by breaking each value into a "stem" part and a "leaf" part. [p. 35]

straight angle   An angle formed by two rays pointing in opposite directions. [p. 413]

subtraction   An operation that tells the difference between two numbers, or how many are left when some are taken away.

sum   The result of adding numbers. [p. 114]

supplementary angles   Two angles whose measures add up to 180°. [p. 417]

surface area (SA)   The sum of the areas of each face of a polyhedron. [p. 584]

symmetry   See *line symmetry* and *rotational symmetry*.

T-table   A table showing corresponding *x*- and *y*-values for an equation. [p. 499]

tally marks   Marks used to organize a large set of data. Each mark indicates one time a value appears in the data set. [p. 25]

terminating decimal A decimal number that ends on the right. [p. 304]

tessellation A pattern of congruent shapes covering a surface without gaps or overlaps. [p. 454]

translation The image of a figure that has been slid to a new position without flipping or turning. [p. 453]

trapezoid A quadrilateral with exactly two sides parallel. [p. 437]

tree diagram A branching, tree-like diagram showing all possible outcomes of a situation. [p. 642]

trend A relationship between two sets of data that shows up as a pattern in a scatterplot. [p. 18]

triangle A closed figure made from three line segments. [p. 424]

turn See *rotation*.

unfair game A game in which not all players have the same probability of winning. [p. 651]

unit One of something. An amount or quantity used as a standard of measurement.

unit fraction A fraction with a numerator of 1.

unit rate A rate in which the second number in the comparison is one unit. Example: 25 gallons per minute. [p. 524]

unlike denominators Denominators that are different in two fractions. [p. 329]

variable A quantity that can change or vary, often represented with a letter. [p. 111]

Venn diagram A diagram that uses regions to show relationships between sets of things. [p. 315]

vertex The common endpoint of two rays forming an angle. Plural: vertices. [p. 412]

vertical axis The vertical line of the two lines on which a graph is built. [p. 29]

volume The number of cubic units an object contains. [p. 606]

weight A measure of the force that gravity exerts on a body.

whole number Any number in the set {0, 1, 2, 3, 4, ... }.

word form A way of writing a number using only words. Example: forty-five trillion. [p. 67]

x-axis The horizontal axis on a coordinate plane. [p. 489]

x-coordinate The first number in an ordered pair, locating a point on the x-axis of a coordinate plane. [p. 489]

y-axis The vertical axis on a coordinate plane. [p. 489]

y-coordinate The second number in an ordered pair, locating a point on the y-axis of a coordinate plane. [p. 489]

yard A unit in the customary system of measurement equal to 3 feet. [p. 221]

zero pair A number and its opposite. Example: 7 and (–7).

Selected Answers

Chapter 1

1-1 Try It (Example 2)

a. 200 m **b.** 800

1-1 Try It (Example 4)

a. 1993 **b.** Interactive TV

1-1 Exercises & Applications

1. Pictograph **3.** Circle graph
5. 11–50 m; 51–100 m **7.** 3
9. $37 **11.** Medical, clothes;
other, transportation; housing
13. 64,000,000 sq mi **17.** 6 million
21. 5106 **23.** 8022 **25.** 90
27. 806 **29.** 694 **31.** 630
33. 433 **35.** 790 **37.** 1000
39. 1586 **41.** 600 **43.** 1056

1-2 Try It

a. Possible answer: It looks like
Crispies sells almost as much cereal
as Crunchies, but there is $9 million
difference. **b.** Possible answer: It
looks like Pete's Pizza pays twice as
much as Prize Pizza, but they only
pay 50 cents more.

1-2 Exercises & Applications

3. 30 yr; 70 yr **5.** B **7.** Twice; $1\frac{1}{2}$
9. Mouse: 300; robin: 600 **11.** 2
million **15.** Two hundred four
17. Nine hundred thirteen
19. Eight thousand nine hundred
twelve **21.** One thousand forty-five
23. 614 **25.** 772 **27.** 71 **29.** 306

1-3 Try It

a. (80, 40) **b.** (100, 45) **c.** (125, 32)
d. (160, 22) **e.** (200, 20)

1-3 Exercises & Applications

1. a. 15 right, 600 up **b.** 600 lb, 15
ft **3. a.** 20 right, 3000 up **b.** 3000
lb, 20 ft **5.** No trend **7.** A
11. 24; 14 **15.** 6606 **17.** 8900
19. 4329 **21.** 1888

Section 1A Review

3. 3 million **5.** Yes **7.** The daily
garbage per person increases.

1-4 Try It (Example 1)

a.

History Test Scores	Frequency
Under 60	1
60–69	3
70–79	4
80–89	7
90–100	5

b. 7; 4

1-4 Try It (Example 2)

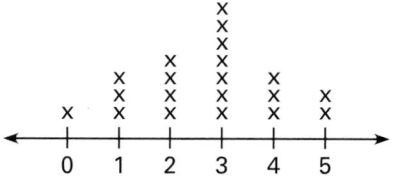

The line plot shows that 3 is the most
common number of phone calls, 0 is
the least common, and 1 and 4
appear with the same frequency.

1-4 Exercises & Applications

1.

a.		**b.**		**c.**	
1	IIII	13	I	1500	I
2	I	17	I	2000	II
3	III	18	I	2500	I
4	III	19	II	3500	I
5	I	20	IIII	4000	II
6	I	21	II	5000	I
7	I	22	II	6000	I
10	I	23	I	6500	I

3.

Shoes in Closet

Shoes	Frequency
2	5
4	6
6	9
8	13
10	16
12	18

11. Two hundred seventeen **13.** Six
hundred sixteen **23.** 25 **25.** 21
27. 11 **29.** 19 **31.** 24 R2 or 24.7

1-5 Try It

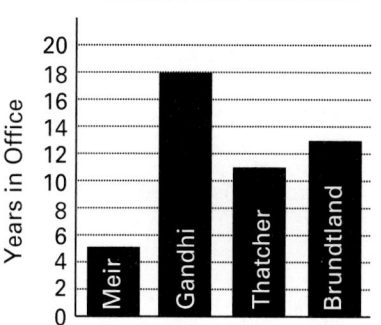

Female Prime Ministers

1-5 Exercises & Applications

1. a. Range 13, interval 2
b. Range 90, interval 25
3.

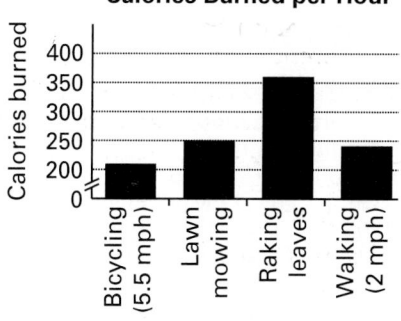

Calories Burned per Hour

5. a. The first graph has range 40,
interval 20. The second has range
40, interval 10. **7.** 8587
9. 718,530 **11.** 32,717 **13.** 3594
15. 153,885 **17.** 13,991

1-6 Try It

Stem	Leaf
9	0 3 3 5 7
10	0 1 5 8 8
11	3 4 5 8
12	4 6 8 8
13	0 0 3 3 6
14	1 1 2 3 4 6 8

1-6 Exercises & Applications

1. a.

Stem	Leaf
1	8 9 0 9
2	7 9
3	8 2 6
4	2 0 7 2

b.

Stem	Leaf
1	0 8 9 9
2	7 9
3	2 6 8
4	0 2 2 7

5. 52 **7.** A **11.** There will be more leaves in the 5 stem. **13.** 1152 **15.** 1360 **17.** 193 **19.** 158

Section 1B Review

1.

No. of Elections Lost	Frequency
1	13
2	3
3	2

3.

Stem	Leaf
1	5 5 7 8 9
2	2 3 3 3 3 4
3	2 2

1-7 Try It

a. 108 **b.** No mode

1-7 Exercises & Applications

1. a. Median $4, mode $10
b. Median 19, modes 12 and 54
c. Median 86, mode 82 **d.** Median 306, no mode **3.** 36 **5.** Median 12, mode 10 **7.** Median 11, mode 13 **9.** Median 21, modes 13 and 31 **11.** Median 10, no mode **13.** Median 25, mode 28 **21.** 2204 **23.** 8918 **25.** 5436 **27.** 32,760 **29.** 48,256 **31.** 517,176 **33.** 95,207 **35.** Basketball **37.** 15 pairs

1-8 Try It

a. $14.39 **b.** 1.5

1-8 Exercises & Applications

1. $5 **3.** 5 **5.** 11.8125 seconds **7.** 3.625 **9.** D **13.** It doesn't change. **15.** 51 R4 or ≈ 51.57 **17.** 88 R5 or 88.625 **19.** 40 R2 or ≈ 40.15 **21.** 49 **23.** 11 **25.** 23 **27.** 3

1-9 Try It

With the outlier: Median 21, no mode, mean 28; Without the outlier: Median 19, no mode, mean ≈ 18.29

1-9 Exercises & Applications

1. 56 **3.** 0 **5.** 3 **7.** 70 **9. a.** With the outlier: Mean 287.4, median 287, mode 287; Without the outlier: Mean 286.25, median 286.5, mode 287. **11. a.** Mean 74.8, median 82, mode 82 **b.** Mean ≈ 69.64, median 82, mode 82 **13.** 1687 **15.** 34 R1 or 34.11 **17.** 83,210 **19.** 30 R14 or ≈ 30.47 **21.** 5

Section 1C Review

1. Mean ≈ 4.81, median 5, modes 5 and 1 **3.** Mean ≈ 15.07, median 12, modes 10 and 25 **5.** The mean **7.** C

Chapter 1 Summary & Review

1. 80 blue jackets **2.** 270 mi
3.

Souvenir	Tally Marks	Frequency
Flags	⊞⊞	5
White House models	III	3
Posters	IIII	4
Uncle Sam hats	I	1

4.

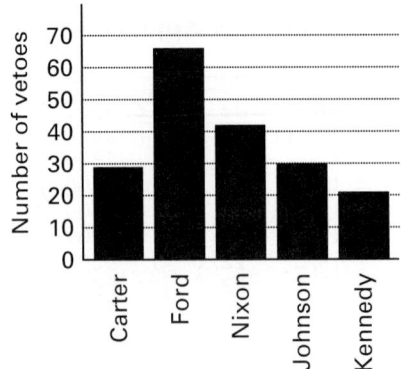

Presidential Vetoes

5. Stems will be 0 through 9. Leaves will be 2, 4, 6, and 8 for the row opposite the zero stem and leaves of 0, 2, 4, 6, and 8 for each row opposite the 1 through 9 stems. **6.** Median, 563; Mode, 521; Mean, ≈ 591.91 or ≈ 592 **7.** The mean

2-1 Try It

a. 1 ten-million **b.** Nineteen million, eight hundred eighty-eight thousand, eight hundred
c. 5,020,000,000,300

2-1 Exercises & Applications

1. Ones **3.** Ten-thousands **5.** Millions **7.** Thousands **9.** Thirty million, eighty thousand, seven hundred five **11.** Eight thousand, two hundred thirty-five **13.** Seven thousand, ninety-eight **15.** Fifty-six million, fifty-six thousand, five hundred sixty **17.** 93 million **19.** 888 million **21.** 2 billion, 791 million **23.** 52,000,000 **25.** 560,000,000 **27.** 9000 **29.** 321,000 **31.** 42,006,000 **33.** 9,020,000,000,030 **35.** 81,500 **37.** Thousand **39.** Billion **45.** D **47.** 3,666,200,000 **49.** 14 **51.** ≈ 1.9

2-2 Try It

a. 70,000 **b.** 74,000 **c.** 74,000

2-2 Exercises & Applications

1. a. 4 **b.** Less than 5 **c.** Leave it the same because the next digit is less than 5. **d.** 1,370,000 **3.** 90,000 **5.** 740 **7.** 3,900,000 **9.** 23,000 **11.** Two billion, seven hundred fifty-eight million, five hundred thirty thousand, nine hundred twenty-eight **13.** B **17.** 9 buses

2-3 Try It

a. 98,419; 138,417; 146,416
b. 190,000 < 198,000

2-3 Exercises & Applications

1. > **3.** < **5.** < **7.** < **9.** 5678; 5687; 5768 **11.** 20,002; 20,200; 22,000 **13.** 10 hundred; 10 million; 1 trillion **15.** 6 hundred; 62 thousand; 29 billion **17.** D **19.** The diameter at the equator is greater. **21.** Calcutta, Rio de Janeiro, Buenos Aires **23.** 268,356,000 > 261,931,000 **29.** 29,297

2-4 Try It

a. 12^4 **b.** $5 \times 5 \times 5 \times 5 \times 5 \times 5$
c. 81 **d.** 161,051

2-4 Exercises & Applications

1. a. 4 **b.** 7 **c.** 4; 7 **d.** 4^7 **3.** 9^5
5. 79^2 **7.** $7^2 \times 3^2$ **9.** 36^1
11. 25×25 **13.** $200 \times 200 \times 200 \times 200$ **15.** $7 \times 7 \times 7 \times 7 \times 7 \times 7 \times 7$
17. $3 \times 3 \times 3 \times 3$ **19.** $5 \times 5 \times 5 \times 5 \times 5 \times 5 \times 5 \times 5 \times 5$ **21.** $9 \times 9 \times 9 \times 9 \times 9 \times 9 \times 9 \times 9$ **23.** 125
25. 243 **27.** 1 **29.** 256 **31.** 729
33. 8^6: base 8, exponent 6, 262,144; 3^5: base 3, exponent 5, 243. **35.** $>$
37. $<$ **39. b.** 2^{50} cells **41.** 6

Section 2A Review

1. 16; 20 **3.** 100,000; 100,000
5. 81; 100 **7. a.** 864°F **9.** 7,000; 17,000; 19,000; 19,000; 20,000; 23,000; 29,000 **11.** $=$ **13.** $<$
15. $>$ **19.** C

2-5 Try It

a. 1,200,000 **b.** 300 **c.** 183
d. 347 **e.** 1300 **f.** 351 **g.** 174
h. 714

2-5 Exercises & Applications

1. a. 240 **b.** 24,000 **c.** 2,400,000
d. 24,000,000 **e.** 70 **f.** 70 **g.** 7
h. 7 **3.** 565 **5.** 1100 **7.** 40
9. 147 **11.** 50 **13.** 900 **15.** 124
17. 693 **19.** 534 **21.** 3500
23. 35,000 **25.** 7,200,000 **27.** 290
29. 2858 **31.** 166 **33.** 200
35. 336 **37.** 525 **39.** 50 **41.** 174
43. 777 **45.** $105 **47.** 50 yards
51. $2.20; No **53.** 335,728,642
57. Three million, ninety-three thousand, two **59.** 73,259
61. 2,674,445 **63.** 61,236
65. 2,146,337

2-6 Try It

a. ≈ 1620 **b.** ≈ 2140 **c.** ≈ 900

2-6 Exercises & Applications

1. a. $\approx 730; \approx 732$ **b.** $\approx 1200; \approx 1195$ **c.** $\approx 72,000; \approx 72,300$
d. $\approx 990; \approx 990$ **3–21.** Possible answers are given: **3.** ≈ 3000
5. ≈ 500 **7.** ≈ 325 **9.** $\approx 3,300,000$

11. ≈ 1000 **13.** $\approx 600,000$
15. $\approx 18,000$ **17.** ≈ 70
19. $\approx 18,500,000$ **21.** ≈ 250
23. ≈ 110 in. **25.** $\approx 99,000,000; \approx 98,400,000$ **27.** D
31. 7,000,000 **33.** 400,000,000
35. $695.86 **37.** $16,402.44

2-7 Try It (Examples 1–2)

a. $\approx 24,000$ **b.** ≈ 200

2-7 Try It (Examples 3–4)

a. ≈ 600 **b.** ≈ 7

2-7 Exercises & Applications

Possible answers: **1. a.** ≈ 2400
b. ≈ 400 **c.** $\approx 35,000$ **d.** ≈ 30
e. ≈ 7 **f.** ≈ 300 **g.** ≈ 1000
h. $\approx 120,000$ **3.** $\approx 56,000,000$
5. $\approx 25,000$ **7.** ≈ 1700 **9.** ≈ 20
11. $\approx 15,000$ **13.** ≈ 4000
15. ≈ 100 **17.** $\approx 350,000$
19. ≈ 6 **21.** $\approx 14,000$ **23.** ≈ 40
25. ≈ 560 **27.** ≈ 50 **29.** ≈ 300
31. ≈ 2 **33.** $\approx 100,000$
35. Under **37.** 60,000 **39.** C
43. $<$ **45.** $<$ **47.** $<$ **49.** 10; 356; 383; 1009; 1023 **51.** 12,140
53. 18,240 **55.** 252 **57.** 3120
59. 144 **61.** 2142

2-8 Try It

a. 25 **b.** 1 **c.** 3 **d.** 48

2-8 Exercises & Applications

1. a. Multiplication **b.** Addition
c. Division **d.** Simplify exponents
e. Subtraction **f.** Multiplication
g. Subtraction **h.** Subtraction
3. 56 **5.** 8 **7.** 48 **9.** 27 **11.** 0
13. 120 **15.** 27 **17.** 300 **19.** 10
21. 0 **23.** 5 **25.** 20 **27.** 33
29. 1 **31.** 66 **33.** 8200 **35.** 190
37. $20 \times (15 - 2) = 260$ **39.** $2 \times (6^2 - 8) = 56$ **41.** $(12 + 10) \div 11 = 2$
43. $(5 + 4) \div 3 = 3$ **45.** B
47. $(4 \times 7 - 2 + 1.96) \div 2 = 13.98$
51. 100,000 **53.** 4096 **55.** 38,416
57. $2^7 = 128$ **59.** 62,103
61. 1,921,899,992

2-9 Try It

a. 30 **b.** 10

2-9 Exercises & Applications

1. a. Add **b.** Add **c.** Subtract
d. Subtract **e.** Subtract
f. Subtract **g.** Subtract **h.** Add
3. Add 3 **5.** Add 13 **7.** Subtract 1
9. Add 11 **11.** Subtract 29
13. Subtract 8 **15.** Add 15
17. Add 58 **19.** 271, 266, 260
21. 76, 70, 64 **23.** 1010, 1028, 1049
25. 10, 9, 11 **27.** 125, 180, 245
29. 1131, 1135, 1139 **31.** 332, 348, 301 **33.** $22 **35.** 550 **41.** 166
43. 1661 **45.** 205 **47.** 6
49. $121.68 **51.** $185,295.50
53. $23.80 **55.** $1453.32

Section 2B Review

1. 60,000 **3.** 879 **5.** 4000
7–17. Possible answers:
7. 30,000 **9.** 300 **11.** 17,000
13. 30 **15.** 23,000 **17.** 1600
19. C **21.** D **23.** E **25.** B

2-10 Try It

a. 21, 28, 35 **b.** 12, 11, 10 **c.** 20, 15, 12 **d.** 26, 27, 28

2-10 Exercises & Applications

1. a. Constant **b.** Variable
c. Variable **d.** Constant
e. Variable **f.** Variable **3.** 9, 10, 11 **5.** 12, 18, 24 **7.** 14, 15, 16
9. 16, 24, 32 **11.** 17, 18, 19
13. 18, 12, 9 **15.** 17, 15, 11
17. 15, 9, 5 **19.** 6, 8, 12 **21.** 3, 5, 9 **23.** 6, 10, 18 **25.** 9, 25, 81
27. 28, 14, 8 **29.** 6, 12, 21
31. 10, 20, 35 **33.** 8, 16, 28
35. 29, 31, 34 **37.** 14, 16, 19
39. Number of stars: 13, 26, 39, 52, $13w$ **41.** A **43. a.** ii **b.** i **c.** iii
Possible answers are given:
45. 7000 **47.** 35,000 **49.** 6400
51. 64, 8, 384 **53.** 24, 30

2-11 Try It

a. $c + 8$ **b.** $\frac{n}{9}$ or $\frac{9}{n}$ **c.** $r + 5$ **d.** $7x$

2-11 Exercises & Applications

1. A **3.** E **5.** $10q$ **7.** $6d$
9. $s - 3$ **11.** $20v$ **13.** $y - 3$
15. $n - 5$ **17.** $n - 4$ or $4 - n$
19. $\frac{x}{8}$ **21.** $4 + s$ **23.** $t - 146$
degrees **25.** $22,278 - m$ square
miles **29. a.** $x + x + x + x$ or $4x$

b. $x + 2 + x + 2 + x + 2 + x + 2$ or $4x + 8$ **c.** $x + 3 + x + 3 + x + 3 + x + 3$ or $4x + 12$ **31.** ≈ 800
33. $\approx 250{,}000$ **35.** ≈ 2 **37.** ≈ 3
39. 122 **41.** 319 **43.** 78
45. 4332

2-12 Try It

a. No **b.** No **c.** Yes

2-12 Exercises & Applications

1. a. True **b.** False **c.** False
d. True **e.** False **f.** False
g. True **h.** False **i.** True **j.** True
3. No **5.** Yes **7.** Yes **9.** No
11. Yes **13.** No **15.** No **17.** Yes
19. Yes **21.** $\frac{12}{p} = 3$ **23.** $1600 + x = 3212$ **25.** $84 + d = 88$
27. $75 - b = 26$ **29.** No
33. $555 \div 111 = 5$ **35.** $1536 \div 48 = 32$ **37.** $546 \div 13 = 42$
39. $1978 \div 86 = 23$ **41.** $8 \times 8 = 64$ **43.** $4 \times 8 = 32$ **45.** $63 \times 56 = 3528$ **47.** $87 \times 12 = 1044$ **49.** 13;
14; 15 **51.** 36; 18; 12 **53.** 6; 12;
18 **55.** 30; 15; 10 **57.** 8; 9; 10

2-13 Try It

a. $a = 15$ **b.** $b = 63$ **c.** $c = 22$
d. $d = 48$

2-13 Exercises & Applications

1. Less **3.** Less **5.** Less
7. Greater **9.** Greater **11.** 2
13. 8 **15.** 8 **17.** 10 **19.** 22; 26;
31; 43 **21.** $j = 6$ **23.** $k = 6$
25. $v = 6$ **27.** $n = 8$ **29.** $z = 80$
31. $g = 5$ **33.** $k = 9$ **35.** $r = 168$
37. B **39.** 1000 ft/hr **41.** 1038 m
43. It must decrease by 2.
45. $200 - 151 = 49$ **47.** $43 + 10 = 53$ **49.** $159{,}000 + 21{,}000 = 180{,}000$

Section 2C Review

1. Constant **3.** $\frac{d}{4}$ **5.** $16m$ **7.** $\frac{d}{17}$
Possible answers are given:
9. ≈ 9000 **11.** ≈ 60 **13.** 17
15. 220 **17.** 4 **19.** 12 **21.** No
23. $x = 22$ **25.** $x = 5$ **27.** 5000 ft
29. D

Chapter 2 Summary & Review

1. Thousands **2.** Twenty-nine
million, one hundred fifty-eight
thousand, six hundred forty-seven

3. a. 29,160,000 **b.** 29,000,000
4. $129{,}058{,}647 < 129{,}186{,}000$
5. 4,067,338; 4,567,238; 40,098,001
6. Base 5, exponent 9 **7.** $7 \times 7 \times 7$
8. 8^2 **9. a.** 16 **b.** 8 **c.** 10,000
d. 9 **e.** 121 **10.** 400 **11.** 1224
12. 900,000 **13.** 700 **14. a.** 320
b. 11,000 **15. a.** 5 **b.** 750 **16.** 9
17. 351 **18.** 29, 22, 15 **19.** 126,
141, 156 **20.** 12, 18, 24 **21.** 4, 3, 2
22. $\frac{m}{11}$ or $\frac{11}{m}$ **23.** Yes; No **24. a.** $x = 61$ **b.** $x = 116$

Cumulative Review
Chapters 1–2

1. C **2.** B **3.** D **4.** B **5.** A
6. B **7.** D **8.** A **9.** D **10.** C
11. A **12.** C **13.** B **14.** D
15. C

Chapter 3

3-1 Try It

a. 0.81 **b.** 0.4

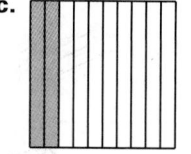

e. Three and fifty-one thousandths
f. One hundred seventy-one
thousandths **g.** Forty-seven
hundredths **h.** Eight and one tenth
i. 0.09 **j.** 2.101

3-1 Exercises & Applications

1. a. 0.6 **b.** 0.43 **c.** 0.312 **d.** 0.9
e. 0.097 **f.** 0.08 **3.** 0.78 **5.** 2.45

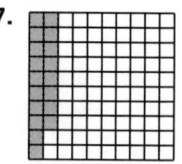
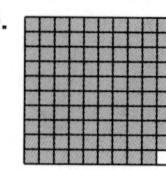

13. 1.067 **15.** 0.08 **17.** 0.2
19. 0.015 **21.** Sixty-seven hundredths **23.** Eight and six hundred
eleven thousandths **25.** Twelve
and six thousandths **27.** Ten and
forty-eight hundredths **29.** B
31. Possible answer: 3.608
33. Infinitely many **37.** 11; 8; 5

39. 1; 8; 11 **41.** 17; 15; 1 **43.** 416
45. 3 **47.** 356 **49.** 2

3-2 Try It (Examples 1–2)

a. 0.8 **b.** 7.05 **c.** 3.462 **d.** 1.9 cm

3-2 Try It (Example 3)

a. 3 cm; 2.7 cm **b.** 13 cm; 13 cm

3-2 Exercises & Applications

1. a. 1 **b.** 3 **c.** 3 **d.** 0 **e.** 1 **f.** 2
3. 5.8 **5.** 0.472 **7.** 4.3 **9.** 0.100
11. 33.5 **13.** 16.13 **15.** 7.30
17. 88 **19.** 7.3 **21.** 8.2
23. 0.7893 **25.** 60 **27.** 1000 cm
29. 2 cm; 2.3 cm **31.** 5 cm; 5.4 cm
33. 2 cm; 2.5 cm **35.** 6 cm; 58 mm
43. $12 + k$

3-3 Try It (Examples 1–2)

a. > **b.** > **c.** > **d.** <

3-3 Try It (Example 3)

1.009, 1.08, 1.6, 1.725, 1.74

3-3 Exercises & Applications

1. a. 0.280 **b.** 1.4500 **c.** 1.670
d. 0.3000 **3.** = **5.** > **7.** = **9.** <
11. < **13.** < **15.** < **17.** <
19. 0.675 in. **21.** 27.939, 27.946,
27.948 **23.** 1.23, 1.5, 2.64
25. 2.84, 2.96, 3.02 **27.** 3.107,
30.17, 31.07, 31.7, 310.7 **29.** A
31. Angela and Temeca
33. Possible answer: 8.743
37. True **39.** False

3-4 Try It

a. 30,000 **b.** 90,620,000,000
c. 5.2×10^4 **d.** 1.74×10^9

3-4 Exercises & Applications

1. a. 4 **b.** 5 **c.** 3 **3.** 75,000
5. 200,000 **7.** 8,890,000
9. 2,459,000,000,000
11. 445,600,000,000
13. 6,900,000,000 **15.** 370,000
17. 57,000,000 **19.** 50,000; 100,000
21. 5×10^3 **23.** 1.6×10^5 **25.** 7.9×10^9 **27.** 5.1×10^7 **29.** 6×10^{12}
31. 5×10^2 **33.** 1.2×10^7 **35.** D
39. 3.65 **41.** Median: 7; modes: 5,
7, 8 **43.** 10 **45.** 12

Section 3A Review

1. 0.7 **3.** 26.5 **5.** 2 cm **7.** 0.1
9. 2.42 **11.** 7.0 **13. a.** KB: 1000;
MB: 1,000,000; GB: 1,000,000,000
b. 2.4×10^9 **15.** 120,000,000
17. 560,000 **19.** 4.5×10^{10}
21. 6.78×10^6 **23.** 6×10^7
25. 5.69×10^4 **27.** A

3-5 Try It

a. $\approx$ \$34 **b.** $\approx$ 35 **c.** $\approx$ 630 **d.** $\approx$ 8

3-5 Exercises & Applications

1. a. 40 or 50 **b.** 25 **c.** 10 **d.** 5
3–33. Possible answers given.
3. $\approx$ \$2 **5.** $\approx$ 5 **7.** $\approx$ 9 **9.** $\approx$ 300
11. $\approx$ \$240 **13.** $\approx$ 6 **15.** $\approx$ 43
17. $\approx$ 73 **19.** $\approx$ 164 **21.** $\approx$ 1800
23. $\approx$ \$2 **25.** $\approx$ 6 **27.** $\approx$ 8100
29. $\approx$ 900 **31.** $\approx$ 10 **33.** $\approx$ 5
35. About \$700 **37.** Yes **39.** About
3 km **45.** 65.625 **47.** 0.32
49. 0.789 **51.** 0.05

3-6 Try It

a. 8.617 **b.** 3.957 **c.** 7.573
d. 2.85

3-6 Exercises & Applications

1. a. i **b.** ii **c.** i **3.** 46.906
5. 8.4 **7.** \$11.25 **9.** 25.904
11. 66.2284 **13.** 0.061 **15.** \$10.01
17. 14.38 **19.** 442.1822 **21.** 41.69
23. 4.947 **25.** 15.678 **27.** 42.63
29. \$76.57 **31.** 104.67 **33.** D
43. 5.998 **45.** 35 **47.** 0.2

3-7 Try It

a. $x = 10.1$ **b.** $n = 10.6$ **c.** $j = 5.1$
d. $p = 2.2$

3-7 Exercises & Applications

1. a. True **b.** False **c.** True
d. False **3.** $d = 0.4$ **5.** $x = 8.1$
7. $u = \$2.37$ **9.** $w = 28.2$
11. $a = 1.22$ **13.** $c = 0.02$
15. $f = \$3.25$ **17.** $i = 87.7$
19. $m = 0.088$ **21.** $w = 2.32$
23. $z = 60$ **25.** $t = 0.67$ **27.** $g = 12.1$ cm **29.** A **31.** $\$26.49 + \$18.50 = s; s = \$44.99$ **37.** 0.123,
0.672, 1.784

Section 3B Review

1. 2.7 cm **3.** 3.3 cm **5.** 2.5
7. 0.88 **9.** 0.03 **11.** 28.4
13. 5.161 **15.** 13.776 cm
17. $x = 24.05$ **19.** $n = 17.5$

3-8 Try It

a. 4.8 **b.** 4.2 **c.** 117.756 **d.** 62

3-8 Exercises & Applications

1. a. i **b.** ii **c.** i **3.** 34.12
5. 24.032 **7.** 872.83 **9.** 357.8
11. 52.2 **13.** 872.3 **15.** \$603.05
17. 12.865 **19.** 80.7 **21.** 3850
23. \$2539 **25.** \$6 **27.** C **29.** Yes
33. 34,790,001; 34,890,000;
34,891,000 **35.** 5540 **37.** 14,200
39. 928,000 **41.** 1,932,000

3-9 Try It

a. 9.44 **b.** 146.72 **c.** 0.0369
d. 56.77 **e.** 0.21 **f.** 0.6

3-9 Exercises & Applications

1. a. i **b.** i **c.** ii **3.** 0.9591
5. 8.19541 **7.** 4238.01 **9.** 0.068
11. 0.0065 **13.** 0.00425 **15.** 38.86
17. 23.22 **19.** 0.546 **21.** 54.288
23. 0.7496 **25.** 0.775 **27.** 4.232
29. $\approx$ \$2; \$2.12 **31.** $<$ **33.** $=$
35. C **41.** 7 **43.** 29 **45.** 2
47. 143 **49.** $\approx$ 3 **51.** $\approx$ 3
53. $\approx$ 10 **55.** $\approx$ 40

3-10 Try It

a. 19.3 **b.** 0.89 **c.** 0.1085
d. 0.262 **e.** 0.003012 **f.** 4.5

3-10 Exercises & Applications

1. a. i **b.** i **c.** i **3.** 5.87 **5.** 0.994
7. 0.0258 **9.** 1.548 **11.** 3.254
13. 0.013 **15.** 0.084 **17.** 1.24
19. 49.75 **21.** 22.476 **23.** 18.96
25. 0.407 **27.** 0.67 **29.** 9.4
31. 137.667 mi **37.** 73, 78, 79
39. 23, 17, 10 **41.** 33, 30, 27
43. 52.07 **45.** 0.007 **47.** 3.53
49. 6.999

3-11 Exercises & Applications

1. a. ii **b.** ii **c.** i **3.** 2.8 **5.** 0.4
7. 4.79 **9.** 1.09 **11.** 8 **13.** 0.07
15. 6.1 **17.** 9.87 **19.** 1.94 **21.** 42

23. 3.7 **25.** 0.6 **27.** 500
29. $\approx$ 14.74 mi per day **31.** A
33. 21,900 **37.** $15 \times 15 \times 15$
49. $e = 8.1$ **51.** $g = 1.2$
53. $j = 1.3$

3-12 Try It

a. $j = 0.7$ **b.** $w = 6$ **c.** $t = 5.5$
d. $f = 0.49$

3-12 Exercises & Applications

1. a. 1000 **b.** 100 **c.** 0.1 **d.** 0.1
3. $e = 0.63$ **5.** $r = 50$ **7.** $w = 0.02$
9. $s = 114.49$ **11.** $u = 45$ **13.** $q = 12.5$ **15.** $h = 6$ **17.** $n = 0.07$
19. $v = 10.8$ **21.** $k = 0.08$
23. $j = 0.14$ **25.** $u = 0.02$
27. $8.3d = 83$; 10 days **29.** $\frac{t}{9} = 0.08$; 0.72 kg **31.** $465 - x = 165.3$;
299.7 kg **33.** 36 **37.** Greek pasta
salad **39.** 8.7 **41.** 21.8 **43.** 54.06

Section 3C Review

1. 5,600,000 **3.** 400,000,000
5. 122,000 **7.** 16,000,000,000
9. 23.5 **11.** 250 **13.** 20.6
15. 60.02 **17.** 2.04 **19.** 310.75
21. 3.6 **23.** 2.793 **25.** 10.78 km
27. $u = 142.2$ **29.** $n = 50$
31. $s = 24.31$ **33.** $v = 830$
35. \$0.36 **37.** B

Chapter 3 Summary & Review

1. a. 0.25 **b.** 0.7 **2. a.** 5.6 **b.** 0.8
3. a. $>$ **b.** $<$ **4. a.** 71,600
b. 395,000 **5.** $\approx$ 700; 729.36
6. $\approx$ 270; 262.277 **7.** 65.92
8. $(7.2 - 2.8) < 4.876$ **9.** 6.4 mm
10. a. $t = 4.6$ **b.** $k = 13.5$
11. $\approx$ 120; 128.8 **12.** $\approx$ 13; 13.25
13. $\approx$ 1; 0.893 **14.** $\approx$ 2; 2.2
15. 0.04533 **16.** 751 **17.** 0.367
18. $m = 3.1$

Chapter 4

4-1 Try It

a. 27 **b.** 46

4-1 Exercises & Applications

1. 180 cm **3.** 100 in. **5.** 8 cm
7. 16 in. **9.** $a = 9$ in.; $b = 3$ in.
11. $f = 12$ mm; $g = 26$ mm **13.** A

19. 90 m/sec **21.** 5.6×10^4
23. 2×10^{12} **25.** 1.6×10^3
27. 9.456×10^7

4-2 Try It (Example 1)

a. km **b.** cm **c.** kg **d.** L

4-2 Try It (Examples 2–3)

a. 7360 **b.** 8 **c.** 0.325

4-2 Exercises & Applications

1. 1 kilometer **3.** 1 meter
5. 1 centimeter **7.** Kilogram
9. Kilometer **11.** Gram **13.** 0.09
15. 100 **17.** 0.00788 **19.** 4.2
21. 0.005 **23.** 131 **25.** 267,000
27. 42,900 **31.** B **33.** 480 mm; 48
cm; 0.48 m **35.** 562 cm **37.** 103
39. 45,000,000,000 **41.** 45,612
43. 0.55 **45.** 0.067 **47.** 0.4
49. 0.02 **51.** 0.008

4-3 Try It (Example 1)

a. Miles **b.** Pounds **c.** Quarts

4-3 Try It (Examples 2–3)

a. 28 **b.** 4 **c.** 10,560

4-3 Exercises & Applications

1. 3 ft **3.** 8 ft **5.** 5 ft **7.** 21 **9.** 12
11. 32 **13.** 36 **15.** 384
17. 21,120 **19.** 7040 **21.** 72 in.;
6 ft **23.** 24 oz **25.** D **31.** 60
points; A and D **33.** B and C
35. 1.06, 1.34, 1.36, 1.66
37. 0.0349, 0.56, 0.678, 0.982
39. 66.3, 67.1, 67.4, 67.5, 68.3

Section 4A Review

1. 35.6 cm **3.** 3120 cm
5. 32,000 cm **7.** 42,240 ft
9. 60 ft **11.** 8000 **13.** 38,000,000
15. 29 **17.** A

4-4 Try It (Example 2)

a. 14 in^2 **b.** 12 cm^2 **c.** 28 ft^2

4-4 Try It (Examples 3–4)

a. 20 in^2 **b.** 54 cm^2 **c.** 28 yd^2

4-4 Exercises & Applications

1. 25 **3.** 24 **5.** 24 cm **7.** 27 ft^2
9. 1.2 km^2 **11.** 132 mm^2 **13.** C
15. 4 cm^2 **17.** 1 cm^2 **19.** 720 in^2
21. C **23. a.** 12,800 ft^2
25. \$60,000 **27.** The mean
29. 70 **31.** 28 **33.** 5 **35.** 143

4-5 Try It

a. 18 **b.** 198 mm^2

4-5 Exercises & Applications

1. 35 **3.** 24 **5.** 44 cm^2
7. 5.52 km^2 **9.** 0.07 in^2
11. 7500 m^2 **13.** 84 yd^2
15. 266.07 cm^2 **17.** 1,000,000 km^2
19. $\approx$ 50,830 mi^2 **21.** 14.57 m^2
25. a. 2.36 m^2 **b.** 384 in^2
c. 132 mm^2 **d.** 456 mm^2 **27.** 81
29. 144 **31.** 64 **33.** 1
35. 2,097,152 **37.** 5,764,801
39. 1.913 **41.** 232.47 **43.** 6.8

4-6 Try It

a. 6 **b.** 4.75 yd^2 **c.** 1.75 in^2

4-6 Exercises & Applications

1. 15 **3.** 6 **5.** 45 cm^2
7. 2,466,000 km^2 **9.** 1581 yd^2
11. 260 **13.** 27 in^2 **15.** 31.5 in^2
17. 1440 **21.** 52 **23.** 6^5 **25.** 7^4
27. 10^4 **29.** $3^4 \times 8$

Section 4B Review

1. 48 in^2 **3.** 0.935 yd^2 **5.** Yes
7. 96 **9.** 3.2 **11.** 48 in.
13. 110 mm

4-7 Try It

a. 37.68 cm **b.** $\approx$ 23.9 ft **c.** 18.84 ft
d. $\approx$ 25.16 cm

4-7 Exercises & Applications

1. True **3.** False **5.** 43.96 cm
7. 37.68 mm **9.** 9 **11.** 7.5 yd;
15 yd **13.** 5.5 m; 34.54 m **15.** 9.3
17. 6.28 cm **19.** 0.83 m **23.** 42
25. 11,658 **27.** $3 \times 3 \times 3 \times 3 \times 3$
29. $9 \times 9 \times 9 \times 9 \times 9 \times 9$ **31.** $12 \times$
$12 \times 12 \times 12 \times 12$ **33.** $6 \times 6 \times 6$
35. $13 \times 13 \times 13 \times 13 \times 13 \times 13 \times$
$13 \times 13 \times 13 \times 13 \times 13$
Possible answers are given:
37. 900 **39.** 10 **41.** 200 **43.** \$6

4-8 Try It

a. 1133.54 cm^2 **b.** 3.14 in^2

4-8 Exercises & Applications

1. True **3.** False **5.** 803.84 yd^2
7. 12.56 ft^2 **9.** 128.6144 ft^2
11. 907.46 ft^2 **13.** 7850 mm^2
15. 1.1304 mi^2 **17.** 1.3 km; 5.4 km^2
19. 0.5 mm; 0.8 mm^2 **21.** 0.2 mi;
0.1 mi^2 **23.** 2.9 m; 25.8 m^2
25. 1.32665 yd^2 **27.** C **29.** A
31. 144 ft^2 **33. a.** C, B, D, A
35. No **37.** 75 **39.** 240 **41.** 1600
43. 800,000

4-9 Exercises & Applications

1. Rectangle, semicircle
3. Semicircle, rectangle **5.** 34.8125
7. 450 ft^2 **9.** $\approx$ 31.8 cm^2
11. $\approx$ 445,000 mi^2 **15.** 289.56 ft^2
17. 21 **19.** 134 **21.** 24 **23.** 6
25. 7 **27.** 8.02 **29.** 162.5 **31.** 5.3

Section 4C Review

1. 12,000 **3.** 9.2 **5.** A: 43.2 mm^2;
P: 28 mm **7.** A: 0.5024 km^2; C:
2.512 km **9.** A: 153.86 in^2; C:
43.96 in. **11.** A: 119.065 units^2; P:
42.71 units **13.** The perimeter of
the square

Chapter 4 Summary & Review

1. 33.6 **2.** 4.14 **3.** 2.407
4. 5300 **5.** 73 **6.** 48 **7.** 14
8. 11,726 **9.** 0.432 **10.** $\approx$ 18.3 ft
11. 19,200 ft^2 **12.** 1200 cm^2
13. 75 ft^2 **14.** 56.25 mm^2
15. 21 ft^2 **16.** 30 ft **17. a.** 9.42 yd
b. 7.065 yd^2 **18.** 167.13 sq. units

Cumulative Review
Chapters 1–4

1. B **2.** A **3.** C **4.** B **5.** D **6.** B
7. C **8.** A **9.** B **10.** D **11.** A
12. A

Chapter 5

5-1 Try It

a. 3 **b.** 5 **c.** 2, 3, 6, 9 **d.** 3, 5
e. 2, 3, 5, 6, 9, 10

5-1 Exercises & Applications

1. a. 2 **b.** 2 **c.** 5 **d.** 2, 5, 10 **e.** 5
f. 2, 5, 10 **3.** 5 **5.** 3, 9 **7.** 2, 5, 10
9. 2, 3, 6 **11.** 2, 3, 5, 6, 9, 10
13. 2, 3, 5, 6, 9, 10 **15.** 2 **17.** 3,
5, 9 **19.** 2 **21.** 2, 3, 6 **23.** 2, 3, 5,
6, 10 **25.** 2, 3, 6 **27.** 3, 5 **29.** 5
31. 2, 3, 6 **33.** Yes **35.** No
37. No **39.** Yes **41.** Yes **43.** Yes
45. No **47.** Yes **49.** No **51.** No
53. Yes **55.** Yes **57. a.** No
b. No **c.** No **d.** Yes **e.** Yes
59. No **61. a.** 2, 5, 10 **b.** 2, 5, 10
c. 2, 5, 10 **73.** 16 **75.** 4.86
77. 6.8 **79.** 13.6

5-2 Try It

a. $2^2 \times 3$ **b.** $2^2 \times 5$ **c.** $2^2 \times 3^2$
d. $3^2 \times 5$ **e.** $2 \times 3 \times 5 \times 7$

5-2 Exercises & Applications

1. a. 3×5 **b.** 3×11 **c.** 2×7
d. 3×7 **e.** 2×3 **f.** 5×7
3. Prime **5.** Composite
7. Composite **9.** 5^2 **11.** 5×19
13. 5^3 **15.** 2×3 **17.** $2^3 \times 11$
19. $2^3 \times 3^2$ **21.** $2^2 \times 3^2 \times 19$
23. $2^2 \times 3 \times 5$ **25.** $3 \times 5 \times 7$
27. $2^4 \times 3$ **29.** 5×17 **31.** 2×3^4
33. $3 \times 5 \times 11$ **35.** $2^2 \times 3^2 \times 13$
37. $2 \times 3 \times 7$ **39.** Composite
41. 101, 103, 107, 109 **43.** 41, 43,
47, 53, 59, 61, 67, 71, 73, 79
49. 5,700,000 **51.** 5,890,000,000
53. 1.2 **55.** 0.25 **57.** 0.25 **59.** 0.5

5-3 Try It (Examples 1–2)

a. 35 **b.** 30 **c.** 20 **d.** 45

5-3 Try It (Example 3)

a. 18 **b.** 8 **c.** 100 **d.** 60 **e.** 55
f. 30 **g.** 54 **h.** 1297

5-3 Exercises & Applications

1. a. 3, 6, 9, 12, 15 **b.** 10, 20, 30,
40, 50 **c.** 11, 22, 33, 44, 55 **d.** 8,
16, 24, 32, 40 **e.** 4, 8, 12, 16, 20
f. 5, 10, 15, 20, 25 **3.** 5, 10, 15
5. 60, 120, 180 **7.** 42, 84, 126 **9.** 8,
16, 24 **11.** 16, 32, 48 **13.** 28, 56,
84 **15.** 33 **17.** 65 **19.** 10 **21.** 12
23. 42 **25.** 42 **27.** 20 **29.** 14
31. 15 **33.** Every 60 minutes
35. D **37.** Every 12 days
39. March 2 **41.** 150 **43.** >
45. > **47.** 2000

Section 5A Review

1. No **3.** Yes **5.** No **7.** Yes
9. Yes **11.** Yes **13.** $2^2 \times 19$
15. 2×11 **17.** $2^2 \times 3$ **19.** $2 \times 3 \times 19$ **21.** 73 is prime **23.** 3^4
25. 2, 4, 6, 8, 10, 12, 14 **27.** 7, 14,
21, 28, 35, 42, 49 **29.** 0, 0, 0, 0, 0,
0, 0 **31.** 6 **33.** 18 **35.** 20
37. 1998, 2000, 2002, 2004 **39.** 585

5-4 Try It

a. $\frac{6}{11}$ are red; $\frac{5}{11}$ are not. **b.** $\frac{7}{8}$; $\frac{14}{16}$

5-4 Exercises & Applications

1. a. $\frac{1}{2}$ **b.** $\frac{1}{4}$ **c.** $\frac{5}{8}$ **d.** $\frac{3}{4}$ **3–19.**
Possible equivalent fractions: **3.** $\frac{14}{18}$
5. $\frac{24}{34}$ **7.** $\frac{4}{6}$ **9.** $\frac{1}{2}$ **11.** $\frac{2}{5}$ **13.** $\frac{6}{16}$
15. $\frac{12}{16}$ **17.** $\frac{4}{8}$ **19.** $\frac{18}{20}$ **21.** $\frac{2}{9}$
23. B **25.** $\frac{6}{7}$ **27.** $\frac{8}{28}$ or $\frac{2}{7}$ **29.** $\frac{10}{16}$ in.
or $\frac{5}{8}$ in. **31.** a, b **33.** 101.9
35. 48.3 **37.** 9 **39.** $n = 100$
41. $h = 2$

5-5 Try It

Possible answers for a–c: **a.** $\frac{3}{5}$; $\frac{12}{20}$
b. $\frac{4}{5}$; $\frac{24}{30}$ **c.** $\frac{1}{3}$; $\frac{14}{42}$ **d.** 5 **e.** 2 **f.** 9
g. $\frac{4}{5}$ **h.** $\frac{3}{4}$ **i.** $\frac{2}{3}$

5-5 Exercises & Applications

1. a. Yes **b.** No **c.** Yes **d.** Yes
e. No **f.** Yes **3–13.** Possible
answers given. **3.** $\frac{2}{6}$; $\frac{1}{3}$ **5.** $\frac{2}{12}$; $\frac{3}{18}$
7. $\frac{3}{7}$; $\frac{18}{42}$ **9.** $\frac{2}{5}$; $\frac{20}{50}$ **11.** $\frac{1}{3}$; $\frac{22}{66}$ **13.** $\frac{8}{18}$;
$\frac{20}{45}$ **15.** $\frac{1}{5}$ **17.** $\frac{1}{3}$ **19.** $\frac{4}{5}$ **21.** $\frac{3}{5}$
23. $\frac{1}{6}$ **25.** $\frac{2}{3}$ **27.** $\frac{1}{4}$ **29.** $\frac{1}{6}$ **31.** $\frac{1}{6}$
33. 5 **35.** 2 **37.** 1 **39.** 8 **41.** 10
43. 4 **45.** 9 **47.** 4 **49.** 3 **51.** C
59. 25 kg **61.** Flyweight and
Cruiserweight; 40 kg

5-6 Try It

a. $4\frac{2}{3}$ **b.** $2\frac{8}{9}$ **c.** $8\frac{3}{4}$ **d.** $\frac{11}{6}$ **e.** $\frac{33}{8}$
f. $\frac{13}{5}$

5-6 Exercises & Applications

1. a. Proper **b.** Improper
c. Improper **d.** Proper
e. Improper **f.** Improper **3.** $\frac{14}{5}$
5. $\frac{10}{3}$ **7.** $\frac{14}{4}$ **9.** $\frac{14}{10}$ **11.** $\frac{31}{10}$ **13.** $\frac{33}{12}$
15. $2\frac{4}{5}$ **17.** $5\frac{1}{2}$ **19.** $2\frac{7}{8}$ **21.** $9\frac{9}{10}$
23. $100\frac{5}{8}$ **25.** $2\frac{7}{11}$ **27.** $\frac{31}{8}$ **29.** Yes
31. 12 **39.** 10,560 **41.** 9
43. 26,400 **45.** 30

5-7 Try It

a. $\frac{4}{5}$ **b.** $\frac{6}{25}$ **c.** $\frac{3}{8}$ **d.** 0.2;
Terminates **e.** 0.65; Terminates
f. $0.\overline{36}$; Repeats

5-7 Exercises & Applications

1. a. $\frac{3}{10}$ **b.** $\frac{7}{10}$ **c.** $\frac{11}{100}$ **d.** $\frac{37}{100}$
e. $\frac{121}{1000}$ **f.** $\frac{333}{1000}$ **3.** $0.\overline{14}$ **5.** $1.\overline{345}$
7. $0.\overline{18}$; Repeats **9.** 0.45;
Terminates **11.** 0.28; Terminates
13. $0.\overline{6}$; Repeats **15.** 2.5;
Terminates **17.** 1.25; Terminates
19. 0.72; Terminates **21.** 0.75;
Terminates **23.** 0.5; Terminates
25. $\frac{2}{5}$ **27.** $\frac{11}{25}$ **29.** $\frac{67}{100}$ **31.** $\frac{7}{20}$
33. $\frac{13}{25}$ **35.** $\frac{24}{125}$ **37.** $\frac{7}{10}$ **39.** $\frac{16}{125}$
41. $\frac{22}{25}$ **43.** $\frac{1}{8}$ in., $\frac{1}{4}$ in., $\frac{3}{8}$ in., $\frac{1}{2}$ in.,
$\frac{5}{8}$ in., $\frac{3}{4}$ in., $\frac{7}{8}$ in. **45.** D **47.** $0.\overline{02}$;
$0.\overline{37}$ **51.** 600 **53.** 2040
55. 15,000 **57.** 102

5-8 Try It

a. $\frac{7}{16}$ **b.** $\frac{5}{6}$ **c.** $\frac{8}{11}$

5-8 Exercises & Applications

1. a. < **b.** > **c.** < **d.** > **e.** <
f. < **3.** 24; > **5.** 18; < **7.** 4; =
9. 132; < **11.** 33; < **13.** 2; =
15. $\frac{4}{8} < \frac{7}{9} < \frac{5}{6}$ **17.** $\frac{3}{11} < \frac{11}{11} < \frac{11}{3}$
19. $\frac{4}{5} < \frac{4}{6} < \frac{4}{5}$ **21.** $\frac{2}{7} < \frac{3}{5} < \frac{3}{5}$
23. $\frac{2}{33} < \frac{3}{22} < \frac{10}{11}$ **25.** $\frac{1}{6} < \frac{7}{36} < \frac{13}{4}$
27. $\frac{7}{8}$; $\frac{10}{16}$; $\frac{3}{8}$; $\frac{10}{32}$; $\frac{1}{4}$; $\frac{2}{16}$ **29.** Renaldo
35. 0; 4; 6 **37.** 198; 110; 90
39. 35; 63; 77 **41.** 8; 4; 2

Section 5B Review

1. Yes; 3^3 **3.** No; 2^5 **5.** Yes; $2^4 \times 3$ **7.** $\frac{1}{2}$; numerator 1; denominator 2 **9.** $\frac{3}{8}$; numerator 3; denominator 8 **11.** $\frac{3}{4}$; 0.75 **13.** $\frac{1}{3}$; $0.\overline{3}$ **15.** $\frac{1}{2}$; 0.5 **17.** $3\frac{2}{10} = 3\frac{1}{5}$ **19.** $\frac{39}{5}$ **21.** $8\frac{2}{5}$ **23.** Beverly; Tom and Maye

Chapter 5 Summary & Review

1. 2, 3, 6, and 9 **2.** 2 **3.** 2, 3, 5, 6, and 10 **4.** 3 and 5 **5.** Composite **6.** Prime **7.** Composite **8.** Composite **9.** 108 **10.** 126 **11.** $\frac{5}{8}$ **12.** $\frac{4}{6}$ or $\frac{2}{3}$ **13.** The numerator is 11, the denominator is 3.
14. $\frac{2}{3}$ **15.** $\frac{1}{8}$ **16.** $\frac{1}{6}$ **17.** $\frac{4}{5}$ **18.** $4\frac{1}{4}$ **19.** $\frac{43}{5}$ **20.** $6\frac{5}{7}$ **21.** $\frac{26}{9}$ **22.** $\frac{7}{8}$ in., $1\frac{1}{4}$ in., $2\frac{3}{4}$ in., $\frac{7}{2}$ in. **23.** $0.\overline{6}$ **24.** 5.5 **25.** 0.375 **26.** 1.4 **27.** $\frac{1}{20}$ **28.** $3\frac{4}{5}$ **29.** $\frac{5}{8}$ **30.** $2\frac{23}{1000}$

Chapter 6

6-1 Try It

a. $\frac{7}{10}$ **b.** $\frac{2}{7}$ **c.** $\frac{17}{2}$ **d.** 0

6-1 Exercises & Applications

1. a. Yes **b.** Yes **c.** No **d.** No **e.** Yes **3.** $\frac{1}{10}$ **5.** 2 **7.** $\frac{1}{3}$ **9.** $\frac{1}{2}$ **11.** $\frac{1}{6}$ **13.** $\frac{4}{9}$ **15.** $\frac{6}{13}$ **17.** = **19.** > **21.** < **23.** > **25.** > **27.** $\frac{7}{13}$ **29.** $\frac{4}{17}$ **31.** $\frac{9}{20}$ **33.** $\frac{3}{10}$ **39.** 16 **41.** 31 **43.** 33, 40, 48

6-2 Try It (Example 1)

a. $\frac{5}{6}$ **b.** $\frac{1}{2}$ **c.** $\frac{17}{20}$ **d.** $\frac{1}{10}$

6-2 Try It (Examples 2–3)

a. $\frac{1}{4}$ **b.** $\frac{2}{3}$ **c.** $\frac{7}{10}$ **d.** $\frac{13}{18}$

6-2 Exercises & Applications

1. Possible answers: **a.** 6 **b.** 18 **c.** 8 **d.** 77 **e.** 24 **3.** $\frac{1}{4}$ **5.** $\frac{1}{6}$ **7.** $\frac{5}{4}$ **9.** $\frac{27}{28}$ **11.** $\frac{17}{30}$ **13.** $\frac{21}{20}$ **15.** $\frac{4}{25}$ **17.** 4, 7 **19.** 15, 4 **21.** 4, 3 **23.** $\frac{37}{7}$ weeks **25.** $\frac{23}{42}$ **27.** $\frac{11}{12}$ **29.** $\frac{1}{2}, \frac{7}{12}, \frac{2}{3}$ **31.** 49 **33.** $4h$

6-3 Try It

a. $\frac{2}{3}$ **b.** $\frac{8}{3}$ **c.** 1

6-3 Exercises & Applications

1. a. 1 **b.** $\frac{2}{7}$ **c.** $\frac{5}{9}$ **d.** $\frac{6}{5}$ **3.** $\frac{3}{10}$ **5.** $\frac{7}{8}$ **7.** 4 **9.** $\frac{25}{7}$ **11.** $\frac{1}{6}$ **13.** $\frac{22}{9}$ **15.** $\frac{2}{11}$ **17.** $\frac{1}{3}$ **19–25.** Possible answers given. **19.** $\frac{3}{4} - \frac{1}{4} = \frac{1}{2}$ **21.** $\frac{1}{6} + \frac{5}{12} = \frac{7}{12}$ **23.** $\frac{90}{81} - \frac{1}{3} = \frac{14}{18}$ **25.** $\frac{2}{12} + \frac{7}{10} = \frac{13}{15}$ **27.** $\frac{7}{15}$ **29.** $\frac{7}{12}$ lb **31.** A **33.** $\frac{1}{2}$ yard **37.** 60 **39.** No **41.** Yes

Section 6A Review

1. $\frac{8}{11}$ **3.** $\frac{1}{2}$ **5.** $\frac{27}{20}$ **7.** $\frac{5}{12}$ **9.** $\frac{2}{9}$ **11.** $\frac{19}{20}$ **15.** $\frac{7}{20}$ **17.** $\frac{1}{4}$ **19.** $\frac{3}{4}$ **21.** $\frac{2}{3}$ **23.** $\frac{3}{8}$

6-4 Try It

a. 6 **b.** 2 **c.** 4 **d.** 16 **e.** 8

6-4 Exercises & Applications

1. 0 **3.** 1 **5.** 1 **7.** 4 **9.** 5 **11.** 26 **13.** 34 **15.** 8 **17.** 7 **19.** 2 **21.** 18 **23.** 9 **25.** 7 **27.** 8 **29.** 5 **31.** 26 **33.** 15 **35.** 19 **37.** 7 **39.** About 21 ft **41.** $4\frac{1}{2}$ **43.** 7 inches **47.** 5 **49.** 16 in² **51.** 21 **53.** 32 **55.** 8 **57.** 22 **59.** 6 **61.** 5

6-5 Try It

a. $8\frac{3}{4}$ **b.** $4\frac{3}{4}$ **c.** $6\frac{1}{2}$ **d.** $7\frac{5}{12}$

6-5 Exercises & Applications

1. $11\frac{2}{3}$ **3.** $6\frac{1}{2}$ **5.** $9\frac{2}{3}$ **7.** $62\frac{3}{4}$ **9.** 11 **11.** $5\frac{17}{24}$ **13.** $6\frac{4}{5}$ **15.** $15\frac{8}{9}$ **17.** $13\frac{1}{9}$ **19.** $14\frac{1}{10}$ **21.** $21\frac{16}{21}$ **23.** 8 **25.** $41\frac{7}{9}$ **27.** $52\frac{1}{12}$ **29.** $38\frac{1}{4}$ ft **31.** $10\frac{3}{4}$ millions of dollars **33.** $15\frac{53}{60}$ millions of dollars **35.** A: $1\frac{2}{3}$ m²; B: 3 m² **37.** 9.42 ft; 62.8 in.; 113.04 in. **39.** 427,000 **41.** 1,124,000 **43.** 9,000,000,000 **45.** 666,300,000,000

6-6 Try It

a. $3\frac{2}{5}$ **b.** $4\frac{5}{6}$ **c.** $2\frac{4}{9}$

6-6 Exercises & Applications

1. $2\frac{3}{4}$ **3.** $2\frac{1}{2}$ **5.** $1\frac{1}{4}$ **7.** $\frac{1}{2}$ **9.** $\frac{2}{3}$ **11.** $1\frac{1}{24}$ **13.** $8\frac{1}{8}$ **15.** $3\frac{1}{5}$ **17.** $4\frac{11}{20}$ **19.** $\frac{3}{4}$ **21.** $3\frac{3}{5}$ **23.** $6\frac{13}{28}$ **25.** $1\frac{1}{5}$ ft **27.** C **29.** $2\frac{1}{4}$ hr **35.** 54.2325 **37.** 3.4×10^5 **39.** 5×10^6 **41.** 6.2×10^6

Section 6B Review

1. $1\frac{3}{5}$ **3.** $\frac{17}{45}$ **5.** $3\frac{5}{9}$ **7.** $111\frac{11}{24}$ **9.** 7 **11.** $4\frac{2}{3}$ **13.** $\frac{1}{18}$ **15.** $3\frac{1}{4}$ **17.** $\frac{1}{21}$ **19.** 6 hours **21.** D

Chapter 6 Summary & Review

1. $\frac{1}{5} + \frac{3}{5} = \frac{4}{5}$ **2.** 12 **3.** 28 **4.** 30 **5.** 63 **6.** $\frac{2}{7}$ **7.** $\frac{11}{15}$ **8.** 1 **9.** $\frac{1}{5}$ **10.** $1\frac{1}{4}$ **11.** $\frac{1}{14}$ **12.** $1\frac{1}{6}$ **13.** $\frac{2}{15}$ **14.** $\frac{15}{22}$ **15.** $\frac{41}{42}$ **16.** $\frac{5}{24}$ **17.** $\frac{7}{72}$ **18.** $\frac{9}{13}$ **19.** $\frac{3}{4}$ **20.** $\frac{7}{10}$ **21.** 3 **22.** 5 **23.** 2 **24.** 79 **25.** 1 **26.** 14 **27.** 20 **28.** 2 **29.** 2 **30.** 4 **31.** $2\frac{3}{4}$ in. **32.** $5\frac{4}{5}$ **33.** $13\frac{2}{3}$ **34.** $4\frac{3}{4}$ **35.** $\frac{7}{17}$ **36.** $8\frac{73}{88}$ **37.** $13\frac{3}{7}$ **38.** $2\frac{1}{6}$ **39.** $16\frac{7}{9}$ **40.** $9\frac{2}{3}$ **41.** $2\frac{5}{6}$ **42.** $28\frac{6}{7}$ **43.** 14 **44.** $10\frac{1}{2}$ m **45.** $28\frac{7}{8}$ yd

Cumulative Review

Chapters 1–6

1. A **2.** C **3.** C **4.** D **5.** B **6.** A
7. D **8.** D **9.** C **10.** C **11.** B
12. C

Chapter 7

7-1 Try It

a. 15 **b.** 3 **c.** 3 **d.** 1

7-1 Exercises & Applications

1. 5 **3.** 6 **5.** 9 **7.** 15 **9.** 50
11. 12 **13.** 72 **15.** 60 **17.** 35
19. 28 **21.** 12 **23.** 40 **25.** 30
27. 20 **29.** 6 **31.** A **33.** No
35. 3 **39.** 800 **41.** 97.6 **43.**
0.453 **45.** No **47.** No **49.** Yes
51. Yes **53.** No **55.** Yes

7-2 Try It

a. $2\frac{2}{3}$ **b.** $5\frac{1}{4}$ **c.** 8 **d.** 25

7-2 Exercises & Applications

1. $3 \times \frac{3}{5}$ **3.** $4 \times \frac{2}{3}$ **5.** $\frac{2}{3}$ **7.** $\frac{3}{5}$
9. $6\frac{2}{3}$ **11.** 2 **13.** $1\frac{1}{2}$ **15.** $6\frac{3}{5}$
17. $2\frac{2}{9}$ **19.** $5\frac{2}{5}$ **21.** $4\frac{3}{4}$ **23.** $12\frac{5}{6}$
25. $9\frac{3}{5}$ **27.** 27 **31.** $2\frac{1}{4}$ lb rice and
$1\frac{1}{2}$ lb sugar **33.** 28 years **37.** 98
39. 8 **41.** 17 **43.** $3^2 \times 7$ **45.** 17
47. 3×19

7-3 Try It

a. $\frac{12}{35}$ **b.** $1\frac{1}{3}$ **c.** $2\frac{8}{21}$ **d.** $\frac{2}{45}$

7-3 Exercises & Applications

1. $\frac{2}{3} \times \frac{2}{4} = \frac{4}{12}$ **3.** $\frac{5}{6} \times \frac{3}{10} = \frac{15}{60}$ **5.** $\frac{2}{7}$
7. $\frac{21}{40}$ **9.** $3\frac{59}{105}$ **11.** $\frac{78}{187}$ **13.** $8\frac{3}{10}$
15. $\frac{13}{60}$ **17.** $1\frac{146}{169}$ **19.** $1\frac{5}{14}$ **21.** $\frac{11}{42}$
23. $\frac{3}{64}$ **25.** $\frac{36}{121}$ **27.** $2\frac{32}{49}$ **29.** $6\frac{1}{4}$ ft
31. $\frac{1}{8}$ cup sugar, $\frac{1}{8}$ cup flour, and $\frac{7}{8}$
cup water **37.** 126,720 **39.** 190,080
41. 63,360 **43.** 6 **45.** 8 **47.** 35
49. 72 **51.** 29 **53.** 9

Section 7A Review

1. 3 **3.** 30 **5.** 2 **7.** 11 **9.** 3 oz
wax; $19\frac{1}{2}$ tbs oil; 9 tbs water; $\frac{3}{4}$ tsp
borax **11.** Yes **13.** $1\frac{2}{3}$ **15.** D

7-4 Try It

a. $6\frac{2}{3}$ **b.** $1\frac{3}{4}$ **c.** $2\frac{6}{17}$ **d.** 5

7-4 Exercises & Applications

1. $\frac{7}{5}$ **3.** $\frac{9}{2}$ **5.** 4 **7.** 9 **9.** $3\frac{1}{2}$
11. $11\frac{1}{4}$ **13.** $1\frac{3}{29}$ **15.** $1\frac{7}{23}$ **17.** $3\frac{3}{10}$
19. 40 **21.** $3\frac{9}{13}$ **23.** $\frac{9}{32}$ **25.** $10\frac{1}{2}$
27. $1\frac{9}{13}$ **29.** $\frac{9}{34}$ **31.** B **33.** 30
35. a. About $3\frac{1}{2}$ **b.** 2 **c.** About 11
37. No **39.** 896 **41.** 400 **43.** 160

7-5 Try It

a. $1\frac{7}{25}$ **b.** $1\frac{1}{2}$ **c.** $\frac{1}{10}$ **d.** $\frac{1}{25}$

7-5 Exercises & Applications

1. $\frac{2}{3} \div \frac{1}{6} = 4$ **3.** $\frac{1}{3} \div \frac{2}{12} = 2$ **5.** $\frac{2}{5}$
7. 7 **9.** $1\frac{1}{4}$ **11.** $\frac{20}{189}$ **13.** $\frac{2}{31}$ **15.** $\frac{5}{16}$
17. 10 **19.** 8 **21.** $\frac{4}{25}$ **23.** $\frac{19}{41}$
25. 7 **27.** B **29. a.** 9 **b.** 108
35. $r = 8$ cm; $d = 16$ cm **37.** $r = 4$
mm; $d = 8$ mm **39.** $\frac{6}{10}$ **41.** $\frac{2}{8}$

7-6 Try It (Example 2)

a. 6 **b.** $\frac{5}{4}$ **c.** 12

7-6 Try It (Example 4)

a. 2 **b.** $\frac{7}{2}$ **c.** $1\frac{1}{2}$

7-6 Exercises & Applications

1. Yes **3.** No **5.** $\frac{24}{133}$ **7.** 15 **9.** $\frac{3}{4}$
11. 2 **13.** $125\frac{1}{45}$ **15.** $2\frac{13}{25}$ **17.** 68
19. $1\frac{1}{3}$ **21.** $1\frac{1}{4}$ **23.** $6\frac{6}{7}$ **33. a.** 256
b. 7000 **c.** 240 **d.** 5760 Possible
answers for 35–39: **35.** $\frac{9}{24}$; $\frac{6}{16}$
37. $\frac{1}{2}$; $\frac{2}{4}$ **39.** $\frac{22}{28}$; $\frac{33}{42}$ **41.** 3 **43.** 1

Section 7B Review

1. 8 **3.** $7\frac{1}{2}$ **5.** $2\frac{4}{7}$ **7.** $4\frac{17}{22}$ **9.** 50
11. 13 **13.** 4 **15.** $v = 32$
17. $x = 2$ **19.** $p = \frac{2}{5}$ **21.** $u = 1\frac{3}{5}$
25. 3 gallons **27.** A

Chapter 7 Summary & Review

1. $2 \times \frac{5}{7} = \frac{10}{7}$ **2.** ≈ 14 **3.** ≈ 5
4. $\frac{3}{32}$ **5.** $\frac{1}{81}$ **6.** $\frac{4}{15}$ **7.** $\frac{12}{49}$ **8.** 25
9. 2 **10.** $11\frac{1}{4}$ **11.** $10\frac{5}{9}$ **12.** $1\frac{1}{4}$
cups **13.** No **14.** $4 \div \frac{2}{3} = 6$
15. $\frac{8}{5}$ **16.** $\frac{1}{3}$ **17.** $4\frac{1}{2}$ **18.** $\frac{5}{6}$
19. $\frac{9}{35}$ **20.** $\frac{8}{35}$ **21.** $\frac{3}{28}$ **22.** $\frac{4}{63}$
23. $\frac{1}{40}$ **24.** $\frac{7}{22}$ **25.** Yes **26.** Yes
27. No **28.** No **29.** $x = \frac{3}{2}$
30. $m = \frac{3}{4}$ **31.** $w = \frac{7}{30}$ **32.** $q = \frac{7}{3}$
33. 10 pieces

Chapter 8

8-1 Exercises & Applications

1. Ray **3.** Ray **5.** Line
13. Parallel **15.** Parallel
17. Intersecting **19.** Perpendicular
31. $1\frac{2}{3}$ **33.** $2\frac{1}{3}$ **35.** $3\frac{1}{2}$ **37.** $1\frac{4}{5}$
39. $1\frac{1}{2}$ **41.** $2\frac{2}{5}$ **43.** 1 **45.** $1\frac{3}{5}$
47. $1\frac{1}{4}$ **49.** $1\frac{2}{3}$ **51.** 1

8-2 Try It

a. Straight **b.** Right **c.** Obtuse
d. Acute

8-2 Exercises & Applications

1. / **3.** B **5.** Obtuse **7.** Acute
9. Acute **11.** Right **13.** $\angle ABC$,
$\angle CBA$, $\angle B$ **15.** $\angle GHI$, $\angle IHG$, $\angle H$
21. Obtuse **23.** Straight
25. Acute **29.** 6 **31.** Acute
33. $\frac{33}{5}$ **35.** $\frac{7}{2}$ **37.** $\frac{119}{11}$ **39.** $\frac{39}{4}$
41. $\frac{13}{6}$ **43.** $\frac{27}{7}$ **45.** $1\frac{19}{36}$ **47.** $1\frac{1}{3}$
49. $\frac{3}{8}$ **51.** $\frac{1}{2}$ **53.** $\frac{9}{11}$

8-3 Exercises & Applications

1. Greater than **3.** Less than
5. 72° **7.** 135° **9.** 180° **11.** 55°
15. Obtuse **17.** Obtuse **19.** 11°
21. 87° **23.** 128° **25.** 90° **29.** B
33. 0.5 **35.** 0.25 **37.** $0.\overline{3}$ **39.** $0.\overline{4}$
41. $0.\overline{54}$ **43.** 1.0 **45.** $\frac{1}{24}$ **47.** $1\frac{25}{66}$
49. $\frac{5}{72}$ **51.** $\frac{9}{10}$

Section 8A Review

1. Parallel **3.** Nonintersecting
5. Right **7.** Obtuse **9.** 37°; C = 53°; S = 143° **11.** 75°; C = 15°; S = 105° **13.** A

8-4 Try It

a. 39°; Right **b.** 122°; Obtuse

8-4 Exercises & Applications

1. 40° **3.** 80° **5.** 100° **7.** Acute
9. Obtuse **11.** Right **13.** Obtuse
15. Acute **17.** Right **19.** 66°, 56°, 58° **21.** 43°, 112°, 25° **23.** 77°, 45°, 58° **25.** 79°, 60°, 41° **27.** 31°
29. 5° **31.** 90° **33.** Yes; Acute
35. Yes; Obtuse **37.** 28°, 45°, 107°
41. 28° **43.** $\frac{39}{50}$ **45.** $\frac{9}{10}$ **47.** $\frac{18}{25}$
49. $\frac{69}{500}$ **51.** $\frac{3}{8}$ **53.** $\frac{999}{1000}$ **55.** 5
57. 16 **59.** 5 **61.** 5

8-5 Try It

a. Yes **b.** No **c.** No

8-5 Exercises & Applications

1. 4 m **3.** 20 ft **5.** 9 yd
7. Scalene **9.** Isosceles
11. Equilateral **13.** Scalene
15. Scalene **17.** Equilateral
19. Yes **21.** Yes **23.** No **25.** Yes
27. Scalene **29.** No **31.** Right scalene **33.** Obtuse scalene
35. Yes **37.** Right scalene triangles
39. > **41.** = **43.** $11\frac{4}{15}$ **45.** $23\frac{1}{2}$
47. $11\frac{17}{35}$ **49.** $7\frac{23}{35}$

8-6 Try It

a. Regular quadrilateral
b. Irregular triangle **c.** Irregular pentagon

8-6 Exercises & Applications

1. Not closed **3.** Not closed
5. Regular pentagon **7.** Irregular hexagon **9.** Regular quadrilateral
11. Regular octagon **19.** Octagon
21. Pentagon **23.** Triangle
25. Quadrilateral **27.** 8 **29.** 40 in.
33. $\frac{4}{5}, \frac{7}{8}, \frac{8}{9}$ **35.** $\frac{6}{9}, \frac{6}{6}, \frac{9}{6}$ **37.** $\frac{1}{4}, \frac{1}{3}, \frac{1}{2}$
39. $\frac{6}{7}, \frac{9}{8}, \frac{7}{6}$ **41.** $1\frac{27}{35}$ **43.** $\frac{1}{8}$ **45.** $3\frac{11}{56}$
47. $6\frac{4}{9}$ **49.** $4\frac{9}{28}$

8-7 Try It

a. False **b.** True **c.** Trapezoid, quadrilateral

8-7 Exercises & Applications

1. 2 **3.** 2 **5.** False **7.** True
23. A **25.** Yes **31.** > **33.** >
35. = **37.** < **39.** = **41.** >
43. 29.4 **45.** 226.8 **47.** 48.23
49. 0.4

Section 8B Review

1. ∠JAH, ∠HAJ, ∠A **3.** ∠IPK, ∠KPI, ∠P **5.** 24° **7.** 135° **9.** 128°
11. Acute; 57° **13.** Acute; 18°
19. Rhombus, parallelogram, irregular quadrilateral, polygon
21. Trapezoid, irregular quadrilateral, polygon

8-8 Try It

a. No **b.** Yes **c.** Yes

8-8 Exercises & Applications

1. **3.**

5. Not symmetric **7.** Not symmetric **9.** Yes **11.** Yes **13.** Yes
17. 2 **19.** Octagon **23.** $\frac{2}{3}$, 0.75, $\frac{7}{9}$
25. 1.1, $\frac{7}{6}$, 1.167 **27.** $\frac{1}{3}$, 1.3, $\frac{3}{1}$
29. 0.25, $\frac{2}{5}$, 2.5 **31.** 30.528
33. 4.3792 **35.** 17.29 **37.** 3.96

8-9 Try It

a. 90° counterclockwise **b.** 270° clockwise **c.** 2

8-9 Exercises & Application

1. **3.**

5. 360° **7.** 180° **13.** 360°
15. 180° **17.** 90° **19.** 72°
25. 3.55 **27.** 0.13 **29.** 0.06
31. 2.37 **33.** 18.2 **35.** 2.69
37. 14.2 **39.** 7

8-10 Try It

Yes

8-10 Exercises & Applications

1. No **3.** Yes **7.** Yes **9.** Yes
11. No **13.** Yes **15.** Hexagon
17. Yes **21.** 28 cm **23.** 26 mm
25. 3100 **27.** 56 **29.** 0.106

Section 8C Review

7. Obtuse, 110°, 40°, 30° **9.** Acute, 65°, 65°, 50° **11.** Regular octagon; Yes; 8 **13.** Irregular triangle; No
15. Yes **17.** Yes **19.** 104°
21. 81° **23.** 90° **25.** C

Chapter 8 Summary & Review

1.

2.

3. a.

b.

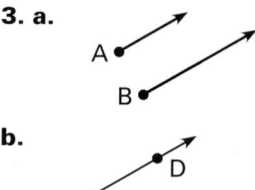

4. Acute triangle **5.** All rectangles are parallelograms because their opposite sides have the same lengths and are parallel. But some parallelograms do not have all 90° angles, which rectangles must have. **6.** Translation **7.** Reflection or rotation **8.** Rotation **9.** Yes. The figures have the same size and shape.

10.

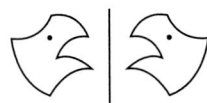

11. Yes

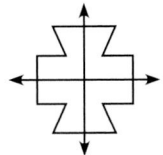

12. 90° clockwise

Cumulative Review
Chapters 1–8

1. B **2.** A **3.** B **4.** C **5.** A **6.** A
7. D **8.** C **9.** A **10.** B **11.** C
12. B **13.** C **14.** D **15.** A

Chapter 9

9-1 Try It

a. 4° **b.** −6° **c.** −10, −3, 0, 1, 7, 10

9-1 Exercises & Applications

1. Yes **3.** Yes **5.** Yes
7–11.

-5 -4 -3 -2 -1 0 1 2 3

13. > **15.** < **17.** > **19.** >
21. > **23.** 3, 2, −4, −5 **25.** 13, −16, −56, −78 **27.** 16, 12, 0, −10
29. 19, 17, 16, −18 **31.** −114
33. 62 **35.** −7 **37.** −213, −211, −107, −76, −52 **39.** −12, 22
41. −20, −15, −5, −4, −3, −2, −1
47. 14 **49.** 3 **51.** 44 **53.** 180
55. Intersecting **57.** Perpendicular
59. Perpendicular **61.** Intersecting

9-2 Try It

a. 10 **b.** −8 **c.** 1 **d.** 0 **e.** 7 **f.** 6
g. 3 **h.** −3

9-2 Exercises & Applications

1. $8 + (-5) = 3$ **3.** $3 + (-1) = 2$
5. −12 **7.** 40 **9.** 1589
11. Negative **13.** Positive
15. Zero **17.** Negative
19. Negative **21.** −12 **23.** −2
25. 6 **27.** −12 **29.** −17 **31.** 1
33. 2 **35.** −6 **37.** 13 **39.** −14
41. 9 **43.** −1 **45.** −31 **47.** −14
49. 0 **51.** Opposite of 211 **55.** B
57. Yes **59.** $34\frac{1}{2}$ **61.** 1 **63.** $6\frac{2}{3}$
65. 50 **67.** Right **69.** Acute

9-3 Try It (Examples 1–2)

a. −2 **b.** −8 **c.** 4 **d.** −1

9-3 Try It (Example 3)

a. 17 **b.** 5 **c.** 26 **d.** −11

9-3 Exercises & Applications

1. $-2 - 4 = -6$ **3.** $-4 - 2 = -6$
5. $-5 - (-2) = -3$ **7.** −9 **9.** 9
11. 12 **13.** 2 **15.** −11 **17.** 19
19. −20 **21.** −11 **23.** −8 **25.** 13
27. −5 **29.** 20 **31.** −13 **33.** 22
35. 11 **37.** 30,300 ft **39.** 16 feet
41. 65° **43. b.** 33 and 26 **45.** 116°
47. 87° **49.** $4\frac{3}{5}$ **51.** $2\frac{3}{40}$

9-4 Try It

a. −36 **b.** 90 **c.** 60 **d.** −10
e. −4 **f.** 3 **g.** −5 **h.** 3

9-4 Exercises & Applications

1. Negative **3.** Negative
5. Negative **7.** 9 **9.** 100 **11.** −12
13. 18 **15.** −20 **17.** −48
19. −32 **21.** −2 **23.** −4 **25.** −7
27. −20 **29.** −2 **31.** −7 **33.** −8
35. 3 **37.** −12; 2; 0; −4; −2; −4, −3, 12 **39.** −2; −3; 0; 3, 3; 3, 2; 9, 3, 3 **43.** His actual average is −3.
45. $4\frac{2}{3}$ **47.** $9\frac{1}{3}$ **49.** 28 **51.** $2\frac{1}{22}$
53. 73 **55.** 11

Section 9A Review

1. −63 **3.** −1 **5.** −4 **7.** 2 **9.** −9
11. −42 **13.** −1 **15.** −2 **17.** −6
19. 10 **21.** −40 **23.** 24 **25.** −23
27. −$4.00 **29.** −4°C **31.** D

9-5 Try It

a. $A(2, 1)$; $B(3, -4)$; $C(0, 5)$; $D(-1, 2)$; $E(4, 0)$; $F(1, -3)$; $G(-2, -3)$
b.

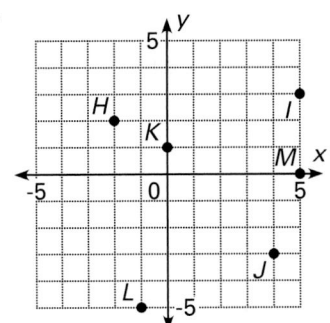

9-5 Exercises & Applications

1. I **3.** III **5.** (−5, 4) **7.** (−3, −2)
9. I **11.** IV **13.** IV **25.** Start at the origin. Go left 35 units and down 18 units. **27.** Start at the origin. Go right 4 units and up 10 units. **29.** Start at the origin. Go right 88 units and down 23 units.
31. a. 1 (300, 100); 2 (400, 300); 3 (0, 400) **b.** 2 **c.** 400
33. a.

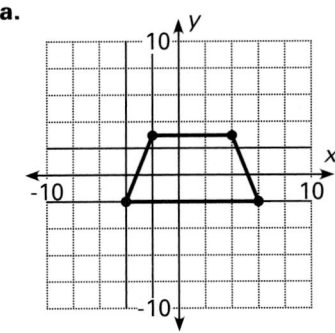

b. Trapezoid, quadrilateral, irregular polygon **35.** (10, 8) **37.** $\frac{147}{256}$
39. $2\frac{13}{144}$ **41.** Yes **43.** Yes

9-6 Try It (Example 1)

$L'(1, -2)$; $M'(2, 0)$; $N'(6, -3)$

9-6 Try It (Example 2)

$X'(-1, -1)$; $Y'(-3, 4)$; $Z'(-5, 1)$

9-6 Exercises & Applications

1. (4, 6) **3.** (7, 4) **5.** (−3, 6)
7. $P'(5, 3)$ **9.** $P'(3, 5)$ **11.** $P'(2, 2)$

13.

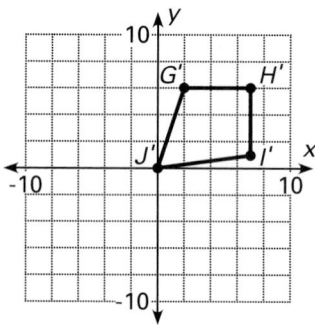

17. c. $R'(2, 3)$, $S'(4, 5)$, $T'(7, 1)$
19. c. $X'(-4, -2)$, $Y'(4, -3)$, $Z'(2, -1)$
21. $A'(2, 3)$, $B'(-1, 3)$, $C'(-1, -3)$,
$D'(2, -3)$ **25.** $p = 4\frac{2}{5}$ **27.** $e = \frac{9}{8}$
29. Irregular octagon   **31.** Irregular
quadrilateral

9-7 Try It

a.

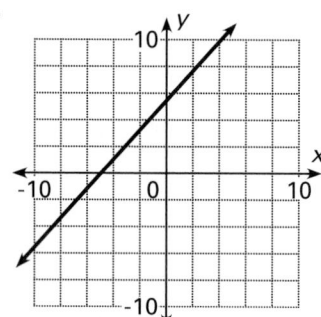

b.

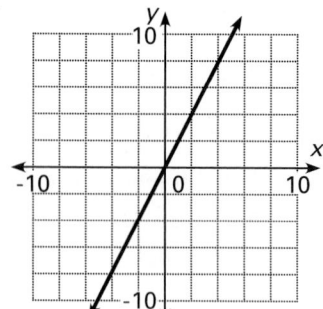

c.

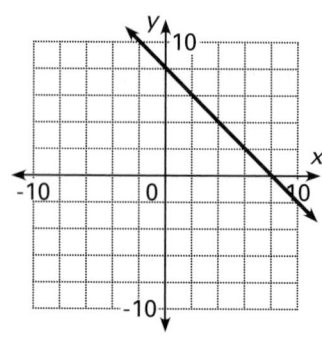

d.

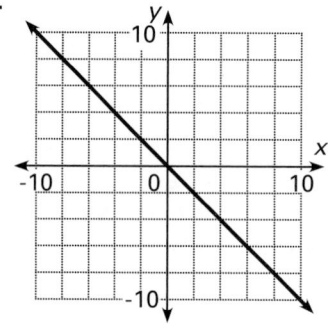

9-7 Exercises & Applications

1. a–d.

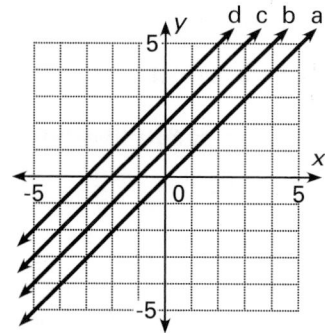

The lines are parallel.

Possible answers for 3–5:

3.

x	y
-2	25
-1	26
0	27
1	28
2	29

5.

x	y
-2	100
-1	50
0	0
1	-50
2	-100

7.

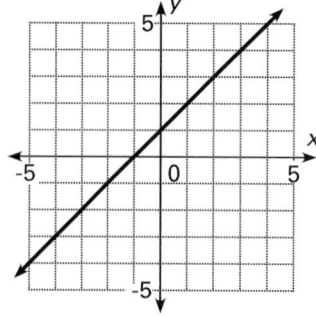

19.

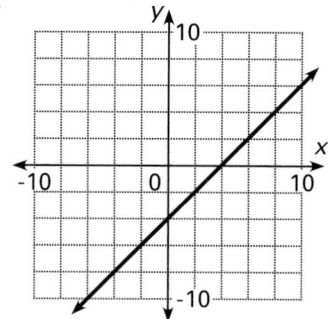

27. 43   **29.** -7 **31.** -2
39. 864   **41.** 36   **43.** 9

Section 9B Review

1. 8   **3.** -12 **5.** -10 **7.** 35   **9.** 5
11. $A(-3, 2)$, $B(2, 1)$, $C(-2, -2)$,
$D(1, -1)$ **13.** $(-2, 1)$ **15.** $(4, 4)$
17.

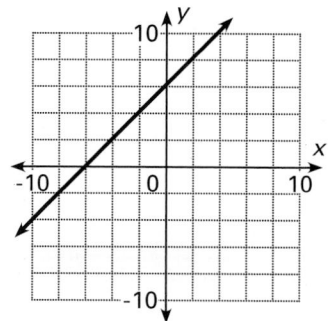

19.

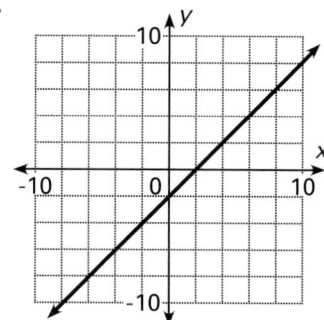

21. $(2, 2)$, $(2, 4)$, $(4, 2)$, $(4, 4)$ **23.** A

Chapter 9 Summary & Review

1.

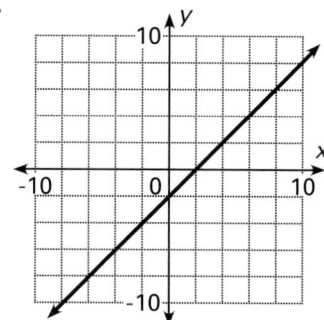

2. -3 **3.** Negative   **4.** Positive
5. $4 + (-5) = -1$ or $4 - 5 = -1$
6. $2 + (-4) = -2$ or $2 - 4 = -2$
7. 4   **8.** -6 **9.** 2   **10.** 0   **11.** -6
12. -10 **13.** 0   **14.** 28   **15.** -21

16. 36 **17.** −8 **18.** 3 **19.** (−6, −5)
20. Quadrant II **21. a.** (5, 0)
b. (0, 5) or (0, −5) **22.** $R'(−4, −2)$, $S'(−3, −4)$, $T'(−2, −2)$ **23.** $A'(0, 2)$; $B'(3, 2)$; $C'(3, 0)$; $D'(0, 0)$

24. a.

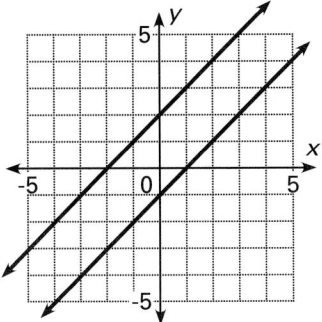

b. Each point on the upper line has been translated down 3 units to create the lower line.

Chapter 10

10-1 Try It

a. 2:5 **b.** 1:2

10-1 Exercises & Applications

1. Yes **3.** Yes **5.** No **7.** 3:2
9. 2:3 **11. a.** 20:9 **b.** 9:29
13. 3:8; $\frac{3}{8}$; 3 to 8 **15.** 1:7; $\frac{1}{7}$; 1 to 7
17. 24:49 **19.** Turtles **21.** Turtles to dogs **23.** You can't tell **25.** Yes
27. No **29.** 9 in. **31.** 2 km

10-2 Try It

Possible answers: **a.** 10:18; 15:27
b. $\frac{6}{16}$; $\frac{9}{24}$ **c.** 3 to 5; 6 to 10 **d.** 2:26; 3:39 **e.** 24:8; 3:1

10-2 Exercises & Applications

1. Yes **3.** Yes **5.** No Possible answers for 7–17: **7.** 8 to 10; 12 to 15
9. 6:4; 3:2 **11.** $\frac{2}{3}$; $\frac{16}{24}$ **13.** $\frac{1}{2}$; $\frac{2}{4}$
15. $\frac{2}{16}$; $\frac{3}{24}$ **17.** $\frac{6}{8}$; $\frac{12}{16}$ **19.** Yes
21. Yes **25.** A Possible answers for 27: **27.** 14:20; 28:40; 21:30
29. Men: 8, 12; Women: 5; 20
31. 5, 10, 15, 20 **35.** 90° **37.** 90°
39. 18 in² **41.** 880 ft²

10-3 Try It

Possible answers: About 0.44 mi in 1 min; 18 miles in 41 min; About 7 mi in 16 min; 72 mi in 164 min

10-3 Exercises & Applications

1. Yes **3.** No **5.** Yes **7.** No Possible answers for 9–11:
9. 7 mi/hr, 21 mi/3 hr **11.** $\frac{15 \text{ j.j.}}{20 \text{ sec}}$; $\frac{3 \text{ j.j.}}{4 \text{ sec}}$ Possible answer for 13:
13. An ostrich runs 5 miles in 10 minutes. **15.** About 25 mi
17. Orange **19.** D **21.** $2\frac{1}{2}$ hours
25. Yes **27.** No **29.** 2.4 m²
31. 0.12 cm² **33.** 120,000 mi²

Section 10A Review

1. 23:30 **3.** Possible answer: $\frac{3 \text{ red}}{5 \text{ blue}}$, $\frac{3 \text{ red}}{4 \text{ green}}$, $\frac{3 \text{ red}}{7 \text{ red or green}}$, $\frac{1 \text{ red}}{3 \text{ blue or green}}$, $\frac{1 \text{ red}}{4 \text{ total}}$ **5.** Possible answers: 3:8, 12:32, 18:48 **7.** 1:3 **9.** Possible answer: $\frac{5 \text{ blue stones}}{28 \text{ stones}}$ **11.** D

10-4 Try It

a. Yes **b.** No **c.** No **d.** Yes

10-4 Exercises & Applications

1. a. II **b.** III **c.** I **d.** IV **3.** No
5. No **7.** No **9.** No **11.** No
13. Yes **15.** b **17.** 254.8 ft **19.** A
21. Ms. Lee and Mrs. Nieto
23. No **25.** Phillip and Janice
27. $0.25 × $0.75 ≠ 3 × 1$
29. 55, 31, −13, −55 **31.** −9, −17, −31, −53 **33.** 44, 41, −14, −41 **35.** 133, 0, −100, −178
37. 4.2 **39.** $r = 4.4$ yd; $d = 8.8$ yd

10-5 Try It

a. 9 **b.** 10 **c.** 1.5 **d.** 7.2

10-5 Exercises & Applications

1. $9x = 36$ **3.** $44j = 275$ **5.** $16s = 56$ **7.** 12 **9.** 25 **11.** 16.5 **13.** 0.96
15. 6 **17.** 3 **19.** $2.\overline{6}$ **21.** 3.6
23. 154 **25.** $23.\overline{3}$ **27.** 12 **29.** $5\frac{1}{3}$ ft
31. A **33.** 6 or −6 **35.** Greater than **37.** −18 **39.** −6
41. 12.56 cm² **43.** 153.86 cm²

10-6 Try It

a. 3600 ft/min **b.** $2.80

10-6 Exercises & Applications

1. 3 **3.** 7 **5.** 8 **7.** 2 houses/mi
9. $5\frac{1}{6}$ holes/in² **11.** 0.6 waves/sec
13. 3 slices/person **15.** $\frac{1}{3}$ m/hr
17. 0.5 cup/serving **19.** 1.5 turtles/mi² **21.** 7.5 m/sec **23.** 252 mi
25. 2.2 points **27.** 9 drips **29.** 1.2 apples **31.** $\frac{70 \text{ apples}}{6 \text{ baskets}} = \frac{x}{3 \text{ baskets}}$; $x = 35$ apples **33.** 3 pounds for 72¢
35. $0.58\overline{3}$ ft, or $\frac{7}{12}$ ft **41.** 33.25 in²
43. 154 mm² **45.** −17 **47.** 14
49. −3 **51.** 6

10-7 Try It

6

10-7 Exercises & Applications

1. Congruent **3.** Neither **5.** $A = B = C = 1$ mm **7.** $A = C = 0.625$ yd, $B = 0.5$ yd **9.** 12.5 m **11. a.** 385 mi; 495 mi; 610 mi **b.** Yes
13. 25 ft or 64 ft **15.** No; Yes
17. −21 **19.** 16 **21.** −70 **23.** 26
25. 12 **27.** Yes **29.** No **31.** Yes
33. Yes **35.** Yes **37.** Yes

Section 10B Review

1. Possible answers: $\frac{5 \text{ cm}}{2 \text{ sec}}$, $\frac{2.5 \text{ cm}}{1 \text{ sec}}$, $\frac{10 \text{ cm}}{4 \text{ sec}}$ **3.** $0.65/min **5.** 0.6 commercials/min **7.** 50.4 **9.** $0.30 **11.** 5
13. $A = 4.\overline{6}$, $B = 3$, $C = 7$ **15.** B

10-8 Try It

a. 25% **b.** 75%

10-8 Exercises & Applications

1. Greater **3.** Less **5.** Less
7. 50% **9.** 25% **11.** 50%
13. 74% **15.** About 12%; About 88% **17.** India, Myanmar, Other
19. 25% **21. a.** 89% **b.** No
23. Yes **25.** Yes **33.** 5^2
35. $5 × 19$ **37.** 5^3 **39.** $2 × 3$
41. $2^3 × 11$ **43.** $2^3 × 3^2$

10-9 Try It

a. 20%　**b.** 70%

10-9 Exercises & Applications

1. 50%　**3.** 40%　**5.** 25%　**7.** 70%
9. 33%　**11.** 25%　**13.** 10%
15. 50%　**17.** 75%　**19.** 60%
21. 1%　**23.** 7%　**25.** C　**27.** 33%
29. $\frac{7}{200}$　**31.** 67% are not　**37.** 6
39. 12　**41.** 10　**43.** 30　**45.** 42
47. 6

10-10 Try It

a. $\frac{83}{100}$; 0.83　**b.** $\frac{7}{100}$; 0.07　**c.** 37.5%

10-10 Exercises & Applications

1. 0.37　**3.** 1.0　**5.** 0.1　**7.** 2.34
9. 0.673　**11.** 0.8887　**13.** $\frac{14}{25}$　**15.** $\frac{3}{4}$
17. $1\frac{1}{2}$　**19.** $\frac{89}{100}$　**21.** $\frac{9}{10}$　**23.** $2\frac{17}{50}$
25. 84%　**27.** 4%　**29.** 110%
31. 85%　**33.** 53%　**35.** 30%
37. 56%　**39.** 48%　**41.** 75%
43. 67.5%　**45.** 33.3%　**47.** 38%
49. 40%, $\frac{2}{5}$, 0.4　**51.** 50%, $\frac{4}{8}$, 0.5
53. 66.$\overline{6}$%　**55.** C　**57.** $\frac{27}{200}$

10-11 Try It (Example 2)

a. 611　**b.** 133

10-11 Try It (Example 3)

a. 70　**b.** 50,000

10-11 Exercises & Applications

1. 50　**3.** 2　**5.** 22.10　**7.** 18.48
9. 104.94　**11.** 54.30　**13.** 22.44
15. 0.38　**17.** 15.20　**19.** ≈ $2.75
21. 6.12　**23.** 8.51　**25.** 250
27. 200　**29.** 88　**31.** 176　**33.** 20
or more　**35.** $36,720　**37.** 249
39. 1,656,000　**41.** Yes
43. Both　**45.** $\frac{1}{2}$　**47.** $\frac{2}{3}$　**49.** $\frac{1}{3}$
51. $\frac{3}{4}$　**53.** $\frac{1}{7}$　**55.** $\frac{3}{5}$　**57.** $\frac{34}{5}$　**59.** $\frac{26}{9}$
61. $\frac{36}{7}$　**63.** $10\frac{1}{2}$　**65.** $\frac{7}{2}$　**67.** $2\frac{4}{5}$

Section 10C Review

1. a. 3:4　**b.** $\frac{3}{4}$; 0.75 lettuce/carrot
c. ≈ 57.14%　**3.** Yes　**5.** Yes　**7.** 4
9. 10　**11.** 1200　**13.** *A* and *C* = 0.2
in.; *B* = 0.3 in.　**15.** 28.86
17. 17.52　**19.** Possible answers:
a. 80%　**b.** 60%　**21.** 95%; 60%

Chapter 10 Summary & Review

1. 6:11, 6 to 11, $\frac{6}{11}$　**2.** $\frac{3}{4}$　**3. a.** 10
to 1　**b.** 1 to 10　**c.** 5 to 1　**d.** 2 to 1
4. 3 to 4; 3 to 7　**5.** A　**6.** B　**7.** No
8. 15　**9.** $4.32　**10.** Possible
answer: The ratios of all the matching sides are equal. The angle
measures are equal.　**11.** $\frac{35}{100}$, $\frac{7}{20}$,
0.35　**12.** $\frac{20}{100}$, $\frac{1}{5}$, 0.2　**13.** $\frac{8}{100}$, $\frac{2}{25}$,
0.08　**14.** $\frac{75}{100}$, $\frac{3}{4}$, 0.75
15. ≈ 4,680,998 people
16. Possible answer: $\frac{6}{4}$, $\frac{12}{8}$, $\frac{18}{12}$, $\frac{24}{16}$
17. $\frac{1.5 \text{ min}}{1 \text{ mi}}$

Cumulative Review
Chapters 1–10

1. D　**2.** B　**3.** A　**4.** C　**5.** C　**6.** B
7. D　**8.** A　**9.** B　**10.** C　**11.** A
12. D　**13.** C　**14.** A

Chapter 11

11-1 Exercises & Applications

1. Triangles and squares or rectangles　**3.** Squares or rectangles
5. Sphere　**7.** Triangular prism;
6 vertices, 9 edges, 5 faces
9. Cylinder　**11.** Cone
17. Rectangular prisms
19. Spheres　**25.** No; No; No
27. 100 to 10　**29.** 2.5　**31.** 0.75
33. 0.8$\overline{3}$

11-2 Try It

a. 6 faces: All rectangles
b. 272 units²

11-2 Exercises & Applications

1. 12 units²　**3.** 18 units²　**5.** 24 cm²;
Cube or rectangular prism　**7.** 60
units²; Triangular prism　**9.** 6 faces:
All rectangles; 310 ft²　**13.** $0.93

15. 35.119 in²　Possible answers
for 19–23:　**19.** 6:8, 9:12　**21.** 2:5,
12:30　**23.** 22:24, 33:36　**25.** 0.23, $\frac{1}{2}$,
1.23　**27.** 8.2, $8\frac{1}{4}$, 8.75

11-3 Try It

a. 358 units²　**b.** 96 units²
c. 380 units²

11-3 Exercises & Applications

1. 6 cm²　**3.** 96 m²　**5.** 48 ft²
7. 268 units²　**9.** 279 cm²
11. 109.8 cm²　**13.** 13.5 cm²
15. C　**17.** 1128 in²　**19.** Yes
21. No　**23.** $\frac{1}{6}$　**25.** $\frac{13}{28}$　**27.** $\frac{10}{63}$

11-4 Exercises & Applications

1. 15.7 cm　**3.** 6.28 ft　**5.** 61.23 m²
7. 17.27 in²　**9.** 150.72 ft²
11. 138.16 units²　**13.** 2110.08 units²
15. a. $1.81　**b.** $2.07　**17.** Possible
answer: *h* = 1 cm, *d* = 4 cm
19. 173.825 in²　**21.** Yes　**23.** No
25. No　**27.** No　**29.** No　**31.** 17.4
33. 0.24

Section 11A Review

1. Sphere　**3.** Triangular prism; 6
vertices, 9 edges, 5 faces　**5.** Cube
or rectangular prism; 8 vertices,
12 edges, 6 faces　**9.** 54 ft²
11. 8800 cm²

11-5 Try It

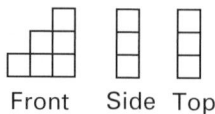

Front　Side　Top

11-5 Exercises & Applications

1. 5　**3.** 12　**13.** 36　**15. a.** 7
b. 5.1 cm　**c.** 6.8 cm　**17. a.** No
b. No　**21.** *f* = 48　**23.** *r* = 3
25. 156%　**27.** 55%　**29.** 28%
31. $\frac{67}{100}$　**33.** $2\frac{1}{2}$　**35.** $\frac{1}{100}$

11-6 Try It

a. 8 units³　**b.** 48 units³
c. 12 units³　**d.** 225 units³

11-6 Exercises & Applications

1. 10 units^3 **3.** 21 units^3 **5.** 360 units^3 **7.** 64 units^3 **9.** 60 units^3
11. 126 **13.** Yes **15.** 4 ways
17. 3 mi per min **19.** 5 bananas per dollar **21.** 0.316 m per sec
23. 4.5 worms per in^2 **25.** About 20% **27.** About 20%

11-7 Try It

a. 105 in^3 **b.** 18 in.

11-7 Exercises & Applications

1. 125 in^3 **3.** 343 ft^3 **5.** 72 yd^3
7. 910 m^3 **9.** 480 units^3
11. 74.088 in^3 **13.** 2907 m^3 **15.** B
17. About 12 inches deep
19. $A = 32$ ft, $B = 80$ ft **21.** 33.$\overline{3}$%
23. 40%

Section 11B Review

1. Rectangular prism; 8 vertices, 12 edges, 6 faces **3.** Triangular prism; 6 vertices, 9 edges, 5 faces
5. C
7.

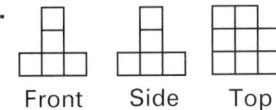
Front Side Top

9.

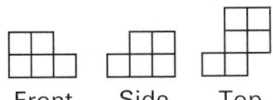
Front Side Top

Chapter 11 Summary & Review

1. Triangular prism; 5 faces, 9 edges, 6 vertices. **2.** Sphere
3. Rectangular pyramid; 5 faces, 8 edges, 5 vertices. **4.** 310 in^2
5. 340 units^2 **6.** 80.07 mm^2
7.

Front Side Top

8.

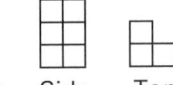
Front Side Top

9. 80 units^3 **10.** 240 cm^3
11. 0.36 units^3 **12.** 477.28 in^2

Chapter 12

12-1 Try It

a. i. $\frac{3}{8}$ **ii.** 0 **b. i.** $\frac{1}{2}$ **ii.** $\frac{3}{5}$

12-1 Exercises & Applications

1. 2 **3.** 6 **5.** $\frac{1}{10}$ **7.** $\frac{1}{10}$ **9.** 0
11. $\frac{1}{2}$ **13.** $\frac{1}{6}$ **15.** $\frac{5}{6}$ **17.** $\frac{1}{6}$ **19.** $\frac{1}{3}$
21. Both are $\frac{1}{8}$ **23.** $\frac{1}{5}$ **25.** Will occur **27.** $\frac{9}{32}$ **29.** No; No
33. Rectangular prism
35. Cylinder **37.** 31.74 cm^2
39. 708 ft^2

12-2 Try It

a. $\frac{13}{61}$ **b.** $\frac{51}{61}$

12-2 Exercises & Applications

1. Yes **3.** No **5.** 3 **7.** $\frac{17}{20}$ **9.** 67
11. 16 **13.** May; $\frac{181}{826} \approx 0.22$
15. Yes **17.** The numbers are considerably above average.
19. First figure **21.** 482.8064 in^2

12-3 Try It

50%

12-3 Exercises & Applications

1. 9 square units **3.** 30% **5.** 37.5%
7. 50% **9.** A **11.** 84 **19.** 18 units^3
21. 16 units^3

Section 12A Review

1. $\frac{1}{6}$ **3.** 0 **5.** $\frac{5}{6}$ **7.** $\frac{5}{8}$ **9.** 1 **11.** C
13. 1000 **15.** B

12-4 Try It

a. Possibilities are: chocolate, hot fudge; chocolate, butterscotch; vanilla, hot fudge; vanilla, butterscotch; mint, hot fudge; mint, butterscotch. **b.** 16

12-4 Exercises & Applications

1. d. 12 outcomes **5.** D **7. a.** 6
b. $\frac{1}{3}$ **9.** 45,697,600 **13.** 12; 12
15. 24 in^3 **17.** $\frac{3}{10}$ **19.** $\frac{1}{5}$ **21.** $\frac{2}{5}$

12-5 Try It

$\frac{1}{3}$

12-5 Exercises & Applications

1. a. 6 **b.** 216 **c.** 1 **d.** 1 **e.** $\frac{1}{216}$
3. $\frac{1}{9}$ **5.** $\frac{4}{27}$ **7.** $\frac{1}{27}$ **9.** About $\frac{1}{32}$
11. $\frac{1}{8}$ **13.** $P(\text{same}) = \frac{1}{6}$; $P(\text{different}) = \frac{5}{6}$ **15.** Winning both the 50-yard dash and the hurdles.
17. $\frac{5}{51}$ **21.** #2

12-6 Try It

a. No
b. Yes

12-6 Exercises & Applications

1. b. $\frac{13}{18}$ **c.** $\frac{5}{18}$ **d.** No
3. Fair **5.** Unfair; Edna **7.** Yes; He got each number about the same amount of times. **9.** Unfair; Either way, you always lose.

Section 12B Review

1. a. 8 **b.** $\frac{1}{8}$ **3.** $\frac{4}{64}$ **5. a.** 42,875
b. $\frac{1}{42,875}$ **7.** No; $P(\text{A win}) = \frac{3}{8}$
$P(\text{B win}) = \frac{5}{8}$

Chapter 12 Summary & Review

1. About $\frac{1}{4}$ **2.** It is likely to occur.
3. $\frac{3}{7}$ **4.** About $\frac{1}{4}$ **5.** 16 **6.** 24 outfits **7.** 180 **8.** 8 **9.** $\frac{1}{3}$ **10.** $\frac{1}{36}$
11. $\frac{1}{16}$ **12.** Yes; Each player has a 50% chance of winning. **13.** No; Player A has a greater chance of winning.

Cumulative Review
Chapters 1–12

1. C **2.** B **3.** D **4.** A **5.** A **6.** D
7. C **8.** D **9.** B **10.** B **11.** C
12. B **13.** A **14.** A

Credits

Photographs

Cover/Spine: Uniphoto Picture Agency, Inc.

Front Matter **iii** GHP Studio* **iii (background)** John Banagan/The Image Bank **v-xvi T** GHP Studio* **xviii L** Cheryl Fenton* **xviii R** George Hunter/Tony Stone Images **xix T** Parker/Boon Productions and Dorey Sparre Photography* **xix B** Ken Karp,* Dennis Geaney* & Parker/Boon Productions and Dorey Sparre Photography* **xxii** Jean-Marc Giboux/Liaison International **xxiii** Pictor/Uniphoto Picture Agency **xxiv** Ken Karp* **xxv** Fridmar Damm/Leo de Wys Inc. **xxvi** John Lund/Tony Stone Images **xxvii** Robie Price* **xxviii** Mark C. Burnett/Stock, Boston

Chapter 1 **2–3 (background)** Ralph Mercer/Tony Stone Images **2 TR (frame)** John Michael/International Stock Photo **2 TR (inset)** Christopher Liu/China Stock **2 BR** NASA/Stock, Boston **2 BL** Robie Price* **3** ZEFA/The Stock Market **4 B** Soames Summerhays/Photo Researchers **4 T** Ed R. Degginger/Photo Researchers **5** Robie Price* **6** Douglas Faulkner/Photo Researchers **8** Blake/Reuters/Corbis-Bettmann **10** Damien Lovegrove/SPL/Photo Researchers **11 L** Marc Chamberlain/Tony Stone Images **11 R** Geoffrey Nilsen Photography* **12** Jeff Rotman **14** W. Gregory Brown/Animals, Animals **15** Bob Daemmrich/Stock, Boston **16** Pete Saloutos/The Stock Market **17** David Hall/Photo Researchers **18 T** David Madison/Bruce Coleman Inc. **18 B** Dr. Nigel Smith/Earth Scenes **19 T** Paul Humann/Jeff Rotman Photography **19 B** Geoffrey Nilsen Photography* **20** Lee F. Snyder/Photo Researchers **21** Robie Price* **23 L** Joseph Nettis/Stock, Boston **23 R** Jon Feingersh/The Stock Market **24** Ron Chapple/FPG International **26 R** UPI/Corbis-Bettmann **26 L** Portrait by Ellis Sawyer/FPG International **28** from HERBLOCK: A CARTOONIST'S LIFE (Macmillan Publishing, 1993) **29** Owen Franken/Stock, Boston **31 BLC** Popperfoto/Archive Photos **31 BR** Ron Thomas/Reuters/Corbis-Bettmann **31 BRC** Mark Reinstein/FPG International **31 T** Worldsat International Inc./SPL/Photo Researchers **31 BL** FPG International **32** Robert Frerck/Tony Stone Images **33** Geoffrey Nilsen Photography* **34 R** Win McNamee/Reuters/Corbis-Bettmann **34 L** Jeffrey Sylvester/FPG International **35** AFP/Archive Photos **36 L** Dennis Geaney* **36 R** Parker/Boon Productions and Dorey Sparre Photography* **38** Archive Photos **39** Jon Feingersh/The Stock Market **40 B** © 89 Mug Shots/The Stock Market **40 T** Geoffrey Nilsen Photography* **41 T** Geoffrey Nilsen Photography* **41 B** Geoffrey Nilsen Photography* **41 (inset)** Mississippi Valley State University **42** Shelley Gazin/The Image Works **43** Bill Reitzel **45** Kevin Lamarque/Reuters/Corbis-Bettmann **46 TL** Berenguier & Jerrican/ Photo Researchers **46 TR** Robie Price* **46 B** Geoffrey Nilsen Photography* **47** Paul Souders/Allsport

48 T Dennis Geaney* **48 B** Al Bello/Allsport **49** Gail Shumway/FPG International **51** Tim DeFrisco/Allsport **52** Otto Rogge/The Stock Market **53** Robie Price* **54** Brad Mangin/Duomo **55 BL** Courtesy of Hank Aaron and the Hank Aaron Chasing the Dream Foundation/National Baseball Hall of Fame © Topps **55 TL** TM/© 1996 Family of Babe Ruth and the Babe Ruth Baseball League, Inc. under license authorized by CMG Worldwide Inc., Indianapolis, Indiana, 46202 USA http://www.cmgww.com. Photo by Geoffrey Nilsen Photography* **55 TR** Geoffrey Nilsen Photography* **55 BR** Geoffrey Nilsen Photography* **56** Popperfoto/Archive Photos **57** Geoffrey Nilsen Photography* **61 T** Stewart L. Craig, Jr./Bruce Coleman Inc. **61 C** Robie Price* **61 B** Geoffrey Nilsen Photography*

Chapter 2 **62-63 (background)** Comstock **62 TL** Erich Lessing/Art Resource, NY **62 TR** David Frazier/Science Source/Photo Researchers **62 B** Cheryl Fenton* **63 T** Robert Fried/Stock, Boston **63 B** Cheryl Fenton* **64 T** Mark Gamba/The Stock Market **64 B** John Terence Turner/FPG International **65 T** Rob Lewine/The Stock Market **65 B** NASA **66 T** Alan Carey/The Image Works **68** Frank Rossotto/The Stock Market **69 L** NASA/Science Source/Photo Researchers **69 R** NASA/Lunar & Planetary Inst. **70** Robert Houser/Comstock **72 L** Lunar & Planetary Inst. **72 R** NASA/ESA/Tom Stack & Associates **73** Robie Price* **74** Tim Flach/Tony Stone Images **75** Lunar & Planetary Institute **77** Sovfoto/Eastfoto **78** Gabe Palmer/Mugshots/The Stock Market **79 T** NASA/JPL/TSADO/Tom Stack & Associates **79 B** NASA **80 L** Parker/Boon Productions and Dorey Sparre Photography* **80 R** Dennis Geaney* **81** NASA/JPL/TSADO/Tom Stack & Associates **82** NIBSC/SPL/Photo Researchers **82 (inset)** CNRI/SPL/Photo Researchers **83 T** Rob Lewine/The Stock Market **83 B** NASA **84** NASA/Mark Marten/Photo Researchers **86 L** Mike Malyszko/FPG International **87** Underwood Collection/Corbis-Bettmann **88** Geoffrey Nilsen Photography* **89** Carl Yarbrough/Uniphoto Picture Agency **90 L** Billy Hustace/Tony Stone Images **90 R** Geoffrey Nilsen Photography* **93** Geoffrey Nilsen Photography* **94 L** John Coletti/Tony Stone Images **94 R** Geoffrey Nilsen Photography* **95** Bob Daemmrich/The Image Works **96 R** Fujifotos **97 T** Geoffrey Nilsen Photography* **97 C** Robie Price* **98 L** Lawrence Migdale/Stock, Boston **98 R** Hewlett Packard **100** Robie Price* **101** Geoffrey Nilsen Photography* **102 TL** Stephen Frisch/Stock, Boston **102 TR** Robie Price* **102 B** Gregory Sams/SPL/Photo Researchers **104 L** Ken Karp* **104 R** Parker/Boon Productions and Dorey Sparre Photography* **105** Anne Dowie* **106** IFA-Bildesteam/Uniphoto Picture Agency **107 L** Geoffrey Nilsen Photography* **108** Anne Dowie* **109** Barry E. Parker/Bruce Coleman Inc. **110 L** Jon Feingersh/Stock, Boston **110 R** Steve Starr/Stock, Boston **113** Martin Rogers/Stock, Boston **114 L** Anne Dowie* **114 R** Robie

Price* **115** Topham/The Image Works **116** Eric A. Wessman/Stock, Boston **117** ©1986 Carmen Lomas Garza, photo by Wolfgang Dietze **118** Jeff Lepore/Photo Researchers **119** Mark Gamba/The Stock Market **120** Navaswan/FPG International **122** Lawrence Migdale/Photo Researchers **123** Brian Parker/Tom Stack & Associates **125** Monteath C./Hedgehog House N. Zeal./Explorer/Photo Researchers **127** Barry E. Parker/Bruce Coleman Inc. **127 TL** Peter David/Photo Researchers **127 BL** Richard Pasley/Stock, Boston **128** Thomas Kitchin/Tom Stack & Associates **129** Geoffrey Nilsen Photography*

Chapter 3 **134-135 (background)** Superstock **134 L** Steven E. Sutton/Duomo **134 TR** J. P. Courau/DDB Stock Photo **134 BR** Stuart Cohen/Comstock **135 T** Cheryl Fenton* **135 B** Kimimasa Mayama/UPI/Corbis-Bettmann **136 T** Anne Dowie* **136 B** Jane Burton/Bruce Coleman Inc. **137** Robie Price* **137 (insets)** Stephen Cooper/Tony Stone Images **138** Doug Wechsler/Earth Scenes **139** G. C. Kelley/Photo Researchers **140** Andrew Syred/SPL/Photo Researchers **141** Popperfoto/Archive Photos **142 L** Gabe Palmer/Mugshots/The Stock Market **142 R** Robie Price* **143 L** Ray Coleman/Photo Researchers **143 R** John Fennell/Bruce Coleman Inc. **144 T** Geoffrey Nilsen Photography* **144 C** Geoffrey Nilsen Photography* **144 B** Rod Planck/Tony Stone Images **145 L** Geoffrey Nilsen Photography* **145 R** Parker/Boon Productions and Dorey Sparre Photography* **146 L** Gilbert S. Grant/Photo Researchers **146 R** John Gerlach/Animals, Animals **148** David Madison **149** Jan C. Taylor/Bruce Coleman Inc. **150 L** Ken Karp* **150 R** Dennis Geaney* **151 L** James H. Carmichael, Jr./Photo Researchers **151 R** L. West/National Audubon Society/Photo Researchers **152** Bob Llewellyn/Uniphoto Picture Agency **153** ATC Productions 1993/The Stock Market **155 T** Astrid & Hanns-Frieder Michler/SPL/Photo Researchers **155 B** Kim Taylor/Bruce Coleman Inc. **156** Geoffrey Nilsen Photography* **157 L** James Carmichael/Bruce Coleman Inc. **157 R** Robie Price* **158 TL** Buddy Mays/FPG International **158 TR** Buddy Mays/FPG International **158 B** David Parker/SPL/Photo Researchers **159** Robie Price* **160** Martin Rogers/Tony Stone Images **161** Geoffrey Nilsen Photography* **162** Geoffrey Nilsen Photography* **163** Robie Price* **164** Jeff Albertson/Stock, Boston **165** Anne Dowie* **166 L** Ken Karp* **166 R** Dennis Geaney* **167** Jeff Greenberg/The Image Works **168 T** Anne Dowie* **169** Robie Price* **170** Robie Price* **171** Robie Price* **172 T** Geoffrey Nilsen Photography* **172 B** Robie Price* **173** Robie Price* **174** Geoffrey Nilsen Photography* **175** Western History Department/Denver Public Library **176** Terry Qing/FPG International **177** Antman Archive/The Image Works **178** Corbis-Bettmann **180** Ron Cronin **181** Bill Stormont/The Stock Market **184 T** Geoffrey Nilsen Photography* **184 B** Robie Price* **185** Geoffrey

Nilsen Photography* **187** Jon Feingersh/The Stock Market **188** McLaughlin Historical File 1/FPG International **189** Doug Pensinger/Allsport **190** Laima Driskis/Stock, Boston **192 L** Parker/Boon Productions and Dorey Sparre Photography* **192 R** Ken Karp* **194** Western History Department/Denver Public Library **195** Shaw McCutcheon/Bruce Coleman Inc. **196** Western History Department/Denver Public Library **197** Richard Price/FPG International **199** Western History Department/Denver Public Library **200** Alan Carey/The Image Works **201** Geoffrey Nilsen Photography* **205 T** Uniphoto Picture Agency **205 CL** Geoffrey Nilsen Photography* **205 TCR** Roy Morsch/The Stock Market **205 BL** Bob Daemmrich/Stock, Boston **205 BCR** Lawrence Migdale/Stock, Boston

Chapter 4 **206-207 (background)** Marc Romanelli/The Image Bank **206 T** Matthew Borkoski/Stock, Boston **206 L** Louis S. Glanzman/National Geographic Image Collection **206 B** Anne Dowie* **207 TL** Michael Macor/San Francisco Chronicle **207 TR** Richard Martin/Agency Vandystadt/Allsport **207 BL** Prim & Ray Manley/Superstock **207 BR** NASA **208 T** Jack Zehrt/FPG International **208 (background)** NASA/SPL/Photo Researchers **208 BL** NASA **208 BC** NASA/The Image Works **208 BR** Owen Franken/Stock, Boston **209** John Elk/Stock, Boston **210** Robie Price* **211** Michael Thompson/Comstock **212 L** Parker/Boon Productions and Dorey Sparre Photography* **212 R** Dennis Geaney* **213** Robie Price* **214** Jerry Wachter/Photo Researchers **215** Donald Carroll/The Image Bank **216** Chuck Place/The Image Bank **217** Andy Snyder/San Francisco Zoo **218 T** Robie Price* **218 C** Robie Price* **218 B** Steve Dunwell/The Image Bank **219 T** Telegraph Colour Library/FPG International **219 B** Norman O. Tomalin/Bruce Coleman Inc. **220** Robie Price* **221** Geoffrey Nilsen Photography* **222** Robie Price* **223 T** Anne Dowie* **223 B** Robie Price* **224** Susan Kuklin/Photo Researchers **225 CL** Yellow Dog Prods./The Image Bank **225 R** John Elk/Stock, Boston **225 BL** Ted Russell/The Image Bank **227 (foregound)** Cheryl Fenton* **227** Kunio Owaki/The Stock Market **228** Julie Houck/Stock, Boston **230** Robie Price **231** NMAA, Smithsonian Institution/Art Resource, NY **233** Comstock **236** Geoffrey Nilsen Photography* **237** Anne Dowie* **239 L** Ken Karp* **239 R** Ken Karp* **241** Robie Price* **243 (foregound)** Cheryl Fenton* **243** Kunio Owaki/The Stock Market **246** Pictor/Uniphoto Picture Agency **247 BL** Robie Price* **247 BR** Robie Price* **248 TR** Arthur Tilley/FPG International **248 BL** Cheryl Fenton* **248 BR** David Sams/Stock, Boston **249 R** FPG International **250** Walter Iooss/The Image Bank **251 BL** Cheryl Fenton* **251 BR** Cheryl Fenton* **252 L** Georg Gerster/Comstock **253** James Carmichael/The Image Bank **254** James Blank/The Stock Market **256 L** Dennis Geaney* **256 R** Parker/Boon Productions and Dorey Sparre Photography* **257 TL** Mark Antman/The Image Works **257 TLC** Cheryl Fenton* **257 TRC** Cheryl Fenton* **257 TR** Andrea Pistolesi/The Image Bank **257 BL** Cheryl Fenton* **257 BR** Cheryl Fenton* **259 TL** Corbis-Bettmann **259 CL** Corbis-Bettmann **261** Geoffrey Nilsen Photography*

Chapter 5 **266-267 (background)** Pierre-Yves Goavec/The Image Bank **266 L** Geoffrey Nilsen Photography* **266 R** Kevin Schafer/Tony Stone Images **267 T** Cheryl Fenton* **267 B** Ellen Beach/Bruce Coleman Inc. **268** Robie Price* **269** NASA **270** Dennis O'Clair/Tony Stone Images **272** Peggy and Ronald Barnett/The Stock Market **274 T** FPG International **274 BL** George Hunter/Tony Stone Images **274 BR** ET Archive/Superstock **275** RLC Trust/Superstock **277 L** Ken Karp* **277 R** Parker/Boon Productions and Dorey Sparre Photography* **279** M. Fischer/Art Resource, NY **280** Pekka Parviainen/SPL/Photo Researchers **281** The Cartoon Bank, Inc. **282 T** Pat Lanza Field/Bruce Coleman Inc. **282 B** Superstock **283** Robie Price* **284** Anne Dowie* **285** NASA **286** Photri/The Stock Market **287** Cheryl Fenton* **288** Robie Price* **289** Cheryl Fenton* **290** Cheryl Fenton* **292** Geoffrey Nilsen Photography* **293** Anne Dowie* **296** Cheryl Fenton* **297** AKG/Superstock **298** Anne Dowie* **300** Robie Price* **301** Anne Dowie* **302** Lee Snider/The Image Works **303** Geoffrey Nilsen Photography* **304 B** Superstock **304 T** M. Greenlar/The Image Works **305** Cheryl Fenton* **308 T** Anne Dowie* **308 B** Cheryl Fenton* **309** Cheryl Fenton* **310** Parker/Boon Productions and Dorey Sparre Photography* **312 L** © Rindy Nyberg/Southern Card and Novelty, Inc. **312 R** © Rindy Nyberg/Southern Card and Novelty, Inc. **313** Cheryl Fenton* **314** Robie Price* **315** Geoffrey Nilsen Photography* **319** Larry Gatz/The Image Bank

Chapter 6 **320-321 (background)** John Elk/Stock, Boston **320 L** Snowdon/Hoyer/Focus/Woodfin Camp & Associates **320 TR** Robie Price* **320 BR** Jane Grushow/Grant Heilman Photography **321 T** Townsend P. Dickinson/Comstock **321 B** Tom Till/Tony Stone Images **322 T** Hans Pfletschinger/Peter Arnold, Inc. **322 BL** Myron J. Dorf/The Stock Market **322 BR** Cheryl Fenton* **324** Geoffrey Nilsen Photography* **325** AP/Wide World Photos **327** Pictos/Uniphoto Picture Agency **328** Anne Dowie* **329** Robie Price* **330** Anne Dowie* **331** David Scharf **332** Geoffrey Nilsen Photography* **333** Texas Instruments **334** Dave Watts/Tom Stack & Associates **335 L** SIU/Peter Arnold, Inc. **335 R** Robie Price* **337** Jay Freis/The Image Bank **338** Larry Mulvehill/Photo Researchers **340** Michael Tamborrino/FPG International **341** Tom Dietrich/Tony Stone Images **342** Kevin Horan/Tony Stone Images **343** Owen Franken/Stock, Boston **344** Tom Till/DRK Photo **346** Peter Beck/The Stock Market **347** Library of Congress/Superstock **348 L** Thomas Dimock/The Stock Market **348 R** Lori Adamski Peek/Tony Stone Images **349** MacTavish/Comstock **350** Robie Price* **351 L** Bob Burch/Bruce Coleman Inc. **351 R** Culver Pictures **352** Parker/Boon Productions and Dorey Sparre Photography* **353** Anne Dowie* **355** Tom Dietrich/Tony Stone Images **356** UPI/Corbis-Bettmann **357** Geoffrey Nilsen Photography*

Chapter 7 **362-363 (background)** Geoffrey Nilsen Photography* **362 TL** Dimitri Messinis/Agence France/Corbis-Bettmann **362 TR** Michele Burgess/The Stock Market **362 BL** Bill Bachmann/The Image Works **362 BR** Ken Cole/Earth Scenes **363 T** David

Woodfall/Tony Stone Images **363 BL** Culver Pictures **363 BR** Draeger/Culver Pictures **364** Bruce M. Herman/Photo Researchers **365** Lawrence Migdale/Stock, Boston **365 (background)** Jeff Schultz/AlaskaStock **366** Grant Heilman Photography **367** R. Dahlquist/Superstock **368** George F. Godfrey/Earth Scenes **369 L** Archive Photos **369 R** Kunio Owaki/The Stock Market **370** M. Timothy O'Keefe/Bruce Coleman Inc. **371** Robert A. Tyrrell **372 L** Dennis Geaney* **372 R** Ken Karp* **373** Geoffrey Nilsen Photography* **374 L** Renee Stockdale/Animals, Animals **374 R** Karl & Kay Ammann/Bruce Coleman Inc. **375** David Hundley/The Stock Market **376** James Carmichael/Bruce Coleman Inc. **377** James H. Robinson/Photo Researchers **378** Robie Price* **379** Lawrence Migdale/Stock, Boston **379 (background)** Jeff Schultz/AlaskaStock **380** Akos Szilvasi/Stock, Boston **381** Steve Liss/People Weekly **381 (inset)** Stanley Tretick/People Weekly **382** Dean Siracusa/FPG International **383** Larry Brownstein/Rainbow **384** Parker/Boon Productions and Dorey Sparre Photography* **385** Kwok Leung Paul Lau/Liaison International **386** Robie Price* **387** John Eastcott/The Image Works **388 L** Culver Pictures **388 R** Simon Bruty/Allsport **389** Robie Price* **390** Geoffrey Nilsen Photography* **391** Texas Instruments **392** Stephen Frisch/Stock, Boston **393** Cheryl Fenton* **395** Geoffrey Nilsen Photography* **396** Bob Daemmrich/Stock, Boston **397 R** Steve Liss/People Weekly **397 L** The MIT Museum **398** Jack Daniels/Tony Stone Images **399** Geoffrey Nilsen Photography **403 TL** Cheryl Fenton* **403 TR** Bruce Wilson/Tony Stone Images **403 BL** Henry Ausloos/Animals, Animals **403 BR** David Madison

Chapter 8 **404-405 (background)** Bruce Hands/Comstock **404 T** Derek Berwin/The Image Bank **404 C** Art Resource, NY **404 B** Symmetry Drawing E67 by M. C. Escher. ©1997 Cordon Art-Baarn, Holland. All Rights Reserved. **405 T** John David Fleck/Liaison International **405 BL** William Johnson/Stock, Boston **405 BR** Kim Taylor/Bruce Coleman Inc. **406 T** Cheryl Fenton* **406 BL** Robie Price* **406 BC** Robie Price* **406 BR** Robie Price* **407** Cheryl Fenton* **408** Steven H. Begleiter/Uniphoto Picture Agency **409** Cheryl Fenton* **410** Cheryl Fenton* **411** Bob Llewellyn/Uniphoto Picture Agency **412 L** Bob Daemmrich/The Image Works **412 R** Cheryl Fenton* **416** Ilene Perlman/Stock, Boston **418 T** Pascal Rondeau/Allsport USA **418 C** Ken Karp* **418 B** Parker/Boon Productions and Dorey Sparre Photography* **419** Cheryl Fenton* **421** Cheryl Fenton* **423** Cheryl Fenton* **424** Bard Wrisley/Liaison International **425** Cheryl Fenton* **427** Cheryl Fenton* **428** Pierre Boulat/Woodfin Camp & Associates **430** Cheryl Fenton* **431** Jenny Thomas* **432** Comstock **433** Cheryl Fenton* **434 L** Eduardo Garcia/FPG International **434 CL** Peter Menzel/Stock, Boston **434 CR** Archive Photos **434 R** S. Vidler/Superstock. **435 T** Dave B. Fleetham/Tom Stack & Associates **435 BL** Cheryl Fenton* **435 BC** Cheryl Fenton* **435 BR** Cheryl Fenton* **436** Bill Gallery/Stock, Boston **438** Archive Photos **441** Cheryl Fenton* **443** Adam Woolfitt/Woodfin Camp & Associates **444** Art Wolfe/Tony Stone Images **445** ©1994, Asian Art Museum of San Francisco **446 TL** Chris

Arend/Tony Stone Images **446 TLC** Barry L. Runk/Grant Heilman Photography **446 TCR** Carl Zeiss/Bruce Coleman Inc. **446 TR** Noble Stock/International Stock Photo **446 B** Robert Fried/Stock, Boston **447** Wolfgang Kaehler/Liaison International **448** Bill Lyons/Liaison International **450 T** Richard Pasley/Liaison International **450 C** Parker/Boon Productions and Dorey Sparre Photography* **450 B** Parker/Boon Productions and Dorey Sparre Photography* **451** ©1994, Asian Art Museum of San Francisco **452** Will & Deni McIntyre/Tony Stone Images **453** Robie Price* **454** Barry Brukoff/Woodfin Camp & Associates **455 T** Sylvain Grandadam/Tony Stone Images **455 CL** A.K.G. Berlin/Superstock **455 CC** Cheryl Fenton* **455 CR** Wolfgang Kaehler/Liaison International **455 B** Bruce Hands/Comstock **456 T** Arvind Garg/Liaison International **456 B** Oddo & Sinibaldi/The Stock Market **457** Adam Woolfitt/Woodfin Camp & Associates **459** Geoffrey Nilsen Photography* **462** Henryk T. Kaiser/Uniphoto Picture Agency

Chapter 9 **464-465 (background)** Gary & Vivian Chapman/The Image Bank **464 T** Bonnie Schiffman **464 B** Joe McBride/Tony Stone Images **465 T** John Lawrence/Tony Stone Images **465 B** Robie Price* **466** Cheryl Fenton* **467** Cheryl Fenton* **468 TL** James Elness/Comstock **468 TC** Parker/Boon Productions and Dorey Sparre Photography* **468 TR** Ken Karp* **468 BL** Parker/Boon Productions and Dorey Sparre Photography* **468 BC** Parker/Boon Productions and Dorey Sparre Photography* **468 BR** Dennis Geaney* **469 L** Charles Thatcher/Tony Stone Images **469 R** Glyn Kirk/Tony Stone Images **470** Chris & Donna McLaughlin/The Stock Market **471** Telegraph Colour Library/FPG International **472** Lambert/Archive Photos **473** Michael Collier/Stock, Boston **474** Ken Chernus/FPG International **475** Ken Karp* **476** Bob Daemmrich/The Image Works **477** Lawrence Migdale/Tony Stone Images **478** Ken Karp* **479** Comstock **481** John Eastcott-Yva Momatiuk/Stock, Boston **484** Don Smetzer/Tony Stone Images **485 L** Laurance B. Aluppy/FPG International **485 R** Cheryl Fenton* **487** Cheryl Fenton* **488** Bruce Silverstein/FPG International **493** Telegraph Colour Library/FPG International **494** Robert DiGiacomo/Comstock **496** Robie Price* **498** Ted Horowitz/The Stock Market **500** Parker/Boon Productions and Dorey Sparre Photography* **501** Ken Karp* **502** Jeffry Myers/Stock, Boston **503** Cheryl Fenton* **505** Geoffrey Nilsen Photography* **509 L** Andrew Unangst/The Image Bank **509 R** Gary S. Chapman/The Image Bank

Chapter 10 **510-511 (background)** Harald Sund/The Image Bank **510 TL** Steve Vidler/Superstock **510 C** Superstock **510 B** Chris Arend/AlaskaStock **511 B** Superstock **511 T** Cheryl Fenton* **512 T** C. M. Fitch/Superstock **512 BL** Patricia J.Bruno/Positive Images **512 BR** Margaret Hensel/Positive Images **513** Superstock **514** Bill Bachmann/Stock, Boston **515 T** Cheryl Fenton* **515 B** Ken Karp* **516 T** Gary Irving/Tony Stone Images **516 B** Cheryl Fenton* **518** Ken Karp* **519** Robie Price* **520** Parker/Boon Productions and Dorey Sparre Photography* **522** Stan Osolinski/Tony Stone Images **523 TL** Ken Karp* **523 TR**

Cary S.Wolinsky/Stock, Boston **523 B** Jack Daniels/Tony Stone Images **525** Kent Knudson/Stock, Boston **527** Superstock **528** Cheryl Fenton* **529** Scott Barrow/Superstock **530** Cary Wolinsky/Stock, Boston **531** Christian Michaels/FPG International **532** Jonathan Wright/Bruce Coleman Inc. **534 T** Liaison International **534 BL** Ken Karp* **534 BR** Rafael Macia/Photo Researchers **535** Russell D.Curtis/Photo Researchers **536 L** Mike Nazzaschi/Stock, Boston **536 R** S. L. Craig, Jr./Bruce Coleman Inc. **537** Jack S. Grove/Tom Stack & Associates **538** Superstock **539** Paul Harris/Tony Stone Images **540** Dennis Geaney* **541** Robert Frerck/Tony Stone Images **542** Robie Price* **543** John Eastcott-Yva Momatiuk/Stock, Boston **545 L** Superstock **545 R** FPG International **547 L** Jerry Jacka Photography **547 CL** Jerry Jacka Photography **547 C** Ron Sanford/Tony Stone Images **547 CR** Chris Arend/AlaskaStock **547 R** Scott Barrow/Superstock **548** Jeff Gnass/The Stock Market **549 (background)** Art Wolfe/Tony Stone Images **549 T** Nancy Adams/Tom Stack & Associates **549 C** David M. Dennis/Tom Stack & Associates **549 BL** Roy Toft/Tom Stack & Associates **549 BR** Gregory G.Dimijian/Photo Researchers **550 L** Superstock **550 C** Ken Karp* **550 R** Ken Karp* **554** Spencer Grant/FPG International **555** Robie Price* **556 L** Fritz Prenzel/Animals, Animals **556 R** John Cancalosi/Stock, Boston **558** Superstock **559** Jeff Lepore/Photo Researchers **560 T** P. Curto/U.P./Bruce Coleman Inc. **560 C** Parker/Boon Productions and Dorey Sparre Photography* **560 B** Parker/Boon Productions and Dorey Sparre Photography* **562** David Austen/Stock, Boston **563** Keith Wood/Tony Stone Images **564** Philippe Plailly/Eurelios/SPL/Photo Researchers **565** Ken Karp* **566 T** Cheryl Fenton* **566 B** Robert A. Tyrell **569 CR** Stuart Westmorland/Tony Stone Images **569 BL** Art Wolfe/Tony Stone Images **569 TR** Art Wolfe/Tony Stone Images **569 BC** Rodolpho Machado/Nexus/DDB Stock Photo **569 BR** Gail Shumway/FPG International **571** Geoffrey Nilsen Photography*

Chapter 11 **576-577 (background)** Geoffrey Nilsen Photography* **576 TL** Mark Segal/Tony Stone Images **576 TR** Christie's Image, London/Superstock **576 BL** Geoffrey Nilsen Photography* **576 BR** Ken Karp* **577 T** Superstock **577 B** Sylvain Grandadam/Tony Stone Images **578 T** B. Cavedo/Superstock **578 B** Ken Karp* **579** Geoffrey Nilsen Photography* **580** Richard Pasley/Stock, Boston **581 L** Corbis-Bettmann **581 C** Cheryl Fenton* **581 R** C. G. Maxwell/National Audubon Society/Photo Researchers **583 L** Joseph Nettis/Stock, Boston **583 R** National Gallery of Art, photo by Philip A. Charles **584** John Blaustein/Liaison International **585** Geoffrey Nilsen Photography* **586** Cheryl Fenton* **587** Geoffrey Nilsen Photography* **588** Superstock **592** Alan Carey/The Image Works **593** Robie Price* **595 L** Ken Karp* **595 R** Dennis Geaney* **596** Geoffrey Nilsen Photography* **599 L** Cheryl Fenton* **599 R** Geoffrey Nilsen Photography* **601** Mike Severns/Tony Stone Images **602** Alfred Pasieka/SPL/Photo Researchers **606** Frank Siteman/Tony Stone Images **607** Jane Burton/Bruce Coleman Inc. **608** Cheryl Fenton* **610** Michael Fisher/Custom Medical Stock **611** Robie Price*

612 Parker/Boon Productions and Dorey Sparre Photography* **613** Jeff Hunter/The Image Bank **614** Jeff Rotman/Tony Stone Images **615 L** Jeffrey Sylvester/FPG International **615 R** Mike Severns/Tony Stone Images **617** Geoffrey Nilsen Photography* **621 T** Robie Price* **621 B** Cheryl Fenton*

Chapter 12 **622-623 (background)** Cheryl Fenton* **622 T** Ken Karp* **622 B** Cheryl Fenton* **623 T** Cheryl Fenton* **623 B** Ken Karp* **624 T** Cheryl Fenton* **624 B** Rafael Macia/Photo Researchers **625** Paul & Lindamarie Ambrose/FPG International **626** Chuck Keeler/Tony Stone Images **627** Ken Karp* **628** Cheryl Fenton* **629** ChinaStock **630 L** John Coletti/Stock, Boston **630 R** Ken Karp* **631** George B. Fry III* **632** Warren Bolster/Tony Stone Images **633** NASA/GSFC/Science Source/Photo Researchers **635** Philippe Brylak/Liaison International **636** Howard Bluestein/Photo Researchers **639** Paul & Lindamarie Ambrose/FPG International **640** Ralph H. Wetmore II/Tony Stone Images **641** Cheryl Fenton* MONOPOLY® is a trademark of Hasbro, Inc. ©1997 Hasbro, Inc. All Rights Reserved. Used with permission. **642** Louis Bencze/Tony Stone Images **644 L** Dennis Geaney* **644 R** Ken Karp* **645** Cheryl Fenton* **646 T** Bob Daemmrich/Stock, Boston **646 B** Robie Price* **647** Ken Karp* **649** Cheryl Fenton* **650** George B. Fry III* **651 L** Ken Karp* **651 R** Michael Stuckey/Comstock **654** Ken Karp* **655** Cheryl Fenton* MONOPOLY® is a trademark of Hasbro, Inc. ©1997 Hasbro, Inc. All Rights Reserved. Used with permission. **656** Robie Price* **657** Geoffrey Nilsen Photography* **659** Cheryl Fenton*

*Photographs provided expressly for Addison Wesley Longman, Inc.

Illustrations

Jenny Ahrens: **407a, 409g, 410o, 412a, 419n** Christine Benjamin: **142b, 205a, 223b, 518b, 664b** Ken Bowser: **538c, 584a** Barbara Friedman: **160a, 191a** Cynthia Gamo: **118a** Joe Heiner Studio: all icons and borders Barbara Hoopes Ambler: **622b** Marlene Howerton: **345d** Dave Jonason: **597a** Jane McCreary: **515b, 517a** Patrick Merewether: **273a, 524a** Karen Minot: **319d, 285a** Andrew Muonio: **23c, 61e, 70a, 225a, 255c** Bill Pasini: **179d, 183d, 186a, 235l, 258d, 439a, 545i, 554e, 557b, 565b, 567a** Matt Perry: **421a, 532b, 545j, 545k** Precision Graphics: All illustrative artwork throughout: all generated electronically QYA Design: **629h** Bill Rieser: **284a, 292a, 297b, 301a, 319b, 591d** Rob Schuster: **9a, 22a, 22d, 24a, 29b, 42a, 44a, 66a, 76a, 96b, 116a, 120b, 148a, 168b, 195a, 198b, 238d, 241b, 244e, 260i, 278a, 291e, 299a, 320c, 320d, 349a, 354a, 357a, 366a, 372e, 379a, 379b, 380a, 385b, 386a, 429a, 441a, 465a, 470b, 480e, 484a, 485a, 508c, 514a, 519e, 521a, 527c, 552b, 582q,r,s, 589c, 590a, 597i, 621a, 633f, 649b, 652b** Bob Ting: **492a, 503a, 509b, 571a** Joe Van Der Bos: **73c, 240l, 243a, 258b** Tom Ward: **7a, 16b, 37a, 38a, 74a, 92a** Sarah Woodward: **323a** Rose Zgodzinski: **525m, 563a, 592a**

Index

INDEX

INDEX

Gems, 423–442

Geography applications, 4, 6, 21, 27, 31, 33, 44, 75, 76, 92, 117, 120, 125, 128, 159, 173, 175, 199, 235, 240, 258, 327, 342, 343, 355, 537, 541, 545, 548, 549, 552, 557, 560, 567, 569, 613, 625

Geography Link, 5, 159, 173, 175, 199, 342, 343, 344, 355, 407, 467, 485, 487, 503, 549, 554, 569, 625, 639

Geometric models of probability, 635–637

Geometry *The development of geometric skills and concepts is a key goal of this math program and is found throughout the book.*
  See also Angle; Circle; Lines; Triangle
  defined, 408
  Euler's formula, 617
  flips, 444–445, 493–495
  glossary entry, 679
  irregular figure, 254–255
  lengths, missing, 169
  line symmetry, 444–445
  perimeter, 210–211
  polygon, 432–433
  problem solving, 210–211, 228–230, 233–234, 237–238, 246–247, 250–251, 254–255, 408–409, 412–413, 416–418, 424–426, 428–429, 432–433, 436–437, 444–445, 448–450, 453–454, 543–544, 602–603
  quadrilateral, 436–437
  rotational symmetry, 448–449
  similar figure, 543–544
  slides, 453–454
  software, 242, 440
  tessellation, 404, 453–454
  transformational, 444–453, 493–495
  translations, 453–454
  turns, 448–449

Geometry software, 242, 440

Gram, 215, 679

Graph
  axis, 29, 488–499
  bar, 7, 11–12, 29–31
  circle, 8, 568
  of coordinate plane, 493–495, 498–499
  of data, 6–15, 29–31
  of equation, 498–499
  of flips, 493–495
  glossary entry, 679
  line, 8
  misleading, 11–13
  pictograph, 7
  of points, 16
  problem solving, 6–8, 11–13, 16–18, 21, 29–31, 66–68
  reading, 6–8
  scale, 29–31, 529
  scatterplot, 17–18
  of slides, 493–495
  trends, 18

Greater than symbol, 75

Greatest common factor (GCF), 295, 679

Greenwich Mean Time, 269
Gretzky, Wayne, 51
Griffith-Joyner, Florence, 141

H

Harrison, Benjamin, 35
Haslam, Pony Bob, 186
Hayes, Rutherford, 35
Health applications, 48, 116, 141, 163, 184, 188, 193, 340, 354, 373, 398, 500, 562, 564
  blood, 323–340
Health Link, 41, 323, 339
Hecto- prefix, 217, 679
Height, 230, 679
Henderson, Ricky, 8
Heng, Zhang, 629
Henry, O., 135
Heptagon, 433, 679
Hexagon, 433, 679
History applications, 4, 27, 28, 37, 113, 140, 180, 194, 244, 252, 269, 272, 274, 279, 297, 368, 374, 381, 395, 397, 430, 438, 498, 529, 536, 547, 629
  inventions, 245–260
  Oregon Trail, 175–200
  Presidents, 23–40
  space, 65–84
History Link, 23, 26, 35, 39, 115, 175, 177, 178, 191, 196, 199, 216, 222, 238, 269, 270, 272, 281, 282, 351, 381, 388, 397, 443, 445, 457, 487, 489, 494, 503, 524, 529, 547
Horizontal axis, 29, 679
Hornsby, Rogers, 143
Hoskins, Patricia, 41
Hydroponics, 477

I

Improper fractions, 298–300, 679
Inches, 221, 229, 679
Industry applications, 22, 96, 110, 209, 211, 225, 227, 243, 245, 259, 289, 292, 312, 313, 340, 365, 379, 381, 390, 397, 423, 434, 441, 513, 516, 525, 527, 566, 579, 587, 596, 599, 641, 646, 655
  fire safety, 513–528
  game design, 641–656
  inventions, 245–260
  packaging, 579–600
  recycling, 209–226
  shopping malls, 227–244
Industry Link, 209, 225, 227, 243, 245, 259, 287, 289, 303, 313, 365, 379, 381, 397, 423, 441, 513, 527, 579, 599, 641, 655
Inequality, 679
Integers
  adding, 472–473
  defined, 469
  dividing, 481–483
  glossary entry, 679
  multiplying, 481–483, 499
  negative number, 469, 473, 476–477, 499

opposite of, 472, 477
  positive number, 469, 473, 477, 499
  problem solving, 468–469, 472–473, 476–478, 481–483
  subtracting, 476–477
  understanding, 468–469
  zero, 469
Internet Link, 2, 3, 5, 8, 23, 41, 62, 63, 65, 85, 109, 134, 135, 137, 159, 175, 206, 207, 209, 227, 245, 266, 267, 269, 287, 320, 321, 323, 341, 362, 363, 365, 381, 404, 405, 407, 423, 443, 464, 465, 467, 487, 510, 511, 513, 529, 549, 576, 579, 601, 622, 623, 625, 641
Intersect, 409, 679
Intersection of lines, 409
Interval, 29, 679
Inventions, 245–260
Irregular figure, 254–255
Islamic art, 443–458
Isometric projection, 603
Isosceles triangle, 428, 679

J

Jordan, Michael, 54
Journal, 20, 22, 38, 73, 84, 89, 93, 97, 106, 113, 117, 141, 146, 156, 163, 168, 184, 189, 198, 214, 219, 236, 241, 253, 258, 279, 284, 292, 297, 301, 306, 312, 327, 338, 354, 369, 374, 386, 415, 420, 427, 435, 439, 447, 471, 475, 484, 491, 502, 517, 526, 533, 542, 562, 587, 629, 638, 650

K

Kasahara, Kunihiko, 421
Kilo- prefix, 216, 679
Kondakova, Elena, 77

L

Language applications, 3, 93, 114, 266, 347, 413
Language Link, 12, 67, 103, 255, 290, 347, 413, 437, 564, 603
Lazarus, Emma, 529
LCD. *See* Least common denominator
LCM. *See* Least common multiple
Least common denominator (LCD), 309, 330, 336, 679
Least common multiple (LCM), 280–282, 336, 679
Length, 169, 221, 229
Less than symbol, 75
Lewis, Carl, 134
Library, 148
Like denominator, 324–325, 679
Line graph, 8, 679
Line of symmetry, 445, 679
Line plot, 26, 679
Lines
  bisecting, 459

INDEX

Ounce, 221, 680
Outcome, 626, 652, 680
Outlier, 51–52, 680
Overestimation, 367

P

Packaging, 579–600
Parallel, 409, 680
Parallel lines, 409
Parallelogram, 233–234, 436–437, 680
Patterns, 236, 604
    binary numbers, 201
    numerical, 87, 102–104
    triangular and square numbers, 129
Pentagon, 404, 433, 680
People of the World, 2, 63, 134, 207, 266, 320, 362, 404, 464, 510, 576, 622
Percent
    connecting to fractions and decimals, 558–559
    defined, 550
    estimating, 554–555
    glossary entry, 680
    of a number, 563–565
    problem solving, 550–551, 554–555, 558–560, 563–565
    understanding, 550–552
Performance Assessment, 61, 205, 319, 403, 509, 621
Performance Task, 60, 132, 204, 264, 318, 360, 402, 462, 508, 574, 620, 660
Perimeter, 210–211, 680
Perpendicular, 409, 680
Perpendicular lines, 409
Perot, Ross, 34
Pi, 247, 250–251, 680
Piccard, Jacques, 127
Pictograph, 7, 680
Place value, 66–67, 138, 680
Planets, 65–84
Plot
    box-and-whisker, 57
    line, 26
Polygon, 432–433, 680
Polyhedron, 580–581, 680
Positive number, 469, 680
Pound, 165, 221, 680
Power, 79, 680
Prediction, 630–631
Presidents, 23–40
Prime factorization, 275–276, 680
Prime number, 276, 680
Prism, 580, 680
Probability
    applications, 76, 278, 567, 625, 638, 639, 650
    compound event, 647–648
    defined, 627
    event, 627
    experiment, 626
    fairness and unfairness, 651–652
    geometric models of, 635–636

    glossary entry, 680
    odds, 657
    outcome, 626, 652
    prediction, 630–631
    problem solving, 626–627, 630–631, 635–636, 642–644, 647–648, 651–652
    tree diagram, 642–643, 652
    understanding, 626–627
Problem Solving *The development of problem-solving skills is a key goal of this math program and is found throughout the book.*
    algebra, 110–112, 114–115, 118–119, 122–123
    area, 228–230, 233–234, 237–238, 250–251, 254–255, 261, 606, 636
    box-and-whisker plot, 57
    circumference, 246
    coordinate plane, 488–489, 493–495, 498–500
    decimals, 138–139, 142–144, 148–150, 160–161, 164–166, 169–170, 176–178, 181–182, 190–192, 195–196, 302–303
    difference, 90–92
    divisibility, 270–272, 295
    equation, 118–119, 122–123, 169–170, 195–196, 334–336, 392–394, 498–499
    estimation, 90–92, 94–95, 160–161, 342–343, 366–367, 554–555
    exponent, 78–79, 153–155
    expression, 110–112, 114–115
    fractions, 288–290, 293–295, 298–300, 302–305, 308–310, 324–325, 328–330, 334–336, 366–367, 375–377, 382–384, 387–388, 391–394
    geometry, 210–211, 228–230, 233–234, 237–238, 246–247, 250–251, 254–255, 408–409, 412–413, 416–418, 424–426, 428–429, 432–433, 436–437, 444–445, 448–450, 453–454, 543–544, 602–603
    graph, 6–8, 11–13, 16–18, 21, 29–31, 66–68
    integers, 468–469, 472–473, 476–478, 481–483
    large numbers, 66–68, 70–72, 74–75
    least common multiples, 280–282, 336
    line plot, 26
    lines, 408–409, 412, 424, 459
    mean, 46–47
    measurement, 144, 210–212, 215–218, 220–222, 228–230, 233–234, 237–239, 246–247, 250–251, 254–256, 606–607, 610–612
    median, 42–43
    mental math, 86–88, 114
    mixed numbers, 298–300, 342–343, 346–347, 350–352
    mode, 42–43
    numerical patterns, 87, 102–104
    order of operations, 98–99
    outlier, 51–52
    percent, 550–551, 554–555, 558–560, 563–565
    perimeter, 210–211
    prediction, 630–631

    prime factorization, 275–277
    probability, 626–627, 630–631, 635–636, 642–644, 647–648, 651–652
    product, 94–95, 366–367, 391
    proportion, 530–531, 534–535, 538–540, 543–544
    quotient, 94–95, 366–367, 391
    ratio, 514–516, 518–520, 523–524
    scale, 29
    scientific notation, 153–155
    solid, 580–581
    stem-and-leaf diagram, 34–36
    sum, 90–92
    surface area, 584–585, 588–590, 593–595
    tally mark, 24–26, 36
    three-dimensional figures, 602–603
    tree diagram, 642–644
    variable, 110–112
    volume, 606–607, 610–612
    whole numbers, 185–187, 370–372, 382–384, 563–565
Problem Solving Focus
    checking for a reasonable answer/solution, 512, 578, 624
    finding unnecessary information, 64, 208
    identifying missing information, 268, 364
    interpreting math phrases, 322, 406
    reading the problem, 4, 136
    solving problems, 466
Problem Solving Strategies
    choose a strategy, 49, 82, 97, 121, 156, 172, 180, 194, 198, 236, 258, 284, 297, 312, 327, 332, 349, 378, 396, 415, 427, 456, 480, 497, 522, 533, 537, 546, 567, 597, 609, 638, 646
    draw a diagram, xxviii
    guess and check, xxv
    look for a pattern, xxii
    make an organized list, xxiii
    make a table, xxiv
    solve a simpler problem, xxix
    use logical reasoning, xxvii
    work backward, xxvi
Problem Solving Tip, 25, 26, 35, 144, 170, 274, 294, 335, 367, 371, 519, 544, 555, 589, 629
Product. *See also* Multiplication
    defined, 115
    estimation of, 94–95, 366–367
    of fraction, 366–367, 391
    glossary entry, 680
    problem solving, 94–95, 366–367, 391
Project Progress, 15, 28, 54, 82, 101, 125, 152, 163, 189, 214, 241, 249, 279, 301, 338, 354, 378, 386, 420, 431, 456, 484, 502, 526, 546, 562, 587, 614, 638, 654
Proper fractions, 299
Proportion *The development of proportional reasoning is a key goal of this math program and is found throughout the book.*
    cross product and, 530, 534–535
    defined, 530
    glossary entry, 680
    measurement and, 534

INDEX

INDEX